D1130967

The Families and Genera of North American Diptera

By C. H. Curran, D.Sc.
Curator Emeritus
American Museum of Natural History
Entomologist
University of Florida Agricultural Experiment Station
Leesburg, Florida

SECOND REVISED EDITION

HENRY TRIPP
92-06 Jamaica Avenue
WOODHAVEN, N. Y. 11421
1965

by
HENRY TRIPP
92-06 Jamaica Avenue
Woodhaven, New York 11421

Library of Congress Catalog Card Number 65-14545

Printed in the United States of America

FOREWORD

An Apology and Acknowledgement

In retrospect, at the time the manuscript of "The Families and Genera of North American Diptera," was completed 25 years had passed since the publication of the third edition of the "Manual of North American Diptera," by Dr. S. W. Williston. With the passage of time the "Manual," as a result of the great advances made due to the stimulation given to the study of flies, had naturally become pretty much out of date. At the completion of the "Manual," Dr. Williston stated that, when it was revised again it would be done by someone else. About 25 years after the "Families and Genera," was published I made a similar remark. One reason: the cost of printing had soared to such heights that the cost of the book would have been prohibitive to the vast majority of students of the Diptera. Reprinting estimates offered no solution until Mr. Henry Tripp, whose interest in Entomology extends far beyond selling books suggested that it be reprinted at a cost that we believe will put it within reach of the average student. I finally agreed despite the fact that after 30 years it was out of date. Unfortunately, nothing has replaced it — so here it is again to fill the gap until a more complete work is produced.

In the appendix corrections have been made, some keys have been modified and generic names brought up to date, with references to pages where they occur. Keys to many of the families need few if any additions. A bibliography has been added listing important publications in various families and genera during the past 30 years.

I am greatly indebted to all those who have made suggestions through the years, and especially so to Drs. Curtis W. Sabrosky and Willis W. Wirth of the United States National Museum for the Bibliographical List. Also to Mr. Henry Tripp, for his keen interest in reprinting the "Families and Genera."

C. H. Curran
Leesburg, Florida
December 8th, 1964

CONTENTS

Preface

Twenty-five years ago Williston's Manual of North American Diptera (third edition), was offered to the public and in the interim it has held the esteem of students of Dipterology in every quarter of the globe. Williston's first synopses of families and genera appeared in 1884 and following years in the Bulletin of the Brooklyn Entomological Society and in 1888 the first edition of the "Manual" appeared. This "pamphlet", as it was modestly termed by its author, contained 88 pages, excluding as it did, the Nematocera and Muscoidea. The second edition appeared in 1896, and included the Nematocera but omitted the Tachinidæ and Dexiidæ. The third edition contained all the families, fifty-eight in number.

The present attempt at a classification of the genera of North American Diptera is the result of many years of study but it is inconceivable that this work should be uninfluenced by such a masterpiece as that of Williston. That a new synopsis is urgently needed becomes obvious when one considers the enormous number of new genera described since the appearance of Williston's Manual, the realignment of genera, the application of newly discovered characters and the increased importance of the study of flies in relation to human welfare.

Knowing, as I do, the excellent quality of Dr. Williston's work it is with temerity that I offer this contribution to a critical public. Even though great pains have been taken in its preparation and every effort has been made to make the keys as complete and simple as possible I fear that some few errors have crept in. That is inevitable. Where they occur I do not know, nor do I offer excuses for them other than to admit an utter ignorance in regard to the characters of thousands upon thousands of Diptera, even though I have had available for study the excellent collections of the Smithsonian Institution, Canadian National Collection and the American Museum of Natural History and the generous assistance of various specialists. If mention is not made of those who have contributed to this work, either wittingly or unwittingly (through their synoptic revisions), it is only because the body of the paper has increased to such proportions that a complete acknowledgment must be omitted.

A few innovations will be found. Where reasonably complete specific keys occur these are referred to in footnotes and the same is true in the case of family revisions. The synonymy has increased so greatly that some indication of it must be given, especially where old familiar names have been changed; this is indicated in the index and while it is far from complete it is hoped that some help may be derived from such an arrangement.

It is my hope that those who may discover errors or omissions may be kind enough to call them to my attention, indicating the manner in which the corrections may be made. Owing to the numerous footnotes it has not been possible to indicate the genera which have been included from description only. Such genera naturally weaken a key as it is impossible to use characters which may be available for a more suitable arrangement. Any specimens representing genera improperly placed, or not common, would be most greatly valued by the author.

Finally I wish to express my unbounded admiration for the late Samuel Wendell Williston. To him I owe, as do very many others, an everlasting gratitude for his kindly encouragement, while he lived, and real inspiration from his printed works. I know of no Dipterologist who has so clearly set forth the facts or who has been so great an inspiration to others. And as a slight token of my appreciation I respectfully dedicate this book to his memory.

C. H. Curran.

American Museum of Natural History,
New York City, 1933.

Introduction

Acknowledgments

It is impossible to express fully my appreciation of the generous cooperation of all those who have assisted in the preparation of this work. It is most fitting that I should mention first the generosity of Mrs. S. W. Williston for not only permitting me to use the illustrations from Williston's "Manual of North American Diptera", but for her offer to furnish the cuts themselves. Needless to say this offer was accepted and many of the illustrations are reproduced from cuts used in the Manual. Unfortunately, due to a rearrangement of many genera and their transfer to different families, it has not been possible to use all of the cuts. Further, in this connection, I owe much to Mrs. George Shor, a daughter of Dr. and Mrs. Williston, for her assistance in this matter, and for her sympathy in the work. It might not be out of place to mention here that, according to Mrs. Shor, her father, upon the completion of the manuscript of the third edition of his Manual, dropped it upon his desk and remarked: "Well, that's finished. When it is revised again, it will be by someone else."

Every request for the loan of specimens and for the review of keys met with a wholehearted response and as a result the value of this book has been greatly enhanced. Dr. C. P. Alexander is deserving of especial thanks for the preparation of the manuscript dealing with the Tipuloidea and the preparation of the illustrations for that superfamily. Drs. Jos. Bequaert, C. T. Brues, O. A. Johannsen, Robert Matheson, F. M. Root and Mr. Marston Bates have assisted very materially in checking over keys and suggesting changes. Dr. E. P. Felt suggested the use of illustrations from his papers published in the Bulletins of the New York State Museum on the Cecidomyidæ (Itonididæ) and Dr. C. C. Adams very generously furnished the cuts. Drs. J. M. Aldrich, F. H. Benjamin and Mr. Marston Bates, and others have loaned specimens not found in the American Museum collection and Dr. Matheson has given permission to use illustrations from his "Handbook of the Mosquitoes". I wish also to express my appreciation to all those Dipterologists of the past and present whose works have been so freely drawn upon.

The preparation of a work of this kind entails a large amount of stenographic and routine work and for the careful typing of the manuscript I am indebted to Miss Ethel Olsen. Mr. Adolph Klein has contributed the excellent colored plate of several typical forms, while my wife has assisted with the illustrations and in many other ways.

For the encouragement he has given during the preparation of the manuscript I shall always feel a deep sense of gratitude to Dr. Frank E. Lutz. The American Museum of Natural History is deserving of particular mention, since the work has been done in this institution without any limitations as to time devoted to it.

If the book should be found useful and helpful, full credit should be given to the Museum as well as to all those who have so generously given of their time and knowledge.

Collection and Care of Diptera

So much has been written about the ease with which collections of insects may be cared for that I feel a word of warning to be not amiss. It is true the Lepidoptera and Odonata may be "papered", Hymenoptera, Hemiptera and Coleoptera may be packed between layers of cotton and Coleoptera may be collected in alcohol but most of the other Orders require more care. With the exception of Coleoptera and the small insects normally collected in alcohol and intended for study in this liquid, or for slide preparation, all insects are much better pinned while fresh. Packing Diptera between layers of cotton may result in recognizable specimens and a small percentage of really good specimens may be secured but the majority can never be made to look attractive.

With small flies pinning should take place within four or five hours of the time of capture and all specimens should be mounted within eight hours. In cold or damp weather a greater time may be allowed to elapse and the time should be shortened in hot, dry weather.

Mounting Diptera should not be a slip-shod process and care should be taken to have the flies an even height on the pins. An excellent practice is to have the mesonotum about one-third the distance from the top of the pin. This permits of careful handling of the specimen and reduces danger of damage to a minimum. Many Entomologists pin Diptera less than a fourth the distance from the head of the pin with the result that the specimens are quickly damaged and ultimately cease to have value. *Double mounts* should never be used for Diptera. If a specimen is too small to be pinned through the thorax it should be fastened to the side of the pin by first circling it (the pin) with a narrow ring of white shellac and touching it to the side of the insect. In this way the specimen may be handled in the usual manner and all parts may be readily seen. If possible, the wings should be arranged so that they extend over the back of the insect in an upright position. Pins of suitable size should be used and it will be found that good, steel No. 00 pins may be used for quite small insects for pinning through the thorax. Some collectors seem to have a craze for double mounts, not realizing that the value of their collection is greatly lessened due to the increased risk during shipping and many of them place the accessory mount much too high on the pin. Another practice, that of placing specimens (nicely spread, it is true) on a circular or oval mount of cardboard by use of minute pins, is to be condemned as the characters available on the under side of the specimen are concealed.

Labelling is an important detail and insufficiently labelled specimens are of little more value than none at all. The fact that a proud collector knows exactly when and where he captured a certain prize is of no value to the student who must needs study the specimen in the absence of the collector. Every specimen should be labelled with the locality, date and name of the collector. Labels should be small and neat and should be placed on the pin along the long axis of the insect, the locality on the right hand side. Labels should never be placed crosswise as they are liable to damage adjacent specimens when the insect is being removed for examination. One guide to labelling all insects is to remember that the label should afford protection to the specimen and not be so large that the collection looks like a collection of locality labels rather than one of insects. The labels should be printed, either by machine or by hand and the month should always be in Roman numerals.

In various places in the following pages will be found instructions for the care of those flies which require special attention. No doubt there are many people who will neglect to read the instructions here but to those who do I offer a few pertinent hints. Never place Diptera in vials or bottles with other insects. Never cram a vial full of flies. Shake them loose occasionally so that the wings will not become folded. Never place small flies in a vial with large ones and be careful not to place more than a few specimens of flies which rub easily in a vial. Always keep mating pairs together: a good plan is to have a vial for this purpose and to put only different species in it.

Collecting outfits need not be elaborate. I usually carry six to eight test tubes and a bottle about an inch across and four inches long. If the collecting is to be general a bottle two inches across may be carried. Such an outfit will suffice for a half day of very good collecting and if the trip be an all-day one the catch may be transferred to a box and stored in a cool place. Empty match boxes are convenient receptacles for the transference of fragile specimens and pairs.

The making of the bottle is a simple affair. Get some fine sawdust, place in the vial or bottle a small amount of sodium or potassium cyanide and add about half an inch of sawdust; wedge this in with a ball of cotton, place in the sun for half an hour and the bottle is ready for use. The cyanide should be broken into small lumps but need not be particularly fine. It must be remembered that *cyanide is a deadly poison* and extreme care is necessary in handling it. Do not use it unless you are properly instructed, and if you do, be sure to destroy by burning or burying all paper, pieces of wood, etc., which the cyanide might have touched and wash thoroughly in running tap water hammers, etc. used in crushing the material, as well as your hands. Never handle cyanide if there is an open sore upon the hands. A little extra care may be worth a lot. It might not be amiss to note here that the most efficient antidote for cyanide poison is the intra-venous injection of methelyne blue, one of the best known aniline dyes.

Flies and Disease

As agents in the spread of diseases of mammals the Diptera undoubtedly rank first in importance among the insects. The chief carriers of diseases are, of course, the biting flies belonging to the families Psychodidæ, Simuliidæ, Culicidæ, Tabanidæ, Glossinidæ, Ceratopogonidæ and Muscidæ. Species of *Flebotomus* carry papataci fever, verruga or oroya fever, kala-azar and oriental sore. Other names are applied to these diseases. The mosquitoes carry blackwater fever, yellow fever, dengue, filariasis and malaria. Onchocerciasis is carried by species of *Eusimulium.* A form of filariasis is believed to be carried by a species of *Culicoides* and species of *Chrysops* are known to transmit the disease. Tularæmia, anthrax and trypanosomiasis are other diseases transmitted by Tabanids. The stable-fly, *Stomoxys calcitrans,* is known to carry a number of species of trypanosomes and may also be responsible for the spread of poliomyelitis (infantile paralysis), although no definite proof has been obtained. Sleeping sickness is carried by the Tse-tse flies.

In addition to carrying diseases the biting flies themselves cause a great deal of irritation by their bites, especially in the vicinity of water. Life is often made miserable in northern regions by the hordes of mosquitoes and black flies while the sportsman is plagued by almost all the biting forms while in the woods and bathers come in for much undesired attention from no-see-ums, mosquitoes and Tabanids, particularly the so-called "green-heads", along the coastal regions.

The house fly carries on its body the germs causing typhoid fever, dysentery, cholera, anthrax and conjunctivitis, while a few other flies carry other diseases. Considerable has been written about myiasis caused by the larvæ of flies living in the human body. If we except the bot-flies, I think that we may regard the occurrence of fly larvæ in the body of man as entirely accidental and dismiss the matter as being a subject of academic interest rather than one calling for serious consideration. There are, of course, the bot-flies, belonging to three distinct families and they are serious pests. In the tropics one species commonly attacks man, but the greatest damage is done to domestic animals. Hides are frequently so greatly riddled with "warble" holes as to be almost valueless.

The bird and bat parasites, as well as the so-called bee-louse (*Braula caeca*), are probably not serious pests although the sheep tick, belonging to the Hippoboscidæ, is often sufficiently numerous to cause serious damage and some species of *Hippobosca* bite humans in addition to their attacks on horses, camels, etc.

In many places the so-called blow-flies cause serious loss to sheep owners by "blowing" the wool.

I have given just a very brief summary of some of the injury caused by flies to animal life, as it affects human welfare, and a very great deal that is of interest has been omitted. One frequently receives inquiries as to the diseases carried by flies, and these few paragraphs may serve to answer the questions. In the following pages, under the families mentioned, additional information is given, particularly concerning diseases carried by flies in North America. If the student desires further information on this important subject he should secure a copy of one of the better books on Medical Entomology.

Flies and Crops

It is impossible to enumerate all the flies attacking field, horticultural and garden crops, but mention might be made of the various root maggots, the leaf miners, gall makers, fruit flies, grass stem flies and the Hessian fly. The amount of damage done by the groups of insects mentioned must be enormous but it must be remembered that there can be no actual measure of crop damage from a financial point of view. A large crop invariably means lower prices and a small crop higher prices. It is only when individuals or limited communities suffer serious loss in the volume of their produce that there is any real loss, and then it is of a local nature and not national for the producers of the crop affected. It so happens in such cases that one man's loss proves to be another man's gain. While flies undoubtedly do a great deal of damage to our crops and flowers, they are of less importance in this respect than some of the other orders of insects and the Diptera are, in actual fact, much more beneficial than injurious.

Beneficial Flies

No group of insects, except, perhaps, the Hymenoptera, are so important to mankind as are the flies. In these two groups are man's best friends among the insects. It would be useless to argue about the relative merits of the two orders because we know so little about them that no one is in a position to make any authoritative statement. It is sufficient to say that flies play an extremely important part in the pollination of flowers, but they undoubtedly occupy second position to the bees. It is in the field of predaceous and parasitic members that these two groups render the greatest service to mankind. If the world should suddenly find itself without flies and bees it would quickly revert to a sphere lacking animal and plant life, so important are these insects in maintaining the "balance of nature".

I believe that the majority of flies, in relation to the number of known species, are either predaceous or parasitic on other insects. Such large families as the Asilidæ, Empidæ and Dolichopidæ are all predaceous in the adult and probably in the larval stage, while the Bombyliidæ, Nemestrinidæ, Conopidæ and Tachinidæ are insect parasites. Other families or groups can be added to the list and we might also include forms which are predaceous in the larval stage. More about the habits of flies will be found in the following pages.

Flies are also beneficial as scavengers and examples of their effectiveness may be found everywhere. They dispose of carcasses, decaying vegetation and waste animal products and in this way do much to keep the air pure and wholesome.

Anent the Insect War

I am aware that there has been some sensational propaganda about "the war against insects" and I cannot forego a few remarks. Insects are our best friends and we owe a great deal to them. They are also our worst enemies but this fact should not be proclaimed from the housetops without at the same time crying much louder of the benefits they give us—flowers, fruits, vegetable, clothes, food, pure air, beauty. The stressing of the danger of the "insect menace" may do entomology a great deal of harm and I think it has already done some. It has taught people to dislike all insects and the fact that the "menace" has not developed perceptably has resulted in some loss of faith in entomologists.

The Diptera contain some of our worst enemies. The public should be made aware of this and steps taken to eliminate the pests in so far as possible. Every effort must be made to keep people suffering from insect-carried diseases out of the country, if such diseases do not occur here and if there are any known carriers of the disease among our insect population. Yellow fever is an excellent example. We have the yellow fever mosquito and if persons suffering from this disease should enter any part of the country where the mosquito occurs the disease might well become established. Every effort should be made to reduce the numbers of the house-fly, stable-fly, and other pests. On the other hand the introduction of parasites, particularly of imported pests, should be encouraged and people should learn to differentiate at least the more beneficial of their insect friends.

Morphology of Diptera

It is not my intention to go into detail concerning the structure or morphology of flies since I have appended a glossary of terms used in this and other works. However, a few remarks on the subject may not be amiss. In Williston's manual a simple system of nomenclature is used and I follow the same system. During recent years attempts have been made to homologize the parts of the various orders of insects and as a result many long and unfamiliar terms have been proposed. To my mind the homologies of the parts are much less important to the systematist than a simple, easily followed and long used terminology. Nevertheless it is important to know the origin of the various parts, especially so to a zoologist, if he deigns to study that group which comprises three-fourths of the animal kingdom. In each order of insects a simple terminology has long been in use and such terms should be employed because the average student can understand them without difficulty. After all, some one has said that "Nature is an open book, and you have but to study nature to understand." Perhaps those are not the exact words, but they will do.

The determination of genera is based upon structure and it is therefore necessary to be acquainted with these parts. The average student will find no difficulty on this score if he will follow the simple expedient of using the keys and consulting the glossary. In this way the terms used will soon be mastered and the student will find little difficulty in tracing out specimens.

The student who desires to delve into the anatomy of Diptera should obtain a bibliography of the works on this subject, particularly those by Crampton and Snodgrass. Many references will be found in Imms' "Recent Advances in Entomology" and "Biological Abstracts"

It will be found that authorities differ as to the origin and homology of different organs. A comparison of the Comstock-Needham system as used by Dr. Alexander in this work and that of Comstock will show certain differences while others disagree in the terminology as applied to the veins in other families of Diptera as well as in other orders of Insects. It must be pointed out that the Comstock-Needham terminology of wing venation is very widely used, probably by more students of Diptera than any other system, and if American students desire to study exotic flies they must familiarize themselves with this system as well as the system used by many Europeans. Explanations of these systems will be found in the glossary.

Classification of Diptera

The classification of any group of animals is a complex problem having its basis in the morphology, histology, embryology and general biology of the phylum, and without a knowledge of these "ologies" no satisfactory classification can be obtained. In addition we must also turn our attention to palæontology, although it must be confessed that very little is known concerning the Diptera of the past ages. In the present work we deal almost entirely with morphology of the adult flies, not from any desire to ignore the other phases of study, nor from any lack of interest in them, but because our space is so limited and each field is so vast that a lifetime of study would leave any field almost untouched. The truth is that we know practically nothing about the biology of flies although we may say, in a general way, that we are acquainted with their mass biology and that we can usually place a species biologically by associating it with some related form.

The taxonomist, however, is forced to deal with adult structures, to classify the creatures by characters he may select and to leave to some one else the pleasure of working out the biology of the insects studied. If you are at heart a taxonomist and are informed that you know nothing of biology unless you study life histories, do not be discouraged. Instead, feel rather strongly inclined to turn a deaf ear to your adviser, taking solace in the fact that even though you may spend all your available time at the systematic study of the adult insects, and gleaning what you may from the writings of others on biology and life history studies, you will never be able to fully master the field you have chosen. There are so many flies that no one can ever truly profess to know them all and their very numbers preclude a thorough survey of the order tending to a complete classification.

It is well, and necessary, to warn against too great specialization, and at the same time it is realized that many students with limited time are unable to study more than one or two families. The great trouble with the intensive specialist is that he loses his sense of proportion and relatively minor details are liable to assume the greatest importance in his mind. In order to overcome this intra-specialization the student should enlarge his outlook by collecting in other families and also in other orders, even though no time be available for a study of his complete catch. The collector who studies a single family may produce a monumental work providing he is painstaking and accurate while the general worker is less liable to accomplish lasting results.

I hope I may be excused if I wander a little aside from a technical discussion of classification to discuss lighter but equally important matters. The real object of this work is not the classification of the Diptera but the presentation of keys to enable the student to place his specimen in the proper genus—or, in short, the generic identification of flies. Nevertheless, we must glance below the generic classification and find out something about species, and it is about the description of species of which I wish to say a few words here.

There is nothing more pleasing than a good description and nothing more aggravating than a poor one. All of us, in our ignorance, may offer poor descriptions at times but we should always strive to make them clear and concise. We should try to step beyond ourselves and look at the description from the viewpoint of another student. If two animals are different, in our estimation, we should clearly express the differences, laying special stress upon the outstanding characters. A description should not be too long, nor should it be brief and stilted. I can do no better than recommend that every Dipterist read the descriptions contained in Williston's "Synopsis of North American Syrphidæ" and pattern descriptions after those. The elimination of words and the excessive use of abbreviations is scarcely to be condoned, even on the ground that it is "scientific". If "science" is to be measured by a stilted language and a lack of consideration for others, it deserves little consideration from humanity as a whole and we should divorce "science" and study insects just for the fun of the thing.

Today the student need not worry a great deal about some one "stealing his thunder". Most eminent entomologists are only too glad to be of assistance to the young student and to leave to him the description of new species. This does not mean that the specialist is willing to name large collections and return all the material. If he were he would be so swamped with work that he would have no time for his other duties. Most specialists name material on the understanding that they may retain what they wish, and as a rule they desire very little. The beginner should be only too glad to assist the specialist by filling in gaps in his collection, because every species added makes his work that much easier in future. It must also be remembered that many specialists are employed by institutions having large collections of unworked material and that every collection named means less time for institutional work and, to make a blunt statement, it is only fair to expect the institution to look for some return from the labor of its employees. However, I do not know of anyone who is not happy to verify a student's findings and to give opinions and suggestions concerning the distinctness of specimens, and, of course, in such cases they are returned if desired.

I cannot condemn too strongly the professor who permits a student to work on a systematic or biological paper and to allow or even urge that the results be published unless the material has been examined by a specialist, or the species of which the biology is being studied has been identified by one in authority. Each year many students are given such problems and the results are frequently very unsatisfactory. Too much care can not be exercised in the preparation of scientific descriptions of either genera or species and it should be realized that a good collection must be available before any work can be faithfully undertaken.

The preparation of keys is a very important matter and their incorporation in a contribution adds greatly to its value. Some authors attempt, in their keys, to portray what they term a "natural classification", but it should be borne in mind that this is impossible. We know too little about the insects with which we are dealing to produce any such result. In preparing keys we arbitrarily accept one or more characters for the separation of groups and, if the key is to be useful, the characters used for each separation must be clean-cut. In any large group it will be found to be very difficult to find clean-cut characters in every case, some forms apparently going into either group although the character used may serve for the vast majority. In cases of this kind the doubtful forms should be run through both categories. In the so-called "natural" grouping it is very frequently necessary to employ characters which are not conspicuous and such keys are liable to prove very difficult to use. Characters expressing a degree of variation should be avoided wherever possible, i. e. front produced vs. front less produced. These characters may be obvious to the maker of a key but are certainly not recognizable to other students whose collections may be limited. It is usually easy to use a key if you know most of the forms but often difficult or impossible otherwise.

All keys should be dichotomous and the use of more than two alternatives should always be avoided. In a short key one may use the "a" and "aa" system but it is not to be recommended in any case. Keys so constructed are more time consuming than such as are used in the present work. In the present case an attempt has been made to produce simple keys, amply illustrated. It must be remembered, however, that the illustrations will not serve for all species in a genus but represent, as a rule, typical forms.

No use has been made, in general, of subfamilies or subgenera. The use of such almost always calls for many exceptions and also unnecessarily encumbers the literature. A sub-family is supposedly a distinct entity within a family, a group separable upon certain characters, but that such classification is unnecessary is evidenced by the exceptions. As an example—the Tachinidæ have been divided into many sub-families, or even families, upon such characters as the absence of abdominal bristles, shape of head, etc., etc., but there is not a single character, nor for that matter group of characters, upon which any of these groupings may be retained. Many of the characters in this family are excellent up to a certain point, but every character falls down, not once, but in many instances throughout the family. It is entirely impossible to separate the Tachinidæ and Dexiidæ, just as it is to separate the Muscidæ, Anthomyidæ and Scatophagidæ.

Subgenera are superfluous. They are proposed as a rule because the author hopes that some day some character may be found upon which a distinct genus may be based. It is well to remember that in nature there is no such thing as a subgenus, genus or family. Their use is a human creation made possible because links connecting the groups have either entirely disappeared or have not been discovered by man. Genera are therefore artificial and the answer to the question of "what is a genus?" is that it is something limited in some way by some one. This may sound facetious but it is not meant to be so. The truth is that certain arbitrary characters have been set up, all the species falling within the limits set forth constituting a genus (or a species or family). It is presumed, but by no means certain that connecting links do not exist.

Many people describe sub-species, varieties, races, forms, etc., especially in the Lepidoptera, but, fortunately, the fad has not become extensive in Dipterology and it is to be hoped that it may never do so. In actual fact there is no difference in a sub-species, race or variety. A variety is something which differs from the typical or first described form in some definite way. They are explained as potential species, ignoring the fact that no two specimens are exactly alike and that if two extremes of similar type should mate a new race would be formed. In each batch of eggs there are produced forms possessing characters somewhat different from the parents. But the species does not change because the average is maintained by the resultant mating. It is only when forms become more or less isolated that a definite trend occurs and so-called races (supposedly geographic forms) are developed. In such cases connecting or transition forms usually occur and it is almost always true that the races, say northern and southern, are connected in the intervening region by a perfect transition of the characters of the two races. Races are interesting but it is not necessary to give them names. Moreover, "variety" was used in the same sense long before people thought of "races" for biological classification and I think we may extend the law of priority and use it in this sense, thus eliminating "race" and "sub-species".

The naming of aberrations, transition forms and such things should be beyond the pale in true science and such a practice must eventually result in ridicule of the science as a whole. It is, of course, very necessary to call attention to these forms but to name them is utterly needless. Knowledge of them is essential in tracing out the relationship and development of species, and of great interest, too, but we should not lose our perspective and attach exaggerated importance to names.

How to Use the Keys

The use of keys is not a difficult matter but there may be some who have not had experience with them. Some keys may not be altogether simple and may not run as smoothly as others. To find the genus to which your specimen belongs turn to the table of families (on the following page) and read over couplet 1. Two alternatives are given: the insect must go in either section. If it has large wings you go to couplet 2 and you repeat the process until it is found that your specimen comes to a section where it agrees with the diagnosis ending in a family name. You have now found the "family", but to be sure read over the other alternative so that the characters in both may be checked. Now turn to the family indicated and continue in the same way until the genus is reached.

It should be remembered that keys are merely guides and the fact that a species traces out to a certain place in a key is no guarantee that it actually belongs there. If one is familiar with the genera of a family he may be reasonably certain either that the insect belongs where it traces or that it is quite different; in either case he should check with descriptions of genera not included in the key or with the genus included, either by means of determined specimens or with the generic description. If a specimen does not seem to agree with the genus to which it traces check back and try one of the other alternatives since there may have been an error in interpretation of the characters used or the specimen may be one that is somewhat aberrant.

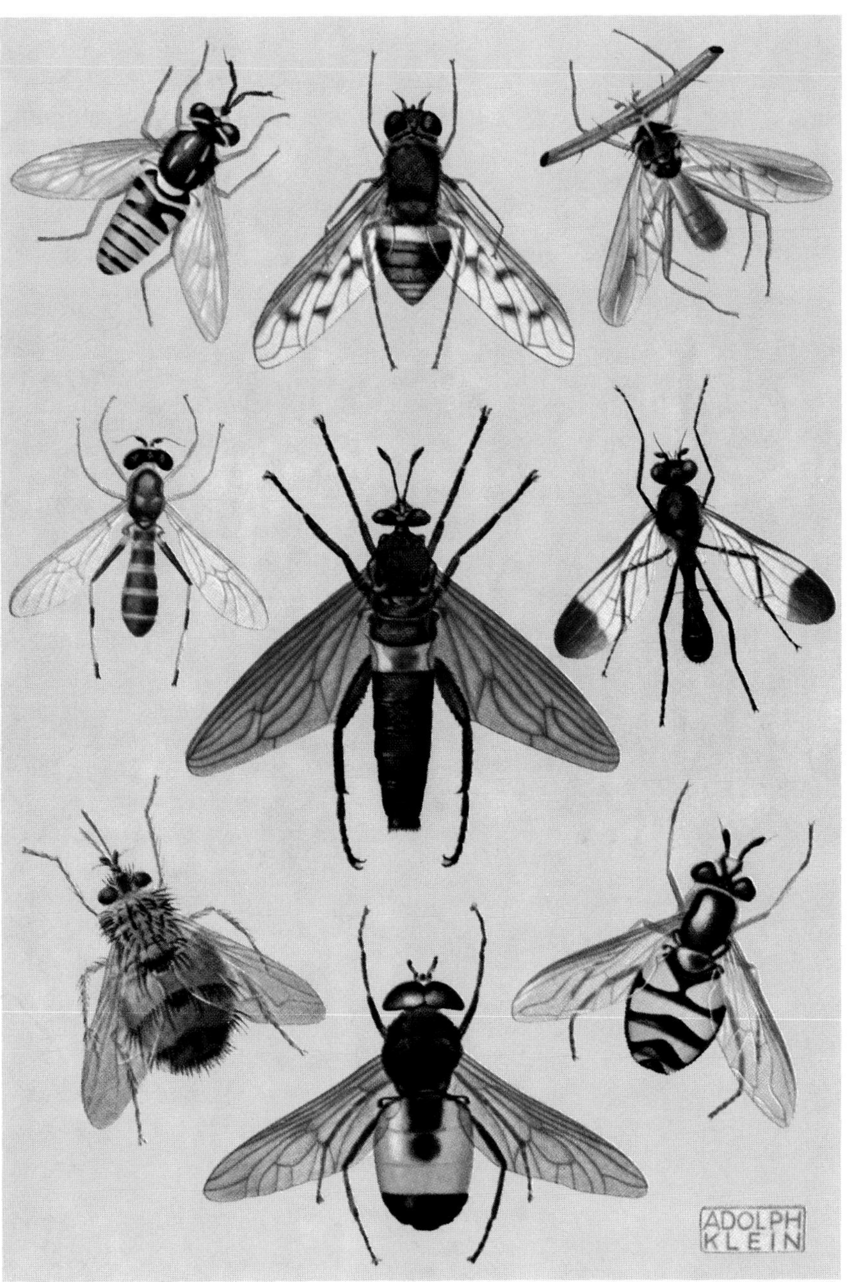

Sphecomyia vittata Wied.
(Syrphidae)

Aloipha cingulata Schiner.
(Stratiomyidæ)

Dejeania vexatrix O. S.
(Tachinidæ)

Hyperalonia hela Erichs.
(Bombyliidæ)

Mydas clavatus Fabr.
(Mydaidæ)

Tabanus cinctus Drury.
(Tabanidæ)

Richardia telescopica Gerst.
(Otitidæ)

Michogaster niger Schm.
(Otitidæ)

Didea fuscipes Macq.
(Syrphidæ)

TABLE OF FAMILIES

1. Wings absent or greatly reduced 91
   Wings present, rarely reduced 2

2. Antennæ composed of six or more freely articulated segments......... 3
   Antennæ composed of not more than five freely articulated segments, the third segment sometimes complex, usually bearing a style or arista 22

3. Mesonotum with an entire V-shaped suture............................ 4
   Mesonotal suture transverse, not V-shaped 7

4. Ocelli absent 5
   Ocelli present ....(p. 31) **TRICHOCERIDÆ**

5. Only one anal vein reaches the wing margin.......................... 6
   Two anal veins reach the wing margin..............(p. 33) **TIPULIDÆ**

6. Second and third veins each with two branches (radius 5-branched) (Tipulidæ plate II, fig. 11)....................(p. 29) **TANYDERIDÆ**
   Second and third veins with only three branches reaching the wing margin (radius 4-branched) (Tipulidæ plate II, fig. 12) (p. 30). **PTYCHOPTERIDÆ**

7. Wings without a network of folds or creases......................... 8
   Wings with a network of fine folds or creases (p. 61) **BLEPHARICERIDÆ**

8. Ocelli present 9
   Ocelli absent 14

9. Costa continuing around the wing, although weakened behind. (p. 101) **CECIDOMYIDÆ**
   Costa ending at or near the wing-tip 10

10. Discal cell present 21
    Discal cell absent 11

11. Tibiæ with apical spurs 12
    Tibiæ without apical spurs, though produced spur-like. (p. 131) **SCATOPSIDÆ**

12. Eyes more or less connected by a projection above the base of the antennæ ....(p. 118) **SCIARIDÆ**
    Eyes separated 13

13. Antennæ placed below the compound eyes, usually close to the oral margin ....(p. 128) **BIBIONIDÆ**
    Antennæ situated at most slightly below the middle of the compound eyes ....(p. 120) **MYCETOPHILIDÆ**

14. Costa continued around the margin of the wings, though weaker behind the apex 17
    Costa ending at or near the apex of the wing 15

15. Wings very broad, the posterior veins weak and poorly developed. (p. 63) **SIMULIIDÆ**
    Wings narrow and long, the posterior veins stronger 16

16. Wings lying flat over the back when at rest; metanotum short and without a longitudinal groove; femora sometimes swollen.
(p. 74) **CERATOPOGONIDÆ**
Wings lying roof-like over the back when at rest; metanotum long and with a median longitudinal groove; legs long and slender.
(p. 69) **CHIRONOMIDÆ**

17. Wings short and broad, folded roof-like over the body when at rest, usually pointed ....(p. 78) **PSYCHODIDÆ**
Wings long, or if broad, the apex very broadly rounded, always lying flat over the back when at rest 18

18. Venation very much reduced, several of the veins lacking.
(p. 101) **CECIDOMYIDÆ**
Venation not reduced, the veins strong 19

19. Basal cells long, extending to or beyond the middle of the wing......20
Basal cells, especially the second, short, not extending nearly to the middle of the wings ....(p. 67) **THAUMALEIDÆ**

20. Apical veins strongly arched ....(p. 80) **DIXIDÆ**
Veins straight or nearly so.........................(p. 83) **CULICIDÆ**

21. Fourth posterior cell widely open...............(p. 59) **ANISOPODIDÆ**
Fourth posterior cell closed ....(p. 133) **RACHICERIDÆ**

22. Empodium developed pulvilliform, the three pads nearly equal........23
Empodium hair-like or absent 29

23. Third antennal segment compound, composed of annuli 24
Third antennal segment simple, usually bearing an elongated style or arista 27

24. Squamæ large and conspicuous ....(p. 148) **TABANIDÆ**
Squamæ small or vestigial 25

25. At least the middle tibiæ with spurs ....(p. 146) **CŒNOMYIDÆ**
Tibial spurs absent 26

26. Posterior branch of the third vein ending before the wing-tip.
(p. 134) **STRATIOMYIDÆ**
Posterior branch of the third vein ending well behind the wing-tip.
(p. 155) **PANTOPHTHALMIDÆ**

27. Squamæ very large; head very small, placed low down, composed almost entirely of the eyes, the face and front very narrow or obliterated.
(p. 203) **CYRTIDÆ**
Squamæ small; head larger, the face or front broad..................28

28. Middle tibiæ with spurs; venation not complex...(p. 157) **RHAGIONIDÆ**
Tibiæ without spurs; venation intricate, many veins ending before the wing-tip ....(p. 201) **NEMESTRINIDÆ**

29. Wings rounded apically, with strong veins anteriorly and very weak, oblique ones; coxæ not widely separated by the sternum.
(p. 234) **PHORIDÆ**
Wings with normal venation or pointed at the apex, or the coxæ broadly separated by the sternum 30

30. Wings pointed at the apex, without crossveins.
(p. 232) **LONCHOPTERIDÆ**

31. Two or more submarginal cells, the third vein furcate................32
Only one submarginal cell, the third vein simple.....................38

32. Front hollowed between the eyes, strongly concave from anterior view..33
Front scarcely or not at all concave from anterior view..............34

33. At most one ocellus; at most two veins reach the wing margin behind the apex ....(p. 163) **MYDAIDÆ**
Three ocelli; at least four veins reach the wing margin, or extend toward it, behind the apex ....(p. 167) **ASILIDÆ**

34. Costa continuing around the wing; fourth vein ending beyond the wing-tip 35
Costa not continued beyond the apex of the wing; fourth vein ending before the wing-tip ....(p. 161) **SCENOPINIDÆ**

35. Five posterior cells 36
At most four posterior cells 37

36. Fourth vein ending before the apex of the wing..(p. 189) **APIOCERIDÆ**
Fourth vein ending behind the apex of the wing...(p. 185) **THEREVIDÆ**

37. Anal cell open or closed near the wing margin, the anal vein reaching the margin ....(p. 191) **BOMBYLIIDÆ**
Anal cell closed far from the wing margin, the anal vein never extending to the margin, sometimes absent..............(p. 205) **EMPIDÆ**

38. Anal cell elongate, tapering and acute apically, closed near the border of the wing; basal cells usually elongate.........................39
Anal cell short, transverse, oblique, or convex apically, if somewhat pointed the apex partly transverse, partly drawn out into a triangular point posteriorly 40

39. Anal cell closed very close to the wing margin; a spurious vein running obliquely between the third and fourth longitudinal veins. (p. 247) **SYRPHIDÆ**
Anal cell usually shorter; no spurious vein..........................40

40. Head extremely large, hemispherical, the front and face very narrow; arista dorsal ....(p. 245) **PIPUNCULIDÆ**
Head not unusually large; face or front usually wide.................41

41. Frontal lunule entirely absent, the parafacials not differentiated by a suture 42
Frontal lunule present; parafacials differentiated by a suture which extends above the antennæ and is indistinct only in some Conopidæ....44

42. Anterior crossvein situated at or before the basal fourth of the wing; second basal and discal cells always united...(p. 215) **DOLICHOPIDÆ**
Anterior crossvein situated far beyond the basal fourth of the wing or the second basal cell complete 43

43. Anal cell pointed posteriorly; proboscis never rigid and adapted for piercing ....(p. 242) **PLATYPEZIDÆ**
Anal cell not pointed posteriorly; proboscis usually rigid; never a single row of acrostical hairs ....(p. 205) **EMPIDÆ**

44. Coxæ close together at the base, the legs attached ventrally...........45
Coxæ widely separated at the base, the legs attached toward the sides of the thorax; usually leathery or coriaceous flies; ectoparasites (Pupipara) 91

45. Second antennal segment with a longitudinal seam along the upper outer edge extending almost the whole length; posterior calli definitely formed by a depression extending from behind the base of the wings to above the base of the scutellum (Calypteratæ; Muscoidea)..85
Second antennal segment rarely with a well developed dorsal seam, the posterior calli not differentiated (except in Gasterophilus); squamæ small (Acalypteratæ) 46

46. Mouth parts vestigial, sunken in a very small oral pit.
(p. 400) **GASTEROPHILIDÆ**
Mouth parts well developed, the oral opening large..................47

47. Posterior spiracle with several hairs on the border in addition to the pubescence, (visible only with high magnification) 50
Posterior spiracle with pubescence only 48

48. Subcosta complete, free from the first vein and ending in the costa (cf. Trypaneidæ) 64
Subcosta incomplete, or not ending in the costa or the apex curved forward beyond the bend 49

49. Subcosta curved forward at nearly a right angle and weakened beyond the bend, the costa fractured at the apex of the subcosta; wings almost always pictured....................(p. 285) **TRUPANEIDÆ**
Subcosta not angularly curved and weakened.........................51

50. Head broad, flattened above; scutellum and thorax flattened, the former elongate; large flies....................(p. 299) **ROPALOMERIDÆ**
Head rather spherical; scutellum usually convex, not elongate; small, cylindrical flies ....(p. 313) **SEPSIDÆ**

51. First segment of the posterior tarsi shortened and incrassate.
(p. 360) **BORBORIDÆ**
First segment of the posterior tarsi normal, usually longer than the second 52

52. Anal cell absent 53
Anal cell present 55

53. Postocellar bristles divergent....................(345) **EPHYDRIDÆ**
Postocellars convergent or absent.....................................54

54. Ocellar triangle large; fifth vein with a distinct curvature near the middle of the discal cell...................(p. 339) **CHLOROPIDÆ**
Ocellar triangle small; fifth vein straight or without a sharp curvature.
(p. 325) **DROSOPHILIDÆ**

55. Costa broken at the humeral crossvein..............................56
Costa not broken at the humeral crossvein............................58

56. Postocellars divergent, if absent the arista absent.
(p. 332) **AGROMYZIDÆ**
Postocellars convergent, parallel or absent, arista present............57

57. A pair of convergent frontal bristles anteriorly; interfrontals often present ....(p. 334) **PHYLLOMYZIDÆ**
Anterior frontals not convergent.............(p. 325) **DROSOPHILIDÆ**

58. Postocellar bristles convergent..................(p. 329) **OPOMYZIDÆ**
Postocellar bristles divergent or absent..............................59

59. Ocellar triangle large and shining, reaching the anterior edge of the front ....(p. 356) CANACEIDÆ
Ocellar triangle short 60

60. Second vein joining the costa just beyond the apex of the first.
(p. 328) ASTEIIDÆ
Second vein joining the costa far beyond the apex of the first........61

61. Costa fractured or weakened at the apex of the auxiliary vein.........62
Costa not at all weakened..................(p. 323) PERISCELLIDÆ

62. Oral vibrissæ present ....(p. 332) AGROMYZIDÆ
Oral vibrissæ absent 63

63. Sternopleural bristle present..................(p. 329) OPOMYZIDÆ
Sternopleural bristle absent..........................(p. 374) PSILIDÆ

64. Oral vibrissæ present 65
Oral vibrissæ absent 71

65. Mesonotum and scutellum convex, if rather flattened the abdomen and legs not bristly 66
Mesonotum and scutellum flattened; legs and abdomen conspicuously bristly ....(p. 376) CŒLOPIDÆ

66. Postvertical bristles divergent 68
Postvertical bristles convergent 67

67. Orbital plates bearing the frontal bristles short and oblique.
(p. 378) HELOMYZIDÆ
Orbital plates long, extending to the anterior margin of the front or almost so ....(p. 371) CHYROMYIDÆ

68. Second basal and discal cells separated 69
Second basal and discal cells confluent......(p. 325) DROSOPHILIDÆ

69. Anterior half of the front with strong bristles, two to four pairs present on the front; third antennal segment short and rather orbicular, the arista subapical ....(p. 362) CLUSIIDÆ
At most two pairs of rather weak frontal bristles situated on the posterior half; arista sub-basal 70

70. Eyes round; occiput convex and prominent.......(p. 310) PIOPHILIDÆ
Eyes, vertical, elongate; occiput concave; antennæ long.
(p. 298) LONCHÆIDÆ

71. Legs long and slender, stilt-like; apical cell narrowed...............72
Legs shorter and more robust, if rather long the apical cell not strongly narrowed 75

72. Propleura haired 73
Propleura bare in the middle..74

73. Pteropleura haired on whole surface...........(p. 301) TANYPEZIDÆ
Pteropleura bare on anterior half; second basal cell confluent with the discal ....(p. 306) MICROPEZIDÆ

74. Arista apical ....(p. 308) NERIIDÆ
Arista dorsal ....(p. 303) CALOBATIDÆ

75. Apical cell closed or almost so in the wing margin; abdomen cylindrical, the genitalia usually large....................(p. 265) CONOPIDÆ
Apical cell not strongly narrowed or the abdomen short and broad......76

76. Some or all of the tibiæ with preapical dorsal bristle..................77
Tibiæ without preapical bristle..80

77. Postocellar bristles parallel, divergent or absent......................78
Postocellar bristles convergent................(p. 315) **LAUXANIIDÆ**

78. Clypeus never prominent; femora with bristles..........................79
Clypeus very prominent; femora without bristles.(p. 382) **DRYOMYZIDÆ**

79. Ovipositor flat and wide; front long and moderately narrow; head short, hemispherical, the antennæ never porrect; shining blackish flies. (p. 298) **LONCHÆIDÆ**
Ovipositor not prominent; front wide; head more or less orbicular or the front produced; antennæ usually porrect; very rarely shining black ....(p. 367) **TETANOCERIDÆ**

80. Antennæ situated on the eye-stalks or at their base.(p. 358) **DIOPSIDÆ**
Antennæ situated on the front, though widely separated, regardless of the presence of eye-stalks..81

81. Ocelli absent ....(p. 268) **PYRGOTIDÆ**
Ocelli present 82

82. Postocellar bristles convergent or absent 83
Postocellar bristles divergent or parallel 84

83. Posterior femora swollen and spinose beneath; abdomen clavate; small, slender flies ....(p. 373) **MEGAMERINIDÆ**
Posterior femora not swollen and spinose; abdomen short and rather broad, never clavate ....(p. 365) **CHAMÆMYIDÆ**

84. Presutural dorsocentrals absent or the subcostal and first veins end far apart ....(p. 271) **OTITIDÆ**
Presutural dorsocentrals present or the thorax bearing very long, fine pile ....(p. 296) **PALLOPTERIDÆ**

85. Metascutellum developed, appearing as a strong convexity below the scutellum; hypopleura with strong bristles.....(p. 415) **TACHINIDÆ**
Metascutellum weak or absent, or if developed there is only hair on the hypopleura 86

86. Oral opening and mouth parts very small; hypopleura with abundant long hair 87
Oral opening normal; hypopleura with a row of bristles or only short, sparse hair 88

87. Scutellum extending far beyond the base of the metanotum; metascutellum never developed...................(p. 411) **CUTEREBRIDÆ**
Scutellum very short; metascutellum usually strongly developed; palpi usually large ....(p. 413) **ŒSTRIDÆ**

88. Hypopleura with a row of bristles.......................................89
Hypopleura with fine, short hair or bare 90

89. Apical cell strongly narrowed apically...........(p. 402) **METOPIIDÆ**
Apical cell not at all narrowed apically.............(p. 384) **MUSCIDÆ**

90. Oral vibrissæ absent; mesonotum without bristles except above the wings ....(p. 374) **PSILIDÆ**
Oral vibrissæ present; mesonotum with bristles......(p. 384) **MUSCIDÆ**

PUPIPARA AND FLIES WITHOUT OR WITH ABORTED WINGS

91. Coxæ widely separated by the sternum; usually parasitic on warm blooded animals 92
Coxæ approximate basally; not parasitic on warm blooded animals (except Streblidæ) 95

92. Mesonotum short, resembling the abdominal segments; antennæ inserted in lateral grooves........................(p. 472) **BRAULIDÆ**
Mesonotum and abdomen differentiated 93

93. Head small and narrow, folding back into a groove on the mesonotum; prosternum produced ....(p. 476) **NYCTERIBIIDÆ**
Head not folding back in a special groove; prosternum not produced....94

94. Palpi broader than long; wings uniformly veined..(p. 477) **STREBLIDÆ**
Palpi elongate, forming a sheath for the proboscis; wing veins crowded anteriorly, weak or absent posteriorly.......(p. 473) **HIPPOBOSCIDÆ**

95. Antennæ and mouth parts present 96
Antennæ and mouth parts absent................(p. 477) **STREBLIDÆ**

96. Antennæ consisting of six or more freely articulated segments 97
Antennæ consisting of at most three freely articulated segments......103

97. Mesonotum without a complete, V-shaped suture 98
Mesonotum with a complete V-shaped suture........(p. 33) **TIPULIDÆ**

98. Eyes meeting over the antennæ 99
Eyes widely separated above the antennæ..........................101

99. Abdomen enormously swollen, the apical four segments slender; termite guests ....(p. 101) **CECIDOMYIDÆ**
Abdomen normal 100

100. Scutellum and halteres present.................(p. 131) **SCATOPSIDÆ**
Scutellum and halteres absent.....................(p. 118) **SCIARIDÆ**

101. Termite guests; ocelli absent; wings with several veins.
(p. 78) **PSYCHODIDÆ**
Not termite guests 102

102. Halteres present ....(p. 69) **CHIRONOMIDÆ**
Halteres absent ....(p. 120) **MYCETOPHILIDÆ**

103. Antennæ apparently consisting of one more or less globular segment; posterior femora robust and laterally compressed..(p. 234) **PHORIDÆ**
Antennæ with two or three quite evident segments; posterior femora not laterally compressed 104

104. Frontal lunule present 105
Frontal lunule absent ....(p. 205) **EMPIDÆ**

105. First segment of the posterior tarsi short and swollen.
(p. 360) **BORBORIDÆ**
First segment of the posterior tarsi longer than the second segment and not swollen 106

106. Arista with long, sparse rays................(p. 325) **DROSOPHILIDÆ**
Arista pubescent or bare; third antennal segment orbicular; wings mutilated by the fly.......................(p. 378) **HELOMYZIDÆ**

Superfamily Tipuloidea

These are the "Crane Flies" and include the families Tanyderidæ, Ptychopteridæ, Trichoceridæ, Tipulidæ and Anisopodidæ. The first four mentioned families are characterized by the presence of a V-shaped suture on the mesonotum, and have, until recent years constituted the family Tipulidæ. In the Ptychopteridæ this suture is more or less obsolete posteriorly where it extends into the prescutellar depression but its form is always very well marked. The inclusion of the Anisopodidæ with the Crane-Flies may be questioned by some students of the Order. I think the question is a debatable one: at any rate, the family seems to form more or less of a connecting link between the Tipulids and Mycetophilids.

The manuscript for the Tipuloidea has been prepared by Dr. C. P. Alexander and this fact assures the student of thorough and accurate keys together with the latest views on generic limits and classification. The study of this group might almost be said to be a "world apart" in the study of Diptera and I cannot fully express my gratitude to Dr. Alexander for the service he has rendered in preparing this part of the work.

Family Tanyderidæ—The Primitive Crane Flies

Generalized flies of medium size, usually with a handsomely banded wing-pattern. Mouthparts often produced. Antennæ with from 15 to 25 segments; flagellar segments simple, cylindrical. Eyes with erect setæ between ommatidia; ocelli lacking. Latero-cervical sclerites sometimes greatly elongated, short in the local species. Wings with five branches of Radius reaching the margin (*Fig. 11); most genera with one or two supernumerary crossveins in the outer radial or medial fields, these never exceeding two in any one genus, usually with a single such element. Male hypopygium with a single dististyle, usually simple, weakly bifid in the two regional genera. Aedeagus trifid.

The immature stages occur in sandy soil at margins of major streams, the larva being aquatic or nearly so.

There are 23 recent species of Tanyderidæ, distributed in 10 genera, chiefly Australasian in distribution. Two genera with three species occur in North America.

KEY TO GENERA

1. A supernumerary crossvein in cell M_3 of the wing (*Fig. 11). **Protoplasa** Osten Sacken

   Wings without supernumerary crossveins....... **Protanyderus** Handlirsch

The most important recent literature is as follows:

Alexander, C. P.

1919. The crane-flies of New York. Part I. Distribution and taxonomy of the adult flies. Cornell Univ. Agr. Expt. Sta., Mem. 25: p. 883, 1 fig.

1927. Diptera. Fam. Tanyderidæ. Genera Insectorum, Fasc. 189.

1930. Observations on the Dipterous family Tanyderidæ. Proc. Linn. Soc. New South Wales, lv, pp. 221-230, 2 pls., 1 fig. (larva and pupa).

Crampton, G. C.

1925. A phylogenetic study of the thoracic sclerites of the non-Tipuloid Nematocerous Diptera. Ann. Ent. Soc. America, xviii, pp. 49-74, 5 pls.

1926. The external anatomy of the primitive Tanyderid Dipteran **Macrochile spectrum** Lœw, preserved in Baltic Amber. Bull. Brooklyn Ent. Soc., xxi, pp. 1-14, 2 pls.

1930a. Some anatomical details of the pupa of the archaic Tanyderid Dipteron **Protoplasa fitchii** O. S. Proc. Ent. Soc. Washington, xxxii, pp. 83-98, 3 pls.

1930b. A comparison of the more important structural details of the larva of the archaic Tanyderid Dipteron **Protoplasa fitchii,** with other Holometabola, from the standpoint of phylogeny. Bull. Brooklyn Ent. Soc., xxv, pp. 239-258, 4 pls.

Williams, Inez

1933. The external morphology of the primitive Tanyderid Dipteron **Protoplasa fitchii** O. S., with notes on the other Tanyderidæ. Journ. N. Y. Ent. Soc., xli, pp. 1-36, 7 pls. (anatomy of adult; comparative wing-figures of all genera of Tanyderidæ).

---

* Plate II, Tipuloidea.

Family Ptychopteridæ—The False Crane Flies

Antennæ elongate, with 16 (Ptychopterinæ) to 20 segments (Bittacomorphinæ); flagellar segments cylindrical. Suture between praescutum and scutum obsolete—posteriorly. Wings with R_2 preserved as a distinct element, lying far distad, subequal in length to R_{1+2}; three branches of Radius reach margin; two or three branches of Media; a single Anal vein (*Fig. 12).

The immature stages occur in saturated organic earth, the larvæ with an elongate caudal breathing-tube, the pupæ with a single greatly elongated pronotal breathing-horn.

There are two subfamilies, with 3 genera, *Ptychoptera* with 24 species, *Bittacomorphella* with 3 species, *Bittacomorpha* with 2 species. In the New World, the family is found only in the Nearctic region, all genera being found on the eastern and western coasts but rare or lacking in the plains region.

KEY TO GENERA

1. Antennæ 16-segmented; wings with cell M_1, present (*Fig. 12); (Ptychopterinæ) .... **Ptychoptera** Meigen
   Antennæ 20-segmented; wings with cell M_1 lacking; (Bittacomorphinæ).. 2

2. Wings with macrotrichia in distal ends of radial and medial cells; basitarsi of legs not dilated .... **Bittacomorphella** Alexander
   Wings without macrotrichia in cells; basitarsi of legs conspicuously dilated .... **Bittacomorpha** Westwood

The latest literature on the family:

Alexander, C. P.

1919. The crane-flies of New York. Part I. Distribution and taxonomy of the adult flies. Cornell Univ. Agr. Expt. Sta., Mem. 25, pp. 884-886, figs. 2-4.

1920. The same, Part II. Biology and Phylogeny. Ibid., Mem. 38, pp. 772-787, pls. 14-18, incl. (larva and pupa).

1927. Diptera. Fam. Ptychopteridæ. Genera Insectorum, Fasc. 188, pp. 1-12, 1 pl.

* Plate II, Tipuloidea.

Family Trichoceridæ—The Winter Crane Flies

Small or medium-sized flies of slender build, the antennæ elongate, setaceous. Three ocelli. Wings with m-cu lying far distad; two complete Anal veins, 2nd A very short, incurved to anal angle, slightly longer and more extended in *Diazosma.* Male hypopygium with a single dististyle, this cylindrical or with a variously developed lobe on basal portion of mesal face. Ovipositor with cerci upcurved, the convexity being on the ventral surface.

The so-called "winter crane flies" are most numerous in Spring and Fall, though sometimes abundant during mild days of Winter. They are usually found in large to small swarms in the open, but may be found in cellars, mines and similar places. The immature stages occur in decaying vegetable matter.

There are 4 valid genera with about 45 described species. *Trichocera* is essentially a genus of the northern Hemisphere; *Diazosma* is represented only by 2 species, with a wide distribution in the Holarctic region. *Paracladura* has several species in New Zealand and Chile, with a few others in eastern Asia; a single species (*trichoptera* O.S.) is found on our Pacific coast.

KEY TO GENERA

1. Wings with vein 2nd A subsinuate, not short and curved abruptly into the anal angle; north temperate.................. **Diazosma** Bergroth
   Wings with vein 2nd A short, curved abruptly into the anal angle...... 2

2. Tibial spurs present; tarsi with basitarsus longer than segments 2 and 3 taken together; (* fig. 13); north temperate to arctic.
   Trichocera Meigen
   Tibial spurs lacking; basitarsus very short, only two or three times as long as wide, shorter than the third tarsal segment; western.
   Paracladura Brunetti

The most important recent literature:

Alexander, C. P.

1919. The crane-flies of New York. Part I. Distribution and taxonomy of the adult flies. Cornell Univ. Agr. Expt. Sta., Mem. 25, pp. 887-888, figs. 165, 166.

1920. The same. Part II. Biology and Phylogeny. Ibid. Mem. 38, pp. 789-791, pl. 19 (larva and pupa).

1926. The Trichoceridæ of Australia (Diptera). Proc. Linnean Soc. New South Wales, 51, pp. 299-304, 11 figs. (key to genera).

---

* Plate II, Tipuloidea.

Edwards, F. W.

1928. Diptera. Fam. Protorhyphidæ, Anisopodidæ, Pachyneuridæ, Trichoceridæ. Genera Insectorum, Fasc. 190, pp. 1-41, 2 pls.

Rhynehart, J. G.

1925. The larva and pupa of **Trichocera regelationis** L. Proc. Belfast Nat. Hist. and Phil. Soc., sess. 1922-1923, pp. 3-14, pls. 1-3.

Family Tipulidæ—The Crane Flies

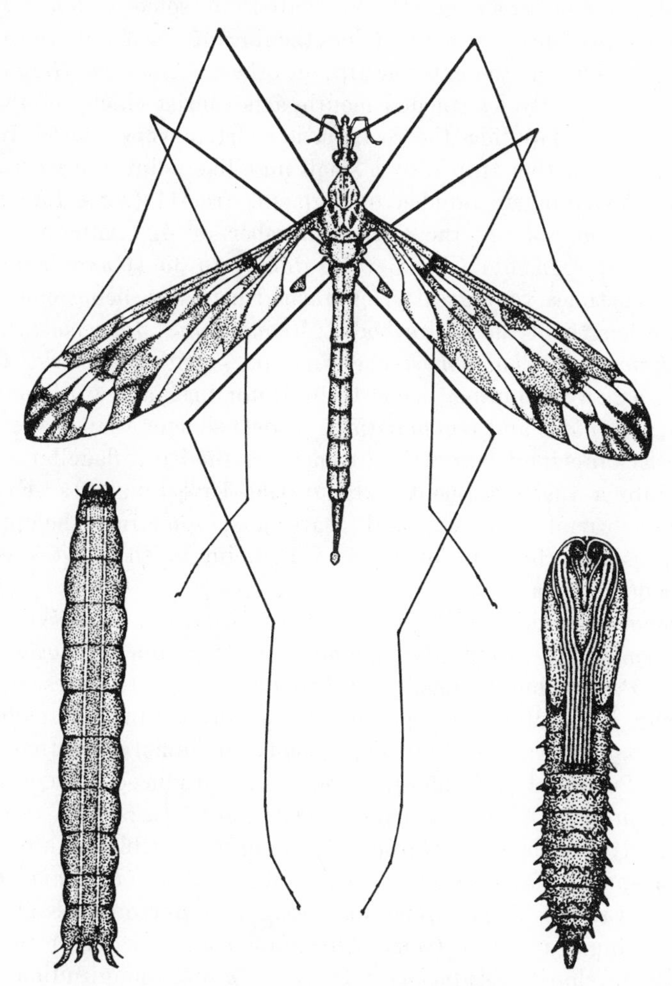

Tipula trivittata—adult, larva, pupa.

The present family, commonly called "crane flies", includes slender-bodied flies, having long to very long, unusually brittle legs that break readily between the trochanter and femur. From allied families of Nematocera, they are readily told by the lack of ocelli, two Anal veins, and the presence of the so-called V-shaped suture between the mesonotal præscutum and scutum. In many species there is a closed discal (1st M_2) cell. In size, the various species show a range almost as great as that found in the entire order, from tiny flies with a wing-length of about 2 millimeters (as *Dasymolophilus*) to gigantic forms with a wing-length in excess of 45 millimeters (*Ctenacroscelis*).

Rostrum sometimes greatly elongated, in some (*Elephantomyia: Toxorhina*) produced by a great lengthening of the front, the reduced mouthparts being at the extreme tip; in others (*Limonia: Geranomyia*) the similarly greatly lengthened mouthparts consist chiefly of the labial palpi. In most Tipulidæ the rostrum is short to very short. In many Tipulinæ it is further tipped by a small nose-like point, the *nasus*. Maxillary palpi ranging in number of segments from 1 (some *Limonia* and *Hexatoma: Conosia*) to the normal number of 4. Antennæ ranging in number of segments from 6 (*Hexatoma*) to 39 (*Gynoplistia: Cerozodia*); sometimes very greatly lengthened in males, being one or more times the length of the entire body (*Megistocera; Macromastix; Hexatoma: Eriocera; Rhabdomastix*); sometimes with branched flagellar segments (many Tipulinæ; some Cylindrotominæ; a few Limoniinæ, as *Limonia: Rhipidia* and *Gynoplistia*); pedicel shorter than scape (except in some Eriopterine Claduraria); sometimes the basal flagellar segments united into a fusion-segment (Claduraria, Toxorhinaria). Eyes with ommatidia variable in size and coarseness; sometimes holoptic (*Limonia*), usually broadly dichoptic. Pediciini with short erect setæ between ommatidia.

Pronotum sometimes lengthened (some *Limonia, Toxorhina*). Præscutum sometimes produced cephalad over pronotum (*Conosia, Trentepohlia*). Paired double dots, the *tuberculate pits*, often present, one on either side of midline on cephalic half of præscutum. *Pseudosutural foveae* often present as shiny depressions on humeral portion of præscutum. Postnotal pleurotergite sometimes produced into a tubercle (some Tipulinæ). Halteres long to very long. Legs with trochanters short, rarely lengthened (*Atarba, Rhabdomastix*); tibiæ with or without terminal spurs; claws simple or variously toothed (*Limonia, Tipula*). Wings of various shapes, sometimes long and narrow, the anal angle correspondingly reduced (some *Limonia*), sometimes with the region squarely developed (*Antocha*). In cases, a pale longitudinal fold in cell Cu of wings (*Dicranoptycha*). The details of venation are not discussed here, having been thoroughly considered by the present writer in recent papers that are cited in the morphological bibliography at end of paper and which may be consulted for details. The chief premise of the interpretation of the radial field is that the so-called radial cross-vein, r, of the Comstock-Needham system, has never been developed in the Diptera, the vein that has been so interpreted in the few families where it is found being the transverse free portion of R_2. The anterior branch of the radial field is labelled R_{1+2}, except in the subtribe Limoniaria, where the free tip of vein Sc_2 has migrated along vein R_1 to occupy the extreme tip of the vein. A series of diagrams (Figs. 3 to 10) indicates this tendency, which involves many hundreds of species in the vast genus *Limonia.* The medial and cubital fields are interpreted according to the Tillyard modification of the Comstock-Needham system.

Male hypopygium usually simple, the basistyles (coxites) bearing the dististyles (styles) at or near apex. Aedeagus and its subtending gonapophyses furnishing characters of paramount importance for specific determination. A dorsal lobe of the basistyle, the interbase, sometimes present. Ovipositor with the tergal valves (cerci) lengthened, heavily sclerotized, usually gently to strongly upcurved, exceeding the short, straight sternal valves (hypovalvæ); in a few cases (as some Tipulinæ; Cylindrotominæ; Styringomyia and others), the valves of the ovipositor are short and fleshy.

Tipulidæ are great lovers of moist conditions, being chiefly restricted by humidity. Species have been taken within 600 miles of the North Pole, while others occur at altitudes of over 17,000 feet in Thibet. The majority of the species occupy the intermediate zone, the family being very numerous in species in all temperate parts of the World and similarly numerous in the subtropical and temperate portions of the mountainous regions of the Tropics. Lowland tropical species are fewer in number and are apt to have a very wide distribution. The lesser oceanic islands are practically devoid of the larger crane flies (Tipulinæ) while having numbers of species of the small fragile Limoniinæ (as *Limonia,* s.l.; *Styringomyia; Gonomyia: Lipophleps; Trentepohlia*). Under rigorous conditions, as the arctic, wind-swept coasts, high mountains and the like, species with reduced wings are frequently found, being most numerous in the female sex. The greatest reduction of wings is found in *Chionea,* which is virtually apterous in both sexes.

The Tipulidæ of the World now include more than 6000 species, arranged in 283 genera and subgenera (Tipulinæ, 76, Cylindrotominæ, 9; Limoniinæ, 198, the latter further distributed in the following tribes: Lechriini, 4; Limoniini, 37; Pediciini, 12; Hexatomini, 70, and Eriopterini, 75). Representatives of all three subfamilies and of all tribes with the exception of the Lechriini occur in the area under consideration.

Keys available for the identification of the adult flies are very few in number. The writer's preliminary study on the "Crane flies of New York", is now seriously out-of-date due to the great additions made in intervening years. The forthcoming volume on Diptera in the "Insects of Connecticut" series will largely supercede the earlier work. Both of these reports are restricted to the area embraced in northeastern

North America. No keys are available for most of the groups in other regions of the continent, with the exception of the papers listed in the bibliography on certain groups of Tipulidæ, which are lessened in value due to the great additions that have been made in later years.

KEYS TO SUBFAMILIES AND TRIBES, GENERA, ETC.

1. Terminal segment of maxillary palpus elongate, whiplash-like; nasus usually distinct; antennæ usually with 13 segments; wings with Sc_1 usually atrophied; vein Cu_1 constricted at m-cu, the latter usually at or close to fork of M_{3+4} (**1, 17 to 20**); body-size usually large. (Tipulinæ) 2
   Terminal segment of maxillary palpus short; no distinct nasus; antennæ usually with 14 or 16 segments; wings with Sc_1 present, its extreme tip atrophied in some Cylindrotominæ; vein Cu_1 straight, not constricted at m-cu, the latter placed far before the fork of M_{3+4}, usually at or close to fork of M (**21 to** 44); body-size usually small or medium.. 19

2. Legs unusually long and filiform; wings with vein R_{1+2} atrophied and with Sc_2 ending in Sc close to origin of Rs (**Dolichopeza, 19**), when R_{1+2} is preserved (**Brachypremna, 18; Tanypremna; Megistocera, 17**), vein Sc is very long, Sc_1 reaching C as a distinct element some distance beyond fork of Rs and with cell 2nd A usually very narrow (Dolichopezaria) 3
   Legs of normal stoutness for the family; wings with vein R_{1+2} preserved (**20**); when atrophied (a few species of **Tipula**) with Sc of moderate length, Sc_1 atrophied before fork of Rs and Sc_2 ending at or near midlength of Rs (exception, some species of **Longurio**); cell 2nd A of normal width.. 8

3. Wings with origin of vein M_4 basad of that of M_{1+2}; R_{2+3} angularly bent at near midlength (**17**); tropical, subtropical.
   Megistocera Wiedemann
   Wings with origin of vein M_4 distad of that of M_{1+2}, usually far beyond; R_{2+3} straight or nearly so, not angulated.................. 4

4. Wings with R_{1+2} pale, perpendicular to R_{2+3}; Rs strongly arcuated at origin (**18**)..........................**Brachypremna** Osten Sacken
   Wings with R_{1+2}, when present, oblique; Rs straight or gently arcuated throughout length, sometimes very short and transverse............ 5

5. Rs of moderate length, subequal to m-cu; Sc long, Sc_1 preserved, ending beyond fork of Rs; R_{1+2} pale but preserved; tropical.
   Tanypremna Osten Sacken
   Rs short, transverse, simulating a crossvein, about equal in length to one-half m-cu; Sc unusually short, Sc_1 atrophied, Sc_2 entering Sc before to just beyond origin of Rs; R_{1+2} atrophied. (**Dolichopeza**) 6

6. Wings with cell 1st M_2 open by atrophy of basal section of M_3, the outer medial field thus appearing pectinately branched (**19**); temperate ....**Dolichopeza: Dolichopeza** Curtis
   Wings with cell 1st M_2 closed.. 7

7. Cells beyond cord with abundant macrotrichia; tropical.
   Dolichopeza: Megistomastix Alexander
   Cells beyond cord glabrous; temperate....**Dolichopeza: Oropeza** Needham

8. Antennal flagellum of male branched, of female branched or serrate; legs relatively short and stout. (Ctenophoraria) 9
   Antennal flagellum simple (serrate in **Prionocera**, readily told by lack of antennal verticils); legs usually more slender. (Tipularia) 11

9. Antennæ of both sexes with two short branches at extreme base of flagellar segments two to seven inclusive; tropical. **Ozodicera: Dihexaclonus** Enderlein
   Antennæ of male with three or four branches on each of flagellar segments two to nine, of female merely serrate; north temperate.. 10

10. Antennæ of male with three pectinations on flagellar segments two to nine, each segment with a single branch on apical half, in addition to the usual basal pair; ovipositor greatly elongated, sabre-like .... **Tanyptera** Latreille
   Antennæ of male with two pairs of pectinations on flagellar segments two to nine, one pair being subbasal, the other subapical; ovipositor short and of normal Tipuline structure........**Ctenophora** Meigen

11. Wings with vein R_3 bent strongly caudad before end, thence angularly deflected cephalad, cell R_3 thus being much constricted at near midlength; western and tropical................**Holorusia** Lœw
   Wings with vein R_3 straight or only gently arcuated throughout its length, not constricting the cell **(20)**......................... 12

12. Flagellar segments without verticils, the lower face of individual segments produced to give the organ a serrate appearance; terminal flagellar segment abruptly more slender, north temperate to arctic. **Prionocera** Lœw
   Flagellar segments verticillate, simple or nearly so................ 13

13. Abdomen in both sexes greatly elongated, somewhat resembling that of a dragon-fly; verticils of outer flagellar segments very long and conspicuous; valves (cerci) of ovipositor with smooth margins; eastern. **(Longurio)** 14
   Abdomen not so elongated (except in female of **Tipula longiventris** Lw., which has the cerci of ovipositor serrate on margins); antennal verticils of moderate length only.......................... 15

14. Wings with cell M_1 sessile.............**Longurio: Æschnasoma** Johnson
   Wings with cell M_1 petiolate.................**Longurio: Longurio** Lœw

15. Wings with Rs short and oblique in position, shorter than m-cu; cell M_1 sessile or very short-petiolate; vein M_4 arising opposite or basad of origin of M_{1+2}; body-coloration highly polished, often black and yellow .... **Nephrotoma** Meigen
   Wings with Rs elongate, exceeding m-cu; cell M_1 petiolate; vein M_1 arising distad of origin of M_{1+2}; body-coloration usually opaque, pruinose or pollinose **(20)**. **(Tipula)**......................... 16

16. Wings with cell M_1 lacking; arctic.........**Tipula: Nesotipula** Alexander
   Wings with cell M_1 present 17

17. Size very small (wing not exceeding 9 mm.); vein R_{1+2} entirely atrophied; tropical ....**Tipula: Microtipula** Alexander
   Size larger (wing over 10 mm.; in species with R_{1+2} atrophied, wing over 12 mm.); R_{1+2} usually preserved.......................... 18

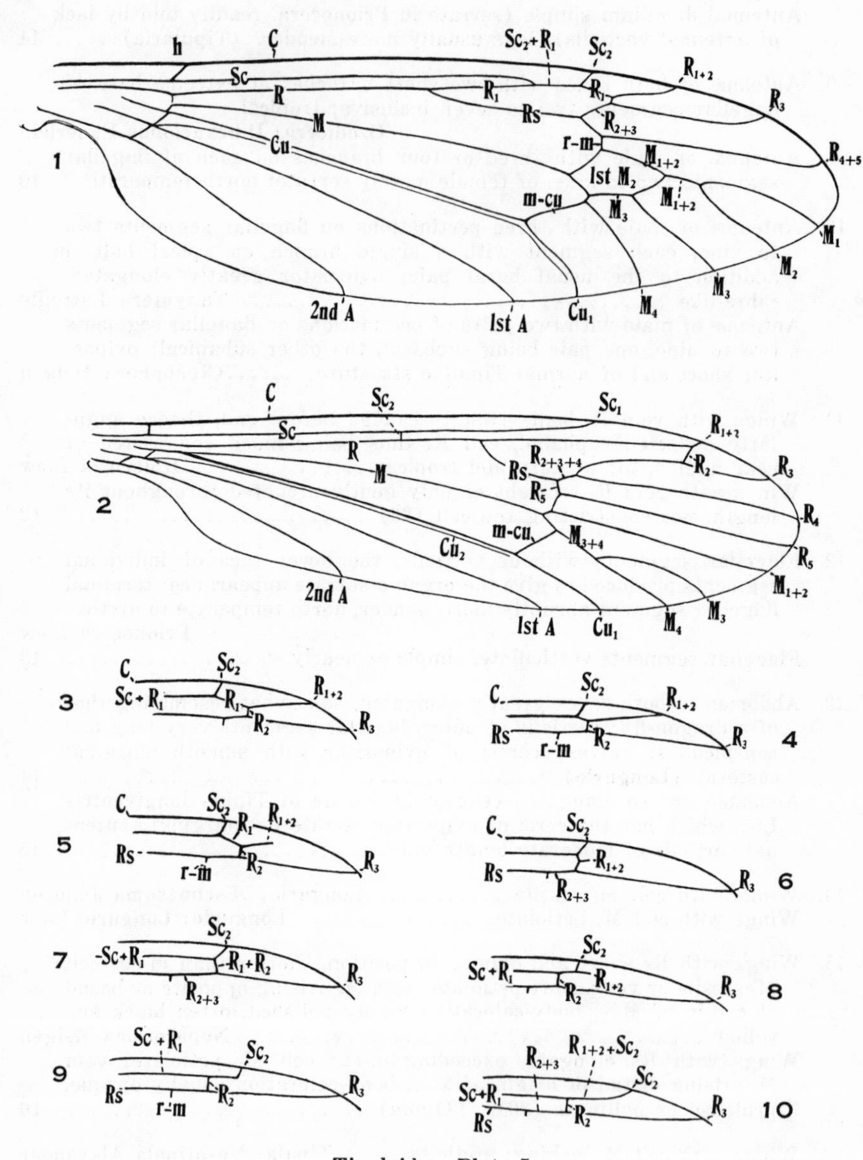

Tipuloidea, Plate I.

EXPLANATION OF PLATE

1. **Tanyptera fumipennis,** venation.

2. **Dicranota (Plectromyia) modesta,** venation.

3-10. A series of diagrams to illustrate the modification of the outer subcostal and radial fields of the wing, as found in the Tipulinæ, Cylindrotominæ, Lechriini and Limoniini.

3. The type found in the Orimargaria: Sc_2 preserved, R_{1+2} complete, attaining the wing-margin.

4. A further development of 3. Sc_2 has moved distad, shortening R_1; R_{1+2} still entire.

5. Condition as in 4 but with tip of R_{1+2} atrophied. Found in several Orimargaria, Limoniaria.

6. An accentuation of 5. The atrophy of R_{1+2} is still greater, R_1 more shortened and more or less in transverse alignment with the free tip of Sc_2. Condition found in numerous Limoniaria.

7. A still further modification of 5. The atrophy of R_{1+2} is now complete and R_1 is in direct transverse alignment with R_2, both in turn being in transverse alignment with the free tip of Sc_2. This is the commonest type in the Limoniaria, being found in most members of the following subgenera of **Limonia,—Dicranomyia, Geranomyia** and **Rhipidia,** as well as in some **Limonia,** s.s.

8. A type that reverts back to condition 5, with a long spur of R_{1+2} persisting, with the free tip of Sc_2 migrated distad along this spur to lie beyond the level of R_2. A condition found in several subgenera of **Limonia,** as **Peripheroptera, Limonia** and **Libnotes.**

9. A further modification of 8, where Sc_2 has migrated to the extreme tip of the spur of R_{1+2} but still forms a rectangular bend. **Limonia: Libnotes.**

10. The culmination of the series, where the free tip of Sc_2 has migrated to the extreme tip of the spur of R_{1+2} and then bends to the costal margin at a gently oblique angle. This condition is common in many **Limonia** of the subgenera **Limonia** and **Discobola.**

EXPLANATION OF SYMBOLS

Comstock-Needham system, as modified by Alexander and Tillyard

C = Costa; Cu = Cubitus; 1st M_2 = cell 1st M_2; M = Media; m-cu = medial-cubital crossvein; R = Radius; r-m = radial-medial crossvein; Rs = Radial sector; s = supernumerary crossvein; Sc = Subcosta; A = Anal veins.

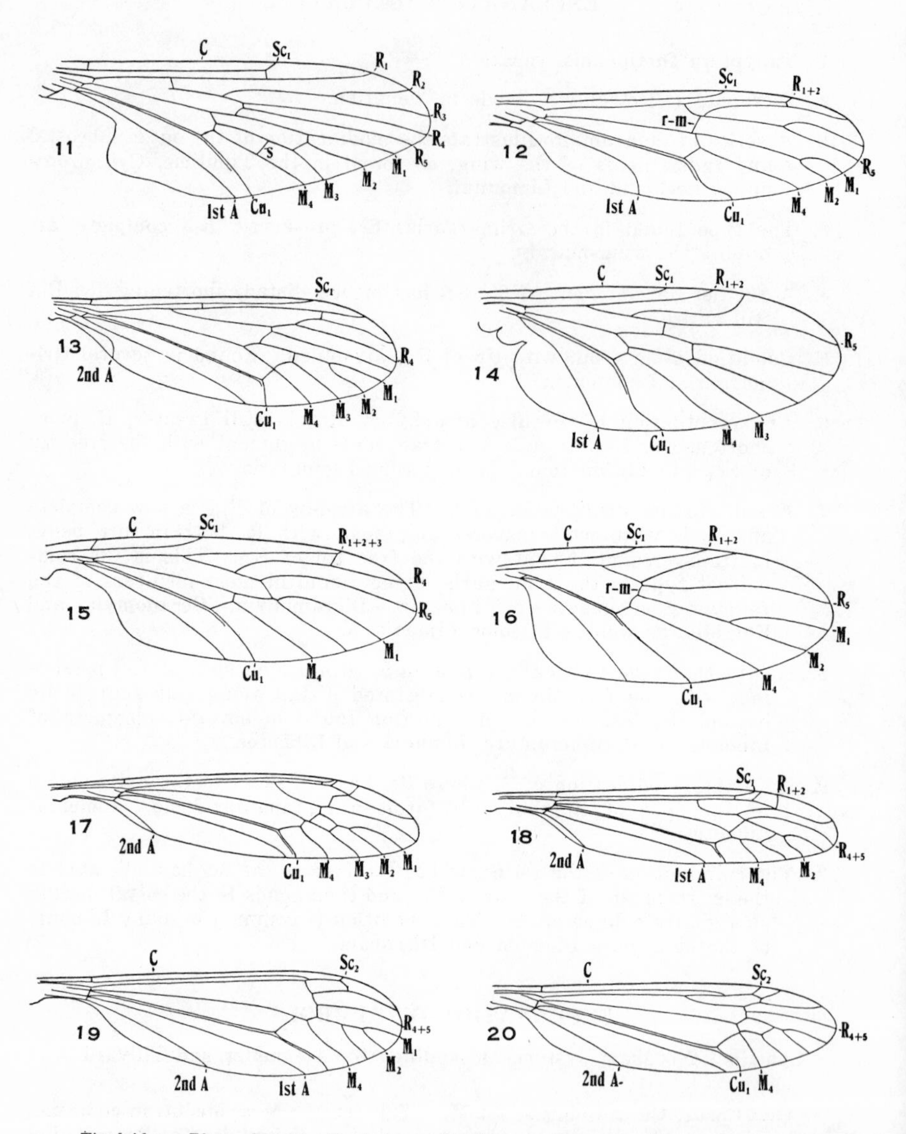

Tipuloidea, Plate II.—11. **Protoplasa fitchii,** venation; 12. **Ptychoptera rufocincta,** venation; 13. **Trichocera colei,** venation; 14. **Anisopus alternatus,** venation; 15. **Axymyia furcata,** venation; 16. **Mycteboia divergens,** venation; 17. **Megistocera longipennis,** venation; 18. **Brachypremna dispellens,** venation; 19. **Dolichopeza (Dolichopeza) americana,** venation; 20. **Tipula (Tipula) dorsomacula,** venation.

18. Wings with macrotrichia in apical cells...**Tipula: Trichotipula** Alexander
Wings with cells glabrous......................**Tipula: Tipula** Linnæus

19. Wings with tip of R_{1+2} atrophied, giving the appearance of a long fusion back from margin of veins R_1 and anterior branch of Rs; free tip of Sc_2 preserved (**21, 22, 23**) (Cylindrotominæ)........... 20
Wings sometimes with tip of R_{1+2} atrophied (some Limoniini) but not giving the appearance of a long fusion backward from margin of veins R_1 and anterior branch of Rs; free tip of Sc_2 preserved in many species of tribe Limoniini, lacking in other tribes in this fauna (**24 to 44**) (Limoniinæ)................................ 24

CYLINDROTOMINÆ: GENERA

20. Head and intervals of mesonotal præscutum with numerous deep punctures; a deep median groove on præscutum.... **Triogma** Schiner
Head and intervals of mesonotal præscutum smooth; no median præscutal groove 21

21. Three branches of Radius reach the margin, R_{1+2} being preserved as a distinct element .... **Phalacrocera** Schiner
Two branches of Radius reach the margin, R_{1+2} being entirely atrophied, giving the appearance of a long backward fusion of veins R_1 and anterior branch of Rs (**21-23**)..................... 22

22. Four branches of Media reach the margin (**21**)..**Cylindrotoma** Macquart
Three branches of Media reach the margin......................... 23

23. Wings with crossvein r-m present; outer end of cell 1st M_2 almost always closed by a single transverse vein, cell M_1 being present, sessile to short-petiolate; cells 2nd M_2 and M_3 confluent by atrophy or partial atrophy of distal section of vein M_3; antennæ nearly simple, the lower face of individual segments not produced (**22, 23**) ....**Phalacrocera** Schiner
Wings with crossvein r-m usually shortened to quite obliterated by the approximation or fusion of veins R_{4+5} and M_{1+2}; outer end of cell 1st M_2 closed by two transverse veins, these being M and the basal section of M_3; cell M_1 lacking, cells 2nd M_2 and M_3 distinct; antennæ strongly nodulose, especially in male, the individual flagellar segments nearly cordate...................**Liogma** Osten Sacken

TRIBES OF LIMONIINÆ

24. Eyes hairy; wings with vein Sc_1 very long, Sc_2 lying basad of origin of Rs (**2, 30**). (Pediciini)..................................... 41
Eyes glabrous; wings with Sc_1 short or of moderate length, when long (some Eriopterini), Sc_2 lying distad of origin of Rs; where Sc_2 lies basad of origin of Rs (some Limoniini, Eriopterini), the entire vein Sc is shortened.................................... 25

25. Wings with free tip of Sc_2 often present; veins R_4 and R_5 fused to margin, only two branches of Rs being present; antennæ usually with 14 (Limoniaria) or 16 segments; (**4-10, 24-29**) (Limoniini).. 27
Wings with free tip of Sc_2 atrophied; veins R_4 and R_5 separate, the former usually transferred to the upper branch, R_{2+3}, to form a distinct element R_{2+3+4}; usually with three branches of Rs present (except in **Atarba, Elephantomyia, Styringomyia, Teucholabis, Gonomyia** and **Toxorhina,** where R_4 is captured by R_{2+3}, as above); antennæ usually with 16 segments; (**31-44**).................... 26

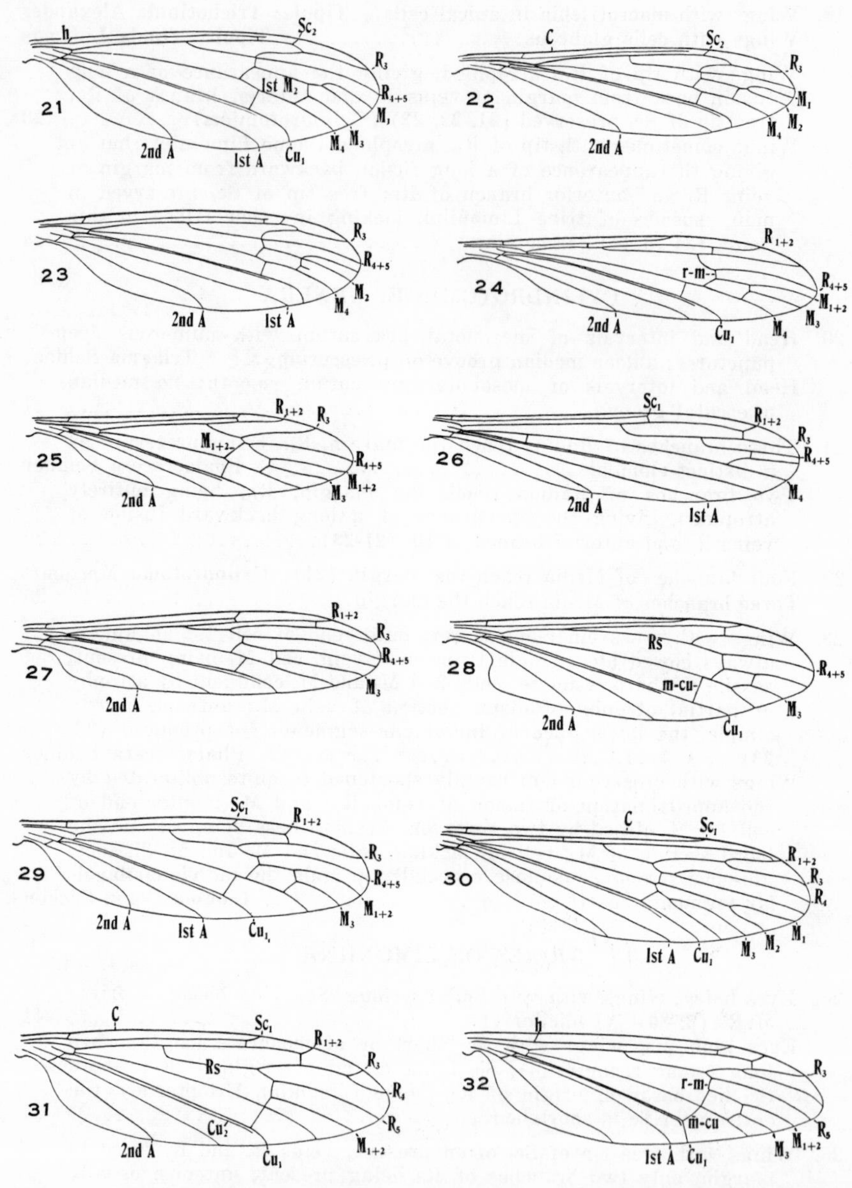

Tipuloidea, Plate III.—21. **Cylindrotoma tarsalis,** venation; 22. **Phalacrocera tipulina,** venation; 23. **Phalacrocera occidentalis,** venation; 24. **Elliptera tennessa,** venation; 25. **Helius (Helius) flavipes,** venation; 26. **Orimarga (Diotrepha) mirabilis,** venation; 27. **Dicranoptycha tigrina,** venation; 28. **Antocha saxicola,** venation; 29. **Limonia (Limonia) immatura,** venation; 30. **Pedicia (Tricyphona) protea,** venation; 31. **Hexatoma (Hexatoma) megacera,** venation; 32. **Hexatoma (Eriocera) longicornis,** venation.

26. Tibial spurs present. (Hexatomini) 51
Tibial spurs lacking. (Eriopterini) 78

LIMONIINI: SUBTRIBES, GENERA, SUBGENERA

27. Wings with vein R_2 lacking (25) 28
Wings with vein R_2 present (24, 26, 29) 29

28. Rostrum short and inconspicuous; Rs long and straight, running close to R_1 and in alignment with R_{2+3}; r-m distinct. (Ellipteraria). **Elliptera** Schiner
Rostrum of moderate length, about equal in length to remainder of head; Rs short, gently arcuated, not in alignment with R_{2+3}; r-m often shortened or obliterated by approximation of adjoining veins (25). (Heliaria) ....**Helius** St. Fargeau

29. Wings with m-cu more than three, (and usually much more), times its own length before the fork of M (26). (Orimargaria, **Orimarga**) 30
Wings with m-cu close to or beyond the fork of M, if before, the distance not or scarcely exceeding the length of the vein itself (24, 27, 29) 31

30. Wings with three branches of Media reaching margin, cell M_3 being present; m-cu beneath Rs..........**Orimarga: Orimarga** Osten Sacken
Wings with two branches of Media reaching margin, cell M_3 lacking; m-cu far before origin of Rs (26)..**Orimarga: Diotrepha** Osten Sacken

31. Wings with vein R_2 lying far distad, beyond level of outer end of cell 1st M_2; m-cu beyond fork of M (27) (Dicranoptycharia). **Dicranoptycha** Osten Sacken
Wings with vein R_2 in almost transverse alignment with r-m and basal half of cell 1st M_2; m-cu at or slightly before fork of M (24, 28, 29) 32

32. Wings with Rs long and straight (24, 28); antennæ 16-segmented... 33
Wings with Rs shorter and more arcuated (21); antennæ 14-segmented. (Limoniaria, **Limonia**) 34

33. Anal angle of wing very prominent, almost square; Rs long, diverging at an acute angle from R_1, ending approximately between the branches of Rs or in alignment with R_{4+5} (28) (Antocharia). **Antocha** Osten Sacken
Anal angle of wing normally rounded; Rs long, lying very close to R_1 and nearly parallel to it, its end in alignment with R_{2+3}; basal section of R_{4+5} short and arcuated, diverging from the end of Rs at nearly a right angle (24) (Ellipteraria)..........**Elliptera** Schiner

34. Wings with M and both sections of M_3 lacking, cell M_3 thus entirely obliterated ....**Limonia: Alexandriaria** Garrett
Wings with at least the distal section of M_3 preserved and usually with both sections, together with m, cell M_3 thus usually present (29) 35

35. Supernumerary crossveins present in certain cells of wing.......... 36
No supernumerary crossveins in cells of wing (excepting a weak element sometimes evident in cell Sc) (29) 37

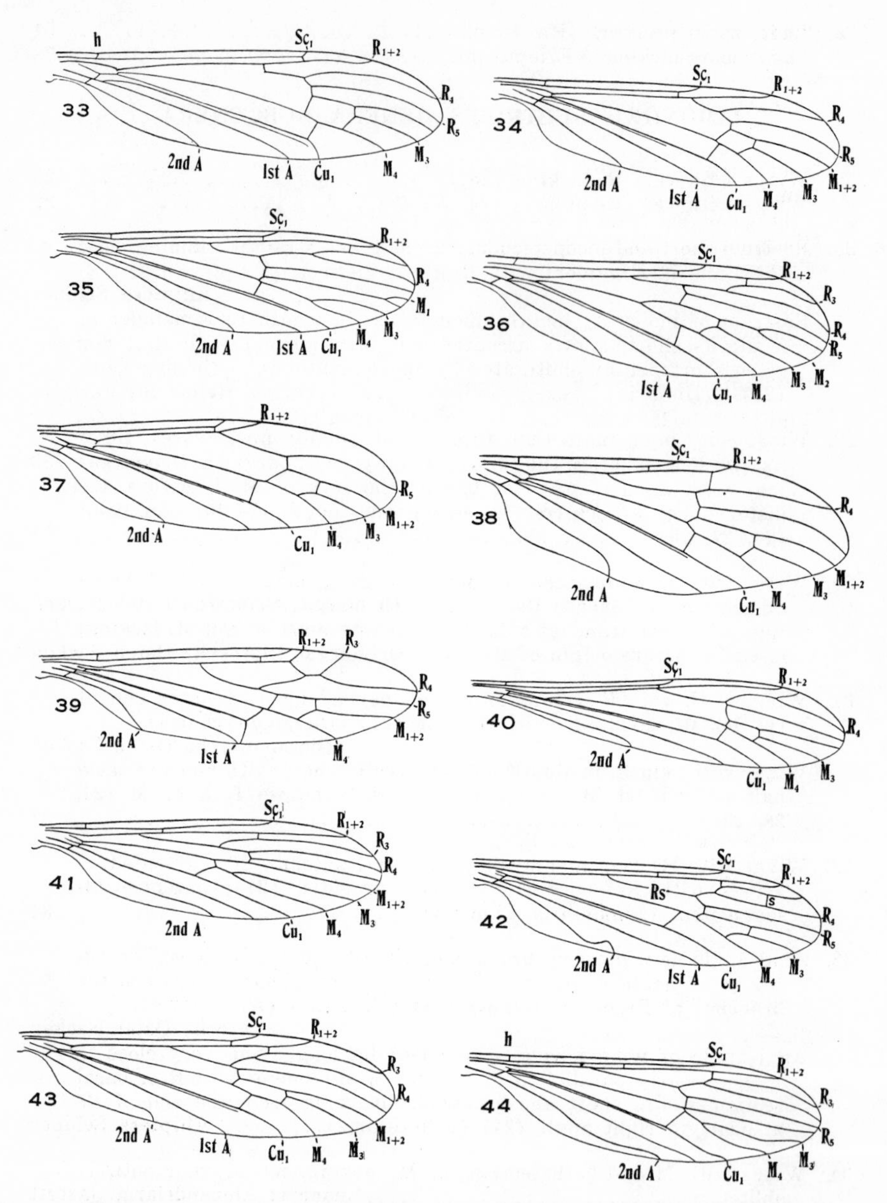

Tipuloidea, Plate IV.—33. **Elephantomyia westwoodi**, venation; 34. **Atarba (Atarba) picticornis**, venation; 35. **Polymera (Polymera) rogersiana**, venation; 36. **Prolimnophila areolata**, venation; 37. **Toxorhina (Toxorhina) muliebris**, venation; 38. **Teucholabis (Teucholabis) complexa**, venation; 39. **Trentepohlia (Paramongoma) bromeliadicola**, venation; 40. **Gonomyia (Gonomyia) subcinerea**, venation; 41. **Molophilus nitidus**, venation; 42. **Helobia hybrida**, venation; 43. **Gnophomyia tristissima**, venation; 44. **Erioptera (Erioptera) septemtrionis**, venation.

36. Wings with Sc short, Sc_1 ending opposite or before origin of Rs; a supernumerary crossvein in cell R_3. . **Limonia: Neolimnobia** Alexander
Wings with Sc long, ending about opposite fork of Rs; a supernumerary crossvein in cell 1st A, connecting the Anal veins. **Limonia: Discobola** Osten Sacken

37. Mouthparts, and especially the labial palpi, lengthened, the rostrum much longer than remainder of head, and usually about as long as the combined head and thorax. . . . . **Limonia: Geranomyia** Haliday
Mouthparts, with the labial palpi, not notably lengthened, shorter than remainder of head 38

38. Antennæ of male more or less branched (bipectinate, unipectinate or subpectinate), of female simply serrate, sometimes very weakly so. **Limonia: Rhipidia** Meigen
Antennæ simple in both sexes 39

39. Wings of male with the prearcular region greatly developed, of female less markedly so; wing-apex very obtuse; Sc_1 ending approximately opposite origin of Rs; tropical. **Limonia: Peripheroptera** Schiner
Wings of both sexes with prearcular cells small and inconspicuous; wing-tip not so obtusely rounded (except in some **Limonia,** s.s., where Sc is elongate, ending beyond midlength of Rs) 40

40. Wings with Sc short, Sc_1 ending opposite or before origin of Rs. **Limonia: Dicranomyia** Stephens
Wings with Sc long, Sc_1 ending beyond midlength of Rs (**29**). **Limonia: Limonia** Meigen

PEDICIINI: SUBTRIBES, GENERA, SUBGENERA

41. Wings with numerous macrotrichia on membrane (Ularia) . . **Ula** Haliday
Wings glabrous 42

42. Rostrum produced into a beak that is subequal in length to remainder of head; western . . . . **Ornithodes** Coquillett
Rostrum only inconspicuously developed 43

43. Antennæ with usually 16 segments; size large, wing usually over 10 mm. (**Pedicia**) 44
Antennæ with usually 13 or 15 segments; size small, wing usually under 8 mm. 45

44. Size very large (wing, 20 mm. or more); wings with a dark pattern that is arranged as a triangle, including broad costal and cubital seams that are connected across the very oblique cord; maxillary palpus with terminal segment elongate. . . . . **Pedicia: Pedicia** Latreille
Size smaller (wing, under 18 mm.); wings without a dark pattern arranged as a triangle, as above described; cord of wing transverse or nearly so (**30**); maxillary palpus with terminal segment short . . . . **Pedicia: Tricyphona** Zetterstedt

45. Wings with four supernumerary crossveins, located in cells R_1, R_3, R_4 and M; western . . . . **Polyangæus** Doane
Wings with at most a single supernumerary crossvein, this in cell R_1, basad of vein R_2 (**Dicranota**) 46

46. A supernumerary crossvein in cell R_1 about opposite end of vein Sc_1. 47
No supernumerary crossveins in cells of wing 49

47. Cell 1st M_2 closed; eastern............**Dicranota: Eudicranota** subg. n.
Cell 1st M_2 open by atrophy of m.. 48

48. Cell M_1 lacking ....**Dicranota: Paradicranota** subg. n.
Cell M_1 present ....**Dicranota: Dicranota** Zetterstedt

49. Cell 1st M_2 closed; eastern ....**Dicranota: Amalopina** Brunetti
Cell 1st M_2 open by atrophy of m.. 50

50. Cell M_1 lacking (2)..............**Dicranota: Plectromyia** Osten Sacken
Cell M_1 present ....**Dicranota: Rhaphidolabis** Osten Sacken

HEXATOMINI: SUBTRIBES, GENERA, SUBGENERA

51. Antennæ with not more than 12 segments (Hexatomaria, **Hexatoma**). 52
Antennæ with more than 14 segments 54

52. Cell 1st M_2 open; two branches of M reach the wing-margin (31); eastern............................**Hexatoma: Hexatoma** Latreille
Cell 1st M_2 closed; three or four branches of M reach the wing-margin (32).. 53

53. Feet snowy-white; eastern and tropical..**Hexatoma: Penthoptera** Schiner
Feet not white (32)......................**Hexatoma: Eriocera** Macquart

54. Wings with only two branches of Rs present; vein R_2 lacking........ 55
Wings with three branches of Rs present; vein R_2 preserved (except in **Phyllolabis**) 56

55. Rostrum elongate, exceeding one-half the length of the entire body (33); (Elephantomyaria)..............**Elephantomyia** Osten Sacken
Rostrum short and inconspicuous, not exceeding the remainder of head (34); eastern and tropical (Atarbaria).
Atarba: Atarba Osten Sacken

56. Apical cells of wing with macrotrichia 57
Cells of wing without macrotrichia (excepting in stigmal area)...... 61

57. A supernumerary crossvein in cell M; eastern (Limnophilaria).
Limnophila: Trichephelia Alexander
No supernumerary crossvein in cell M 58

58. Cell R_3 of wings sessile, subsessile or short-petiolate; R_{2+3+4} lacking or much shorter than m-cu. (Limnophilaria) 59
Cell R_3 of wings long-petiolate, R_{2+3+4} being as long as or longer than m-cu. 60

59. Wings with macrotrichia abundant, involving the cells basad of cord.
Ulomorpha Osten Sacken
Wings with sparse macrotrichia in cells beyond cord only.
Limnophila: Lasiomastix Osten Sacken

60. Small species (wing, ♂, less than 5 mm.); cell M_1 usually present; antennæ short in both sexes (Adelphomyaria)....**Adelphomyia** Bergroth
Larger flies (wing, ♂, over 6 mm.); cell M_1 lacking; antennæ of male very long; tropical (Limnophilaria) ....**Shannonomyia** Alexander

61. A supernumerary crossvein in cell C (Epiphragmaria).
Epiphragma Osten Sacken
No supernumerary crossvein in cell C (35)............................ 62

62\. Wings with vein R_2 lacking; m-cu at outer end of cell 1st M_2; western. **Phyllolabis** Osten Sacken
Wings with vein R_2 present; m-cu at or before two-thirds the length of cell 1st M_2, when the latter is present (35, 36)................ 63

63\. Wings with cell 1st M_2 open by atrophy of m (35); male with elongate nodulose antennæ; tropical and subtropical. **Polymera: Polymera** Wiedemann
Wings with cell 1st M_2 closed; antennæ of male not nodulose....... 64

64\. Wings with Sc very long, Sc_1, R_{1+2} and R_3 all ending close together at costal margin; tropical ....**Psaronius** Enderlein
Wings with Sc short, widely separated from either R_{1+2} or R_3 (36)... 65

65\. Wings with m-cu at or close to fork of M; anterior arculus lacking. (Dactylolabaria) ....**Dactylolabis** Osten Sacken
Wings with m-cu beyond the fork of M, at from one-third to about one-half the length of cell 1st M_2; where close to fork of M (some **Pseudolimnophila**) the arculus complete........................ 66

66\. Wings with the anterior arculus lacking (36) (Pseudolimnophilaria, in part) 67
Wings with the anterior arculus present 68

67\. Cell 1st M_2 of wings very large, its inner end lying far proximad of the other elements of the cord (36)..........**Prolimnophila** Alexander
Cell 1st M_2 of wings of normal size, its inner end straight and in approximate alignment with the elements of the anterior cord. **Archilimnophila,** g. n.

68\. Wings with Sc relatively short, Sc_1 ending before the level of the fork of Rs; where slightly longer (**Limnophila albipes** Leonard) the posterior tarsi snowy-white. (Limnophilaria, in part)................ 69
Wings with Sc longer, Sc_1 ending opposite or beyond the fork of Rs; (compare some species of **Pilaria,** distinguished by having the antennal verticils of unusual length) 70

69\. Antennæ with long conspicuous verticils; tuberculate pits present, small, placed at extreme cephalic end of præscutum; Rs elongate, exceeding vein R_3; cell M_1 present or lacking..........**Pilaria** Sintenis
Antennæ with short verticils; tuberculate pits lacking; Rs short and strongly arcuated or angulated at origin; cell M_1 lacking. **Shannonomyia** Alexander

70\. Head strongly narrowed and prolonged behind; radial and medial veins beyond cord long and sinuous; vein R_3 extending generally parallel to vein R_4, not diverging markedly at tips; vein 2nd A strongly curved to margin (Pseudolinmnophilaria, in part). **Pseudolimnophila** Alexander
Head broad, not conspicuously narrowed behind; radial and medial veins beyond cord more nearly straight; vein R_3 diverging strongly from vein R_4, cell R_3 conspicuously widened at margin; vein 2nd A not curved strongly into margin (Limnophilaria, in part, **Limnophila**).

71\. Supernumerary crossveins in either cell R_3 or cell M of wing....... 72
No supernumerary crossveins in cells of wing..................... 74

72. A supernumerary crossvein in cell R_3; eastern.
Limnophila: Dicranophragma Osten Sacken
A supernumerary crossvein in cell M.......................... 73

73. Rs long-spurred at origin; antennæ of male elongate.
Limnophila: Idioptera Macquart
Rs slightly if at all spurred at origin; antennæ short in both sexes.
Limnophila: Elæophila Rondani

74. Cell R_3 sessile; cell M_1 lacking......**Limnophila: Idiolimnophila,** subg. n.
Cell R_3 petiolate; cell M_1 present.......................... 75

75. Very large species (wing over 16 mm.); wings with the branches of M leaving the main stem at a strong angle, cell 1st M_2 thus being strongly hexagonal; eastern........**Limnophila: Eutonia** Van der Wulp
Smaller species (wing under 14 mm.); wings with the branches of M not strongly divergent, especially M_{3+4}, cell 1st M_2 being more nearly rectangular in outline.............................. 76

76. Wings with vein R_{2+3+4} short, subequal to the basal deflection of R_5; Rs elongate, exceeding four times R_{2+3+4}; coloration polished black or gray, the latter group having the male hypopygium with a series of teeth on margin of outer dististyle, producing a comb-like appearance ....**Limnophila: Prionolabis** Osten Sacken
Wings with R_{2+3+4} longer, usually exceeding the basal deflection of R_5; Rs shorter, not exceeding three times R_{2+3+4}; where the above characters are doubtful, the species have a closely irrorate brown wing-pattern; body coloration never polished black; when gray, male hypopygium without a comb of spines on outer dististyle.... 77

77. Rs short, weakly to more strongly angulated at origin, more rarely merely arcuated; R_{2+3+4} subequal to or shorter than m-cu; antennæ short in both sexes.............**Limnophila: Phylidorea** Bigot
Rs longer, more gently arcuated; in species with shorter Rs, antennæ of male elongate and usually with R_{2+3+4} long, considerably exceeding m-cu............................**Limnophila:** aberrant species

ERIOPTERINI: SUBTRIBES, GENERA, SUBGENERA

78. Nearly apterous, the wings reduced to microscopic structures that are smaller than the halteres; northern. (Claduraria).**Chionea** Dalman
Fully-winged species 79

79. Wings with cell M_1 present 80
Wings with cell M_1 lacking (37-44)............................ 84

80. Antennæ with the basal two to four segments united into a fusion-segment; wings with R_{2+3+4} much longer than the short basal section of R_5; veins Sc_1 and R_{1+2} widely separated at margin, the distance on Costa between them approximately three times r-m; legs plainly colored; temperate. (Claduraria)................................ 81
Antennæ with all flagellar segments distinct; wings with basal section of R_5 elongate, much exceeding R_{2+3+4}; veins Sc_1 and R_{1+2} closely approximated at margin, the distance on costa between them subequal to or shorter than r-m; legs conspicuously hairy, banded with black, rufous and white; tropical. (Lecteriaria).
Lecteria Osten Sacken

81. Wings with R_{2+3+4} subequal to or longer than vein R_3, cell R_3 thus being subequal to its petiole; vein R_2 at or before the fork of R_{3+4}. **Neolimnophila** Alexander
Wings with R_{2+3+4} shorter than vein R_3, cell R_3 being much longer than its petiole; R_2 far beyond fork of R_{2+3+4}.................... 82

82. Wings with cell M_1 very small, about one-third its petiole; fusion-segment of antenna very long, about equal to the succeeding four segments combined; western..................**Pterochionea** Alexander
Wings with cell M_1 subequal to or longer than its petiole; fusion-segment of antennæ shorter, about as long as the succeeding two or three segments combined. (**Cladura**)......................... 83

83. Wings with R_{1+2} elongate, exceeding R_{2+3+4}; R_{2+3} subequal to m-cu; male hypopygium with two dististyles..**Cladura: Neocladura** Alexander
Wings with R_{1+2} shorter than R_{2+3+4}; R_{2+3} approximately twice m-cu; male hypopygium with a single powerful dististyle. **Cladura: Cladura** Osten Sacken

84. Rostrum very long and slender, approximately one-half the entire body or longer; setæ of legs profoundly bifid (Toxorhinaria, **Toxorhina**) 85
Rostrum short, not exceeding remainder of head; setæ of legs simple. 86

85. Wings with Rs having a single branch (**37**); eastern and tropical. **Toxorhina: Toxorhina** Osten Sacken
Wings with Rs having two branches; tropical. **Toxorhina: Ceratocheilus** Wesché

86. Two branches of Rs reach the wing-margin (**38**).................. 87
Three branches of Rs reach the wing-margin (**39-44**).............. 89

87. Wings with R_1 ending before midlength; anterior branch of Rs diverging strongly from posterior branch, arising at or close to r-m, straight and oblique; tropical. (Styringomyaria)..**Styringomyia** Lœw
Wings with R_1 ending about opposite two-thirds their length; branches of Rs subparallel on basal half. (Gonomyaria).................. 88

88. Wings with R_2 present, close to fork of Rs; Sc usually long, Sc_1 ending beyond origin of Rs (**38**); some eastern, but chiefly tropical.......................**Teucholabis: Teucholabis** Osten Sacken
Wings with R_2 lacking; Sc short, Sc_1 ending opposite or before origin of Rs; chiefly tropical (Gonomyaria)...**Gonomyia: Lipophleps** Bergroth

89. Wings with R_5 fused with M_{1+2} to form the entire cephalic face of cell 1st M_2, r-m thus obliterated; only two branches of M reach the margin; vein 2nd A very short (**39**); tropical. (Trentepohliaria). **Trentepohlia: Paramongoma** Brunetti
Wings with R_5 entirely distinct from M_{1+2}, being separated by the r-m crossvein (the veins fused only in a few species of **Paratropesa,** where the alternative characters hold); three branches of M reach the margin; vein 2nd A of normal length (**40-41**).......... 90

90. Wings with cell R_3 short, vein R_3 shorter than the petiole of cell R_3 (**40**) 91
Wings with cell R_3 deep, vein R_3 longer than the petiole of cell R_3 (**42-44**); shortest in **Progonomyia** and **Empedomorpha**.......... 99

91. Wings with vein R_2 present 92
Wings with vein R_2 lacking 95

92. R_2 at end of Rs, in alignment with the other elements of the cord; r-m obliterated by the long fusion of veins R_{4+5} and M_{1+2}; tropical. (Gonomyaria)......................**Teucholabis: Paratropesa** Schiner
R_2 its length or more beyond the fork of Rs, R_{2+3+4} subequal to or longer than R_2; r-m distinct 93

93. Wings with Rs long and straight, exceeding the distal section of M_{1+2}; tuberculate pits on cephalic portion of præscutum; trochanters elongate; arctic and subarctic. (**Rhabdomastix**).
Rhabdomastix: Sacandaga Alexander
Wings with Rs shorter, less than the distal section of M_{1+2}; tuberculate pits removed from cephalic margin of præscutum; trochanters short. (**Erioptera**).. 94

94. Wings with veins R_3 and R_4 strongly diverging, cell R_3 having a **Gonomyia**-like shape..............**Erioptera: Gonempeda** Alexander
Wings with veins R_3 and R_4 more generally parallel, cell R_3 having the more normal **Erioptera**-shape, but shorter.
Erioptera: Empeda Osten Sacken

95. Wings with Sc long, Sc_1 extending to near opposite or beyond midlength of Rs; m-cu at or beyond fork of M. (Eriopteraria, **Rhabdomastix**) 96
Wings with Sc short, not extending to beyond midlength of Rs; if Sc is relatively long (**Ptilostena**), m-cu lies more than its own length before the fork of M. (Gonomyaria, **Gonomyia**)........... 97

96. Antennæ of male longer than body; chiefly tropical
Rhabdomastix: Rhabdomastix Skuse
Antennæ of male scarcely attaining wing-root; chiefly temperate.
Rhabdomastix: Sacandaga Alexander

97. Wings with m-cu more than its own length before form of M.
Gonomyia: Ptilostena Bergroth
Wings with m-cu at or very close to fork of M (**40**) 98

98. Wings with cell R_3 very small, at margin subequal in extent to cell R_2; antennal verticils long and conspicuous.
Gonomyia: Lipophleps Bergroth
Wings with cell R_3 larger, at margin considerably exceeding in extent cell R_2; antennal verticils not conspicuously elongated.
Gonomyia: Gonomyia Meigen

99. Wings with distinct macrotrichia in outer cells..................100
Wings with the outer cells glabrous 103

100. Wings with Rs shortened, its union with R_{2+3+4} forming an angle, so cell R_1 is nearly equilateral in outline; chiefly tropical. (Eriopteraria) ....**Cryptolabis** Osten Sacken
Wings with Rs long, normal in position, cell R_1 elongate.........101

101. Size very small (wing, 3 mm. or less); Rs ending in cell R_3, this cell thus being sessile, without element R_{2+3+4}; temperate. (Eriopteraria)................................ **Dasymolophilus** Gœtghebuer
Size larger (wing over 4 mm.); Rs ending in cell R_4, cell R_3 being petiolate by the presence of a distinct element R_{2+3+4}.............102

102. Wings with Sc_2 close to tip of Sc_1, the two veins thus being subequal in length or nearly so. (Gonomyaria)......**Gnophomyia** Osten Sacken
Wings with Sc_2 far removed from tip of Sc_1, the latter vein long, subequal in length to Rs; temperate. (Eriopteraria)....**Ormosia** Rondani

103. Wings with Rs ending in cell R_3, there being no element R_{2+3+4} (41) (Eriopteraria) ....**Molophilus** Curtis
Wings with Rs ending in cell R_4, cell R_3 being petiolate by a distinct element R_{2+3+4} (42-44)....................................104

104. Wings with a supernumerary crossvein in cell R_3; vein 2nd A strongly bisinuate (42). (Eriopteraria)...................**Helobia** St. Fargeau
Wings without a supernumerary crossvein in cell R_3; vein 2nd A straight or simply sinuous (43, 44)..............................105

105. Wings with veins R_3 and R_4 divergent, unequal in length, R_3 being less than two-thirds R_4, cell R_3 at margin much more extensive than cell R_2 106
Wings with veins R_3 and R_4 nearly equal in length, or with R_3 exceeding three-fourths of the length of R_4, the veins extending generally parallel to one another to the margin; cell R_2 at margin wider than cell R_3..107

106. Wings with veins R_3 and R_4 very unequal in length, widely divergent or sprawly, R_3 being only about one-fourth R_4 and ending in costa close to vein R_{1+2}; cell R_3 at margin some eight times as wide as cell R_2; tropical..........................**Neognophomyia** Alexander
Wings with veins R_3 and R_4 less conspicuously unequal, R_3 being about one-half R_4; cell R_3 at margin some three or four times as wide as cell R_2; tropical and subtropical. (**Gonomyia**).
Gonomyia: Progonomyia Alexander

107. Antennæ of both sexes with the flagellar segments more or less kidney-shaped to give a nodulose appearance to the organ; large species (wing, 15 mm. or more); tropical. (Sigmatomeraria).
Sigmatomera Osten Sacken
Antennæ of both sexes simple or nearly so, not nodulose; smaller (wing less than 12 mm., usually less than 10 mm.)...............108

108. Coxæ of middle and hind legs only slightly separated by the small meral region; wings with Sc_1 relatively short, not exceeding one-third the length of Rs. 109
Coxæ of middle and hind legs widely separated by a large "pot-bellied" meral region; wings with Sc_1 very long, exceeding one-half the length of Rs. (Eriopteraria)...............................110

109. Wings with Rs in alignment with R_{2+3+4}; Sc short, Sc_1 ending opposite the fork of Rs and far before R_2; Sc_1 and Sc_2 subequal; male hypopygium with interbasal structures conspicuously developed as blackened spines; temperate.......................**Lipsothrix** Lœw
Wings with Rs in approximate alignment with R_5; Sc long, Sc_1 ending opposite or shortly before R_2, at or beyond midlength of R_{2+3+4}; Sc_1 much longer than Sc_2 (43); male hypopygium without evident interbases ....**Gnophomyia** Osten Sacken

110. Wings with R_2 far before fork of R_{2+3+4}, at or just beyond the fork of Rs; male with a very large hairy stigmal region that more or less distorts the adjoining veins; western plains..**Empedomorpha** Alexander
Wings with R_2 beyond the fork of R_{2+3+4}; stigma normal.............111

111. Wings with vein Cu_1 nearly straight, its distal section not swinging cephalad toward wing-tip; cell 1st M_2 small, less than one-half the distal section of M_{1+2}; terminal three segments of antennæ smaller than the remainder of flagellum...............**Trimicra** Osten Sacken
Wings with vein Cu_1 having its distal section slightly deflected at apex toward wing-tip; cell 1st M_2, when present, elongate, subequal to or longer than the distal section of M_{1+2}; flagellar segments becoming progressively smaller to outer end (44) (**Erioptera**).....112

112. Wings with vein 2nd A arcuated so cell 1st A at midlength is as broad as, or broader than it is at margin; cell 1st M_2 opening into cell 2nd M_2 by atrophy of m; (44); chiefly temperate.
Erioptera: Erioptera Meigen
Wings with anal veins divergent, cell 1st A being widest at margin; cell 1st M_2 generally closed..113

113. Wings with cell 1st M_2 open..114
Wings with cell 1st M_2 closed, the basal section of M_3 greatly exceeding m in length 115

114. Wings with cell 1st M_2 opening into cell M_3 by atrophy of basal section of M_3; where closed, the elements closing outer end not greatly disproportionate in length, m being one-half or more of M_3; chiefly tropical ....**Erioptera: Mesocyphona** Osten Sacken
Wings with cell 1st M_2 opening into cell 2nd M_2 by atrophy of m; northern and western ....**Erioptera: Psiloconopa** Zetterstedt

115. Wings with a spur from the basal section of vein M_3, jutting basad into cell 1st M_2.................**Erioptera: Hoplolabis** Osten Sacken
Wings with no such spur as described.........**Erioptera: Ilisia** Rondani

SUPPLEMENTARY KEY TO THE SUBAPTEROUS TIPULIDÆ

1. Frontal prolongation of head with nasus (Tipulinæ).......**Tipula** Linnæus
Frontal prolongation of head (or rostrum) without nasus............. 2
2. Eyes with numerous short erect setæ between ommatidia (Pediciini).
Tricyphona Zetterstedt
Eyes without setæ 3
3. Tibial spurs present. (Hexatomini)................**Limnophila** Macquart
Tibial spurs lacking. (Eriopterini).....................**Chionea** Dalman

TYPE SPECIES OF THE NEW GENERA AND SUBGENERA PROPOSED

Dicranota: Eudicranota; type, **Dicranota notabilis** Alexander.
Dicranota: Paradicranota; type, **Dicranota rivularis** Osten Sacken.
Archilimnophila; type, **Limnophila unica** Osten Sacken.
Limnophila: Idiolimnophila; type, **Limnophila emmelina** Alexander.

BIBLIOGRAPHY OF IMMATURE STAGES

Alexander, C. P.

1920. The crane-flies of New York. Part II. Biology and Phylogeny. Cornell Univ. Agric. Expt. Sta. Mem. 38; pp. 691-1133, 87 pls. (bibliography to 1920).

1931. Deutsche Limnologische Sunda-Expedition. The Crane-flies. Archiv für Hydrobiologie, Suppl. Bd. IX, Tropische Binnengewässer, 2; pp. 135-191, 51 figs., 1 pl. (bibliography of biology, 1920-30).

Rogers, J. S.

1933. The ecological distribution of the crane flies of northern Florida. Ecological Mon., 3, No. 1, pp. 1-74, figs. 1-25.

BIBLIOGRAPHY OF KEYS TO SPECIES OF NORTH AMERICAN TIPULIDÆ

The genera of which Keys are given follow the reference and the regions covered are indicated: Neo., Neotropical; Nea., Nearctic.

Alexander, C. P.

1912a. On the tropical American Rhipidiæ. Bull. Brooklyn Ent. Soc., VIII, pp. 6-17, 1 pl.
(**Limonia: Rhipidia,** Neo.).

1912b. A revision of the genus **Brachypremna** Osten Sacken. Journ. New York Ent. Soc., XX, pp. 225-236, 1 pl.
(**Brachypremna**).

1912c. New species of **Furcomyia.** Canadian Ent., XLIV, pp. 333-334.
(**Limonia: Dicranomyia,** Neo., in part).

1913a. New Neotropical Antochini. Psyche, XX, pp. 40-54, 1 pl.
(**Orimarga; Toxorhina,** Neo.).

1913b. A synopsis of part of the Neotropical crane-flies of the subfamily Limnobinæ. Proc. United States Nat. Mus., XLIV, pp. 481-549, 4 pls.
(**Epiphragma; Polymera; Lecteria; Trentepohlia; Gonomyia; Gnophomyia; Cryptolabis; Molophilus; Erioptera; Mesocyphona,** Neo.).

1913c. The Neotropical Tipulidæ in the Hungarian National Museum. I, II. Ent. News, XXIV, pp. 404-412, 439-449.
(**Limonia: Peripheroptera; Teucholabis: Paratropesa**).

1914a. New or little-known Neotropical Hexatomini. Psyche, XXI, pp. 33-45, 1 pl.
(**Hexatoma: Eriocera, Penthoptera,** Neo.).

1914b. A revision of the American species of **Tanypremna** Osten Sacken and **Megistocera** Wiedemann. Journ. New York Ent. Soc., XXII, pp. 205-218, 1 pl.
(**Tanypremna**).

1914c. On a collection of crane-flies from British Guiana. Trans. American Ent. Soc., XL, pp. 223-255, 2 pls.
(**Psaronius; Trentepohlia,** part; **Sigmatomera; Teucholabis: Teucholabis; Gonomyia: Lipophleps,** part, Neo.).

1915. Two new crane-flies from Porto Rico. Insec. Inscit. Menst., III, pp. 104-107.
(**Hexatoma: Eriocera,** part).

Alexander, C. P. (Continued)

1916a. New Limnophiline Crane-flies from the United States and Canada. Journ. New York Ent. Soc., XXIV, pp. 118-125, 1 pl.
(Limnophila: Prionolabis, part: Nea.)

1916b. New species of Crane-flies from the West Indies. Ent. News, XXVII, pp. 343-347, 6 figs.
(Hexatoma: Eriocera).

1916c. New or little-known crane-flies from the United States and Canada. Part 3. Proc. Acad. Nat. Sci. Philadelphia, 1916, pp. 486-549, 7 pls.
(**Dicranota: Rhaphidolabis; Gonomyia,** Nea.).

1917. New Nearctic crane-flies. Part 3. Canadian Ent., XLIX, pp. 199-211.
(**Erioptera: Empeda,** Nea.).

1919a. Notes on the genus **Dicranoptycha** Osten Sacken. Ent. News, XXX, pp. 19-22.
(**Dicranoptycha**).

1919b. Records and descriptions of Neotropical craneflies. Journ. New York Ent. Soc., XXVII, pp. 132-154, 1 pl.
(**Trentepohlia,** part; **Gnophomyia,** s.l.).

1919c. The crane-flies of New York. Part I. Distribution and taxonomy of the adult flies. Cornell Univ. Agr. Expt. Sta., Mem. 25; 765-993, 55 pls.
(Tanyptera; Ctenophora; Nephrotoma; Tipula; Dolichopeza; Oropeza; Phalacrocera; Cylindrotoma; Limonia: Dicranomyia, Rhipidia, Geranomyia, Limonia; Helius; Dicranoptycha; Pedicia: Pedicia, Tricyphona; Dicranota: Dicranota, Rhaphidolabis; Ula; Adelphomyia; Epiphragma; Limnophila, s.l.; **Eriocera; Chionea; Cladura; Gonomyia; Teucholabis; Rhabdomastix; Molophilus; Ormosia; Erioptera; Toxorhina).**

1920a. Undescribed Tipulidæ from western North America. Proc. California Acad. Sci., (4), X, pp. 35-46.
(Ulomorpha).

1920b. New or little-known crane-flies from tropical America. Canad. Ent., LII, pp. 141-144.
(**Polymera,** part, Neo.).

1926a. Studies on the crane-flies of Mexico. Part II. Ann. Ent. Soc. America, XIX, pp. 158-179, 2 pls.
(**Atarba;** Nea., Neo.).

1926b. Undescribed species of crane-flies from Cuba and Jamaica. Journ. New York Ent. Soc., XXXIV, pp. 223-230.
(**Gonomyia,** part, Neo.).

1927. Undescribed species of the genus **Limnophila** from eastern North America. Part II. Bull. Brooklyn Ent. Soc. XXII, pp. 56-64.
(Limnophila: Elæophila)

1929. The crane-flies of New York: Fourth Supplementary List. Bull. Brooklyn Ent. Soc., XXIV, pp. 295-302.
(**Pedicia,** Nea.)

1930. The genus **Sigmatomera** Osten Sacken,—with observations on the biology by Raymond C. Shannon. Encycl. Entomol., Diptera, V, pp. 1-8, 8 figs.
(Sigmatomera).

Dietz, W. G.

1913. A synopsis of the described North American species of the Dipterous genus **Tipula** L. Ann. Ent. Soc. America, VI, pp. 461-484.
(Tipula, Nea.).

1914. The **hebes** group of the Dipterous genus **Tipula** Linnæus. Trans. American Ent. Soc., XL, pp. 345-363, 2 pls.
(Tipula, part; Nea.)

1916. Synoptical table of the North American species of **Ormosia** Rondani **(Rhypholophus** Kolenati), with descriptions of new species. Trans. American Ent. Soc., XLVII, pp. 135-146, 1 pl.
(Ormosia, Nea.).

1917. Key to the North American species of the **tricolor** group of the Dipterous genus **Tipula** Linnæus. Ent. News, XXVIII, pp. 145-151, 1 pl.
(Tipula, part; Nea.).

1918. A revision of the North American species of the Tipulid genus **Pachyrhina** Macquart, with descriptions of new species. Trans. American Ent. Soc., XLIV, pp. 105-140, 4 pls.
(Nephrotoma, Nea.).

1919. The **streptocera** group of the Dipterous genus **Tipula** Linnæus. Ann. Ent. Soc. America, XII, pp. 85-94, 1 pl.
(Tipula, part; Nea.).

1921a. The **impudica** group of the Dipterous genus **Tipula** Linnæus. Ann. Ent. Soc. America, XIV, pp. 1-15, 1 pl.
(Tipula, part; Nea.).

1921b. Description of two new species of the **angustipennis** group of the Dipterous genus **Tipula** Linnæus, with table of species. Ent. News, XXXII, pp. 299-302.
(Tipula, part; Nea.).

Doane, R. W.

1908a. Notes on the Tipulid genus **Dicranomyia.** Ent. News, XIX, pp. 5-9.
(Limonia: Dicranomyia, Nea.).

1908b. New North American **Pachyrhina,** with a table for determining the species. Ent. News, XIX, pp. 173-179.
(Nephrotoma, Nea.).

1908c. New species of the Tipulid genus **Rhypholophus,** with a table for determining the North American species. Ent. News, XIX, pp. 200-202.
(Ormosia, Nea.).

Garrett, C. B. D.

1922. New Tipulidæ from British Columbia. Proc. Ent. Soc. Washington, XXIV, pp. 58-64, 13 figs.
(Limonia: Alexandriaria, Nea.)

Hine, J. S.

1903. The genus **Peditia,** with one new species. Ohio Nat., III, pp. 416-417.
(Pedieia, Nea.)

Johnson, C. W.

1909. New and little known Tipulidæ. Proc. Boston Soc. Nat. Hist., XXXIV, pp. 115-135, 2 pls.
(Dolichopeza: Oropeza, Nea.)

Osten Sacken, C. R.

1869. Diptera of North America, Part 4. Smithson. Miscel. Coll. 219, pp. 1-345, 4 pls., 7 figs.
(Limonia: Geranomyia, Dicranomyia, Rhipidia, Limonia; Pedicia: Tricyphona; Limnophila; Eriocera; Gonomyia; Ormosia; Erioptera).

1886. Biologia Centrali-Americana. Insecta, Diptera, I, pp. 1-216, 3 pls.
(Nephrotoma; Hexatoma: Eriocera, Neo.)

GENERAL BIBLIOGRAPHY OF MORPHOLOGICAL TERMS OF ESPECIAL VALUE IN A STUDY OF THE TIPULIDÆ.

Alexander, C. P.

1927. The interpretation of the radial field of the wing in the Nematocerous Diptera, with special reference to the Tipulidæ. Proc. Linn. Soc. New South Wales, LII, pp. 42-72, 92 figs.

1929. A comparison of the systems of nomenclature that have been applied to the radial field of the wing in the Diptera. IVth Internat. Congress Ent., Trans., II, pp. 700-707, 3 pls.

Cole, F. R.

1927. A study of the terminal abdominal structures of the male Diptera. Proc. California Acad. Sci., (4), XVI, pp. 397-499, 287 figs.

Crampton, G. C.

1923a. The genitalia of male Diptera and Mecoptera compared with those of related insects, from the standpoint of phylogeny. Trans. American Ent. Soc., XLVIII, pp. 207-225, 3 pls.

1923b. Preliminary note on the terminology applied to the parts of an insect's leg. Canadian Ent., LV, pp. 126-132, 1 pl.

1925. Evidences of relationship indicated by the thoracic sclerites of certain Eriopterine Tipuloid Diptera. Insec. Inscit, Menst., XIII, pp. 197-213, 2 pls.

1926. The external anatomy of the primitive Tanyderid Dipteran **Macrochile spectrum** Loew, preserved in Baltic Amber. Bull. Brooklyn Ent. Soc., XXI, pp. 1-14, 2 pls.

1928. The eulabium, mentum, submentum and gular region of insects. Journ. Ent. and Zool., XX, pp. 1-18, 3 pls.

1931. A phylogenetic study of the posterior metathoracic and basal abdominal structures of insects, with particular reference to the Holometabola. Journ. New York Ent. Soc., XXXIX, pp. 323-357, 4 pls.

Snodgrass, R. E.

1903. The terminal abdominal segments of female Tipulidæ. Journ. New York Ent. Soc., XI, pp. 177-183, 2 pls.

1904. The hypopygium of the Tipulidæ. Trans. American Ent. Soc., XXX, pp. 179-236, 11 pls.

SYSTEMATIC ARRANGEMENT OF GENERA AND SUBGENERA, WITH CITATIONS TO THE ABOVE BIBLIOGRAPHY OF KEYS

Tipulinæ

Ctenophora (Alexander, 1919c)
Tanyptera (Alexander, 1919c)
Nephrotoma (Alexander, 1919c; Dietz, 1918; Doane, 1908b; Osten Sacken, 1886.)
Tipula, s.l. (Alexander, 1919c; Dietz, 1913, 1914, 1917, 1919, 1921a, 1921b.)
Brachypremna (Alexander, 1912b)
Tanypremna (Alexander, 1914b)
Dolichopeza: Oropeza (Alexander, 1919c; Johnson, 1909)

Cylindrotominæ

Phalacrocera (Alexander, 1919c)
Cylindrotoma (Alexander, 1919c)

Limoniinæ
Limoniini

Limonia: Limonia (Alexander, 1919c; Osten Sacken, 1869)
Dicranomyia (Alexander, 1912c, 1919c; Doane, 1908a; Osten Sacken, 1869)
Alexandriaria (Garrett, 1922)
Peripheroptera (Alexander, 1913c)
Rhipidia (Alexander, 1912a, 1919c; Osten Sacken, 1869)
Geranomyia (Alexander, 1919c; Osten Sacken, 1869)
Orimarga: Orimarga (Alexander, 1913a)
Dicranoptycha (Alexander, 1919a, 1919c)
Helius (Alexander, 1919c)

Pediciini

Pedicia: Pedicia (Alexander, 1919c, 1929; Hine, 1903)
Tricyphona (Alexander, 1919c; Osten Sacken, 1869)
Dicranota: Dicranota (Alexander, 1919c)
Rhaphidolabis (Alexander, 1916c, 1919c)
Plectromyia (Alexander, 1919c)
Ula (Alexander, 1919c)

Hexatomini

Adelphomyia (Alexander, 1919c)
Epiphragma (Alexander, 1913b, 1919c)
Polymera (Alexander, 1913b, 1920b)
Dactylolabis (Alexander, 1919c; Osten Sacken, 1869)
Pseudolimnophila (Alexander, 1919c)
Limnophila, s.l. (Alexander, 1919c; Osten Sacken, 1869)
Prionolabis (Alexander, 1916a, 1919c; Osten Sacken, 1869)
Eutonia (Alexander, 1919c)
Lasiomastix (Alexander, 1919c; Osten Sacken, 1869)
Phylidorea (Alexander, 1919c)
Elæophila (Alexander, 1919c, 1927; Osten Sacken, 1869)
Idioptera (Alexander, 1919c)
Dicranophragma (Alexander, 1919c)
Pilaria (Alexander, 1919c)
Ulomorpha (Alexander, 1920a)

Psaronius (Alexander, 1914c)
Hexatoma: Eriocera (Alexander, 1914a, 1915, 1916b, 1919c; Osten Sacken, 1869, 1886)
Penthoptera (Alexander, 1914a)
Atarba: Atarba (Alexander, 1926a)

Eriopterini

Chionea (Alexander, 1919c)
Cladura, s.l. (Alexander, 1919c)
Lecteria (Alexander, 1913b)
Sigmatomera (Alexander, 1914c, 1930)
Trentepohlia: Paramongoma (Alexander, 1913b, 1914c, 1919b)
Teucholabis: Teucholabis (Alexander, 1914c, 1919c)
Paratropesa (Alexander, 1913c)
Gonomyia, s.l. (Alexander, 1916c, 1919c; Osten Sacken, 1869)
Progonomyia (Alexander, 1916c)
Lipophleps (Alexander, 1914c, 1916c, 1919c)
Gonomyia (Alexander, 1913b, 1916c, 1919c, 1926b; Osten Sacken, 1869)
Ptilostena (Alexander, 1916c)
Gnophomyia, s.l. (Alexander, 1913b, 1919b)
Rhabdomastix: Sacandaga (Alexander, 1919c)
Erioptera, s.l. (Alexander, 1919c; Osten Sacken, 1869)
Erioptera (Alexander, 1919c; Osten Sacken, 1869)
Mesocyphona (Alexander, 1913b, 1919c; Osten Sacken, 1869)
Ilisia (Alexander, 1919c)
Empeda (Alexander, 1917, 1919c)
Cryptolabis (Alexander, 1913b)
Ormosia (Alexander, 1919c; Dietz, 1916; Doane, 1908c; Osten Sacken, 1869)
Molophilus (Alexander, 1913c, 1919c)
Toxorhina: Toxorhina (Alexander, 1913a, 1919c)

Family Anisopodidæ

Moderately small, elongate flies with long legs and three ocelli.

Head subspherical or hemispherical, the eyes of the males holoptic or dichoptic, usually rounded. Proboscis moderately prominent, with small labella; palpi long, four segmented. Antennæ usually about as long as the thorax, cylindrical, composed of twelve to sixteen segments. Thorax convex, without distinct transverse suture; scutellum semicircular, short and broad, the metanotum well developed. Abdomen more or less cylindrical, flattened below, the genitalia small. Legs slender, without spines; anterior coxæ and the basal segment of the tarsi elongated; tibiæ with or without apical spurs; pulvilli absent, the empodia pad-like. Wings rather large, lying flat on the abdomen when at rest; auxiliary vein present; radius with 3 or 4 (*Axymyia*, Fig. 15*) branches; cell 1st M_2 closed or open (Figs. 14, 16*); a single anal vein reaches the margin.

The adults are frequently common, particularly those belonging to the genus *Anisopus* which sometimes occur in small swarms near the edges of woods in the vicinity of swamps and also on the trunks of trees. The other genera occur in moist places, particularly upon foliage. The members of this family, insofar as known, breed in wet or moist decaying organic matter, as fermenting sap, rotten wood and similar situations.

There are about 80 described species, distributed in 6 genera and 3 subfamilies, all of the latter being found in the North American fauna.

* Plate II, Tipuloidea.

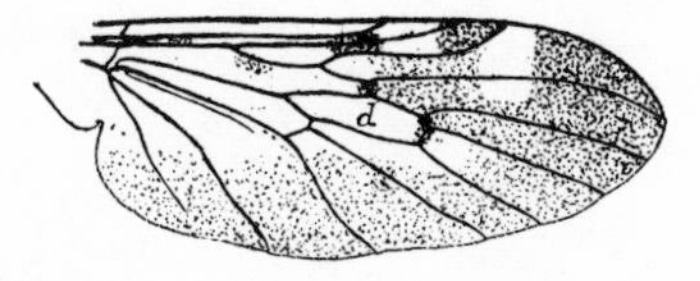

Fig. 1. **Anisopus** species.

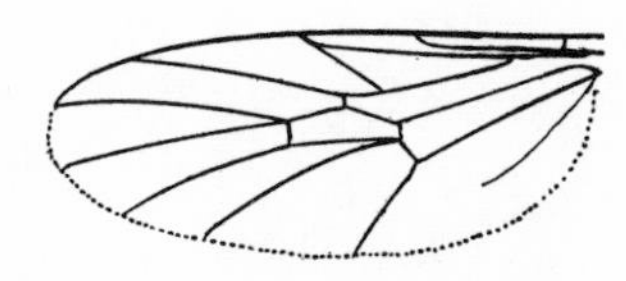
Fig. 2. **Olbiogaster** species.

KEY TO GENERA

1. Wings with cell 1st M_2 present. (Anisopodinæ)........................ 2
   Wings with cell 1st M_2 open by the atrophy of basal section of M_3...... 3
2. Wing-membrane with macrotrichia (14*; also 1); posterior tibia with a comb of spinous setæ ....**Anisopus** Meigen
   Wing-membrane without macrotrichia; posterior tibia without spinous comb; tropical (2)..........................**Olbiogaster** Osten Sacken
3. Wings with vein R_3 present as a nearly transverse element, connecting with vein R_{1+2} at margin (15*); eastern (Axymyiinæ)..**Axymyia** McAtee
   Wings with vein R_3 lost by atrophy, there being only two branches of Rs (16*); north temperate (Mycetobiinæ).............**Mycetobia** Meigen

The most important paper:

Edwards, F. W.

1928. Diptera. Fam. Protorhyphidæ, Anisopodidæ, Pachyneuridæ, Trichoceridæ. Genera Insectorum, Fasc. 190, pp. 1-41, 2 pls.

---

* Plate II, Tipuloidea.

Family Blephariceridæ—The Net-Winged Midges

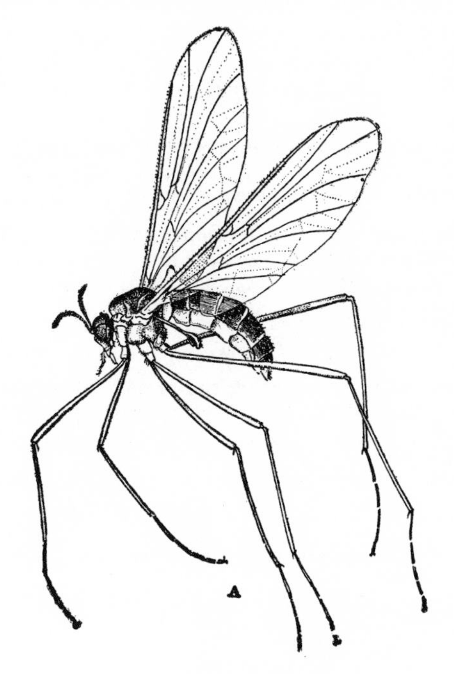

Agathon elegantula.

Moderate sized, elongate, nearly bare species with long legs and rather wide, delicate wings.

Eyes sometimes holoptic in one or both sexes and usually bisected below the middle by a narrow, unfaceted line below which the facets are smaller; three ocelli present. Antennæ slender, composed of nine to fifteen segments and clothed with pubescence. Mouth parts more or less elongate, the females with slender, flattened elongate serrate mandibles. Mosontum with distinct, broadly interrupted transverse suture. Legs rather slender, the posterior pair longer than the others; tibiæ with or without spurs; pulvilli and empodium absent or nearly so. Wings broad, bare, the anal angle projecting, almost always with a network of delicate lines due to the creasing of the folded wings in the pupal case.

The adults are not common in most collections but are often found in large numbers near fast-flowing streams. I have found them chiefly on the foliage of evergreens or on the sides of cliffs or rocks.

The larvæ live in swift water, clinging to the rocks or stream bed by a series of ventral suckers, pupation taking place in the stream. The immature stages are even more easily identified than the adults. The latest revision of the family is contained in Williston's Manual of North American Diptera, 3rd edition.

KEY TO GENERA

1. An incomplete longitudinal vein between the fourth and fifth longitudinals (1) 3
   No incomplete vein between these veins (2) 2
2. Proboscis long; palpi but little developed (2, 5) .... **Paltostoma** Schiner
   Proboscis not longer than the vertical diameter of the head; palpi well developed, four-segmented .... **Kelloggina** Williston
3. Second basal cell closed apically 4
   Second basal cell open apically (1) .... **Blephariceraa** Macquart
4. Second longitudinal vein branched, the branch either simulating a cross-vein near the base of the second vein, or elongate 5
   Second vein not branched (3) .... **Philorus** Kellogg
5. Pleura pilose or haired (4) .... ***Bibiocephala** Osten Sacken
   Pleura bare .... **Agathon** Röder

* **Bibionus** Curran is a synonym but the two species upon which the genera were based are distinct.

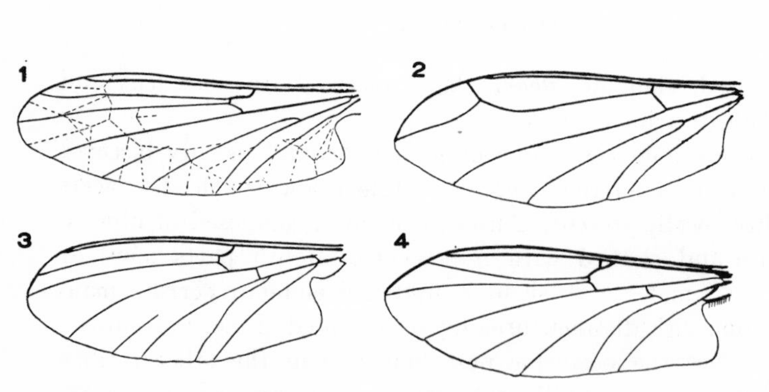

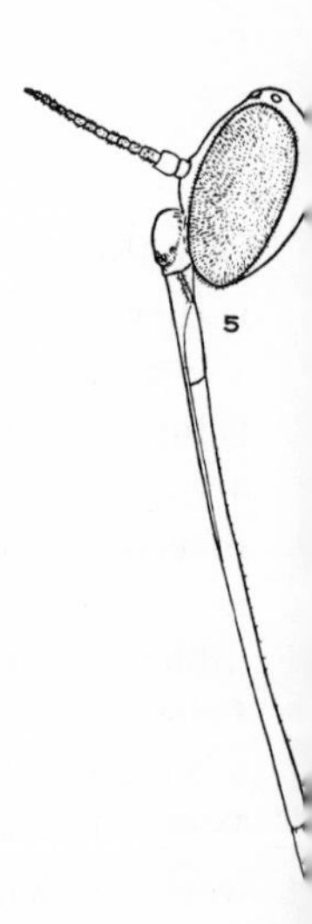

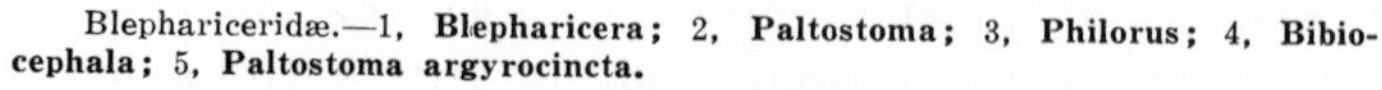
Blephariceridæ.—1, **Blepharicera**; 2, **Paltostoma**; 3, **Philorus**; 4, **Bibiocephala**; 5, **Paltostoma argyrocincta.**

Family Simuliidæ—The Black Flies

Larva of **Simulium venustum** showing the mouth fans (left) used for securing food. (After Metcalf and Sanderson).

Small, usually dark colored flies, rarely over 5 mm. in length, with short, thick legs.

Head rather hemispherical; face short, eyes round or reniform, holoptic in the males; ocelli absent. Proboscis rather short, with small, horny labellæ, palpi incurved, four segmented, the basal segment short, the two following of equal length, the fourth longer and more slender than the preceding. Thorax arched, without transverse suture; scutellum small. Abdomen rather cylindrical, tapering in the males, composed of seven or eight segments; genitalia concealed. Legs short and strong, the femora broad and flat; tibiæ usually with terminal spurs; basal segment of the tarsi elongate, the apical segment small. Wings large and broad, with distinct allulæ, the anterior veins thickened, the others weak. Auxiliary vein ending in the costa near the middle of the wing, the second vein absent, the first and third approximate; anterior cross-vein very short; fourth vein curved, forked nearly opposite the anterior cross-vein, the branches terminating near the apex of the wing.

The Black-Flies, Buffalo Gnats, Turkey Gnats, to use some of the common names for these pests, need no introduction to the hunter or fisherman. To most people they are extremely annoying and as they frequently occur in enormous numbers in the neighborhood of streams fishermen are only too well acquainted with them. As a rule their bites do not attract immediate attention but after a short time they cause painful swellings and, if in sufficient numbers, may result in the serious illness of the sufferer and even death. The adults attack all warm blooded animals and are known from all parts of the world, being particularly abundant in the north temperate and subarctic zones.

In addition to the irritation caused by their bites some members of the family carry disease. In Africa *Onchocerciasis,* a disease caused by a worm (*Onchocerca volvulus* Leuckart) of the family Filariidæ is transmitted by *Eusimulium damnosum* Theobald. In man the disease takes the form of small to rather large, subcutaneous swellings and may or may not be apparent without careful examination. From 40 to 50 per cent of the natives of Sierra Leone were said by Blacklock to be infected in 1926.*

---

* Ann. Trop. Med. & Parasit., xx, pp. 1-48, 203-218.

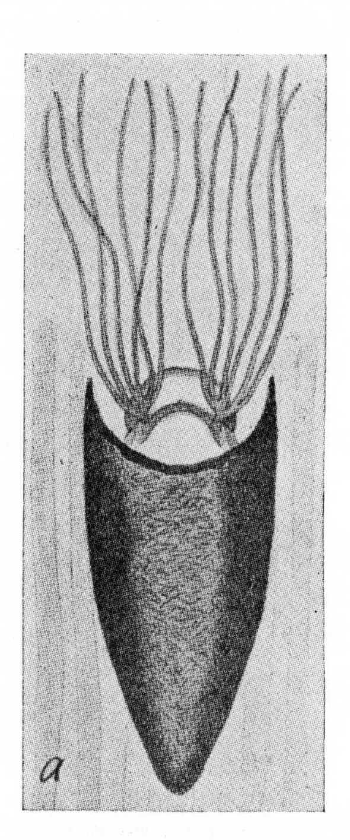

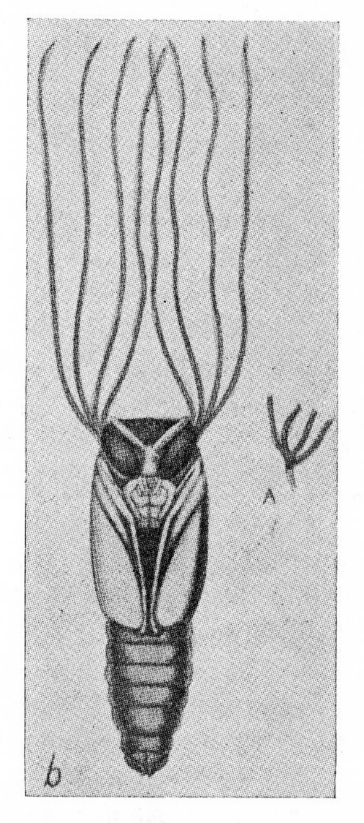

(a) pupa of **Simulium venustum** in pupal cocoon and (b) pupa of S. **bracteatum,** with cocoon removed. (After Metcalf and Sanderson).

In Central America three species of *Simulium* have been shown to carry a disease displaying various symptoms and sometimes resulting in blindness. The causative agent is related to the form described above and was named *Onchocerca cæcutirus* by Brumpt. In some cases of infection there are no clinical symptoms but in others there are erysipelas-like swellings, the name *coastal erysipelas* being applied to the disease in such cases. Nodular swellings may occur on the head, shoulder blades, ribs iliac crests, etc. In the eye the microfilariæ may cause *conjunctivitis, keratitis* and *iritis,* blindness sometimes resulting.

Both the fly and man are necessary for the development of the disease. After being ingested by the fly the microfilariæ pass from the intestine to the muscles of the thorax where further development takes place. The infective stages occur in the proboscis of the fly and are transferred to man during feeding by the insect. Strong has discussed *Onchocerciasis* in Guatemala.*

The larvæ live in streams where they attach themselves to stones, plants, etc. and collect their food from the flowing water. Pupation takes place within the larval cocoon, the adults emerging under water and, quickly reaching the surface, fly away. Under favorable conditions many thousands of larvæ may be found together, being so numerous as to entirely conceal the surface to which they are attached.

The latest revision of the North American species is by Dyar and Shannon.† Unfortunately these authors apparently took greater pains to find fault with the work of others than to clarify their own conclusions and only a study of their material and amplification of the descriptions will result in a clear understanding of the specific limits. In some cases the drawings were evidently made from freshly prepared slides and these show characters which gradually disappear, with the result that the same characters cannot be found in old slides and may not even be present in freshly prepared ones made from old specimens. Just what effect this will have on the validity of several of the forms recognized by the authors it is impossible to say. Malloch‡ has also revised the family: the two contributions should be used together.

---

* 1931, Science, N. S., lxxiii, pp. 593-594.
† 1927, Dyar and Shannon, Proc. U. S. N. M., lxix, Art. 10, pp. 1-54, 7 plates.
‡ 1914, Malloch, Bull. U. S. Dept. of Agric., Bur. Ent., Tech. Ser., No. 26.

KEY TO GENERA

1. Third vein forked 3
   Third vein simple 2

2. Petiole of the second and third veins setulose above... **Eusimulium** Roubaud
   Petiole of the second and third veins bare (1)......... **Simulium** Latreille

3. Fifth vein not forked (3)........................ **Parasimulium** Malloch
   Fifth vein forked (2)............................ **Prosimulium** Roubaud

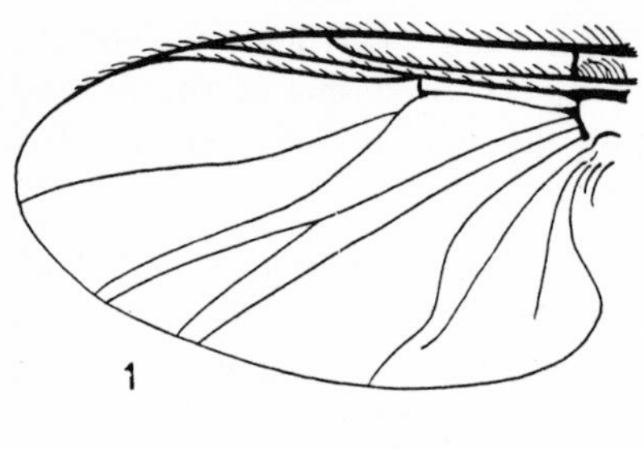

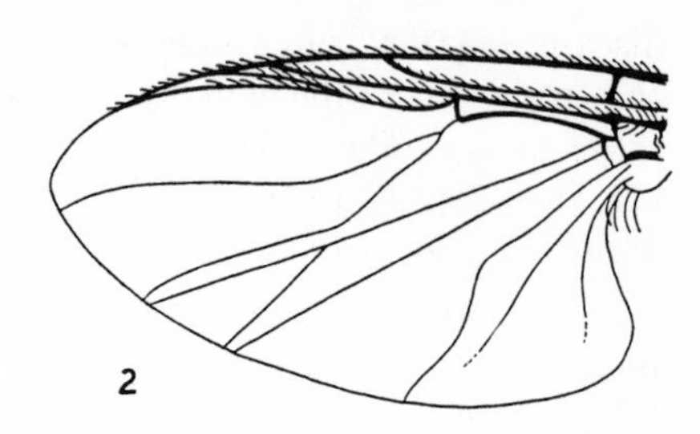

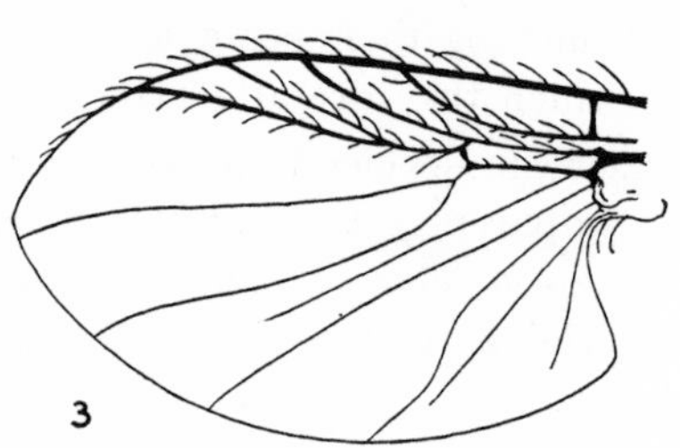

Simuliidæ.—1, **Simulium**; 2, **Prosimulium**; 3, **Parasimulium**

Family Thaumaleidæ

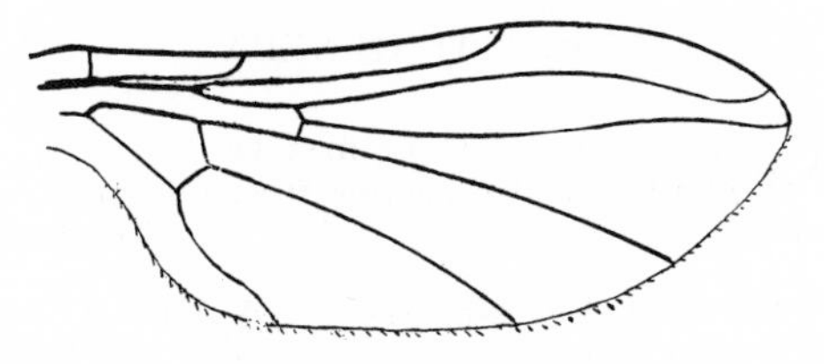

Thaumalea species.

Small, bare, obscurely reddish yellow or brownish flies of peculiar appearance.

Head small, round; eyes holoptic in both sexes; ocelli absent; proboscis short; palpi longer than the antennæ, composed of five segments, the first short, the second thickest; antennæ situated near the oral margin, composed of a scape, pedicel and flagellum, the latter very compact and arista-like, but composed of ten distinct segments, the basal two rather large and globose. Thorax robust, strongly convex, without transverse suture, somewhat depressed before the rather large, obtusely triangular scutellum; metanotum arched. Abdomen narrower than the thorax, cylindrical, composed of seven segments; male genitalia large, the basal piece swollen, bladder-like; ovipositor with broad, rounded lamellæ. Legs simple, comparatively short; coxæ short; tibiæ without spurs; tarsi of moderate length, the anterior pair about as long as the tibiæ, the penultimate segment short; empodia vestigial; claws small. Wings longer than the abdomen; auxiliary vein short, terminating in the costa; second longitudinal vein curved; the third and fourth veins simple; basal cell short; anal angle rounded.

There are about three dozen described species belonging to this family, most of them occurring in the Old World. The adults are found along the edges of streams, particularly those with mossy banks, and are not common in collections. They are small flies, under 6 mm. in length, and the wings bend sharply near the base in death, folding downward as in the Psychodidæ.

The larvæ, which resemble those of the Chironomidæ, are found in small brooks and streams where the clear water flows very thinly over the rocks, so that the back of the larva is always exposed above the surface. They feed on detritus and diatomes, and move about in search of food. The pupæ are found in the bottom of the stream between stones, etc.

The following key will separate the described genera, two of which occur in America. The family has been revised by Edwards.*

KEY TO GENERA

1. Subcostal vein ending in the costa or first vein...................... 2
   Subcostal vein obsolete apically, ending free. (North America, **pluvialis** Dyar & Shannon)...........................**Trichothaumalea** Edwards

2. Subcostal vein ending in the first vein, very short (Australia, N. Zealand, S. America)..........................**Austrothaumalea** Tonnoir
   Subcoastal vein ending in the costa................................ 3

3. Basal segment of ♂ palpi greatly swollen, the second and third segments not much longer than broad; subcosta weak apically (Europe).
   Androprosopa Mik
   Palpi rather stout, alike in both sexes, somewhat longer than the antennæ (N. America, Europe)........................**Thaumalea** Ruthé

North American Species of Thaumalea

1. Thorax and abdomen brown or blackish............................ 2
   Thorax reddish yellow, the abdomen brown........**elnora** Dyar & Shannon

2. Male clasper with two terminal claws....................**americana** Bezzi
   Male clasper with about six terminal claws......**johannis** Dyar & Shannon

* Edwards, 1929, Zool. Anzeiger, pp. 121-142.

Family Chironomidæ—The Midges

Small, slender flies, rarely over 10 mm. in length, thorax large, the legs slender, antennæ of males plumose.

Head small, more or less spherical, partly concealed from dorsal view by the projecting thorax. Antennæ slender, with five to fourteen segments, the basal segment enlarged and globular, plumose in the males, more or less haired in the females. Eyes reniform or oval, the ocelli absent or rudimentary. Proboscis short, not adapted for piercing; palpi with three or four segments. Thorax sub-ovate, or moderately long, more or less projecting in front, without a transverse suture but with a wide, longitudinal impression in front of the scutellum; metanotum with a more or less distinct longitudinal groove in the middle; scutellum small and hemispherical. Legs slender and rather long, especially the front pair; the tarsi often very long; empodium and pulvilli present or absent. Wings bare or haired, long and narrow, usually with a strong anal angle; anterior veins strong; auxiliary vein complete though slender; second longitudinal vein weak or absent, the third vein often forked and connected with the first by a crossvein; fourth vein often with two branches which may or may not be petiolate basally, the fifth vein usually furcate; second basal cell open or closed apically; costa usually ending at the termination of the third vein, usually well before the tip of the wing. Abdomen narrow and long, especially in the males, shorter and more robust in the females, the hypopygium exposed; ovipositor short.

The Certatopogonidæ, formerly included in this family by most authors, have been recognized as a distinct family by Malloch and Edwards, and are so treated here. They may be distinguished by the shape of the thorax and absence of the metanotal depression.

The midges bear little resemblance to mosquitoes when viewed by a careful observer, but to the layman they show no differences and are not differentiated. Many people believe that they are "'young'' mosquitoes and that they will ''grow up'', but there is, of course, no justification for such a belief. In mosquitoes the costa extends entirely around the wing and the wing veins and costa are usually scaled.

The family is a very large one and comprises close to two thousand described species. Midges are found almost everywhere, but since the larvæ are aquatic their distribution is limited to the vicinity of water, although they are frequently found in large numbers at a considerable distance from any visible water supply. While they are not strong fliers they can remain in the air for long periods of time and they often occur in large numbers. Williston states that in the Rocky Mountains he has observed them dancing in the air in incredible numbers and producing a noise like a distant waterfall. As a rule they swarm in the evening, but swarms are not uncommon in sheltered places during the day. For the most part only the males swarm, although an occasional female may be found with them. While, as a rule, only one species will be found in a swarm it is not unusual to find other species among them. The females are found mostly on foliage, where they rest on the under surface during the day. Some forms occur commonly on tree trunks, logs, and in grass. They are attracted to light, frequently in very large numbers.

Since many of the Chironomids are very small they must be handled with care. The larger ones may be pinned in the usual manner, provided fine pins are used; the smaller should be attached to the side of a pin by a ring of shellac, care being taken to leave one wing and the tarsi free. Specimens without front tarsi are almost useless and, since the insects dry quickly, they must be mounted within an hour or two.

The larvæ are elongate, cylindrical, slender and curved more or less downward, particularly when preserved. The head and legs are conspicuous and there may be one or more pairs of leg-like pads posteriorly. They are scavengers and live in water everywhere, also in mud and have been dredged from a depth of nearly a thousand feet in Lake Superior. Some are also found in decaying vegetation, in moss, etc. Many of them are free-living while others make mud cases on stones, leaves and pieces of wood and I have found one undetermined species building almost colorless cases in *Spirogyra*. Many of the larvæ contain hæmoglobin and are red in color, the name "blood-worms" being applied to these.

The classification of the family is not entirely satisfactory and characters for the limitation of genera are few. Edwards* has utilized the tibial spurs and combs for the separation of genera, in addition to other characters. However, the classification must be considered as very artificial, although losing nothing on that account. Since the object of taxonomy is the identification of species the means of obtaining the end is not important. Many papers dealing with the American species have been published since the appearance of Johannsen's monographic revision† in 1905, by Kieffer, Malloch,‡ Johannsen, etc. Some of the more important are listed below.

---

* 1929. British non-biting midges, Tr. Ent. Soc. London, Dec. 1929.
† 1905. New York State Museum Bulletin No. 86.
‡ 1915. Bull. Ill. State Lab. Nat. Hist., x, Art. 6.

KEY TO GENERA*

1. Wings functional 2
   Wings greatly reduced, strap-like, not more than half as long as the abdomen (16) ....**Eretmoptera** Kellogg

2. Second basal cell open apically..14
   Second basal cell closed.. 3

3. Second vein either present and forked near tip or else indistinct or absent (Tanypodinæ) 4
   Second vein not forked apically, simple, and always distinct (Diamesinæ) 10

4. Costa not produced beyond end of third vein, wing hairy; fourth tarsal segment linear (**Ablabesmyia** Johannsen) (11).....**Pentaneura** Philippi
   Costa distinctly produced beyond the end of the third vein........... 5

5. Second vein wanting, the space between first and third veins broad; wings hairy 6
   Second vein present 7

6. Fifth vein with long petiole (7)...................**Trichotanypus** Kieffer
   Fifth vein without petiole (**Linacerus, Paratanypus**) (15).
   Podonomus Philippi

7. Fourth tarsal segment cordiform; wings bare, branches of fifth vein either with or without petiole (**Cœlotanypus**)......**Clinotanypus** Kieffer
   Fourth tarsal segment not cordiform; wings hairy or bare............ 8

8. Fifth vein not petiolate (6).......................**Anatopynia** Johannsen
   Fifth vein petiolate 9

9. Petiole of fifth vein not one-third as long as the posterior branch; wings hairy ....**Tanypus** Meigen
   Petiole of fifth vein at least half as long as posterior branch of this vein; wings bare or hairy (12).....................**Procladius** Skuse

10. Posterior crossvein intersecting the petiole of the fifth vein; eyes bare; fourth tarsal segment cylindrical (14).............**Prodiamesa** Kieffer
    Posterior crossvein intersecting the anterior branch of the fifth vein near its base 11

11. Fourth segment of tarsus more or less cordiform, shorter or at least not longer than the fifth..12
    Fourth tarsal segment cylindrical, longer than the fifth.
    Syndiamesa Kieffer

12. Eyes finely pubescent; antennæ of male plumose (3)....**Diamesa** Meigen
    Eyes bare 13

13. Legs annulate; male antennæ not plumose (8)........**Heptagyia** Philippi
    Legs not annulate ....**Psilodiamesa** Kieffer

14. Terminal segment (style) of hypopygium of male directed rigidly backwards; basal segment of anterior tarsi longer than the tibia, the anterior tibia without distinct spur except in **Pseudochironomus** (Chironominæ) 25
    Terminal segment of hypopygium folded inwards; first segment of anterior tarsus shorter than the tibia; anterior tibia with spur (Orthocladiinæ) 15

---

* Checked by Dr. O. A. Johannsen.

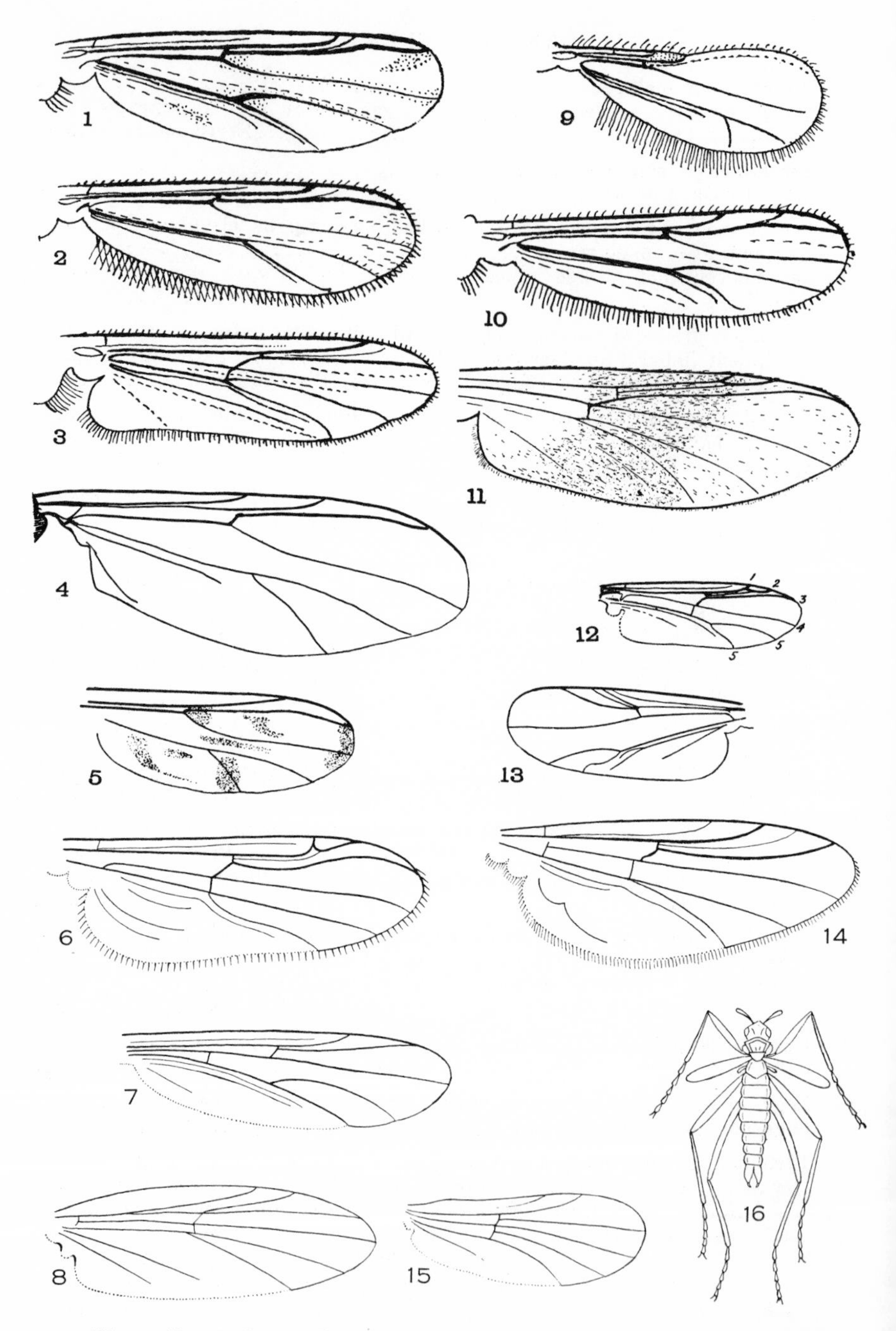

Chironomidæ.—1, **Pentapedilum**, hairs omitted; 2, **Tanytarsus**; 3, **Diamesa**; 4, **Crictopus insolitus**; 5, **Chironomus**; 6, **Anatopynia**; 7, **Trichotanypus**; 8, **Heptagyia**; 9, **Corynoneura**; 10, **Orthocladius**; 11, **Pentaneura algens**; 12, **Procladius**; 13, **Metriocnemus**; 14, **Prodiamesa**; 15, **Podonomus**; 16, **Eretmoptera.**

15. Third vein fused with the costa and not reaching beyond the apical three-fourths of the wing; a false vein running close to anterior margin of wing (9)........................**Corynoneura** Winnertz
    Third vein free, no false vein....................................16

16. Wings with hairs..17
    Wings bare 20

17. The thick crossvein joining the third and fourth vein very long and appearing as the base of the third vein......................... 18
    The crossvein short 19

18. Mesonotum conically produced in front; wings spotted..**Eurycnemus** Wulp
    Mesonotum not produced; wing unicolored...............**Brillia** Kieffer

19. Pulvilli absent; wing hairs decumbent (13)..........**Metriocnemus** Wulp
    Pulvilli present though small; wing hairs suberect (**Spaniotoma** Edwards (10)...................................**Orthocladius** Wulp

20. Mesonotum with a longitudinal fissure; wings black with white markings in most species ....**Chasmatonotus** Lœw
    Mesonotum without longitudinal fissure............................21

21. Claws cleft; large marine species (**Telmatogeton** Coquillett, not Schiner) ....**Paraclunio** Kieffer
    Claws not cleft 22

22. Palpi porrect, 3 segmented (**Symbiocladius**).........**Trissocladius** Kieffer
    Palpi flexible, 4 segmented.......................................23

23. Fourth segment of at least the hind tarsi cordiform, shorter than the fifth (**Thalassomyia** Johannsen, not Schiner)......**Cardiocladius** Kieffer
    Fourth tarsal segment linear......................................24

24. Dorsocentral hairs minute and decumbent; tibiæ usually banded with white; genitalia in most cases in part pure white (4)...**Crictopus** Wulp
    Dorsocentral hairs larger and suberect; tibiæ not banded (**Spaniotoma** Philippi) Edwards, **Psectrocladius, Trichocladius, Dactylocladius, Camptocladius**) (10) ....***Orthocladius** Wulp

25. Wing disc with hairs at least at tip..............................26
    Wings quite bare, the anterior crossvein distinct and oblique.........27

26. Squamæ fringed; anterior crossvein distinct and oblique (1).
    Pentapedilum Kieffer
    Squamæ quite bare, anterior crossvein longitudinal in position or indistinct (2) ....**Tanytarsus** Wulp

27. Eyes widely separated, reniform; all tibiæ with long conspicuous spurs; pronotal collar large; basal segment of anterior tarsus not longer than the tibiæ...........................**Pseudochironomus** Malloch
    Eyes with dorsal projection; front tibial spur indistinct or absent; basal segment of anterior tarsus longer than the tibia (5).
    Chironomus Meigen

The genus **Chirocladius** Picado, represented by a species from Costa Rica, and which seems to belong among the Chironominæ, is too briefly described to place in the key.

---

* **Pseudochironomus** Malloch, with widely separated reniform eyes and very large pronotal collar, in spite of short basal segment of the anterior tarsi and the tibial spurs, belongs with the next section.

Family Ceratopogonidæ—The Biting Midges

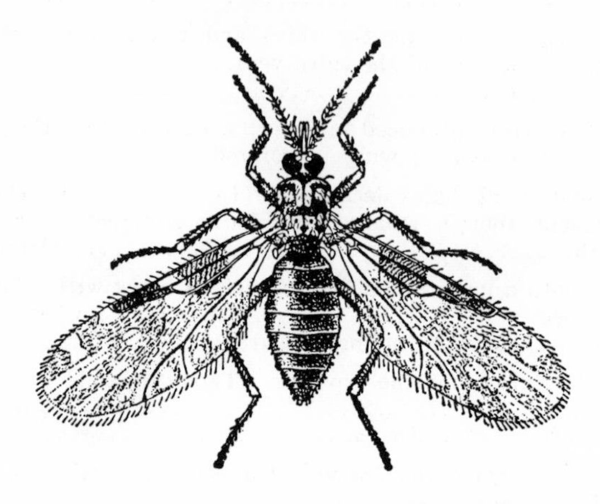

Culicoides species.

Very small, slender flies, rarely 5 mm. in length.

Head small, spheroidal and rounded behind or hemispherical and flattened behind; ocelli absent or practically so; antennæ slender, usually with fourteen segments and a fifteenth microscopic one, the apical three to five segments lengthened, the basal swollen; mouth parts complete, adapted for biting. Thorax rather oval, shorter than in the Chironomidæ; pronotum never prominent; metanotum rather rounded, never with a longitudinal groove; scutellum small, hemispherical, usually bearing distinct bristles. Wings of moderate width, folded flat over the back when at rest; second vein absent, fourth vein generally furcate; alula very narrow; squamæ never completely fringed. Legs moderately long, the posterior pair longest; femora and tibiæ sometimes swollen, the former sometimes with spines beneath; pulvilli present or absent. Abdomen elongate; genitalia exposed; ovipositor small.

The Ceratopogonidæ may be readily distinguished from the Chironomidæ by the characters enumerated above. They are minute or quite small flies and are often serious pests, especially along the seashore, in the tropics and along our rivers and lakes, but are not limited in distribution to large bodies of water. The adults are either predaceous or externally parasitic although no real differentiation can be made. The larger species are known to prey upon small insects while the small forms suck blood and they have been observed more than once attached to "mantids" or "walking sticks", upon which they feed. Warm blooded animals are freely attacked by representatives of the genera *Culicoides, Lasiohelea and Leptoconops* and the tiny creatures sometimes make man miserable by their unceasing attention. They are known commonly as "punkies" and "no-see-ums", the latter name because of their small size, and they are unwitting jokers since almost any large insect is liable to be blamed for the bites of these lilliputians. They are attracted to light in large numbers and are difficult to keep from houses owing to their small size.

In Africa *Culicoides austeni* is known to be the intermediate host of a parasitic worm (*Acanthocheiloneura perstans*), a form occurring also in South America, but the worm is not known to cause any specific disease. Further study may link the members of this family with the transmittal of diseases of a specific nature.

The larvæ are aquatic or semi-aquatic being found in moist places, in mud, sand, decaying vegetation and in tree-holes. It seems likely that most of the marine species live within the tide-zone and for that reason there is no practical means of control, while those living in decaying vegetation form an equally serious problem. The species living in tree holes are seldom abundant and the elimination of their breeding places is a simple matter. It is not known whether the larvæ are scavengers or predators and it may be that they include both groups.

The insects are difficult to capture and require special care in handling. Those which bite may be captured by placing a bottle over them as they suck blood, but the collector will no doubt find it necessary to exercise great self control during the process owing to the numbers which begin feeding at the same time. Specimens seem best when mounted on the side of a pin but some may be kept in alcohol and mounted on slides. Owing to the delicate nature of the hairs on the wings they are easily abraded and the characteristic wing pattern disappears. For this reason dried specimens should always be preserved. Edwards* has dealt with the British species and his paper will be found invaluable. Malloch†, Johannsen‡, Root, Hoffman and others have published on the North American forms and a great deal of research is being conducted at the present time by the last two mentioned authors. I am indebted to Drs. Johannsen and Root for checking and revising the key to this family.

---

* 1926, Trans. Ent. Soc. London, pp. 389-426.
† 1915, Bull. Ill. State Lab. Nat. Hist., x, Article vi; id, xi, Article 4.
‡ 1905, N. Y. State Mus. Bull. #86.

KEY TO GENERA

1. Empodium as long as claws.. 2
   Empodium very short or absent....................................... 3

2. Costa extending to about middle of wing; wings with dense macrotrichia all over (**Euforcipomyia** Malloch) (3)............**Forcipomyia** Meigen
   Costa extending well beyond middle of wing; macrotrichia sparser, sometimes absent (4) ....*__Atrichopogon__ Kieffer

3. A fold looking like a simple vein between third and fourth veins; first and third veins indistinct, more or less fused. (**Tersesthes** Townsend). **Leptoconops** Skuse
   No vein-like fold between third and fourth veins.................... 4

4. Costa extending to about middle of wing; second radial cell short and square-ended, first radial cell obliterated; macrotrichia usually dense (**Pseudoculicoides** Malloch, **Isoecacta** Garrett)=(5)....**Dasyhelea** Kieffer
   Costa extending well beyond middle of wing; radial cells usually otherwise 5

5. Humeral pits present and conspicuous; microtrichia of wings distinct; claws of female small and equal; at least some macrotrichia present. (**Æcacta** Poey) (**9, 10**)..........................†**Culicoides** Latreille
   Either humeral pits absent or else microtrichia absent or else claws of female very unequal.. 6

6. The two radial cells small and equal or one or both of them obliterated; wings finely punctuate but without distinct microtrichia; legs not thickened 7
   Either second radial cell much longer than broad or else wings with distinct microtrichia or else legs modified.......................... 8

7. Wings with at least one dark spot and with some macrotrichia; female claws unequal (**Neoceratopogon** Malloch)........**Alluaudomyia** Kieffer
   Wings whitish, without dark markings, and without macrotrichia; female claws equal (8)........................**Ceratopogon** Meigen

8. Hind femora noticeably thicker than the others...................... 9
   Hind femora not thickened...10

9. Hind femora much thickened and spinose beneath; hind tibiæ not thickened (**Ceratolophus** Kieffer) (**1**)..............**Serromyia** Meigen
   Hind femora not spinose; both hind femora and hind tibiæ moderately thickened (**7**) ....**Monohelea** Kieffer

10. First and third veins connected by a crossvein, 2 radial cells...........11
    First and third veins not connected, one long radial cell...............15

11. Front femora spinose beneath...12
    Front femora not spinose beneath.....................................13

12. Front femora conspicuously swollen...................**Heteromyia** Say
    Front femora not conspicuously swollen...............**Palpomyia** Meigen

13. The branches of the fourth vein petiolate basally (**Hartomyia** Malloch). **Stilobezzia** Kieffer
    The branches of the fourth vein arise at or before the cross vein.......14

14. Last segment of front tarsi much swollen (2)..........**Clinohelea** Kieffer
    Last segment of front tarsi not swollen (**6**)......**Johannsenomyia** Malloch

---

* Malloch, 1915, Bull. Ill. State Lab. Nat. Hist., x, p. 304 (Ceratopogon).
† Hoffman, 1925, Amer. Journ. Hygiene, v, pp. 274-301.

15. Branches of fourth vein petiolate basally............................16
    Branches of fourth vein arise at or before the crossvein...............17

16. At least one pair of femora with spines beneath.....**Pseudobezzia** Malloch
    Femora without spines beneath......................**Parabezzia** Malloch

17. Posterior branch of the fourth vein elbowed basally in the female (12).
    Stenoxenus Coquillett
    Posterior branch of fourth vein not elbowed........................ 18

18. At least one pair of femora with spines beneath (11)......**Bezzia** Kieffer
    Femora without spines beneath......................**Probezzia** Kieffer

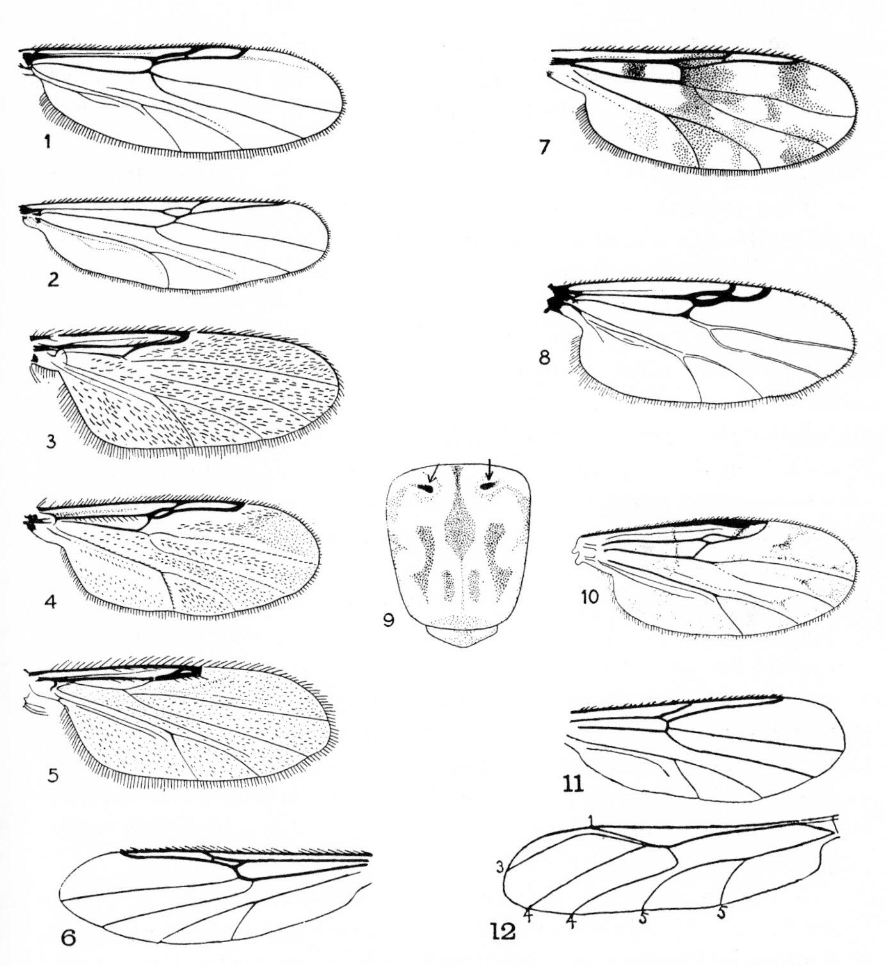

Ceratopogonidæ.—1, **Serromyia**; 2, **Clinohelea**; 3, **Forcipomyia**; 4, **Atrichopogon**; 5, **Dasyhelea**; 6, **Johannsenomyia**; 7, **Monohelea**; 8, **Ceratopogon**; 9, **Culicoides**, thorax; 10, **Culicoides cockerelli**; 11, **Bezzia**; 12, **Stenoxenus**.

Family Psychodidæ—The Moth Flies

Thickly haired, small flies, rarely exceeding 5 mm. in length, the wings clothed with hairs or scales and folded roof-like over the back.

Head small; ocelli absent. Antennæ usually as long as the head and thorax together, the segments usually bead-like and sometimes so densely haired as to appear very thick; composed of from twelve to sixteen segments, the basal segments usually short and cylindrical. Proboscis usually short but more or less elongate and rigid in *Flebotomus;* palpi composed of four segments, hairy. Thorax without transverse suture, not very convex; scutellum rounded. Abdomen rather cylindrical, composed of six to eight segments; male genitalia prominent, the female ovipositor usually projecting. Wings large, ovate, often pointed, when at rest lying roof-like over the abdomen, the base being bent at more than a right angle, the veins and border densely haired, the integument often with hairs or scales; veins strong, usually concealed by the dense hair; crossveins restricted to the basal third of the wing; two or three of the veins furcate. Legs rather short, elongate in *Flebotomus* and usually thickly haired.

The adults occur commonly in shady places in the vicinity of water and may often be found in large numbers on dense foliage in swamps, where they crawl about on the under surface of leaves, occasionally alighting on the upper surface after a short flight. I have seen them in thousands on tree-trunks after a heavy rain and they are not rare on logs and fallen trees where they walk about in a peculiar, jerky manner or remain perfectly still. One or more species of *Psychoda* breeds in drain pipes and they often cause uneasiness by appearing in the bath room. Their presence should incite interest rather than fear as the larvæ survive hot water and soap alike, and do no harm. The adults are not common in collections, chiefly because they are so easily damaged. The hairs brush off and they become useless unless unusual care is taken of the specimens. No recent revision of the family has appeared and the synonymy is badly mixed and is not to be trusted. The male genitalia offer excellent characters. There are dozens of species and the family offers an excellent opportunity for a thorough, monographic work.

In America two diseases are known to be carried by species of *Flebotomus.* The disease known as *Verruga Peruviana, Oroya Fever* or *Carrion's Disease* has been found only in narrow valleys on the western slopes of the Peruvian Andes. *Verruga* is said not to be serious but *Oroya Fever* (*Carrion's Disease*), the malignant form, is responsible for many deaths annually. *Local Leishmaniasis* or *Espundia* occurs in South and Central America. The causative organism is *Leishmania braziliensis* but it is not known definitely which species of *Flebotomus* carry the disease. It is possible that most of them are capable of doing so. The statement has been made that the adults of *Flebotomus* are nocturnal and that protection against disease may be obtained by remaining indoors at night. Most of the nocturnal blood-sucking flies may be found on the wing on dull cloudy days.

The larvæ live in decaying vegetable matter, dung, or water and are peculiar in possessing both open spiracles and tracheal gills; the head bears eye-spots; in the aquatic forms there are sucking discs on the segments behind the head, but no feet.

KEY TO GENERA

1. Two longitudinal veins behind the posterior forked vein............. 2
   Three longitudinal veins behind the posterior forked vein............ 3
2. Two forked veins in front of the middle of the wing. ***Flebotomus** Rondani
   One forked vein in front of the middle of the wing (3)...**Maruina** Müller
3. Wings with scales or scale-like hairs on the veins or membrane...... 4
   Wings with hairs only 5
4. Wing membrane with broad scales over most of the surface.
   Parabrunettia Brunetti
   Wings with scales on the veins only...............**Brunettia** Annandale
5. Two longitudinal, unforked veins between the anterior and posterior furcate veins 6
   Only one longitudinal vein between the anterior and posterior furcate veins (4) ....**Trichomyia** Haliday
6. The second simple vein behind the anterior furcate vein ends in the tip of the wing (1)............................**Psychoda** Latreille
   The second simple vein ends behind the tip of the wing (2).
   Pericoma Walker

* **Phlebotomus** of authors.

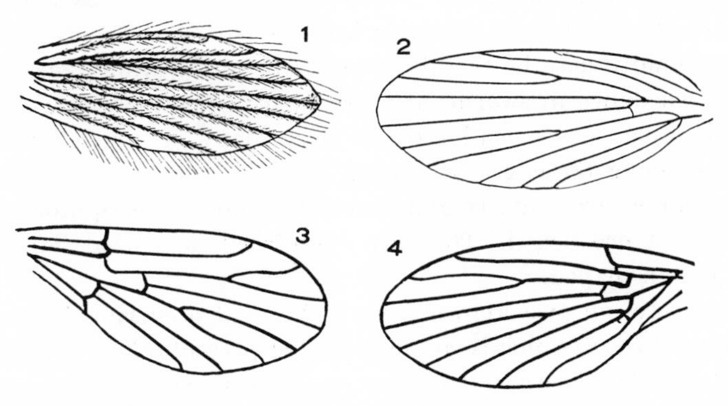

Psychodidæ.—1, **Psychoda**; 2, **Pericoma**; 3, **Maruina**; 4, **Trichomyia**. Hairs omitted from figures 2-4.

Family Dixidæ

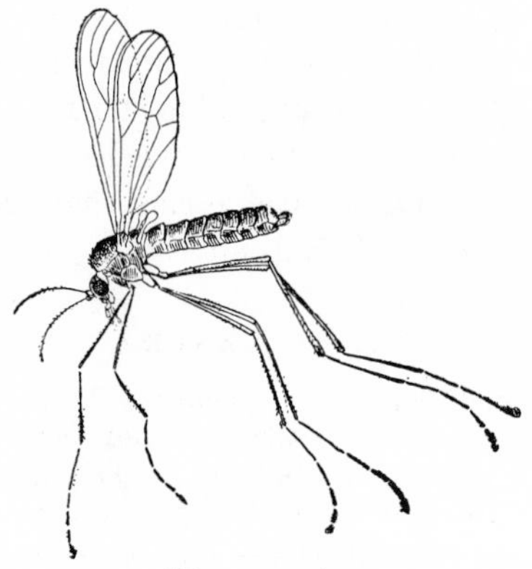

Dixa species.

Rather small, slender, nearly bare species occurring near running water.

Proboscis somewhat projecting; palpi four-segmented; antennæ long, the basal segments swollen, the flagellar segments hair-like and poorly separated; ocelli absent; eyes round. Thorax strongly convex, without transverse suture; metanotum arched; scutellum transverse. Abdomen long and slender, composed of seven or eight segments, thickened posteriorly in the male, pointed in the female. Legs long and slender, the coxæ somewhat elongated; tibiæ without terminal spurs. Wings rather large; auxiliary vein present, ending in costa before the middle of the wing; two complete basal cells.

This family may be readily recognized by the wing venation. The adults often dance in swarms at a height of a few inches to a few feet above the surface of small streams in swampy or wooded areas and occur also along the edges of ponds.

The larvæ are aquatic and resemble those of mosquitoes but the thorax is not broadened. They are cylindrical, somewhat flattened beneath, and n-shaped.

There are but two known genera, *Neodixa* occurring only in New Zealand, and *Dixa*, which is cosmopolitan. I present a key, adapted from Edwards, to the genera and subgenera of the world.

KEY TO GENERA

1. Second vein branched .... **Dixa** Meigen
   Second vein simple (New Zealand) .... **Neodixa** Tonnoir

Subgenera of **Dixa**

1. Hind margin of the wing evenly rounded 2
   Hind margin of wing produced at end of fifth vein; all veins in apical part of wing parallel..................... **Dixapuella** Dyar & Shannon

2. Crossvein connecting the fourth vein and anterior branch of the fifth vein strong 3
   Crossvein connecting anterior branch of the fifth vein and the fourth vein faint .... **Dixella** Dyar & Shannon

3. First flagellar segment fusiform or oval 4
   First flagellar segment cylindrical, five times as long as wide. **Paradixa** Tonnoir

4. First flagellar segment oval, about two and one-half times as long as wide .... **Nothodixa** Edwards
   First flagellar segment fusiform; at least three times as long as wide. **Dixa** Meigen

LIFE STAGES OF MOSQUITOES

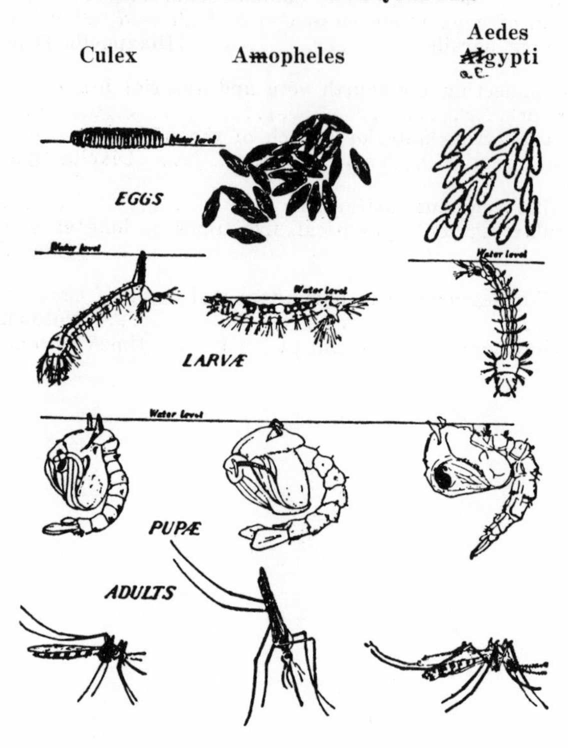

The life stages of three different genera of mosquitoes showing characteristic types of each and resting position of the adults (After Pieper and Beauchamp, from Metcalf and Sanderson).

Family Culicidæ—The Mosquitoes

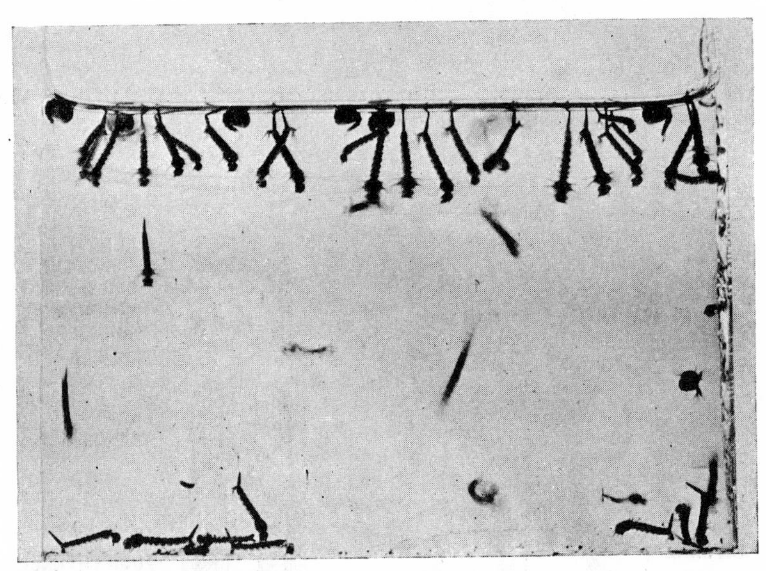

Aëdes larvæ. Note position at surface of water characteristic of the Culicini. (After Matheson, courtesy C. C. Thomas).

Slender, delicate flies, with slender legs and usually with scales upon the body and appendages.

Head small, subspherical; eyes reniform; ocelli absent. Antennæ slender, elongate, composed of fourteen or fifteen segments, densely plumose in the males; first segment reduced to a narrow ring, second globose, the following elongated, nearly or quite cylindrical and with whorls of hairs, in the male the apical two segments elongated and nearly bare. Thorax ovate, arched but not projecting over the head, without transverse suture; scutellum short, evenly rounded or trilobate; metanotum usually arched. Abdomen long and narrow, somewhat arched, composed of nine or ten segments; male genitalia prominent but not large; ovipositor short. Legs long and slender, the coxæ not elongate; tarsi long, the claws often denticulate. Wings long and narrow, at rest lying flat over the abdomen, with six fully developed longitudinal veins reaching the margin, the posterior margin fringed with hairs or scales, the costal vein extending around the wing; venation as in figure; two basal cells, the veins usually clothed with scales.

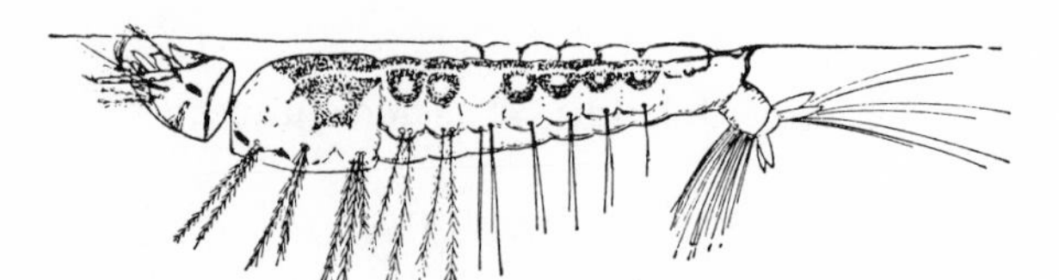

Anopheles larva. Compare position at surface of water with that of **Aëdes.** (After Matheson, courtesy C. C. Thomas).

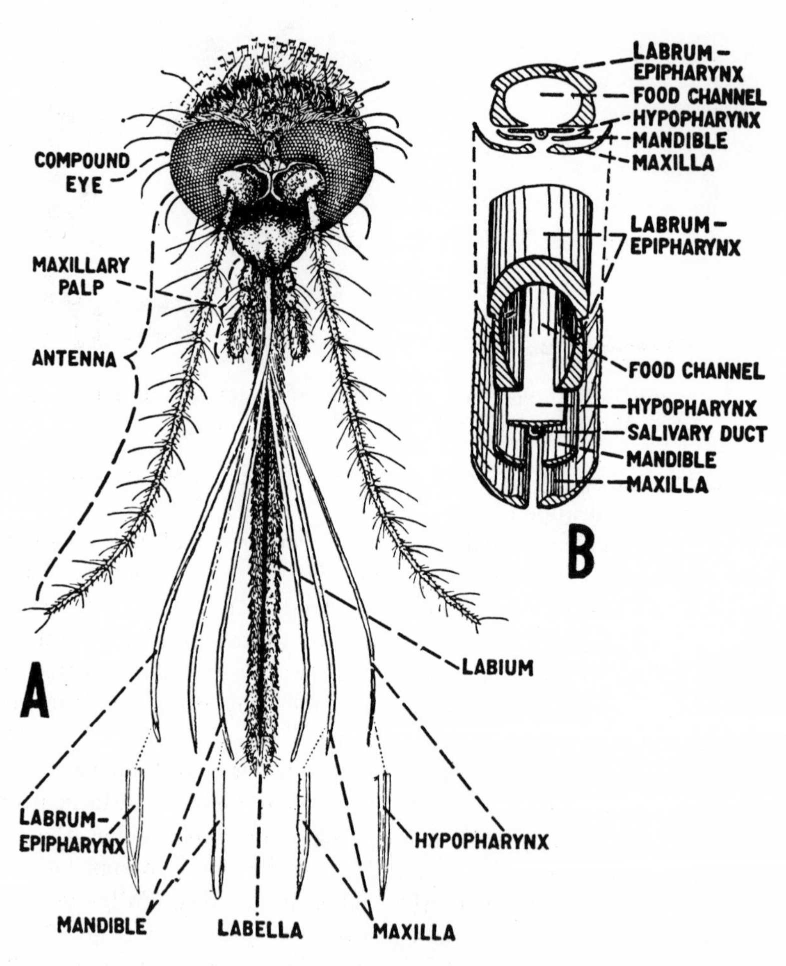

Head and mouth-parts of a mosquito.
(After Metcalf and Sanderson).

The mosquitoes are too well known to require hints as to where they may be found although it may be well to remark that a "swatted" mosquito does not make a suitable study specimen. Despite the fact that these flies are not altogether fragile it is nevertheless true that most specimens in collections are in poor condition because the preservation of the insects in good state depends upon care in handling immediately after capture. Few specimens should be placed in a killing bottle and they should be mounted while fresh. All but the very small species should be pinned on fine steel pins and not mounted on points; the small ones should be fastened on the sides of pins, using a ring of white shellac. With careful collecting, care in pinning and proper preservation, a collection of these insects may be very attractive. Many of the adults are extremely beautiful although it must be admitted that most of those in the Nearctic region do not go in for fine colors: in the tropics many of the species are clothed in nature's most beautiful colors.

All mosquitoes are not injurious and many of them do not bite. Some are predaceous upon other mosquitoes in the larval stage and this is true of the Chaoborinæ, which should, perhaps, be ranked as a distinct family, since they almost entirely lack scales. Their larvæ are called "Phantoms" because they are practically colorless.

So much has been written about mosquitoes during the present century that it would be impossible to review the entire literature in the space available but mention may be made of two books which will furnish a basis for intensive study for anyone interested. Matheson's "Handbook of the Mosquitoes of North America" deals with most of the species occurring in the United States and Canada and gives a thorough resumé of the medical and control aspects of the subject. Dyar's "The Mosquitoes of the Americas" deals entirely with the taxonomy of the group, but the descriptions are too brief and often omit important details: nevertheless it is an indispensable work and with careful study and use of the figures will be found fairly satisfactory.

I may say that the Culicidæ are one of the most important families of the Diptera insofar as human welfare is concerned. The diseases carried by them are not only lethal but cause extreme suffering and agony. Without doubt a much more extensive account of these insects might well be included in this work but space does not permit.

The diseases known to be transmitted by mosquitoes are *Malaria, Blackwater Fever, Yellow Fever, Dengue, Filariasis, Bird Malaria* and *Fowl-pox*. Of these Malaria and Yellow Fever are the most widely distributed and much has been written about them. In at least the first five both the mosquito and man are essential in the life cycle of the

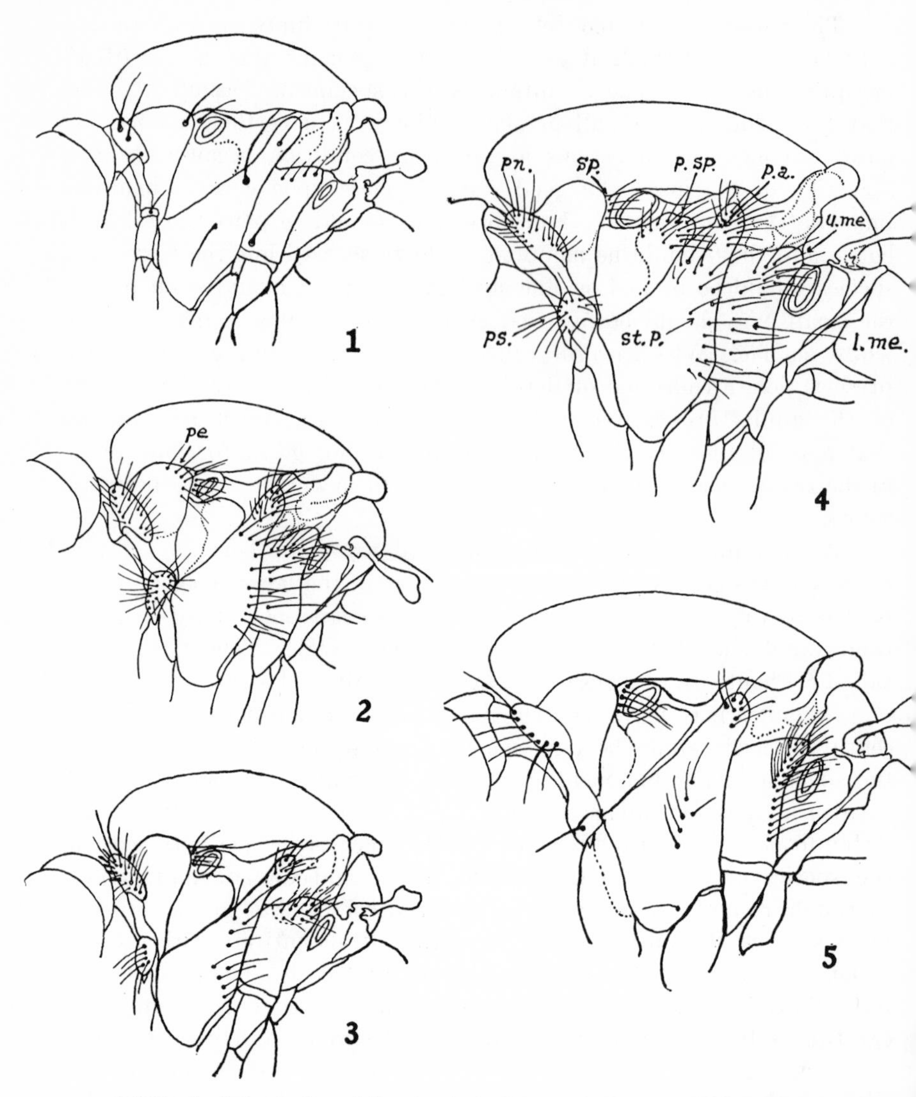

Culicidæ I.—Lateral view of thorax of: 1, **Uranotænia lœwii**; 2, **Theobaldia morsitans**; 3, **Anopheles punctipennis**; 4, **Psorophora ciliata**; 5, **Megarhinus septentrionalis.** (After Matheson, courtesy C. C. Thomas).

l.m.e., lower mesepimeral bristles; pa., prealar bristles; pe., prothoracic bristles; pn., pronotal bristles; p.sp., postspiracular bristles; ps., prosternal or propleural bristles; sp., spiracular bristles; st.p., sternopleural bristles; u.me., upper mesepimeral bristles.

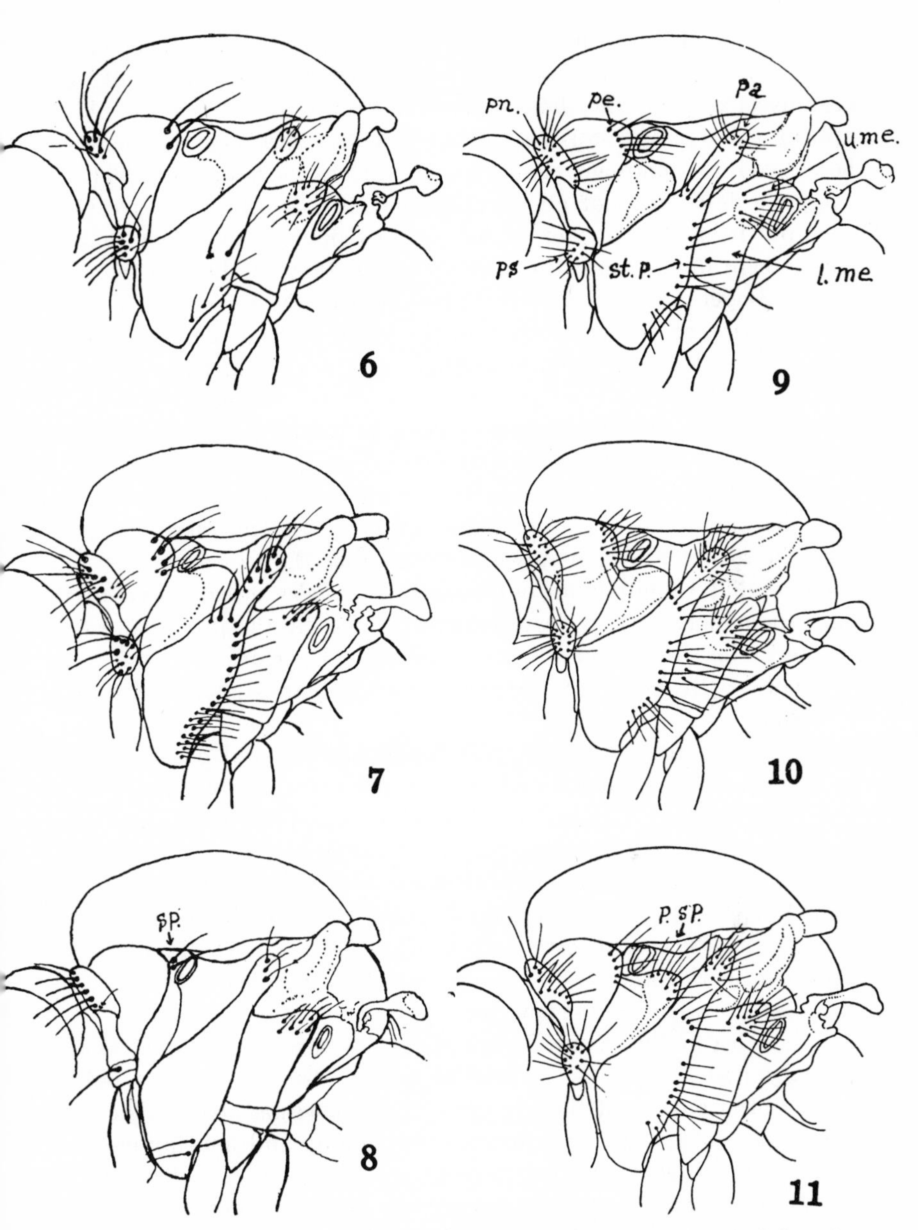

Culicidæ II.—Lateral view of thorax of: 6, **Orthopodomyia signifer**; 7, **Deinocerites pseudes**; 8, **Wyeomyia smithii**; 9, **Culex pipiens**; 10, **Mansonia perturbans**; 11, **Aedes vexans.** (After Matheson, courtesy C. C. Thomas).

causative organism, although other warm blooded animals may take the place of man. If the mosquitoes essential for the development of the organisms causing the disease were destroyed the disease would disappear entirely and it is because of this that such vigorous steps have been taken to stamp out mosquitoes in various parts of the world. The complete destruction of all disease carrying mosquitoes is scarcely possible but it has been demonstrated in the Panama Canal Zone that they can be kept under control to such an extent that the diseases they carry are no longer a serious menace to residents of the region. It is now so well known that the construction of the Panama Canal was made possible only by the control of mosquitoes that no more than mention of the fact need be made here.

Malaria is still a common disease in many parts of the United States. Many of us think of it as a tropical or subtropical disease, but nothing could be further from the truth. *Malaria* has raged at one time or another over rather large areas of the northern states and may do so again if patients suffering from the disease in its active stage should be bitten by our native *Anopheles* mosquitoes and they have the opportunity of developing and injecting the protozoan causing the fever into the blood stream of uninfected persons.

The North American *Anopheles* known to transmit the disease are *quadrimaculatus, maculipennis, punctipennis, crucians,* and *atropus* in the United States, *albimanus, pseudopunctipennis* and *quadrimaculatus* in Mexico, and *albimanus* and *tarsimaculatus* in Central America and the West Indies. The last three species named for the United States are not considered important vectors of the disease.

The causative organisms of *Malaria* are *Plasmodium vivax* for tertian, *P. malariæ* for quartan, and *P. falciparum* for the pernicious type. Tertian is our commonest type, being approximately three times as prevalent as the other two combined, while the pernicious form is almost twice as prevalent as the quartan.

An idea of the essential part played by insects which act as intermediary hosts for parasites causing human diseases, may be obtained from a brief outline of the life cycle of *Plasmodium vivax.* The organism passes an asexual stage in man, developing and multiplying in the red corpuscles, causing them to enlarge. In a little less than two days the *trophozoites* are mature, having absorbed the contents of the cell and the term *schizont* is now applied to them. These divide into from 15 to 24 *merozoites* and are discharged into the blood stream by rupturing of the cell wall. The cycle now begins over again and the same process is repeated, but after a time certain of the *merozoites* develop into male (*microgametocytes*) and female (*macrogametocytes*) which remain in the red blood cells, no further development taking place. From this point on the mosquito becomes an essential factor since, unless they are ingested by a mosquito, the *gametocytes* are capable of no further development.

When the *gametocytes* are taken into the mosquito further development occurs, commencing in the stomach of the host. The female (*macrogametocytes*) mature into what is called a *macrogamete,* corresponding to a ripened but unfertilized ovule, while the *microgametocytes* give off a number of thin, elongate, worm-like bodies, the male elements or *microgametes.* These travel about by a lashing motion until they come in contact with a *macrogamete,* when they penetrate the cell wall and fertilization takes place, producing a *zygote,* a round body which soon elongates into an *ookinete* which becomes active, penetrates the wall of the stomach and establishes itself between the epithelial and muscular layers. In this position it absorbs food from the surrounding tissue, becomes spherical and very large, and in this stage is termed an *oocyst.* In this stage the spores (corresponding to eggs) are developed, and are called *sporozoites.* They escape by the breaking of the *oocyst* and enter the body cavity, where they are carried to all parts of the body by the free-flowing blood, many of them finding their way to the salivary glands and into the blood streams of human beings where they penetrate the red blood cells and develop into *schizonts.*

It will be seen from this that the sexual stage occurs in the mosquito, occupying from eight to fourteen days, and probably results in no ill effects to its host, since it is a cold-blooded creature.

In *tertian malaria* a chill is produced about every three days, followed by fever, while in *quartan malaria* the chill occurs every four days, due to the longer incubation period of the *merozoites,* while in *pernicious malaria* the chills and fever are irregular.

Blackwater Fever is now believed to be the result of numerous attacks of malaria or a more or less continuous infection and derives its name from the fact that the patient's urine is of a dark mahogany color due to the presence of broken down red corpuscles.

Yellow Fever may be carried by at least three species of mosquitos in America *Aëdes* (*Stegomyia*) *aegypti, Aëdes fluvialtilis* and *Aëdes scapularis.* Possibly other species might carry the disease as well but we fortunately do not have it in the United States, even though *A. aegypti* is common in the south. With present facilities for rapid transportation there is danger of travellers from yellow fever areas entering the country and developing the disease after arrival. If we were sure that the disease would be quickly diagnosed and the patient isolated in a mosquito-proof room we might feel much more certain

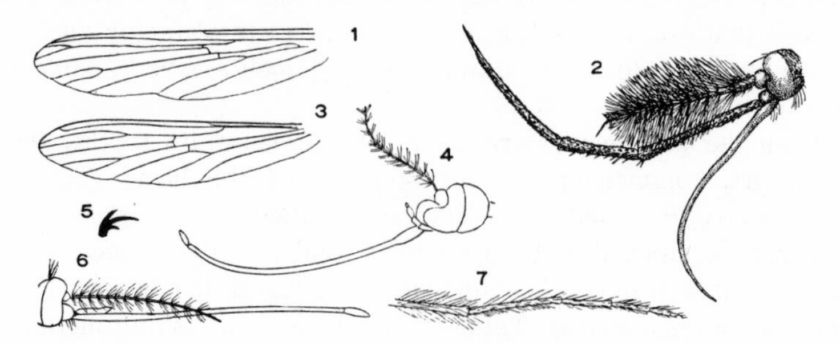

Culicidæ III.—1, **Megarhinus;** 2, **Megarhinus,** ♂ head; 3, **Aëdes,** wing venation; 4, **Hæmagogus;** 5, **Hæmagogus,** front claws of ♂; 6, **Wyeomyia,** ♀; 7, **Chaoborus,** posterior tarsus.

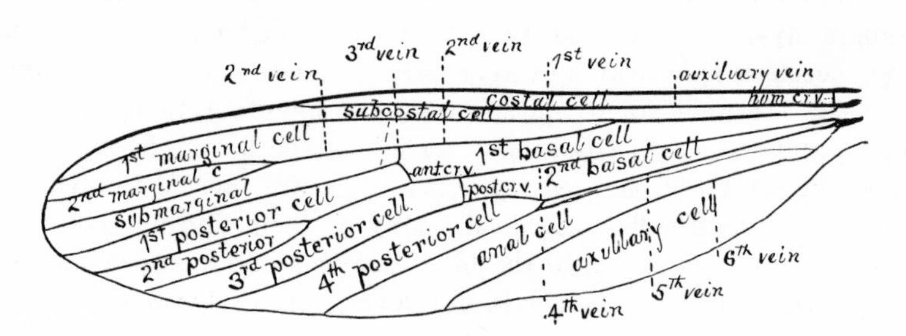

Venation of **Aëdes.**

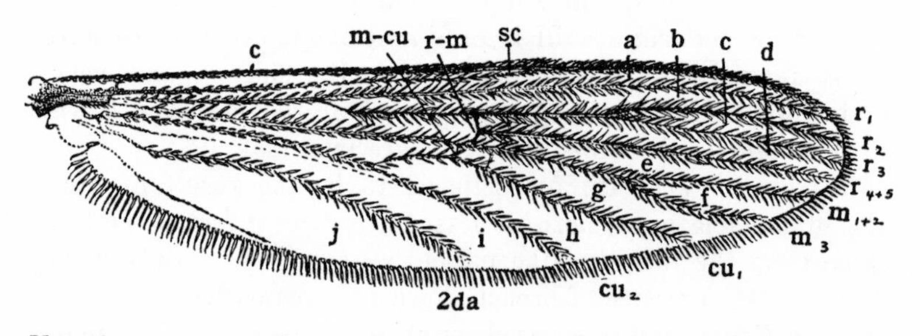

Venation of **Anopheles,** giving Comstock-Needham terminology and that of Schiner, etc. (in brackets). Veins.—C, costal; Sc., subcostal (auxiliary); R, (first longitudinal); R_2, R_3, (second longitudinal); R_{4+5}, (third longitudinal); M_{1+2}, M_3 (fourth longitudinal); Cu_1, Cu_2 (fifth longitudinal); 2 da., (sixth longitudinal); r-m, radio-medial crossvein (anterior crossvein); m-cu, medio-cubital crossvein (posterior crossvein). Cells.—a, Sc., (subcostal); b, R_1, (first marginal); c, R_2 (second marginal); d, R_3 (submarginal); e, R_5 (first posterior); f, M_2, (second posterior); g, M_3 (third posterior); h. Cu, (fourth posterior); i, Cu_2 (anal); j, 2a, (axiliary). (After Matheson, courtesy C. C. Thomas).

that the disease would not become established in this country, but, unfortunately, few doctors are familiar with the symptoms of yellow fever and there is grave danger of the disease remaining undiagnosed until it is too late to take precautionary measures. Even though steps have been taken to quarantine all persons coming from known yellow fever areas the danger of introduction of the disease is an ever present menace.

Dengue or Break-bone Fever is another disease carried by the *Yellow Fever* mosquito (*Aëdes aegypti*). It is a common tropical and subtropical disease and there are occasional outbreaks in the Southern States, corresponding to the distribution of the mosquito. After biting a patient it requires from eight to eleven days before the mosquito is capable of transmitting the disease.

The microfilariae of *Wuchereria bancrofti* Cobbold are taken up (in America) by *Culex fatigans* Wiedemann and undergo development in the muscles of the mosquito, in much the same way as described for *Malaria* but there is no increase in numbers and they do not become sexually mature until they have been returned to the human body. The worms occur in the lymphatic system and may be responsible for a number of organic disturbances. The region about Charleston, South Carolina is the only area in the United Staates where *Filariasis* is prevalent but it is common in the tropics of both hemispheres.

Since writing the foregoing and preparing the following key, Edwards' fascicle in the "Genera Insectorum" (194), has appeared. In this work the Dixidæ are included as a subfamily of the Culicidæ, a course I do not follow. An examination of this important fasicle of "Genera Insectorum" will disclose the fact that Edwards makes free use of subgenera. My views on this question are expressed elsewhere in this work. With the author's view that genera should be limited to groups readily characterized in both sexes I most heartily agree. The quality of the scientific work of this author is of too high a standard to warrant criticism except of a most favorable nature and one can disagree with him only on questions of minor importance. The question of subgenera is really one of likes and dislikes, and I prefer to keep as close as possible to a binomial system of nomenclature.

Most of the cuts used to illustrate this family are from "A Handbook of the Mosquitoes of North America" by Dr. Robert Matheson and I wish to express my indebtedness to him and to Mr. C. C. Thomas, the publisher, for furnishing them, and also my appreciation of their wholehearted cooperation.

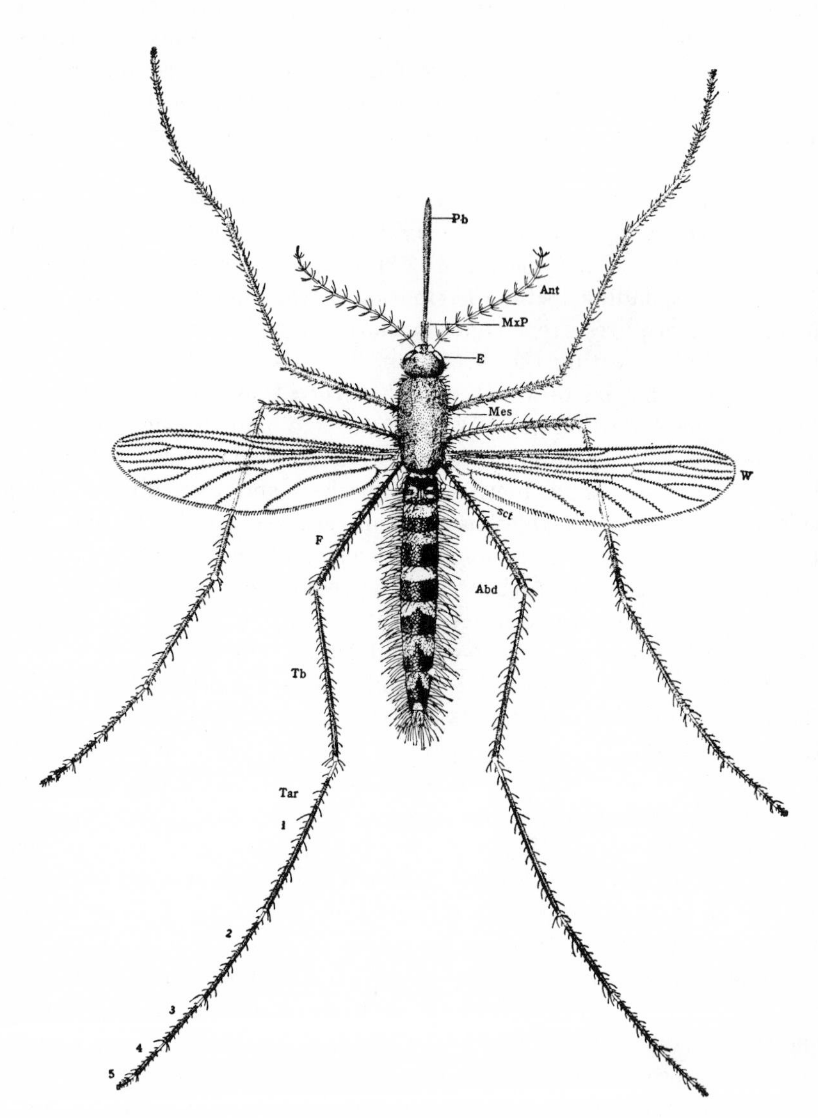

Aëdes vexans. (After Matheson, courtesy C. C. Thomas).

KEY TO GENERA*

1. Proboscis not elongate, extending but little beyond the clypeus; wings with scales (when present) confined mostly to the fringe. (Chaoborinæ) 2
   Proboscis elongate, extending far beyond the clypeus; wings with the veins and margins with scales (Culicinæ) 5

2. Anal vein ends beyond the fork of the fifth vein........ 3
   Anal vein ends before the fork of fifth vein.......**Eucorethra** Underwood

3. First tarsal segment longer than the second........ 4
   First tarsal segment shorter than the second...........**Mochlonyx** Lœw

4. First vein ending much closer to the tip of the anterior branch of second vein than to that of the auxiliary vein (**III-7**). **Chaoborus** Lichtenstein
   First vein ending nearer to tip of auxiliary vein than to anterior branch of second vein ....**Corethrella** Coquillett

5. Abdomen without scales, or at least with the sternites largely bare; scutellum with the margin convex, evenly setose; never a spurious vein behind fifth vein (**I-3**, and text figure of larva)..**Anopheles** Meigen
   Abdomen with both tergites and sternites completely clothed with scales; scutellum trilobed, the lobes alone setose; if scutellum evenly convex then a spurious vein behind fifth vein........ 6

6. Proboscis rigid, the outer half more slender and bent backwards; a spurious vein behind the fifth vein (**I-5, III-1, III-2**). **Megarhinus** Desvoidy
   Proboscis more flexible, of uniform thickness (at times swollen at tip), outer half not bent back; never a spurious vein behind fifth vein... 7

7. Base of hind coxæ in line with or above the upper margin of the metasternal sclerite 8
   Base of hind coxæ below upper margin of metasternal sclerite....... 16

8. Pronotal setæ absent; prothoracic lobes not widely separated......... 9
   Pronotal setæ present; prothoracic lobes widely separated........... 14

9. Prealar setæ absent 10
   Prealar setæ present 11

10. Propleural setæ absent ....**Sabethes** Desvoidy
    Propleural setæ present ....**Sabethoides** Theobald

11. Spiracular setæ present 12
    Spiracular setæ absent ....**Limatus** Theobald

12. Lower sternopleurals distinctly below the upper margin of metasternal sclerite 13
    Lower sternopleurals extending to or above the upper margin of the metasternal sclerite ....**Dendromyia** Theobald

13. Outstanding scales on at least the basal portion of the second and third veins broad........**Miamyia** Dyar
    These scales usually narrow (**II-8, III-6**) ....**Wyeomyia** Theobald

* Checked by Dr. R. Matheson.

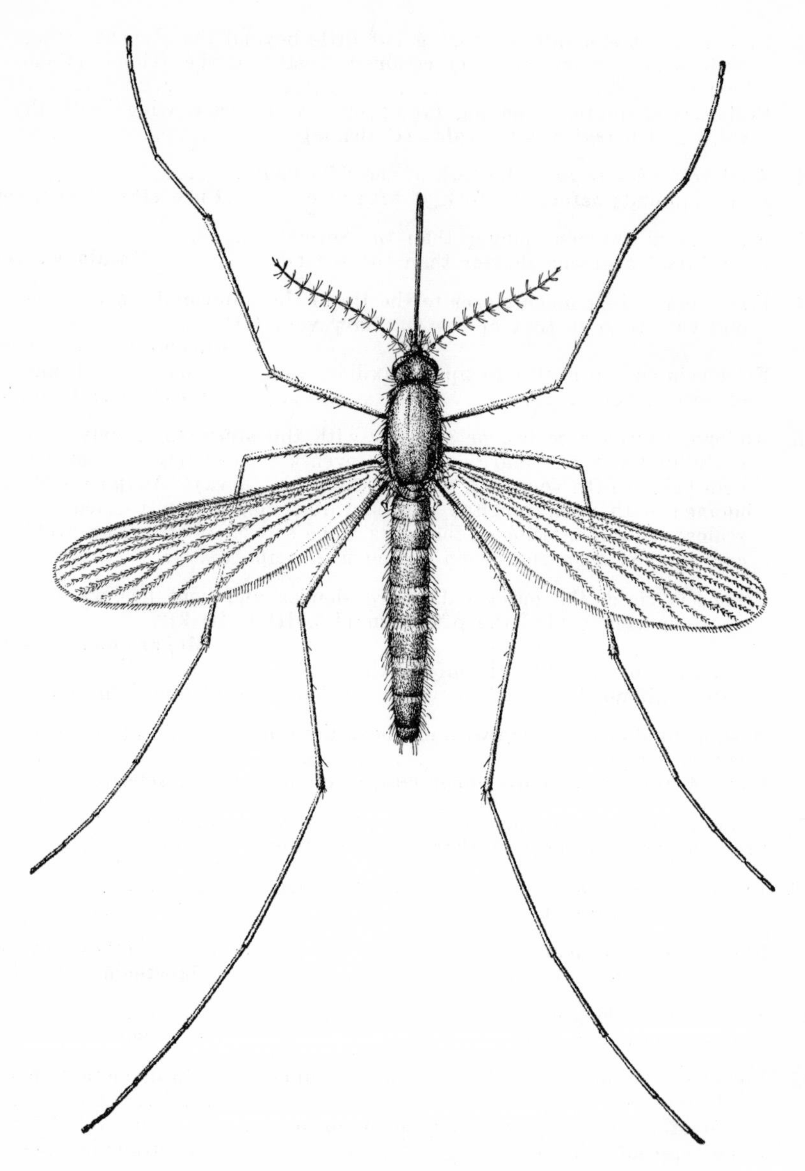

Culex pipiens. (After Matheson, courtesy C. C. Thomas).

14. Clypeus with setæ.............................**Joblotia** Blanchard
Clypeus without setæ.. 15

15. Lower sternopleural setæ extending above the upper margin of the metasternal sclerite ....**Gœldia** Theobald
Lower sternopleural setæ not extending above the upper margin of the metasternal sclerite (I-1)..................**Isostomyia** Coquillett

16. Anal vein ending opposite or before the fork of the fifth vein. **Uranotænia** Arribalzaga
Anal vein ending well beyond the fork of the fifth vein............. 17

17. Prescutellar setæ and postspiracular setæ absent (III-4, III-5). **Hæmagogus** Williston
Prescutellar setæ present 18

18. Postspiracular setæ present 19
Postspiracular setæ absent 21

19. Spiracular setæ absent 20
Spiracular setæ present (I-4 and text figure)........**Psorophora** Desvoidy

20. Wing scales narrow (rarely broad) or the base of first vein with setæ posteriorly on the upper side (II-11, III-3, and text figs.).**Aëdes** Meigen
Wing scales broad; base of first vein bare (II-10)....**Mansonia** Blanchard

21. Spiracular setæ present (I-2)...............**Theobaldia** Neveu-Lemaire
Spiracular setæ absent 22

22. First vein without setæ basally on upper side; wing scales broad..... 23
First vein with setæ basally on upper side; wide scales narrow....... 25

23. Fourth segment of front tarsi at least as broad as long (II-6). **Orthopodomyia** Theobald
Fourth segment of front tarsi longer than wide.................... 24

24. Antennal segments little longer than wide..........**Aedeomyia** Theobald
Antennal segments much longer than wide (II-10)....**Mansonia** Blanchard

25. Antennæ much longer than the length of the proboscis (II-7). **Deinocerites** Theobald
Antennæ not longer than the length of the proboscis................ 26

26. Wings yellowish, spotted with black...................**Lutzia** Theobald
Wings never black-spotted (II-9 and text figure).......**Culex** Linnæus

KEY TO THE GENERA OF THE WORLD

1. Scales almost confined to the wing-fringe; mouth-parts short, the palpi incurved (Chaoborinæ)...................................... 2
Wing-veins and legs scaled; proboscis long; palpi not incurved (Culicinæ) 7

2. Clypeus large and hairy; R_1 ending close to tip of R_2............... 3
Clypeus small and nearly bare; R_1 ending far from tip of R_2. **Corethrella** Coquillett

3. First tarsal segment much shorter than the second................. 4
First tarsal segment longer than the second........................ 6

4. Tibiæ spurred 5
Tibiæ not spurred; metapleural hairs absent...........**Mochlonyx** Lœw

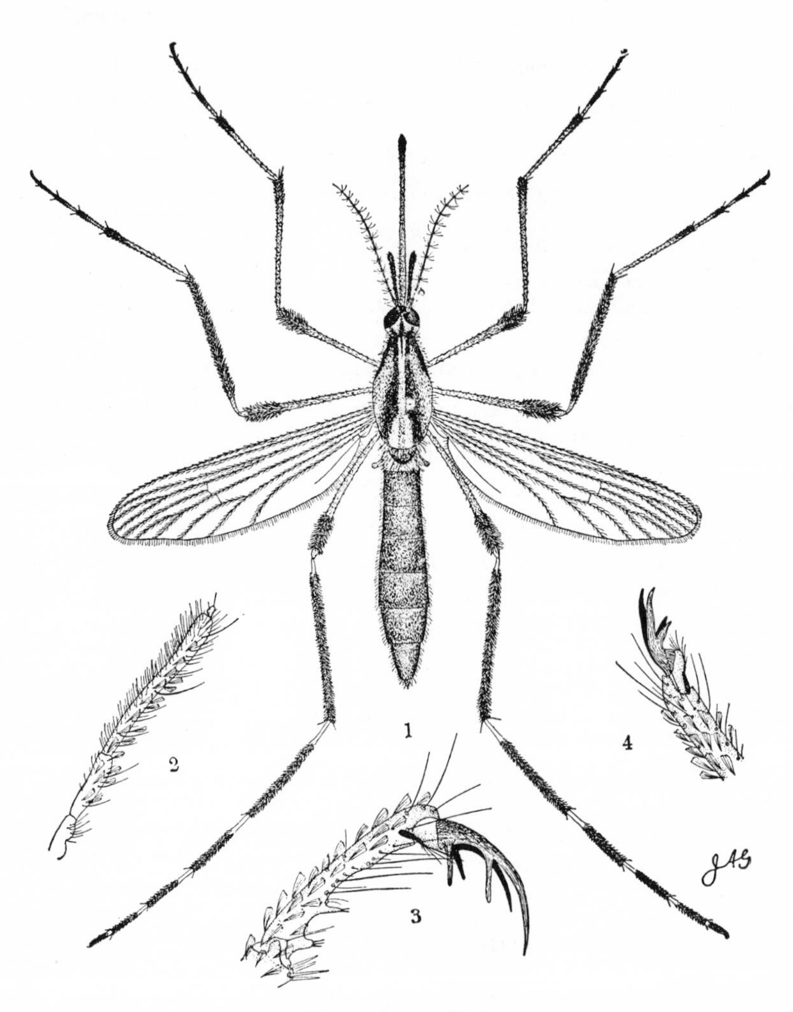

Psorophora ciliata.

5. Tibial spurs 1-2-2*; metapleural hairs present........**Cryophila** Edwards
Tibial spurs 1-1-1; metapleura bare.............**Promochlonyx** Edwards

6. Clypeus as long as the head; claws larger and toothed.
Eucorethra Underwood
Clypeus shorter than the head; claws small and simple.
Chaoborus Lichtenstein

7. Abdomen without scales; or at least with the sternites largely bare (Anophelini) 8
Abdomen with both tergites and sternites completely clothed with scales 10

8. Scutellum slightly trilobed ....**Chagasia** Cruz
Scutellum evenly rounded 9

9. Stem of median fork wavy.........................**Bironella** Theobald
Stem of median fork straight........................**Anopheles** Meigen

10. Proboscis not rigid, of uniform thickness (unless swollen at tip), outer half not bent backwards (Culicini)............................ 11
Proboscis rigid, outer half slender and bent backwards (Megarhinini).
Megarhinus Desvoidy

11. Squama fringed (fringe usually complete, rarely interrupted); vein An reaching well beyond base of cubital fork........................ 12
Squama bare or rarely with 1-4 short hairs........................ 30

12. Pulvilli present; pleural chætotaxy well developed, but spiracular and post-spiracular bristles absent 13
Pulvilli absent or rudimentary.................................. 14

13. Second antennal (first flagellar) segment short in both sexes; antennæ of ♂ nearly always plumose..........................**Culex** Linnæus
Second antennal (first flagellar) segment elongate in both sexes; antennæ of ♂ not plumose......................**Deinocerites** Theobald

14. Post-spiracular bristles absent; claws of ♀ simple (except in **Leicesteria, Hæmagogus,** and **Heizmannia**)............................ 15
Post-spiracular bristles present, even if only one or two; claws of ♀ usually toothed; dorsocentral and upper sternopleural bristles nearly always well developed.. 25

15. Spiracular bristles present (sometimes only one or two)............. 16
Spiracular bristles absent.. 19

16. Several upper sternopleural bristles; stem-vein usually hairy beneath.
Theobaldia Neveu-Lemaire
At most one or two upper sternopleural bristles; stem-vein bare beneath 17

17. Postnotum nearly always bare (Oriental and Australasian).
Tripteroides Giles
Postnotum with bristles (Neotropical)............................ 18

18. Clypeus with setæ...........................**Trichoprosopon** Theobald
Clypeus bare ....**Gœldia** Theobald

* Posterior four tibiæ each with two apical spurs.

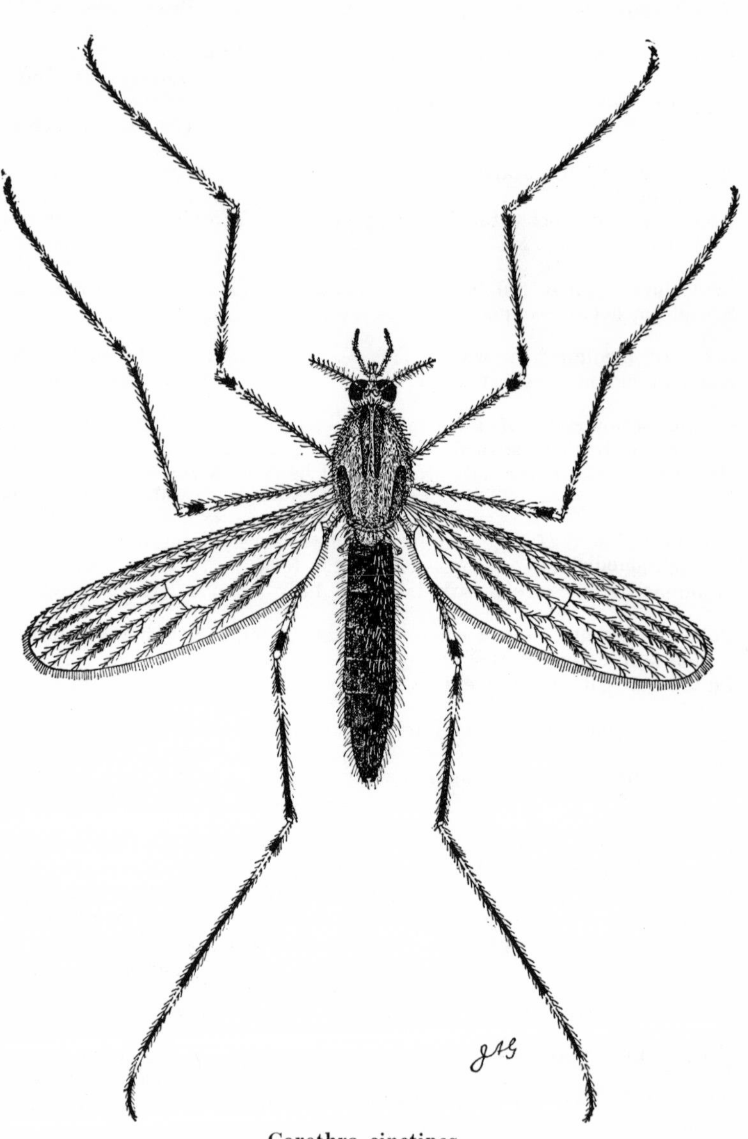

Corethra cinctipes.

19. Dorsocentral and pre-scutellar bristles absent; pronotal lobes approximated 20
    Dorsocentral and pre-scutellar bristles well developed; pronotal lobes well separated 21

20. Postnotum usually bare (Neotropical) .... **Hæmagogus** Williston
    Postnotum usually with bristles (Oriental) .... **Heizmannia** Ludlow

21. Post-spiracular area scaly; ♀ claws usually toothed; ♀ palpi more than half as long as proboscis .... **Armigeres** Theobald
    Subgen. **Leicesteria** Theobald
    Post-spiracular area bare; ♀ claws simple 22

22. All segments of ♀ antenna, and last two of ♂ antenna short and thick; middle femora with scale-tuft .... **Aëdeomyia** Theobald
    Antennæ normal, slender; middle femora without scale-tuft 23

23. First segment of front tarsi longer than the last four together; fourth very short in both sexes .... **Orthopodomyia** Theobald
    First segment of front tarsi not longer than last four together; fourth not shortened in ♀ 24

24. Proboscis of ♂ much swollen apically, of ♀ slightly so, or else cell R_2 shorter than its stem .... **Ficalbia** Theobald
    Proboscis not swollen apically; cell R_2 at least as long as its stem.
    Mansonia Blanchard

25. Head with numerous short hairs on vertex in addition to the orbital row; antennæ thick in both sexes, not plumose in ♂ .... **Opifex** Hutton
    Head without hairs on vertex apart from the orbital row; antennæ slender in ♀, nearly always plumose in ♂ 26

26. Spiracular bristles present, even if few (American) .. **Psorophora** Desvoidy
    Spiracular bristles absent 27

27. Eyes widely separated, space between them clothed with metallic silvery scales (Ethiopian) .... **Eretmopodites** Theobald
    Eyes less widely separated (sometimes touching), space between them not covered with metallic silvery scales 28

28. Wing-scales generally mostly narrow (when, rarely, all are broad, the ♀ claws are toothed); usually a few hairs on upper surface of stem-vein 29
    Wing scales all very broad; ♀ claws simple; stem-vein bare.
    Mansonia Blanchard

29. Proboscis more slender, not recurved at tip in repose; ornamentation various .... **Aëdes** Meigen
    Proboscis rather stout, recurved at tip in repose; dark species with flat scales on vertex and scutellum .... **Armigeres** Theobald

30. Wing-membrane without microtrichia (or these only visible under a high magnification); cell R_2 shorter than its stem; An ends about opposite base of cubital fork .... **Uranotænia** Arribalzaga
    Wing-membrane with distinct microtrichia (visible under a magnification of 50) 31

31. Postnotum bare; An (except in some species of Topomyia) ending little if at all beyond base of cubital fork; two or more posterior pronotal bristles present (Palæotropical) 32

Postnotum with bristles; An ending well beyond base of cubital fork; posterior pronotal bristles usually absent; spiracular bristles present (except in **Limatus**) (Neotropical) 35

32. Spiracular bristles absent; clypeus normal.......................... 33
Spiracular bristles present (one or more); clypeus rather small and narrow; cell R_2 longer than its stem............................ 34

33. Cell R_2 shorter than its stem; several posterior pronotal bristles; wing scales normal...................................**Zeugnomyia** Leicester
Cell R_2 longer than its stem; two posterior pronotal bristles; wing-scales emarginate at tips..........................**Hodgesia** Theobald

34. Proboscis very hairy, much enlarged at tip......**Harpagomyia** de Meijere
Proboscis not hairy, rarely enlarged at tip...........**Topomyia** Leicester

35. Middle legs with "paddles" formed of very long erect scales.
Sabethes Desvoidy
Middle legs without "paddles".. 36

36. Clypeus with hairs; large species with long ♂ palpi.
Trichoprosopon Theobald
Clypeus bare, or with scales only..................................... 37

37. Hind tarsi with long suberect scales; large species with long ♂ palpi.
Gœldia Theobald
Hind tarsi with appressed scales only; smaller species with short ♂ palpi 38

38. No bristles on subalar knob; pronotal lobes large and almost in contact; mesonotal scales all metallic...............**Sabethoides** Theobald
Bristles present on sub-alar knob; pronotal lobes more widely separated; mesonotal scales rarely metallic.......................... 39

39. Spiracular area with scales only; hind tarsus with one claw.
Limatus Theobald
Spiracular area with 1-4 bristles, no scales; hind tarsus with two claws.
Wyeomyia Theobald

Family Cecidomyidæ—The Gall Midges

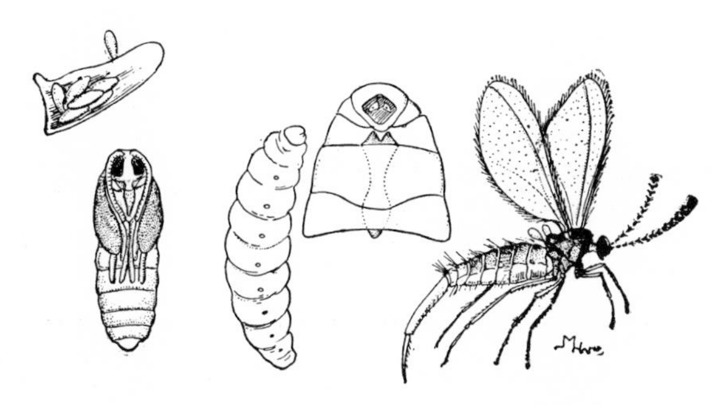

Cecidomyidæ—Thecodiplosis piniradiatæ Snow and Mills. Eggs, pupa, larva, "breast-bone" and imago. (Williston).

Small, delicate flies with broad wings and long antennæ and legs.

Head small; eyes round or reniform, sometimes holoptic; ocelli usually absent; antennæ long, cylindrical, the segments usually with bead-like swellings, ten to thirty-six in number; proboscis short, rarely elongated; palpi with one to four segments. Thorax ovate, more or less convex, without transverse suture; abdomen composed of eight segments; hypopygium small but projecting; ovipositor sometimes very long. Legs long and slender; coxæ rather short; tibiæ without terminal spurs, basal tarsal segment sometimes very short. Wings large, usually hairy, narrowed basally and without alula; three to five longitudinal veins, usually with only the first, third and fifth; humeral crossvein indistinct or absent; costal vein extending around the entire wing, the veins all weak, the fifth usually furcate; anterior crossvein situated very near the base of the wing, often appearing as the beginning of the third vein, the base of the third vein having the appearance of a crossvein; only one basal cell present.

These small flies may be found everywhere but the most satisfactory means of collecting them is to rear them. The larvæ of most of the species live in living plants where they form galls, or deformities of various kinds, in the axils of the leaves, etc. Others live under bark, in decaying vegetation and in fungi while a few live upon plant lice, being found for the most part under the colony of aphids or in axils of the leaves during the day. Many of the species are inquilines in the galls formed by other members of the family or even by other orders of insects. The galls occur on all parts of plants, on the flowers, leaves,

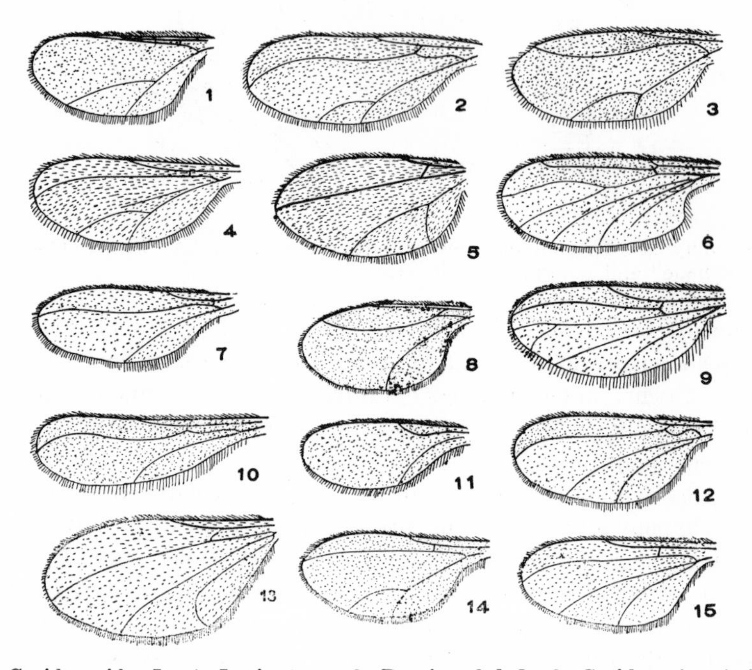

Cecidomyidæ I.—1, **Lasioptera**; 2, **Porricondyla?**; 3, **Cecidomyia**; 4, **Hormomyia**; 5, **Trichopteromyia**; 6, **Lestremia**; 7, **Miastor**; 8, **Spaniocera?**; 9, **Catocha**; 10, **Colpodia**; 11, **Heteropeza**; 12, **Asynapta**; 13, **Winnertzia**; 14, **Lestodiplosis**; 15, **Winnertzia**.

stems and roots and are usually characteristic for each species. The larvæ may be recognized by the presence of a "breast bone" or chitinized process lying within the thorax and terminating behind the head. The phenomenon of pædogenesis occurs in some species belonging to the genus *Miastor,* that is the larvæ produce eggs from ovary-like organs, the eggs hatch within the body and the young larvæ devour the parent, later escaping and completing their development externally; several generations may be produced in this way, before the development of adult insects occurs.

The classification of the family is difficult and I have merely emended the key given by Dr. Felt.* For the most part little can be done without preparing slides of the adults, the whole insect being mounted. It is advisable to preserve dried specimens as well as the mounts, and the galls should always be kept along with the adults. Study of the group should not be attempted by anyone who is not prepared to spend years of painstaking work on his hobby. Such a study would prove of inestimable value and would fully repay the student for the time spent. Many of the species are serious pests, the chief among these being the Hessian fly.

I may add that the study of the galls themselves constitutes a fascinating past-time and Dr. Felt has given us an excellent treatise on this subject† and is, I believe, preparing a new and enlarged edition. The series of papers published by Dr. Felt is copiously illustrated and I have made free use of these illustrations. In connection with their use I cannot help but call attention to the splendid cooperation of Dr. C. C. Adams, of the New York State Museum, in furnishing the cuts used for this family and of Dr. Felt for assistance and suggestions. Most of the illustrations of *Cecidomyidæ* are from cuts furnished by the New York State Museum.

KEY TO GENERA

1. Circumfila present 23
   Circumfila absent 2

2. Wings with four longitudinal veins 3
   Wings with at most three longitudinal veins 17

3. Fourth vein forked 4
   Fourth vein simple 10

4. Second antennal segment greatly enlarged 5
   Second antennal segment normal 7

---

* 1925. Key to Gall Midges (A resume of Studies, i-vii, Itonididæ), N. Y. State Mus. Bull. No. 257. References to Parts i-vii will be found in this Bulletin.

† 1918. Key to American Gall Insects, N. Y. State Mus. Bull. No. 200.

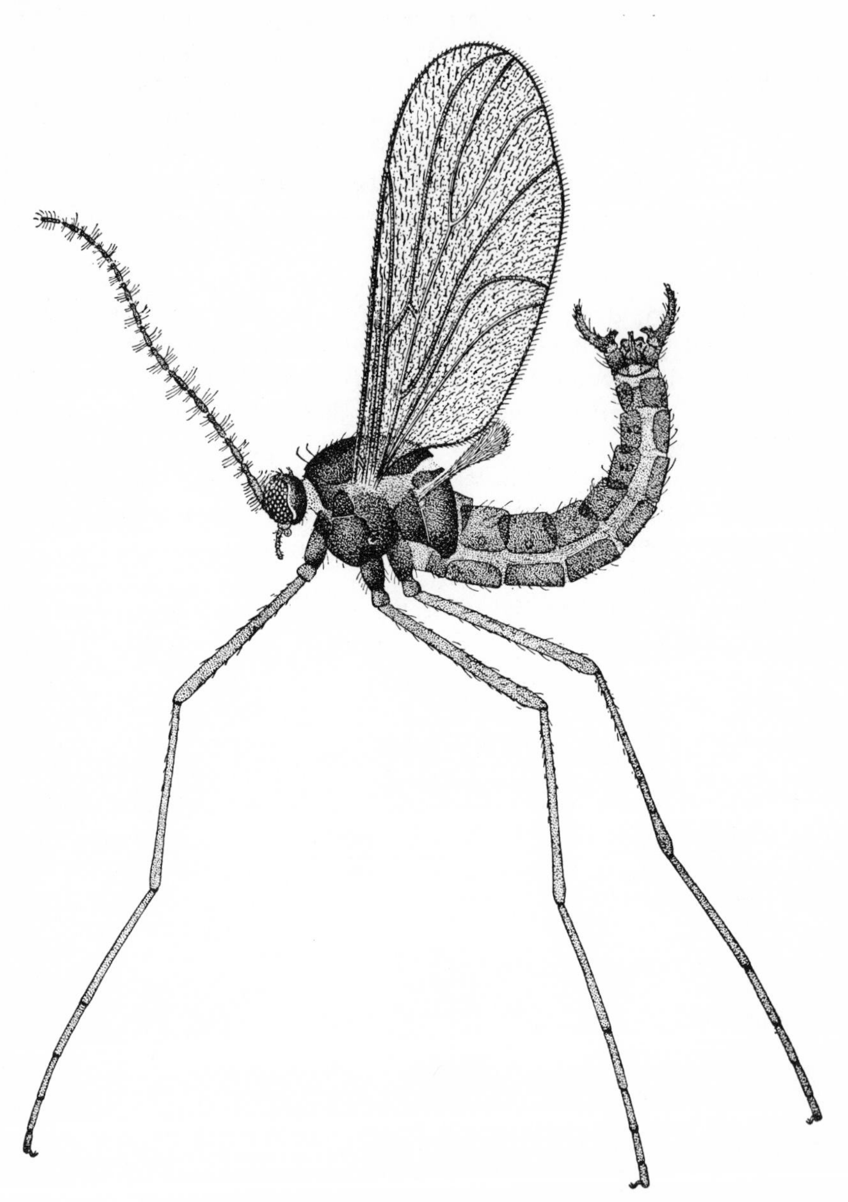

Cecidomyidæ II. 16, **Catocha Americana.**
(Courtesy New York State Museum, Albany, N. Y.)

5. Subcosta and third vein united as though by a very short crossvein. **Microcerata** Felt
   Subcosta and third vein separate and with no trace of a crossvein... 6

6. Branches of the fork of the fourth vein even...........**Konisomyia** Felt
   Branches of the fork of the fourth vein irregular (22)...**Tritozyga** Lœw

7. Flagellate antennal segments sessile, with a length only a little greater than their diameter........................**Neocatocha** Felt
   Antennal segments not sessile, more elongate.................... 8

8. Antennæ with not more than ten segments...........**Neptunimyia** Felt
   Antennæ with at least eleven segments.......................... 9

9. Costa ending at or a little beyond the tip of the third vein (**6, 26**). **Lestremia** Meigen
   Costa extending beyond the apex of the wing (**9, 16**)...**Catocha** Haliday

10. Third vein usually well separated from the costa and frequently uniting with it at or beyond the apex......................... 11
    Third vein rarely extending to the apex of the wing; flagellate antennal segments subsessile in female, ornamented with crenulate whorls or structures more complex than irregular whorls of simple hairs.. 14

11. Flagellate antennal segments globose, stemmed in both sexes, or the second enlarged 12
    Flagellate antennal segments cylindrical, sub-sessile, the second not enlarged (**23**)...**Mycophila** Felt

12. Fourth vein absent 13
    Fourth vein present (**28**) ....**Joannisia** Kieffer

13. Antennal segments stemmed (**5**)............**Trichopteromyia** Williston
    Antennal segments sessile, the second enlarged.........**Ceratomyia** Felt

14. Flagellate antennal segments with a more or less distinct subapical collar forming a more or less cup-shaped cavity; claws denticulate. **Prionellus** Kieffer
    Flagellate segments with subapical whorl of stemmed disks or spines. 15

15. Flagellate segments with subapical whorl of stemmed disks; claws with minute apical tooth ....**Monardia** Kieffer
    Flagellate segments with spines 16

16. Flagellate segments with short, stout, usually recurved spines (**24, 27**) ....**Cordylomyia** Felt
    Flagellate segments with short, stout, curved spines (**32**). **Corinthomyia** Felt

17. First segment of the tarsi shorter than the second................ 19
    First segment of the tarsi longer than the second................ 18

18. Tarsi with four segments; three longitudinal veins (**7, 18**). **Miastor** Meinert
    Tarsi with three segments; two longitudinal veins (**11**). **Heteropeza** Winnertz

19. Tarsi with five segments 20
    Tarsi with two segments..........................**Oligarces** Meinert

20. Wing membrane finely haired..................................... 21
    Wing membrane scaled ....**Kronomyia** Felt

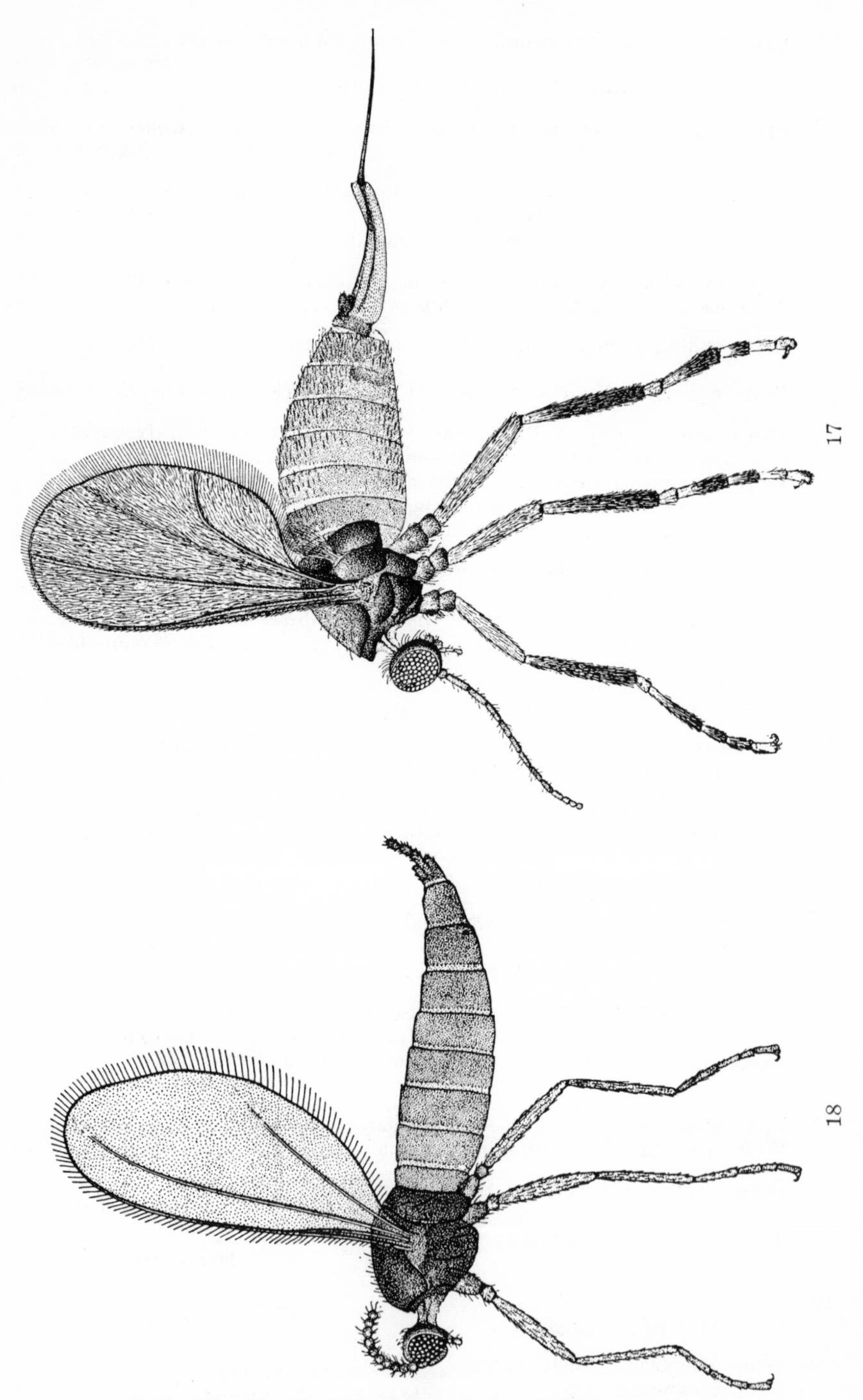

Cecidomyidæ III.—17, **Asphondylia monacha**; 18, **Miastor americana.** (Courtesy New York State Museum, Albany, N. Y.)

21. Third vein extending to the apex of the wing.................... 22
    Third vein not extending to the apex of the wing.........**Epimyia** Felt

22. Palpi with four segments.........................**Johnsonomyia** Felt
    Palpi with only one segment (29)..................**Leptosyna** Kieffer

23. No crossvein uniting the third and first veins..................... 29
    A distinct crossvein uniting the third and first veins.............. 24

24. Crossvein parallel or nearly so with the costa and apparently forming a continuation of the third vein............................. 27
    Crossvein forming a well-marked angle with the costa............. 25

25. Four longitudinal veins... 26
    Three longitudinal veins (**10**)......................**Colpodia** Winnertz

26. Fifth vein absent ....**Parawinnertzia** Felt
    Fifth vein well developed (**13, 15, 25**).............**Winnertzia** Rondani

27. Three or five longitudinal veins.................................. 28
    Four longitudinal veins (**12**)...........................**Asynapta** Lœw

28. Three longitudinal veins ....**Dirhiza** Lœw
    Five longitudinal veins...........................**Hormosomyia** Felt

29. Costa thickly scaled; third vein usually very close to anterior margin of wings; antennal segments cylindrical, sessile, short, never produced 30
    Costa rarely thickly clothed with scales, the third vein well separated from it; antennal segments usually longer than wide............ 36

30. Third vein lying very close to the costa and uniting with it at or before the middle of the wing, rarely at the distal third.......... 32
    Third vein well separated from the costa and uniting with it beyond the middle of the wing...................................... 31

31. Third vein and body thickly clothed with scales......**Trotteria** Kieffer
    Third vein and body not thickly clothed with scales.
    Camptoneuromyia Felt

32. Mouth parts and thorax normal, not greatly prolonged.............. 33
    Mouth parts and thorax prolonged.................**Clinorhyncha** Lœw

33. Palpi with one or two segments......................**Asteromyia** Felt
    Palpi with three or four segments................................. 34

34. Third and fourth antennal segments coalescent or closely fused..... 35
    Third and fourth antennal segments at least separated by a distinct constriction ....**Protaplonyx** Felt

35. Three longitudinal veins, the fifth forked (**1, 21**).....**Lasioptera** Meigen
    Four simple longitudinal veins.....................**Neolasioptera** Felt

36. Flagellate antennal segments cylindrical, never binodose in the male.. 37
    Flagellate antennal segments in the male greatly produced, binodose; circumfila usually forming long loops.......................... 60

37. Claws on at least one pair of legs toothed........................ 38
    Claws simple 50

38. Palpi with four segments.. 39
    Palpi with not more than three segments........................... 45

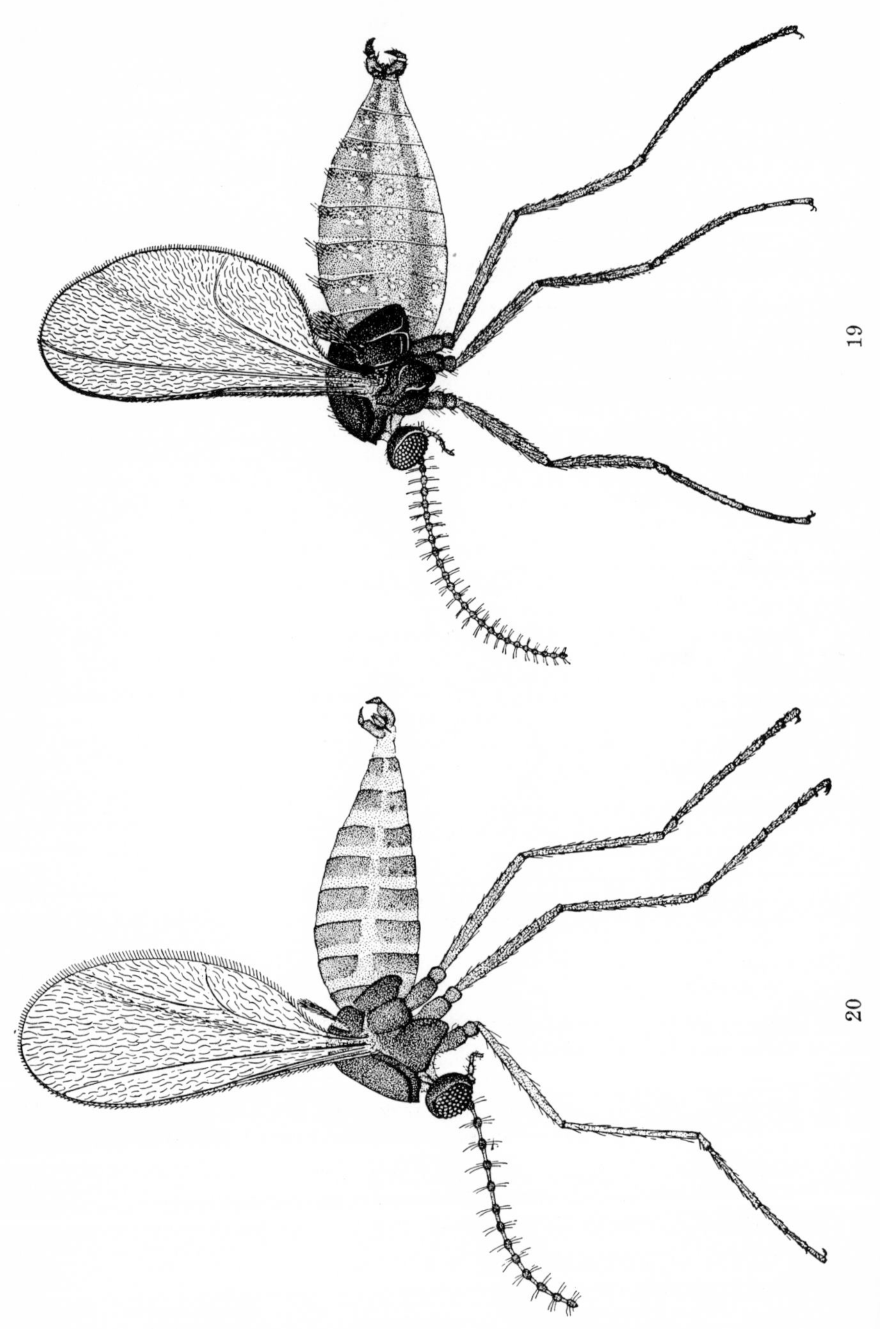

Cecidomyidæ IV.—19, **Rhabdophaga** sp.; 20, **Dasyneura gibsoni.**
(Courtesy New York State Museum, Albany, N. Y.)

39. Antennæ with fourteen or more segments.......................... 40
Antennæ with ten to thirteen, rarely with fourteen segments........ 43

40. Third vein uniting with the costa at or near the apex of the wing.... 41
Third vein uniting with the costa well before the apex of the wing... 42

41. Ovipositor not chitinized apically; claws with one strong tooth (19).
Rhabdophaga Westwood
Ovipositor chitinized apically, blade-like, the claws weakly toothed.
Procystiphora Felt

42. Wing veins scaled, the membrane more or less brownish.
Lasiopteryx Stephens
Veins not distinctly scaled, the membrane hyaline (20).
Dasyneura Rondani

43. Third vein uniting with the costa near the apex of the wing......... 44
Third vein uniting with the costa well before the apex of the wing.
Neuromyia Felt

44. Antennæ with thirteen or fourteen segments.........**Cystiphora** Kieffer
Antennæ with twelve segments, genital harpes sickle-shaped, greatly produced ....**Harpomyia** Felt

45. Palpi with two or three segments.................................. 46
Palpi with only one segment...........................**Ficiomyia** Felt

46. Palpi with three segments.. 48
Palpi with two segments.. 47

47. Antennæ with twelve segments....................**Coccidomyia** Felt
Antennæ with fourteen to eighteen segments.....**Diarthronomyia** Felt

48. Claws with a single tooth... 49
Claws pectinate.................................**Ctenodactylomyia** Felt

49. Ovipositor with apical spine; male clasper short, swollen.
Cystiphora Kieffer
Ovipositor without apical spine; pulvilli nearly three times as long as the claws...**Allomyia** Felt

50. Flagellate antennal segments cylindrical, not greatly elongated, usually stalked in the male; ovipositor not aciculate................. 51
Flagellate segments cylindrical, elongate, sessile; ovipositor usually aciculate 56

51. Palpi with one to three segments.................................. 53
Palpi with four segments.. 52

52. Third vein joining the costa at or near the apex of the wing (34).
Phytophaga Rondani
Third vein joining the costa well before the apex of the wing.
Janetiella Kieffer

53. Ovipositor distinctly chitinized, aciculate or cultriform.
Sackenomyia Felt
Ovipositor not chitinized.. 54

54. Palpi with only one or two segments............................... 55
Palpi with three segments......................**Oligotrophus** Latreille

55. Pulvilli nearly twice as long as the empodium........**Walshomyia** Felt
Pulvilli shorter than the empodium............**Rhopalomyia** Rübsaamen

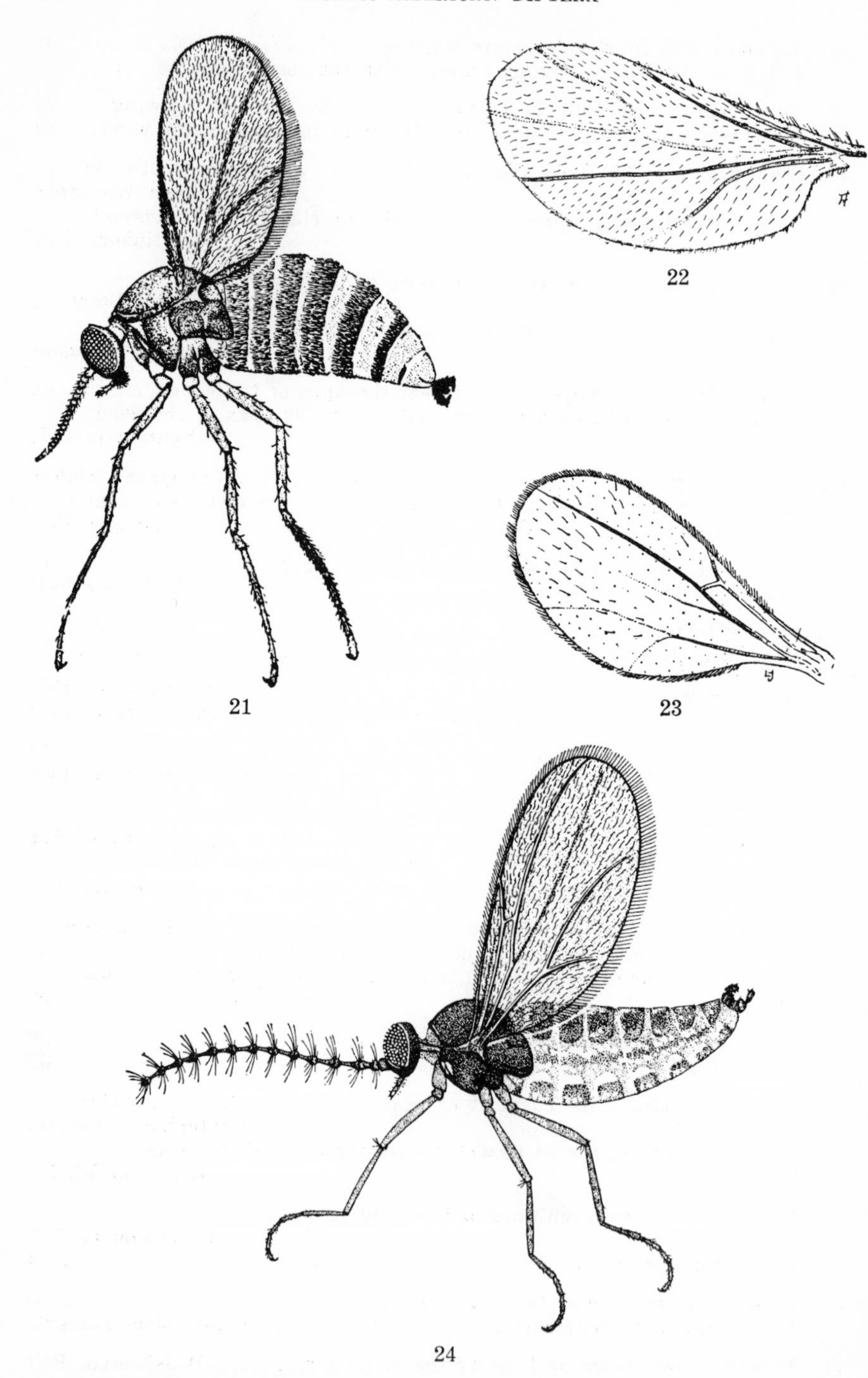

Cecidomyidæ V.—21, **Lasioptera veroniæ**; 22, **Tritozyga sackeni**; 23, **Mycophila fungicola**; 24, **Cordylomyia coloradensis.**

(Courtesy New York State Museum, Albany, N. Y.)

56. Ovipositor protractile, aciculate or nearly so; terminal clasper of male usually unidentate or bidentate.................................. 57
Ovipositor exserted, with lobes or triangular plates apically; terminal clasper of male usually serrate apically.......................... 58

57. Palpi with four segments (33)......................**Schizomyia** Kieffer
Palpi with two or three segments (17)..............**Asphondylia** Lœw

58. Palpi with four segments... 59
Palpi with three segments...........................**Feltomyia** Kieffer

59. Flagellate antennal segments cylindrical, not strongly constricted; circumfila usually with many fine reticulations in the male; pulvilli usually shorter than the claws (31)................**Cincticornia** Felt
Flagellate segments cylindrical, sometimes rather strongly constricted; circumfila forming transverse series of low lines or loops; lobes of ovipositor subtriangular...................**Caryomyia** Felt

60. Nodes of the male flagellate antennal segments equal, only two circumfila 61
Nodes of male flagellate segments plainly unequal, three circumfila.. 71

61. Palpi with three or four segments.................................. 62
Palpi with one segment ....**Kronodiplosis** Felt

62. Palpi with four segments... 64
Palpi with three segments.. 63

63. Terminal clasp segment irregular, pectinate apically.
Pectinodiplosis Felt
Terminal clasp segment normal........................**Dentifibula** Felt

64. Claws on all the legs simple... 67
Claws on at least the front legs toothed.............................. 65

65. Claws on all the legs toothed....................................... 66
Only the anterior claws toothed........................**Toxomyia** Felt

66. Internal basal lobe of the basal clasp segment smooth, the dorsal and ventral plates broadly and slightly emarginate, the ovipositor with a length one-half that of the abdomen, protractile...**Erosomyia** Felt
Internal basal lobe of the basal clasp segment rudimentary, smooth; dorsal plate truncate, ventral plate broadly and roundly emarginate; ovipositor moderately long..............**Mangodiplosis** Tavares

67. Wings of males with the posterior area greatly produced and broadly rounded ....**Lobopteromyia** Felt
Wings normal, not unusually broad.................................... 68

68. Costa not clothed with scales.. 69
Costa thickly clothed with scales.....................**Endaphis** Kieffer

69. Third vein interrupting the costa at its union with the margin...... 70
Third vein not interrupting the costa at its union with the margin (See text fig.)...............................**Thecodiplosis** Kieffer

70. Wings hyaline...................................**Contarinia** Rondani
Wings spotted ....**Stictodiplosis** Kieffer

71. Claws toothed on all the legs.. 72
Claws of at least the posterior legs not toothed..................... 84

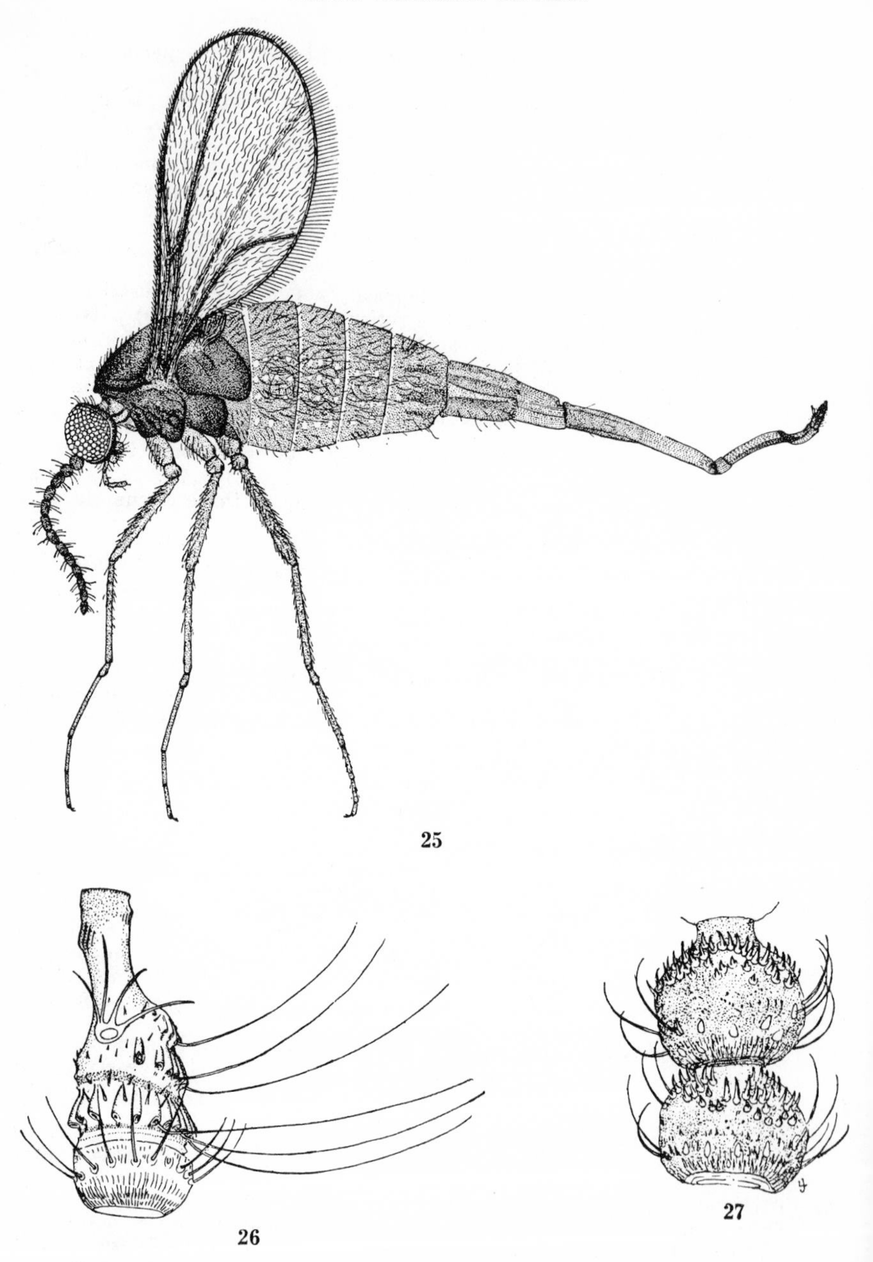

Cecidomyidæ VI.—25, **Winnertzia pectinata; 26, Lestremia pini,** fifth antennal segment of ♂; 27, **Cordylomyia** brevicornis, fourth and fifth antennal segments of ♂.
(Courtesy New York State Museum, Albany, N. Y.)

72. Palpi with four segments.. 75
Palpi with three segments.. 73

73. Basal clasp segment of male distinctly lobed...........**Peridiplosis** Felt
Basal clasp segment of male not lobed.................................. 74

74. Flagellate antennal segments of female subcylindrical.
Kalodiplosis Felt
Flagellate antennal segments of female binodose (Brit. Guiana).
Epihormomyia Felt

75. Circumfila with one or more greatly produced bows or loops having a length five to ten times that of the enlargement and extending at approximately right angles to it.................................. 76
Circumfila all about equal, nearly regular.............................. 80

76. Three well-developed circumfila on each flagellate antennal segment.. 77
Two well-developed, irregular circumfila; basal circumfila on the distal enlargement forming a low band; pulvilli small.**Bremia** Rondani

77. All three circumfila irregular, the pulvilli rudimentary.
Tribremia Kieffer
At most two circumfila irregular.. 78

78. Pulvilli shorter than the claws; two circumfila irregular............ 79
Pulvilli as long as or longer than the claws; one circumfila irregular.
Aphidoletes Kieffer

79. Pulvilli slightly shorter than the claws, conspicuous...**Isobremia** Kieffer
Pulvilli rudimentary or wanting.................**Cryptobremia** Kieffer

80. Basal clasp segment of male genitalia with basal lobe; ovipositor short and with large, orbicular lobes...............**Youngomyia** Felt
Basal clasp segment without basal lobe.................................. 81

81. Claws curved at nearly right angles....................................... 82
Claws curved but not at nearly right angles.............................. 83

82. Ventral plate moderately long, broadly emarginate; dorsal plate moderately long, broad, deeply triangularly emarginate, the lobes triangular; ovipositor short........................**Cleodiplosis** Felt
Dorsal and ventral plates short, broad, deeply emarginate.
Thomasia Rübsaamen

83. Ovipositor slightly protractile, the lobes long, curved, and with two or three subventral rows of obtuse spines........**Dicrodiplosis** Kieffer
Ovipositor about half the length of the abdomen, the lobes with a length about six times the width; mouth parts prolonged (Brit. Guiana) ....**Delphodiplosis** Felt

84. Claws not toothed on any of the legs.................................... 92
Claws toothed on at least the front legs................................ 85

85. Palpi with four segments.. 86
Palpi with three segments..........................**Diadiplosis** Felt

86. Basal clasp segment lobed.. 87
Basal clasp segment not distinctly lobed................................ 89

87. The lobe basal or sub-basal 88
The lobe apical, setose or spinose; terminal clasp segment subapical.
Lobodiplosis Felt

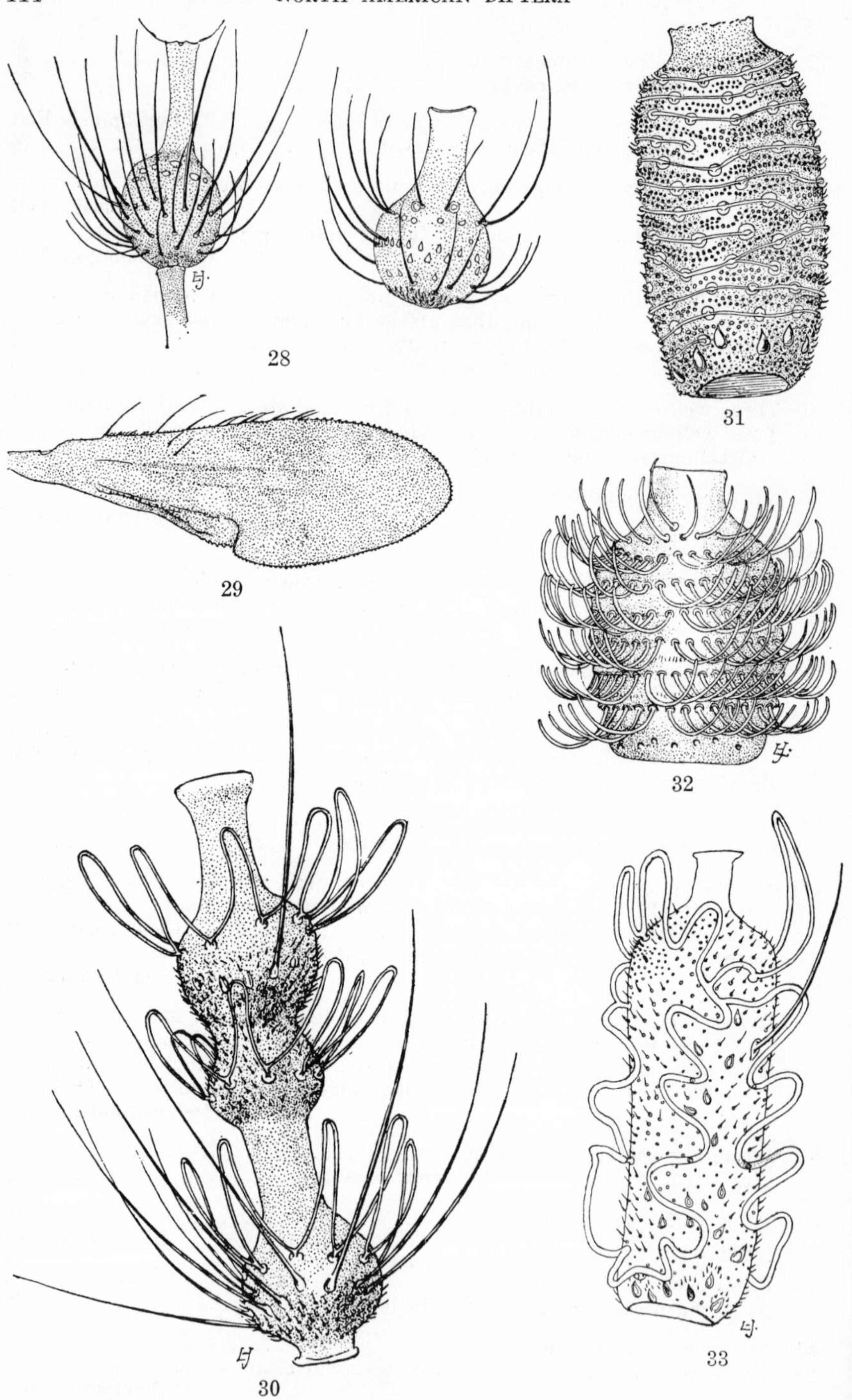

Cecidomyidæ VII.

88. Ventral plate or harpes strongly chitinized.........**Coquillettomyia** Felt
Ventral plate or harpes not chitinized..............**Feltiella** Rübsaamen

89. Terminal clasp segment sub-fusiform, distinctly dilated; harpes strongly chitinized and very complex (**30**)........**Karschomyia** Felt
Not as above 90

90. Claws curved at nearly right angles...............**Clinodiplosis** Kieffer
Claws not curved at nearly right angles.......................... 91

91. Ventral plate almost linear, straight and much longer than the dorsal plate ....**Acaroletes** Kieffer
Ventral plate not greatly produced.............**Mycodiplosis** Rübsaamen

92. Palpi with fewer than four segments..............................108
Palpi with four segments.. 93

93. Third vein uniting with the costa behind the apex of the wing...... 94
Third vein uniting with the costa before the apex of the wing.
Arthrocnodax Rübsaamen

94. Circumfila with short bows or wanting........................... 95
Circumfila well developed and not conspicuously irregular, the loops mostly as long as or longer than the diameter of the enlargement.. 97

95. Some of the flagellate antennal segments cylindrical............... 96
Flagellate antennal segments binodose in the male or presumably so.
Caryomyia Felt

96. Circumfila rudimentary or wanting; tenth to fourteenth segments cylindrical; harpes somewhat inflated................**Prodiplosis** Felt
Circumfila distinct though low, all the flagellate or only the distal segments cylindrical; ovipositor short..............**Caryomyia** Felt

97. Claws bent at nearly right angles................................ 98
Claws not bent at right angles................................... 99

98. Ventral plate long, slender, slightly expanded and roundly emarginate apically; dorsal plate short, triangularly emarginate..**Giardomyia** Felt
Ventral plate long, broad, very deeply and broadly emarginate; dorsal plate deeply and roundly emarginate...........**Hyperdiplosis** Felt

99. Basal clasp segment lobed...100
Basal clasp segment not lobed.....................................103

100. The lobe apical 101
The lobe basal 102

101. The lobe very long, curved, setose; terminal clasp segment swollen basally ....**Epidiplosis** Felt
The lobe triangular; terminal clasp segment short, greatly constricted near the middle and enormously swollen and recurved apically ....**Metadiplosis** Felt

102. Wings spotted ....**Lestodiplosis** Kieffer
Wings not spotted ....**Coprodiplosis** Kieffer

103. Antennal segments plainly trinodose................**Obolodiplosis** Felt
Antennal segments not plainly trinodose...........................104

Cecidomyidæ VII.—28, **Joannisia photophila,** fifth and tenth antennal segments of male; 29, **Leptosyna quercivora**; 30, **Karschomyia viburni,** fifth antennal segment of ♂; 31, **Cincticornia transversa,** sixth antennal segment of ♂; 32, **Corinthomyia cincinna,** fourth antennal segment of ♂; 33, **Schizomyia macrofila,** sixth antennal segment of ♂.

(Courtesy New York State Museum, Albany, N. Y.)

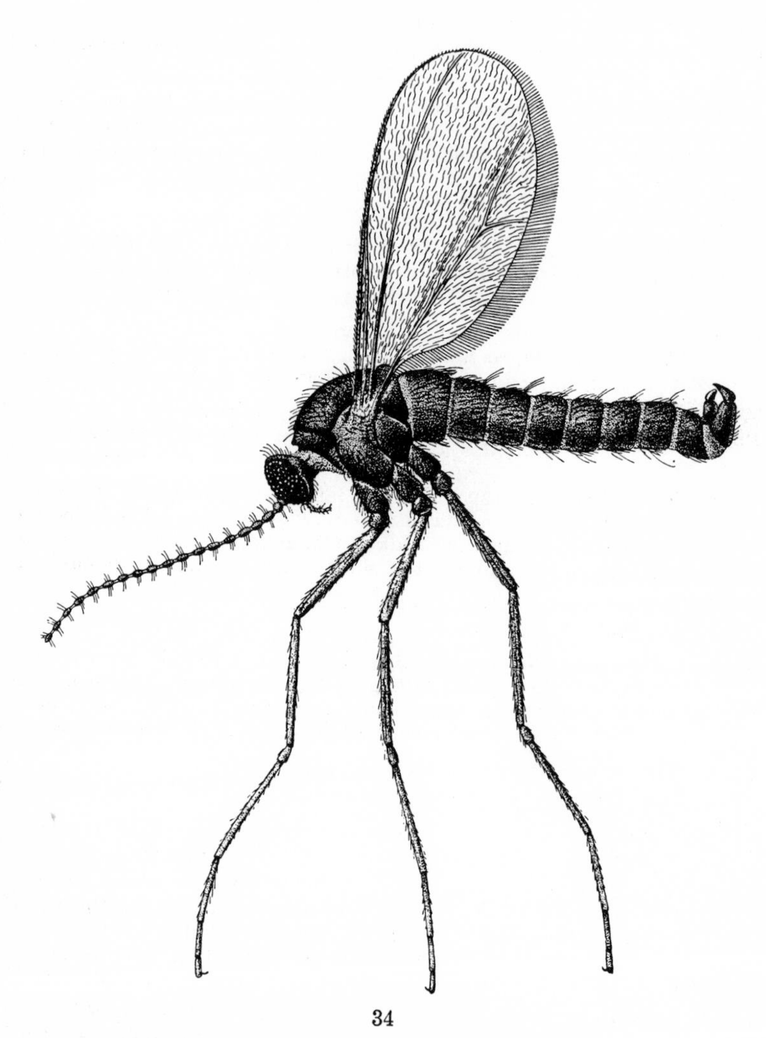

34

Cecidomyidæ VIII.—34, **Phytophaga destructor.**
(Courtesy New York State Museum, Albany, N. Y.)

104. Antennal segments short, thick, the stems transverse, the enlargements short and broad; circumfila fine, rather short, each with about twenty loops............................**Retinodiplosis** Kieffer
Antennæ of normal form..105

105. Ventral plate linear or long and spatulate............................106
Ventral plate broad and broadly or triangularly emarginate........107

106. Ventral plate linear, rounded apically; dorsal plate shorter than the ventral, the lobes truncate...............**Parallelodiplosis** Rübsaamen
Ventral plate spatulate, the dorsal plate moderately long, deeply and triangularly emarginate, the lobes broad, obliquely and roundly emarginate ....**Hypodiplosis** Kieffer

107. Dorsal plate deeply incised, the lobes narrowly rounded; terminal clasp segment with serrate margin.................**Paradiplosis** Felt
Dorsal plate not incised or very narrowly emarginate; terminal clasp segment smooth (3)...........................**Cecidomyia** Meigen

108. Palpi with three segments...109
Palpi with only one or two segments.................................113

109. Circumfila with short bows or loops, their length being one-half the diameter of the enlargement or less...........................110
Circumfila loops with a length equal to the diameter of the enlargement or longer..112

110. Thorax plainly extending over and concealing the head to a certain extent 111
Thorax not produced over the head to a marked degree..**Caryomyia** Felt

111. Males with fifteen to at least twenty-seven antennal segments; female with fourteen or more antennal segments; ovipositor short (4). **Hormomyia** Lœw
Male and female with fourteen or fifteen antennal segments, the fifteenth rudimentary; ovipositor moderately long. **Trishormomyia** Kieffer

112. Basal clasp segment lobed..........................**Odontodiplosis** Felt
Basal clasp segment simple..............................**Adiplosis** Felt

113. Palpi with two segments.......................**Dishormomyia** Kieffer
Palpi with one segment...114

114. Wings hyaline 115
Wings marked with black and yellow...............**Astrodiplosis** Felt

115. Fourteen antennal segments in both sexes.........................116
Thirteen segments in female, the third and fourth fused, the basal and distal nodes in the male flagellate antennal segments globose and ovoid respectively; dorsal and ventral plates bilobed; ovipositor short, chitinous, aciculate..............**Cystodiplosis** Kieffer & Jorg

116. Both dorsal and ventral plates deeply emarginate; ovipositor short, chitinous, falcate......................**Monarthropalpus** Rübsaamen
Ventral plate not deeply emarginate...................................117

117. Dorsal plate deeply and ventral plate broadly emarginate; ovipositor stout, half as long as the abdomen, the distal part thickly clothed with long, silky hairs...........................**Onodiplosis** Felt
Dorsal plate deeply, broadly and roundly emarginate, the lateral margin extended ventrally; ventral plate broadly emarginate; ovipositor stout, about two-thirds as long as the abdomen. **Horidiplosis** Felt

Family Sciaridæ—The Dark Winged Fungus Gnats

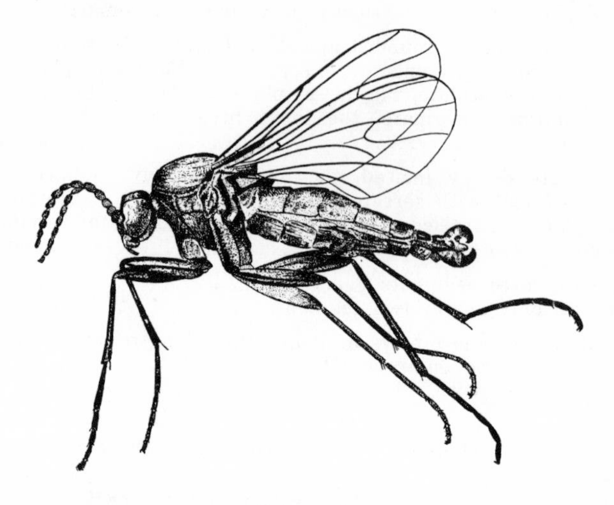

Sciara ♂.

Usually small, blackish, brownish or testaceous species, the abdomen cylindrical and tapering, especially in the females.

The insects belonging to this family are related to the Mycetophilidæ, with which they have, until recently, been united. They differ in having the eyes produced toward each other above the antennæ, instead of being regularly convex in outline, and in having shorter coxæ. As a general rule the wing venation is typical although a very few genera of the Mycetophilidæ have similar venation.

The adults inhabit moist places or any place where fungus growth occurs, particularly manure. The larvæ frequently become pests in mushroom cellars, feeding upon the mycelium of the fungi. The females are difficult to determine, the classification being based mainly on the male genitalia although the ovipositors of the females also offer good characters. The larvæ, like those of the Mycetophilidæ, have some very interesting habits, some of them sometimes travelling over the ground in snake-like masses. The family is treated by Johannsen in the reference given under the Mycetophilidæ.

KEY TO GENERA

1. Proboscis longer than the thorax (2)............**Eugnoriste** Coquillett
   Proboscis not greatly elongate 2
2. Wings conspicuously hairy; claws never denticulate...**Trichosia** Winnertz
   Wings with microscopic setulæ but not hairy...................... 3
3. Claws toothed 4
   Claws not toothed 5
4. Forks of the fourth vein arcuate................**Metangela** Rübsaamen
   Forks of the fourth vein not arcuate............**Phorodonta** Coquillett
5. Face strongly produced.....................**Rhynchosciara** Rübsaamen
   Face not produced 6
6. Forks of the fourth vein arcuate; antennæ of the male pedicellate and with whorls of hair (1).........................**Zygoneura** Meigen
   Forks of the fourth vein not arcuate; antennæ never pedicellate (**Neosciara**) (6, 7, Mycetophilidæ)...................**Sciara** Meigen

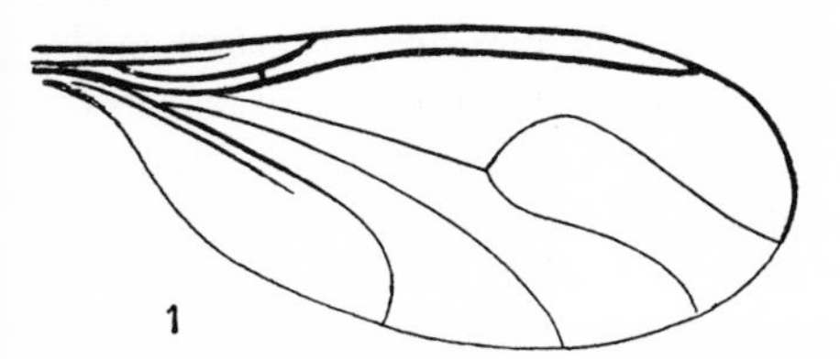

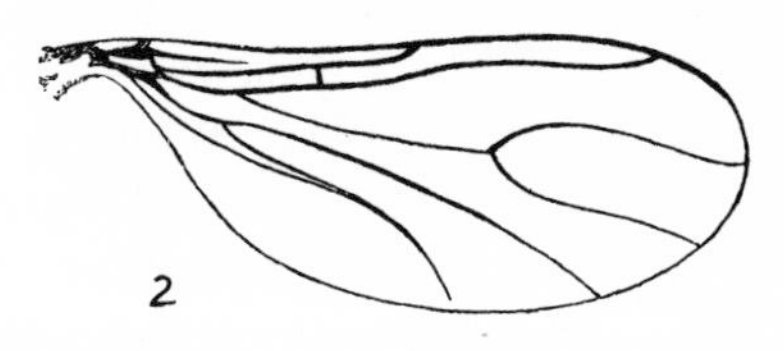

Sciaridæ.—1, **Zygoneura**; 2, **Eugnoriste**.

Family Mycetophilidæ—The Fungus Gnats

Moderately small, rather delicate, slender flies with elongated coxæ.

Head small, rounded or somewhat elongate, usually closely applied to the thorax. Eyes round, rather prominent; ocelli three, two or none, the median one often small, the lateral ones frequently close to the orbits; front broad in both sexes. Antennæ elongated, composed of twelve to seventeen segments, the two basal segments large or differentiated, the others cylindrical, flattened or petiolated. Proboscis usually short, rarely greatly lengthened; palpi rarely absent, composed of three or four segments, usually inflexed. Thorax distinctly to strongly arched, without transverse suture; scutellum small; metanotum large. Abdomen composed of six or seven segments, cylindrical or compressed either laterally or dorsoventrally, sometimes narrowed basally; male genitalia projecting; ovipositor pointed, usually with two terminal lamellæ. Legs more or less elongated, the femora usually thickened; coxæ elongated; tibiæ with spurs and usually with series of short or conspicuous bristles. Wings large; auxiliary vein present though sometimes very short; second longitudinal vein absent, or simulating a crossvein; third vein arising from the first vein, usually at such an angle as to simulate a crossvein, the crossvein sometimes appearing to form the base of the third vein; fourth and fifth veins usually furcate, sometimes simple; sixth vein sometimes rudimentary, never furcate; the seventh usually short, often rudimentary or entirely absent; discal cell absent, the second basal cell often open apically.

The adults are found in moist places, especially about decaying wood, on mossy rocks or moist humus, and prefer dark places. Many of the species are quite small only a few being large and conspicuous. They occur in a variety of habitats and some species are very restricted in habitat although occurring over a very wide geographical range. They may be collected throughout most of the year and when encountered often occur in large numbers. The larvæ live in moist soil, wood, fungi, etc., and probably feed upon fungus growth. Pupation takes place outside the larval skin, some species spinning cocoons. The habits of the larvæ are particularly interesting and their investigation should provide an entertaining and profitable field of study to some one interested in pure science for the fun of the thing. Johannsen* has monographed the family and only a small number of North American species have been described since.

* Maine Agric. Exp. Sta. Bulls. 172, 180, 196, 200, 1909-12.

KEY TO GENERA*

1. Second basal cell closed apically 2
   Second basal cell open apically 12

2. Anterior branch of third vein at least half as long as posterior branch; auxiliary vein short, ending free; posterior divisions of pronotum with one or more long bristles (Ditomyiinæ) 11
   Anterior branch of third vein less than half as long as posterior branch, in some cases vestigial or absent; auxiliary vein in most cases long and ending in the costa; posterior divisions of pronotum without long bristles 3

3. The second basal cell much shorter than the first; first and second basal cells separated (Bolitophilinæ) (18) .... **Bolitophila** Meigen
   The second basal cell almost as long as the first or the basal sections of the third and fourth veins fused for a short distance 4

4. Both crossveins closing the basal cells present, nearly in a straight line; basal section of fourth vein lacking (Diadocidinæ) (19). **Diadocidia** Ruthé
   Basal sections of third and fourth veins fused for a short distance except in **Palæoplatyura** in which basal section of fourth vein is present 5

5. Antennæ long and slender, in most cases longer than the body (Macrocerinæ) (4) .... **Macrocera** Meigen
   Antennæ more robust, in some cases distinctly thickened and flattened (Ceroplatinæ) 6

6. Proboscis prolonged into a snout .... **Asindulum** Latreille
   Proboscis not prolonged into a snout 7

7. Antennæ conspicuously flattened; palpi porrect (**Heteropterna, Cerotelion, Euceroplatus**) (5) .... **Ceroplatus** Bosc
   Antennæ not conspicuously flattened, palpi curved 8

8. The anterior crossvein not obliterated by the fusion of the bases of the third and fourth veins (20) .... **Palæoplatyura** Meunier
   The anterior crossvein not obliterated by the fusion of the base of the third and fourth veins 9

9. Basal section of fourth vein absent (**Isoneuromyia, Neoplatyura, Proceroplatus, Lapyruta, Micrapemon**) (9) .... **Platyura** Meigen
   Basal section of fourth vein present 10

10. Ocelli wanting; anterior branch of third vein ending in the costa. **Hesperodes** Coquillett
    Ocelli present, anterior branch of third vein ending in the first vein (21) .... **Apemon** Johannsen

11. Fork of fourth vein distal of fork of third vein (22) ... **Ditomyia** Winnertz
    Fork of fourth vein basal of fork of third vein (14) ... **Symmerus** Walker

12. First and third veins arising separately at base of wing; venation defective; proboscis elongate (Lygistorrhinæ) (**Probolæus**) (2, 3). **Lygistorrhina** Skuse
    First and third veins arising from a common stem well beyond base of wing 13

---

* Checked by Dr. O. A. Johannsen.

13. Eyes joined above the antennæ by a narrow bridge; anterior crossvein long, appearing like the base of the third vein, the latter short and transverse, resembling a crossvein........................See Sciaridæ
    Eyes not joined by a narrow band above the antennæ; base of third vein and the anterior crossvein in most cases oblique............ 14
14. Prothorax without long bristles, antennæ inserted above the middle of the head, occiput flat or concave, venation defective (Manotinæ) (1). **Manota** Williston
    Prothorax with long bristles, occiput convex, antennæ inserted at or below the middle of the head.................................... 15
15. Microtrichia of wings irregularly arranged or absent; auxiliary vein usually long; lateral ocelli in most cases far from margin of compound eyes (Sciophilinæ Edwards = Sciophilinæ Johannsen + Series I of Mycetophilinæ Johannsen 1911)............................ 16
    Microtrichia in more or less definite longitudinal lines; auxiliary vein usually short; lateral ocelli touching compound eyes (Mycetophilinæ Edwards, Mycetophilinæ Johannsen 1911, Series II)................ 44

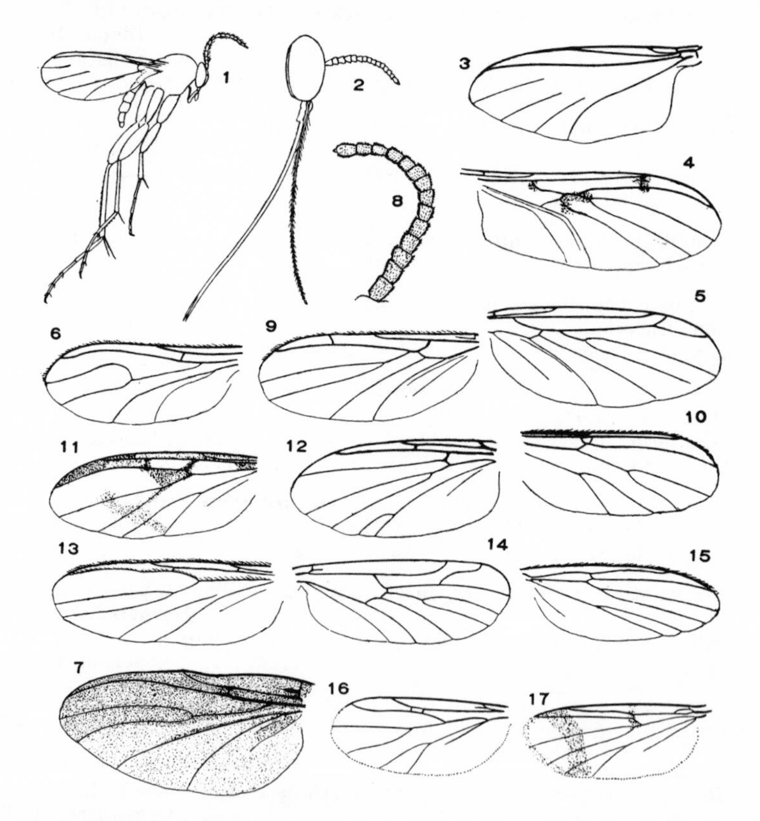

Mycetophilidæ I.—1, **Manota defecta**; 2, 3, **Lygistorrhina singularis**; 4, **Macrocera concinna**; 5, **Ceroplatus longimana**; 6, 7, 8, **Sciara (Sciaridæ)**; 9, **Platyura ignobilis**; 10, **Sciophila diluta**; 11, **Neoempheria maculipennis**; 12, **Phthinia fraudulenta**; 13, **Leia nitens**; 14, **Symmerus**; 15, **Mycetophila insipiens**; 16, **Tetragoneura sylvatica**; 17, **Dynatosoma fuscicornis**.

16. Ocelli two, approximated; wings without macrotrichia (hairs) on membrane; auxiliary vein reaching at least the base of the third vein; fine tibial setæ in regular longitudinal rows.......................... 19
   Ocelli three, if but two (in **Eudicrana**) they are close to the eye margin. 17

17. Wing with macrotrichia (hairs) on membrane.................... 20
   Wing without macrotrichia on membrane.......................... 18

18. Apical segment of first vein several times longer than the anterior crossvein; branches of fourth vein longer than the petiole.......... 32
   Apical segment of first vein short, in most cases not much longer than the crossvein, or if longer the branches of fourth vein scarcely longer than the petiole 38

19. Costa not produced beyond tip of third vein; no spurious vein between third and fourth veins; wing not banded **(23)**.......**Mycomya** Rondani
   Costa produced beyond tip of third vein; spurious vein usually present between third and fourth veins; wing banded or spotted **(11)**. **Neoempheria** Osten Sacken

20. Ocelli two, contiguous to eye margin...................**Eudicrana** Lœw
   Ocelli three, remote from compound eyes.......................... 21

21. Fork of fifth vein situated nearer to wing base than is the fork of fourth vein 22
   Fork of fifth vein, if present, situated beyond fork of fourth vein.... 27

22. Postnotum with hairs or bristles................................ 23
   Postnotum bare 26

23. Anterior branch of fourth vein complete or nearly so............... 24
   Anterior branch of fourth vein faint or defective at base; third vein undulate (**Odontopoda**). **(24)**.....................**Neuratelia** Rondani

24. Subcostal crossvein before middle of auxiliary vein **(25)**..**Allocotocera** Mik
   Subcostal crossvein beyond middle of auxiliary vein................. 25

25. Third vein straight; costa not produced beyond its tip (**Diomonus**) **(26)**. **Leptomorphus** Curtis
   Third vein undulate; costa produced beyond its tip **(27)**. **Polylepta** Winnertz

26. Metapleura hairy; auxiliary vein ending in first vein; body stout **(28)**. **Syntemna** Winnertz
   Metapleura bare; auxiliary vein ending in the costa; body long and slender **(29)** ....**Paratinia** Mik

27. Legs slender and extremely long; basal tarsal segment of anterior legs twice as long as the tibia; fourth vein forks broadly **(12)**. **Phthinia** Winnertz
   Legs normal; fork of media pointed 28

28. Second branch of fourth vein complete........................... 29
   Second branch of fourth vein detached, present only as a short element on the wing margin **(30)**...........................**Azana** Walker

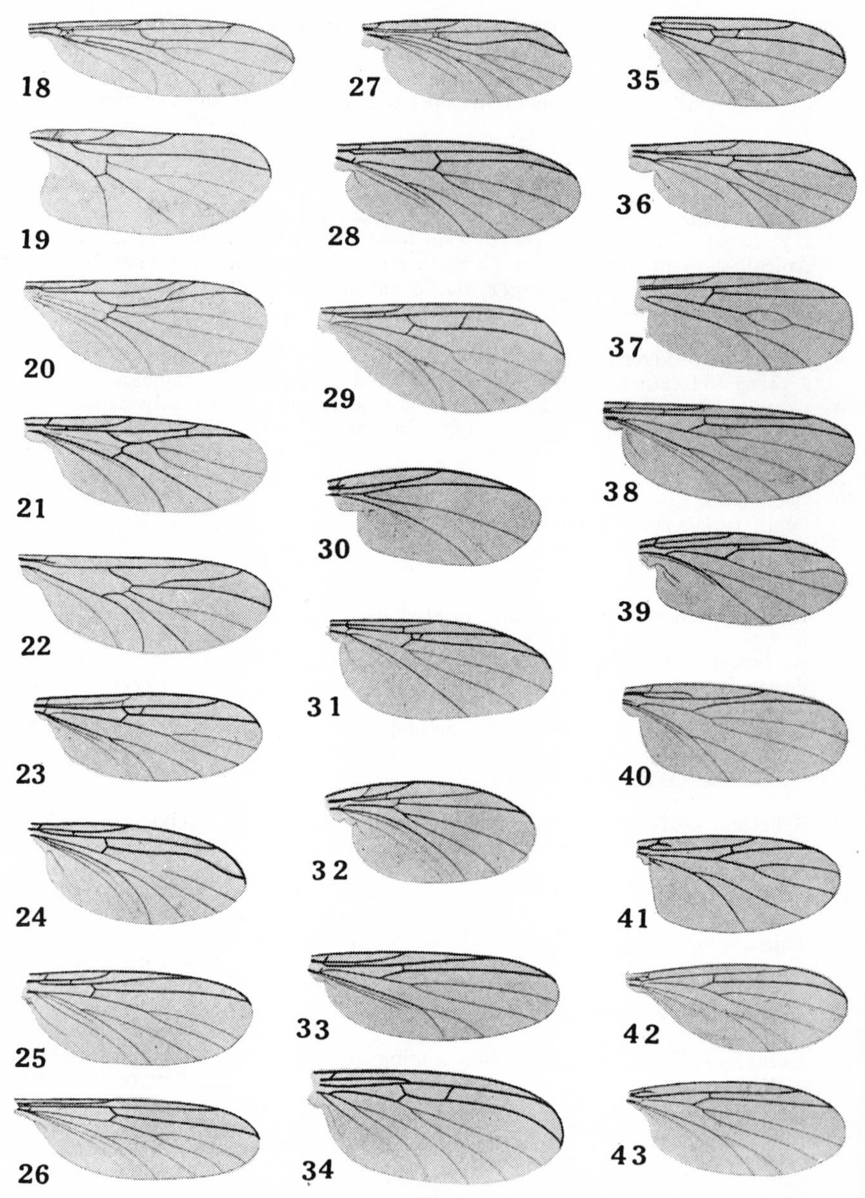

Mycetophilidæ II.—18, **Bolitophila**; 19, **Diadocidia**; 20, **Paleoplatyura**; 21, **Apemon**; 22, **Ditomya**; 23, **Mycomya**; 24, **Neuratelia**; 25, **Allocotocera**; 26, **Leptomorphus**; 27, **Polylepta**; 28, **Syntemna**; 29, **Paratinia**; 30, **Azana**; 31, **Monoclona**; 32, **Acnemia**; 33, **Cœlosia**; 34, **Hadroneura**; 35, **Dziedzickia**; 36, **Gnoriste**; 37, **Synapha**; 38, **Boletina**; 39, **Rondaniella**; 40, **Docosia**; 41, **Megophthalmidia**; 42, **Anatella**; 43, **Exechia**.

29. Subcostal crossvein well beyond origin of third vein; mesopleura bare. **Megalopelma** Enderlein
    Subcostal crossvein just before, above or immediately beyond origin of third vein 30

30. Fifth vein forked; mesopleura with small hairs (**10**)...**Sciophila** Meigen
    Fifth vein simple; mesopleura bare.. 31

31. Macrotrichia (hair) reflexed toward base of wing (**31**)...**Monoclona** Mik
    Macrotrichia decumbent (**32**) ....**Acnemia** Winnertz

32. Seventh abdominal segment large in both sexes (for **Polylepta leptogaster**) ....**Speolepta** Edwards
    Seventh abdominal segment small and retracted, at least in the male.. 33

33. Fifth vein forks well beyond fork of fourth (**33**)......**Cœlosia** Winnertz
    Fifth vein forks before, below or just beyond fork of fourth........ 34

34. Auxiliary vein ends in the first vein 35
    Auxiliary vein ends in the costa 36

35. Proboscis produced, about as long as the head (34) **Hadroneura** Lundstrom
    Proboscis not produced (**35**)......................**Dziedzickia** Johannsen

36. Proboscis very elongate (**36**)..........................**Gnoriste** Meigen
    Proboscis not elongate 37

37. Subcostal crossvein well beyond middle of auxiliary vein (**Empalia**) (**37**) ....**Synapha** Meigen
    Subcostal crossvein absent or near middle of auxiliary vein (**38, 55**). **Boletina** Stæger

38. Auxiliary vein ends in the costa (extremity may be faint in species of **Leia**) 39
    Auxiliary vein short, ending free or in the first vein................ 40

39. Last section of first vein over twice as long as anterior crossvein; anterior branch of fourth vein in most cases detached at base; subcostal crossvein wanting (**39**)..................**Rondaniella** Johannsen
    Last section of first vein scarcely longer than the crossvein, in some cases shorter (**13**) ....**Leia** Meigen

40. Palpi minute, consisting of a single segment; female wingless; in the male the basal section of fourth and fifth veins are coalescent so that both branches of the fifth appear to arise from the basal section of the fourth vein (**47**)......................**Pnyxia** Johannsen
    Palpi well developed, female winged, venation various.............. 41

41. Lateral ocelli contiguous with the margin of the compound eyes; last section of first vein long, petiole of fourth vein short; hypopleura hairy (**40**) ....**Docosia** Winnertz
    Lateral ocelli remote from eye margins; last section of first vein shorter 42

42. Hypopleura hairy; hind tibial comb present (**41**). **Megophthalmidia** Dziedzicki
    Hypopleura bare; no tibial comb 43

43. Auxiliary vein rather long, ending in first vein; fifth vein forks near base of wing ....**Ectrepesthoneura** Enderlein
    Auxiliary vein very short, ending free; fifth vein forks near the middle of the wing (**16**)..........................**Tetragoneura** Winnertz

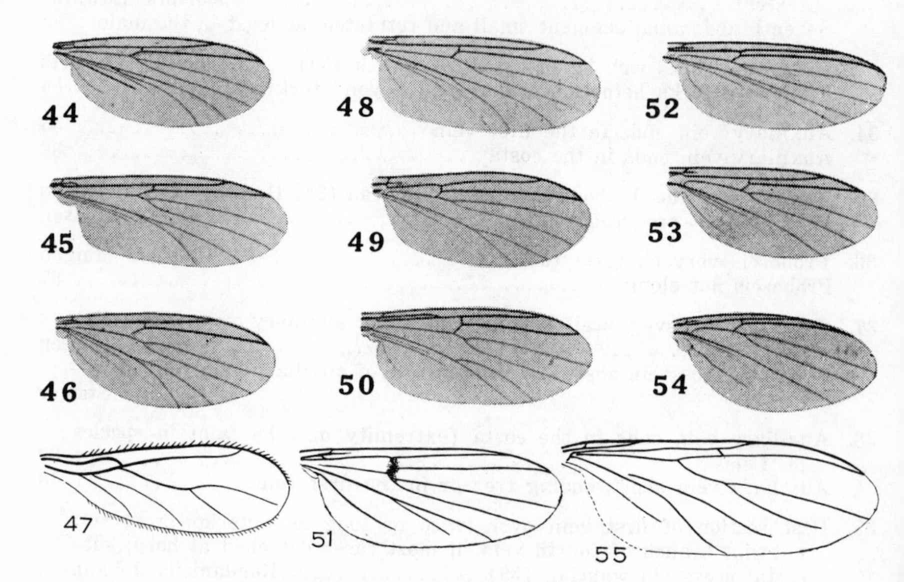

Mycetophilidæ III.—44, **Rhymosia**; 45, **Brachypeza**; 46, **Allodia**; 47, **Pnyxia scabei**; 48, **Cordyla**; 49, **Phronia**; 50, **Trichonta**; 51, **Mycetophila dominicana**; 52, **Epicypta**; 53, **Zygomyia**; 54, **Sceptonia**; 55; **Boletina incompleta.**

44. Mesopleural and hypopleural bristles absent; hind coxa with a fairly strong bristle at base.. 45
Mesopleural bristles present; hind coxa usually without basal bristle... 49

45. Costa produced beyond tip of third vein (42)..........**Anatella** Winnertz
Costa ends at tip of third vein.. 46

46. Fifth vein forks beyond fork of fourth (43)...........**Exechia** Winnertz
Fifth vein forks below or before fork of fourth 47

47. Second anal vein strong and distinct (44)...........**Rhymosia** Winnertz
Second anal vein weak or absent.. 48

48. First anal vein very long and distinct, attaining the middle of the fork of the fifth vein (45)..........................**Brachypeza** Winnertz
First anal vein shorter and less distinct (46)..........**Allodia** Winnertz

49. Pteropleural bristles present; tibial bristles long and strong.......... 53
Pteropleural bristles absent 50

50. Tibial bristles long and strong; auxiliary vein ends in first vein (= **Johannsenia**) (17) ....**Dynatosoma** Winnertz
Tibial bristles small, at most a little longer than the diameter of the tibia 51

51. Second palpal segment greatly thickened (48)...........**Cordyla** Meigen
Second palpal segment normal 52

52. Fifth vein forks beyond fork of fourth; auxiliary vein ends free (including **Telmaphilus**) (49).......................**Phronia** Winnertz
Fifth vein forks below or before fork of fourth; auxiliary vein ends normally in the first (50).........................**Trichonta** Winnertz

53. Fifth vein forked 54
Fifth vein simple 56

54. Anterior branch of fifth vein slightly divergent apically from second branch of fourth but parallel with or convergent towards second branch of fifth; hypopleura and pteropleura generally quite large (including **Mycothera** and **Opistholoba**) (15, 51)....**Mycetophila** Meigen
Anterior branch of fifth parallel with second branch of fourth but slightly divergent from second branch of fifth..................... 55

55. Pronotal lobes with long bristles; fifth vein forks scarcely if any before the anterior crossvein (82).......................**Epicypta** Winnertz
Pronotal lobes without long bristles; fifth vein forks well before the anterior crossvein ....**Delopsis** Skuse

56. Second branch of fourth and first branch of fifth vein slightly divergent; hypopleura and pteropleura large; middle tibia with ventral bristles (53) ....**Zygomyia** Winnertz
Second branch of fourth and first branch of fifth vein parallel; hypopleura and pteropleura small; middle tibia without ventral bristles (54) ....**Sceptonia** Winnertz

Family Bibionidæ—The March Flies

Slender flies of small to medium size, ranging from four to twelve millimeters in length.

Head usually somewhat flattened; eyes of the males approximate or contiguous, of the females, broadly separated; face rather short, sometimes elongate in *Dilophus;* eyes round; ocelli large. Antennæ composed of eight to twelve segments, cylindrical or somewhat flattened, the segments rather closely united. Proboscis short, with thickened, hairy labellæ; palpi with two to five segments, usually short, sometimes long. Thorax without transverse suture; scutellum hemicircular. Abdomen composed of seven to nine segments, more or less flattened, the male genitalia rather small. Legs moderately long, the anterior femora usually thickened, sometimes greatly swollen, the other femora usually somewhat swollen; anterior tibiæ usually modified, often greatly swollen in *Bibio;* legs slender in *Plecia.* Pulvilli and usually the empodium distinct. Wings large, the anterior veins stout, the others usually considerably weaker; costa ending at or before the wing-tip; second vein present or absent; fourth vein furcate; basal cells complete; anal cell rarely closed; posterior crossvein absent.

The larvæ feed upon decaying vegetable matter, especially upon the roots of grass, and pupation takes place in the soil. The adults are frequently very common and may be found almost anywhere in the open. The name "March Flies" has been given the family in this country because of the frequent occurrence of *Bibio albipennis* Say in large numbers during this month. "Harlequin Flies" is used in England, while "March Flies" is applied to other flies in Australia. The family has been reviewed by MacAtee*.

KEY TO GENERA

1. Third vein furcate (6, 7) 2
   Third vein not furcate (5) 5
2. Fourth and fifth veins forked 3
   These veins not forked .... **Eupeitenus** Macquart
3. Antennæ with not more than 12 segments 4
   Antennæ with 16 segments (7) .... †**Cramptonomyia** Alexander

---

* 1921. Proc. U. S. N. M. lx, Art. 11.

† For a discussion of the position of this genus and its allies see Alexander, 1931, Bull. Brooklyn Ent. Soc. xxvi, pp. 7-11.

4. Distance between the fork of the fourth vein and the anterior crossvein more than twice the length of the crossvein (4). **Hesperinus** Walker

   Distance between fork of fourth vein and anterior crossvein much less than twice the length of the crossvein (6)........**Plecia** Wiedemann

5. Anterior tibiæ produced apically to form two spurs (3).............. 6

   Anterior tibiæ without such spurs but with two or three series of teeth (2) ....**Dilophus** Meigen

6. Third and fourth longitudinal veins coalescent for a short distance (1) ....**Bibiodes** Coquillett

   Third and fourth veins not coalescent, joined by the anterior crossvein (3, 5) ....**Bibio** Latreille

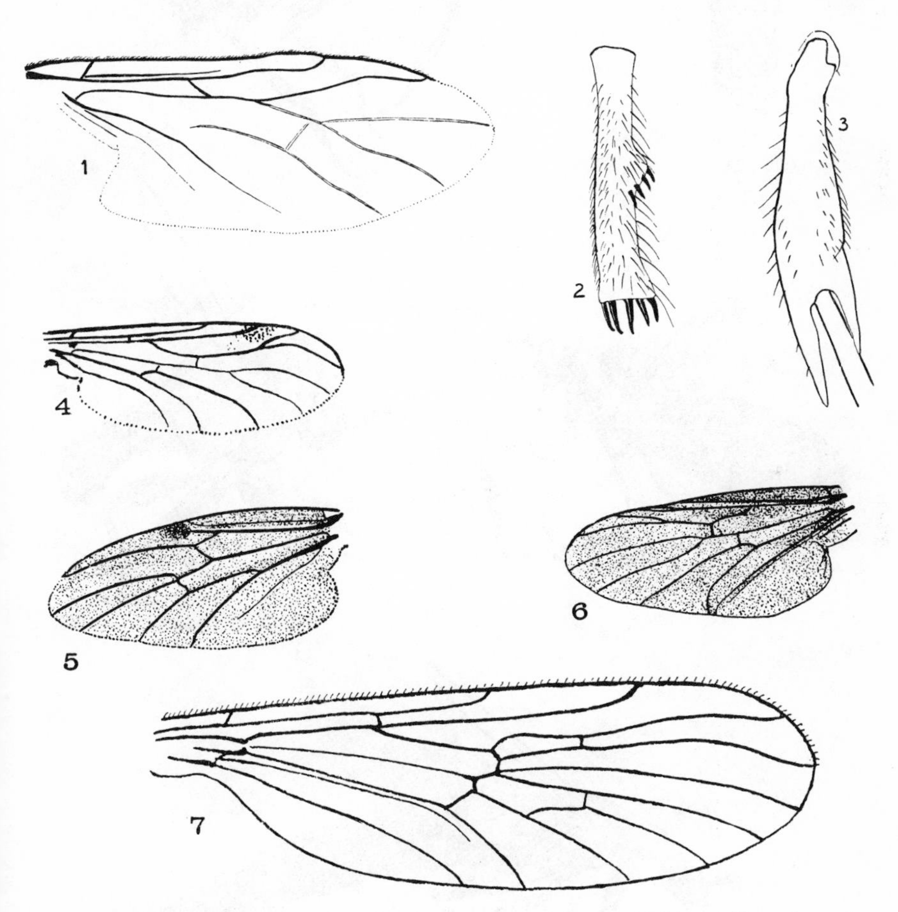

Bibionidæ.—1, **Bibiodes**; 2, **Dilophus**, front tibia; 3, **Bibio**, front tibia; 4, **Hesperinus**; 5, **Bibio**; 6, **Plectia**; 7, **Cramptonomyia.**

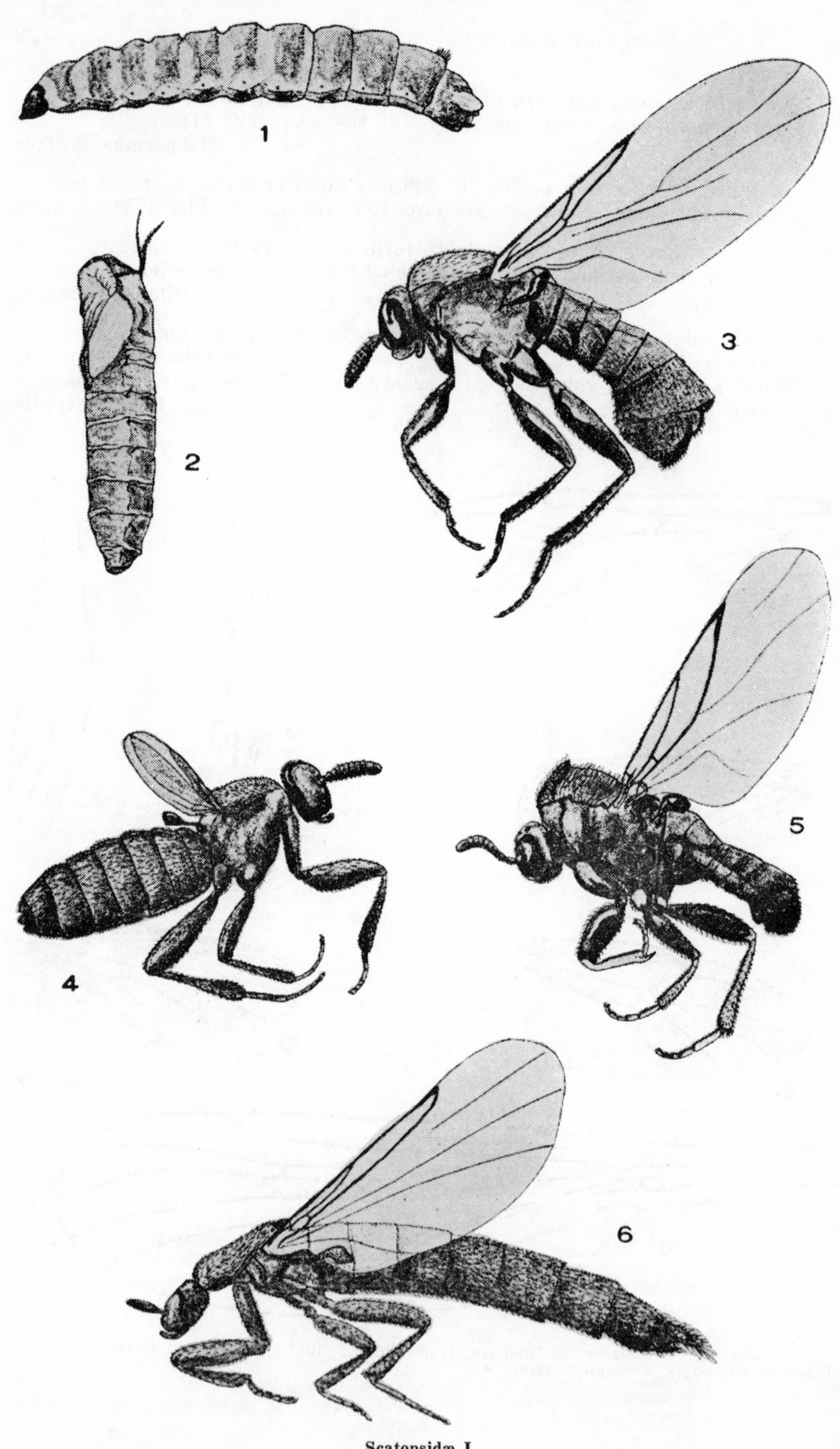

Scatopsidæ I.

Family Scatopsidæ—The Minute Black Scavengers

Small black or brownish flies, the appendages and thorax often partly yellowish.

Head more or less orbicular—subquadrate or elongate oval; antennæ composed of seven to twelve segments; usually slightly longer than the head; three ocelli; proboscis short and stout. Thorax gently convex, rarely flattened. Legs short, the femora robust. Wings with the veins thin, the first and third strong, the second simulating a crossvein, the fourth vein furcate or simple. Abdomen subcylindrical, composed of six or seven segments, the male genitalia large.

The Scatopsidæ breed in decaying vegetable and animal matter and excrement. They often breed in sewers and privies and frequently become very numerous in houses, where they cause more anxiety than harm. In the autumn they are frequently common on windows, when they are most easily collected. The species range in size from .75 to 3 mm. in length and the family may be readily recognized by the wing venation. Melander* has revised the North American species.

KEY TO GENERA

1. Wings of normal size.. 2
   Wings about half normal size, the adults flightless (4).
   Cobaldia Melander

2. Front tibiæ ending in a spur (5)........................**Aspistes** Meigen
   Front tibiæ without apical spur.. 3

3. Anterior branch of the fourth vein without appendage.............. 4
   Anterior branch of the fourth vein with an appendage near the base on the anterior side (12)........................**Scatopse** Geoffroy

4. Anterior branch of the fourth vein not disconnected at the base (10).. 5
   Anterior branch of the fourth vein disconnected basally (7).......... 7

5. Petiole of the fourth vein more than twice as long as the anterior branch (10) ....**Swammerdamella** Enderlein
   Petiole of the fourth vein at most a little longer than the anterior branch 6

---

* 1916, Bull. 130, State Coll. Wash., Agric. Exp. Station.

Scatopsidæ I.—1, 2, 3, **Rhegmoclema atrata**, larva, pupa, adult; 4, **Coboldia formicarum**; 5, **Aspistes berolinensis**; 6, **Psectrosciara californica**.

6. Third vein ending well beyond the middle of the wing (9).
Reichertella Enderlein
Third vein ending before or at the middle of the wing (1, 2, 3, 11).
Rhegmoclema Enderlein

7. Third vein ending at or near the middle of the wing (7).
Aldrovandiella Enderlein
Third vein ending at the apical fourth of the wing (6, 8).
Psectrosciara Kieffer

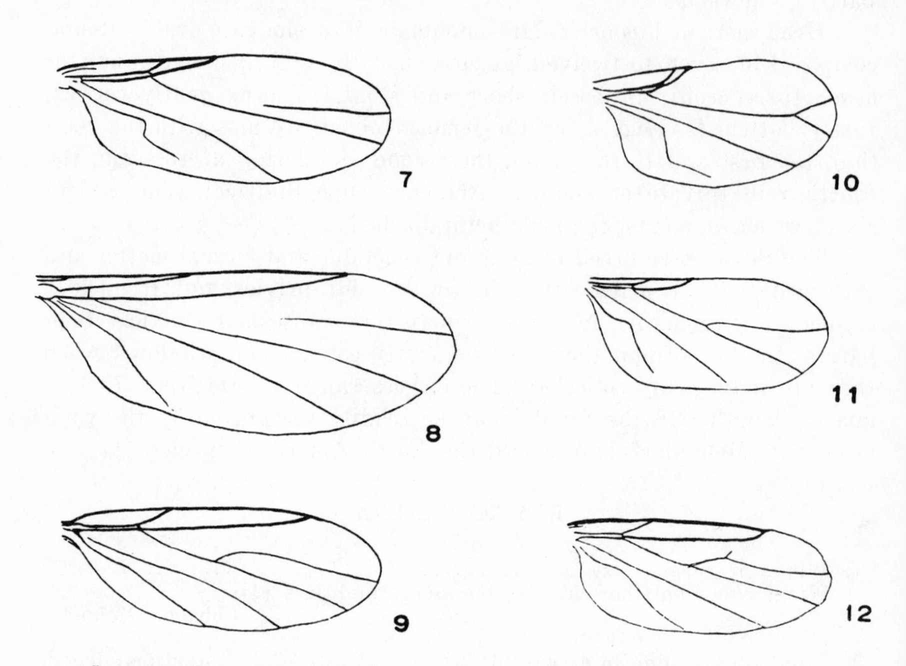

Scatpospidæ II.—7, **Aldrovandiella**; 8, **Psectrosciara**; 9, **Reichertella uncinata**; 10, **Swammerdamella brevicornis**; 11, **Rhegmoclema aterrima**; 12, **Scatopse notata**. (All figures after Melander.)

Family Rachiceridæ

Flies of medium size, elongated, very thinly pilose, resembling sawflies.

Males dichoptic. Empodium developed pulvilliform, the pulvilli present. Antennæ composed of twenty to thirty-eight segments, often strongly serrate. Squamæ small or rudimentary. Veins strong; discal cell three times as long as wide; fourth posterior cell closed and petiolate; anal cell closed apically. Legs moderately long.

The only genus belonging to this family is *Rachicerus* Walker of which only about a score of species are known. Six species have been described from the Nearctic region, but one is unrecognizable.

The larvæ are found in decaying wood and are presumed to be predaceous.

Rachicerus has usually been placed in the Rhagionidæ (s. l.) but should no doubt be isolated since the large number of antennal segments, all of which are freely articulate, indicates a more primitive condition than that accorded even the Cœnomyiidæ of the present work.

KEY TO NEARCTIC SPECIES OF RACHICERUS

1. Antennæ reddish toward the base, pectinate below, the lower processes conspicuously longer than the upper.................**obscuripenis** Lœw
   Antennæ not reddish basally, the lower processes on the segments short, at most slightly longer than the upper.................... 2
2. Mesonotum brownish yellow, sometimes with brown vittæ, never blackish 4
   Mesonotum black or brownish black.............................. 3
3. Halteres yellow; wings hyaline with a dark median cloud in front; mesonotum shining black............................**nitidus** Johnson
   Halteres brownish; wings tinged with brown; mesonotum shining dark brown ....**niger** Leonard
4. Mesonotum without brown vittæ; ♀ antennæ serrate, with 21 or 22 segments, ♂ antennæ sub-pectinate below, with 28 to 35 segments. **fulvicollis** Haliday
   Mesonotum with two broad brown vittæ; antennæ sub-pectinate below, with 22 or 23 segments..................**honestus** Osten Sacken

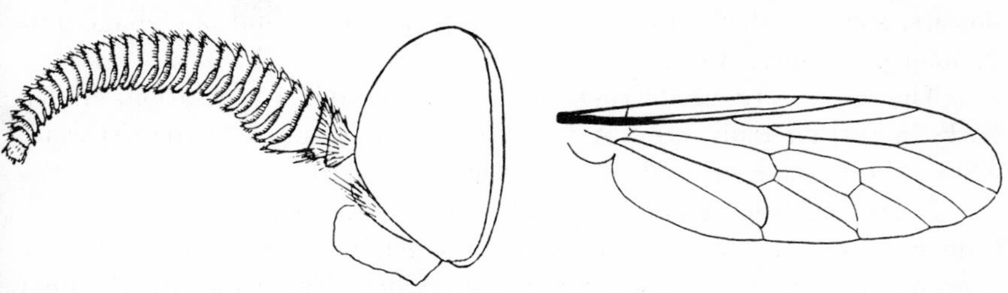

Rachicerus, head and wing.

Family Stratiomyidæ—The Soldier Flies

Cyphomyia species.

Small to moderately large, nearly bare or thinly pilose flies, without bristles.

Head usually short, sometimes produced either at or below the antennæ, usually wider than the thorax; ocelli present; eyes dichoptic in the females, usually holoptic in the males; proboscis short, never longer than the headheight, palpi two segmented or rudimentary. Antennæ with three to ten segments, the third always annulate and usually bearing an apical style or arista or a dorsal arista. Thorax never strongly convex, often elongate; scutellum often with spines, tubercles or projections on the margin. Abdomen composed of five to seven segments, variable in shape, sometimes short and very broad or long and narrow, rarely petiolate. Legs thinly soft haired; pulvilli and empodium padlike, the tibiæ without spurs. Costal vein not reaching beyond the tip of the wing, the veins crowded anteriorly, the posterior ones weak; discal cell present and of characteristic shape; four or five posterior cells and one or two submarginals; anterior branch of third vein short and often indistinct or wanting.

The name "soldier flies" has been given to this family because of their conspicuous markings. Most of the species may be found on flowers, some of them hover, while others may be found on foliage and in long grass near water.

The larvæ are predaceous or live in decaying vegetation, under bark, in rotting fruit, etc. A few species are confined to the sea coast while others occur in fresh water or mud.

I have adopted a number of changes in the nomenclature, and, as I do not use the names proposed in Meigen's "1800" paper *Eulalia* does not replace the well-known *Odontomyia*. The name *Stratiomyia* is an emendation of the original spelling, *Stratiomys*, and not only changes the spelling but also the meaning. I suspect that Geoffroy had in mind the mouse-like character of the typical species of the family when he proposed the name, and that he was better aware of his intentions in this connection than those who have followed the spelling of Macquart. It is unfortunate that such a well known name as *Clitellaria* Meigen must be replaced by *Adoxomyia* for the American species previously listed under *Clitellaria.* The other changes are mostly a return to the original spellings or the realignment of genera based upon structural characters.

The family is a difficult one, the generic limits being, often, difficult to define if they actually exist. Unfortunately I lack representatives of a few of the genera and must rely upon descriptions, so that some characters which might be used have, of necessity, been omitted.

There is great need of a monograph of the American species of this family: my synopsis of the Canadian species* may prove helpful but it contains only keys and these are incomplete for most of the genera.

KEY TO GENERA

1. Abdomen with seven visible dorsal segments 2
   Abdomen with five or six segments 9

2. Three posterior veins or stumps of veins, the third usually arising from the discal cell 4
   Four posterior veins or vestiges of them, all arising from the discal cell 3

3. Posterior femora thickened ....**Neœxaireta** Osten Sacken
   Posterior femora but little thickened, the posterior tibiæ noticeably thickened (82) ....**Actina** Meigen

4. Scutellum with spines or denticulations 6
   Scutellum without spines 5

5. Third vein branched (33)....................**Allognosta** Osten Sacken
   Third vein not branched (1, 87)....................**Chiromyza** Wiedemann

6. Scutellum with fewer than ten spines.................... 7
   Scutellum with ten or twelve spines or teeth.................... 8

7. Head hemispherical; antennæ situated near the middle of the head (2, 3) ....**Beris** Latreille
   Head not hemispherical; antennæ situated well below the middle of the head ....**Berismyia** Giglio-Tos.

8. Scutellar spines long ....**Heteracanthia** Macquart
   Scutellum with about twelve short teeth ....**Antissops** Enderlein

9. Three posterior veins, all arising from the discal cell....................10
   Four posterior veins, the first and third sometimes vestigial but at least represented by angulations of the discal cell....................22

* Curran, 1927, Tr. Roy. Soc. Can., Sec. v, 1927, pp. 191-228.

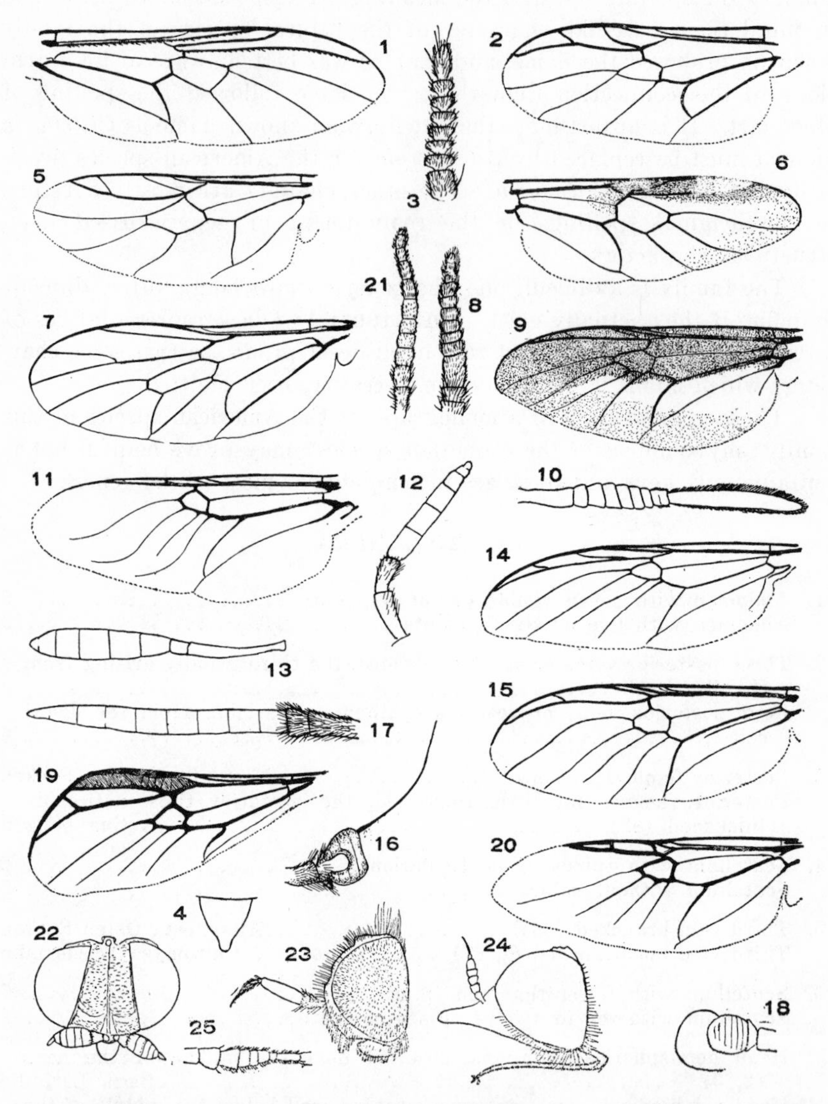

Stratiomyidæ I.—1, **Chiromyza;** 2, **Beris;** 3, **Beris,** antenna; 4, **Psephiocera,** scutellum; 5, **Psephiocera,** wing; 6, **Acanthinomyia;** 7, 8, **Solva aterrima** (Coenomyidæ); 9, **Hermetia;** 10, **Hermetia,** antenna; 11, **Odontomyia;** 12, **Odontomyia,** antenna; 13, **Stratiomys,** antenna; 14, **Pedicella,** antenna; 15, **Ptecticus;** 16, **Ptecticus;** antenna; 17, **Cyphomyia,** antenna; 18, **Merosargus,** antenna; 19, **Histiodroma;** 20, **Euparyphus;** 21, **Euparyphus,** antenna; 22, **Euryneura,** head from in front; 23, **Pelagomyia;** 24, **Nemotelus;** 25, **Aochletus,** antenna.

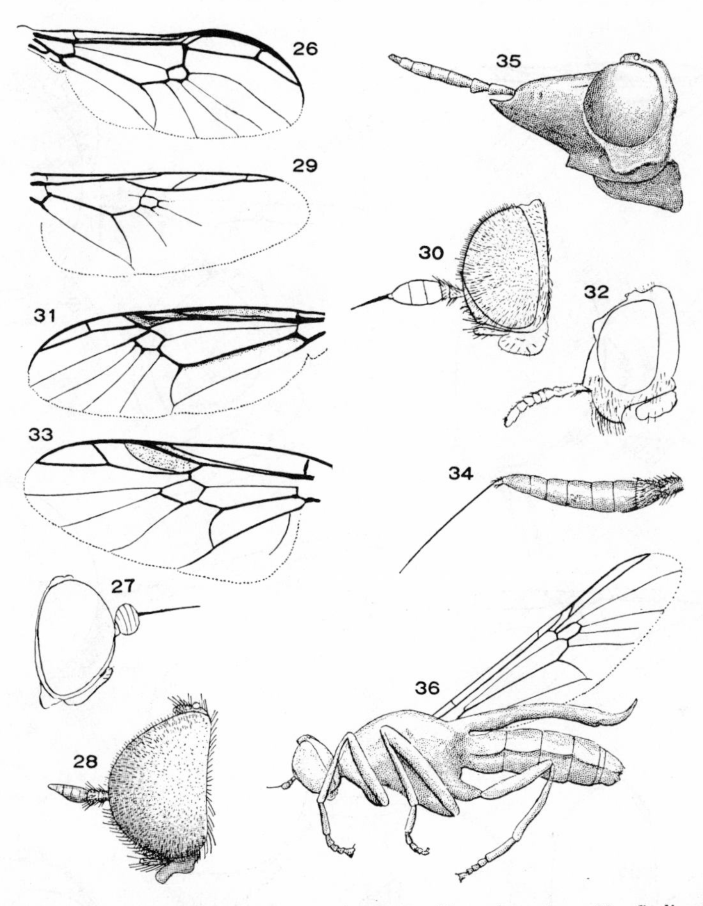

Stratiomyidæ II.—26, **Analcocerus**, wing; 27, **Neopachygaster**; 28, **Scoliopelta**; 29, **Microchrysa**; 30, **Euclitellaria**; 31, **Rhaphiocera**; 32, **Myxosargus**; 33, **Allognosta**; 34, **Chrysochlora**, antenna; 35, **Rhingiopsis**; 36, **Dicranophora** (Brazil).

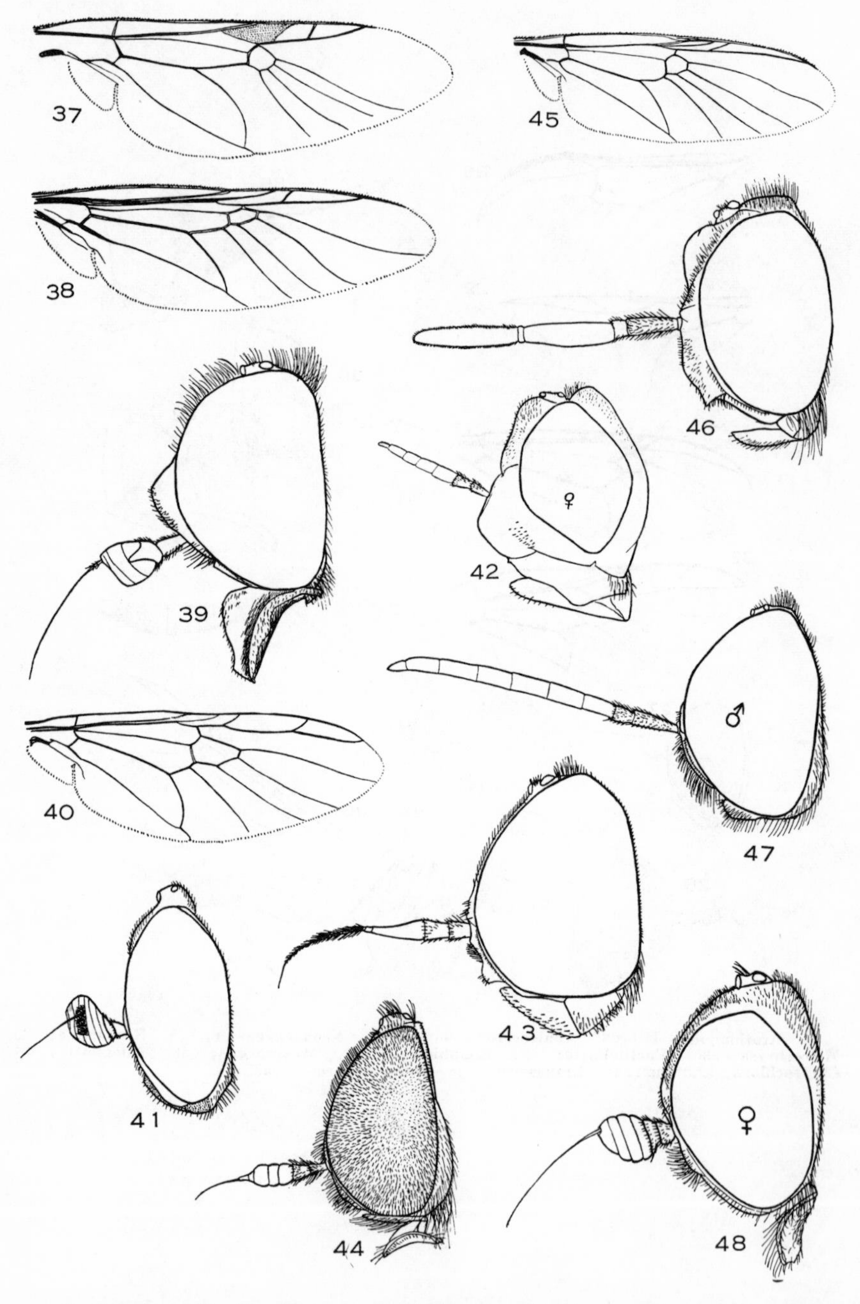

Stratiomyidæ III.—37, **Oxycera albovittata**; 38, **Rhingiopsis rostrata**; 39, **Ptecticus testaceus**; 40, **Neorondania chalybea**; 41, **Gowdeyana mirabilis**; 42, **Odontomyia** (sp. Panama); 43, **Cacosis**; 44, **Euclitellaria**; 45, **Chrysochroma nigricornis**; 46, **Hermetia** (n. sp. Panama); 47, **Cyphomyia**; 48, **Microchrysa polita**.

10. Antennæ situated at most a little below the middle of the head in profile; scutellum never with two spines 13
Antennæ situated far below the middle of the head, near the lower edge of the eyes; scutellum with at least a pair of spines................11

11. Third antennal segment not furcate; scutellum bispinose............12
Third antennal segment furcate, the upper branch with a terminal arista and a lateral process **(72, 78)**....................**Neochauna** Williston

12. Eyes bare ....**Psegmomma** Enderlein
Eyes pilose **(6, 86)** ....**Acanthinomyia** Hunter

13. Third vein branched 15
Third vein simple 14

14. Third antennal segment elongate (55, 56)...........**Berkshiria** Johnson
Third antennal segment short, as broad as long (54, 58).
Zabrachia Coquillett

15. Third antennal segment elongate..16
Third antennal segment as wide as long or nearly so.................17

16. Scutellum prolonged and obtusely pointed, without conspicuous rim on lower edge ....**Cynipimorpha** Brauer
Scutellum broadly rounded apically and with a strong rim on the lower margin (55, 56)...............................**Berkshiria** Johnson

17. Scutellum prolonged, its sides more or less parallel apically or triangular with a very broad preapical depression, the lower edge not margined **(4, 5, 60)**...........................**Psephiocera** Enderlein
Scutellum rounded apically, its lower edge sometimes very strongly margined 18

18. Arista short plumose or with very long pubescence of isolated hairs **(49)** ....**Lophoteles** Lœw
Arista short pubescent or bare..19

19. Antennæ arising at most slightly below the middle of the head........20
Antennæ arising conspicuously below the middle of the head **(61)**.
Pachygaster Meigen

20. Scutellum with a strong marginal rim below..........................21
Scutellum with at most a very weak rim below **(27, 57)**.
Neopachygaster Austen

21. Rim of scutellum strongly serrate **(62)**..........***Eupachygaster** Kertesz
Rim of scutellum so finely serrate as to appear smooth except under high magnification **(41, 51)**.......................**Gowdeyana** Curran

22. All the posterior veins arise from the discal cell.........................23
The fourth posterior vein arises from the second basal cell...........39

23. Scutellum with spines 24
Scutellum without spines, sometimes denticulate...................32

* I have not seen the type of this European genus and it may be that the species described by Malloch as belonging here belongs to **Vittiger** Kertesz.

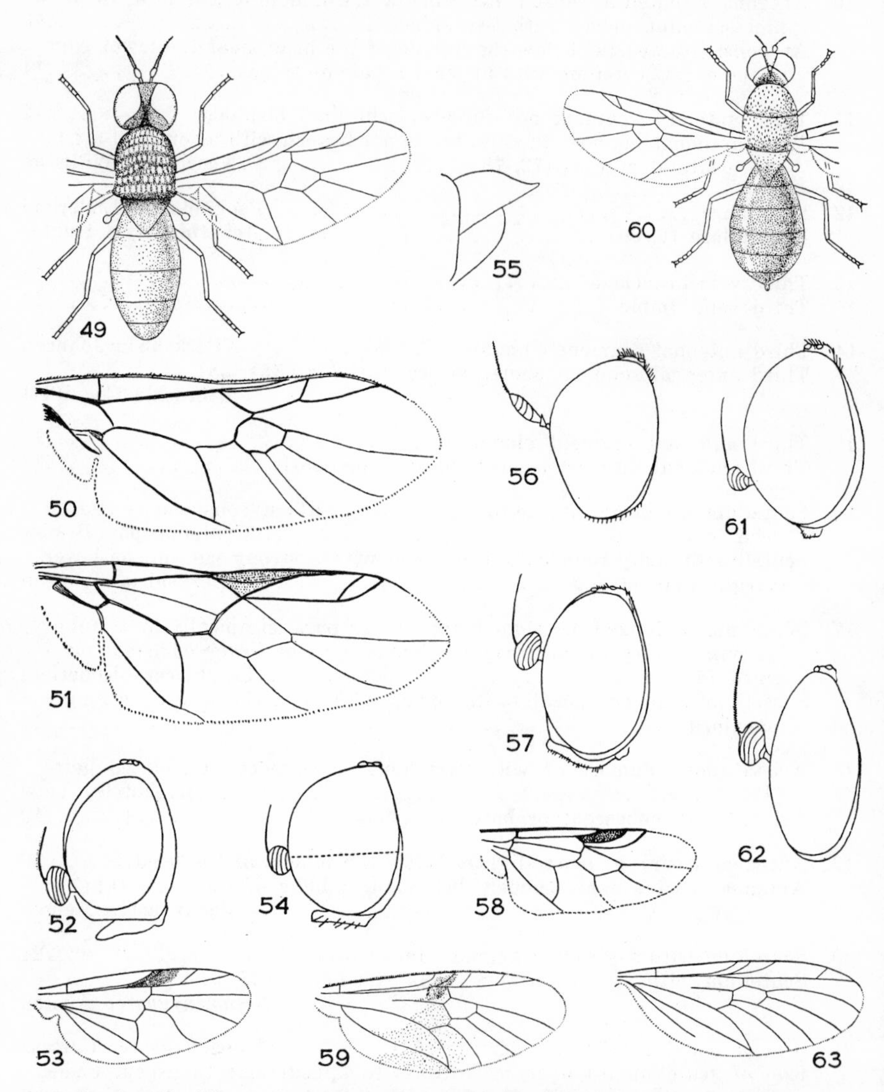

Stratiomyidæ IV.—49, **Lophoteles pallidipennis**, after Williston; 50, **Neurota tricolor**; 51, **Gowdeyana mirabilis**; 52, **Zabrachia polita** ♀; 53, **Berismyia nigrofemorata**; 54, **Zabrachia polita** ♂; 55, **Berkshiria**, scutellum; 56, **Berkshiria**; 57, **Neopachygaster maculicornis**; 58, **Zabrachia polita**; 59, **Gyneuryparea lasiophthalmus**; 60, **Psephiocera minuta**, after Williston; 61, **Brachygaster pulcher**; 62, **Eupachygaster punctifer**; 63, **Merosargus bulbifrons**.

24. Antennæ short, with a sub-terminal arista (37, 84)......**Oxycera** Meigen
Antennæ more or less elongate..................................25

25. Antennæ inserted near the middle of the head......................27
Antennæ inserted close to the oral margin..........................26

26. Eyes bare (22, 68).................................**Euryneura** Schiner
Eyes pilose (30)...............................**Euclitellaria** Kertesz

27. Antennal style not differentiated.................................28
Antennal style distinctly differentiated..........................30

28. Antennæ with eight distinct segments..............................29
Antennæ with three segments, the third annulate (28).
Scoliopelta Williston

29. Second antennal segment twice as long as the first......**Glaris** Kertesz
Second antennal segment not longer than the first (20, 21, 90).
Euparyphus Gerstæcker

30. Eyes bare (**Clitellaria** auct).........................**Adoxomyia** Kertesz
Eyes pilose 31

31. Third vein branched (44, 65).....................**Euclitellaria** Kertesz
Third vein simple (25)........................**Aochletus** Osten Sacken

32. Face conically produced..33
Face not conically produced......................................34

33. Males holoptic (24, 64)..........................**Nemotelus** Geoffroy
Males dichoptic ....**Akronia** Hine

34. Antennal style almost as long as the third antennal segment, quite flat and shining; the thin sides densely fringed with long pubescence (9, 10, 46) ....**Hermetia** Latreille
Antennal style different in structure or the antennæ with an arista....35

35. Eyes pilose on practically the whole surface........................36
Eyes bare, or very thinly pubescent on the upper half only............38

36. Antennæ with a bristle-like style (23).............**Pelagomyia** Williston
Antennal style not well differentiated..............................37

37. Face produced ....**Lasiopa** Brullé
Face receding (50, 66) ....**Neurota** Curran

38. Arista apical and densely plumose on basal half or more (43, 81).
Cacosis Walker
Arista apical but bare (34, 91).................*__Chrysochlora__ Latreille

39. Third antennal segment without an arista, the style absent or but poorly differentiated, rarely short and bristly 40
Third antennal segment with an arista..............................51

40. Third vein with an anterior branch.................................41
Third vein without anterior branch.................................44

41. Head strongly produced anteriorly and with a porrect spine or protuberance below the antennæ (35, 38, 83)..........†**Rhingiopsis** Röder
Head not produced, the face sometimes produced conically downward...42

* Curran, 1929, Amer. Mus. Novitates No. 339, p. 2.
† Curran, 1932, Amer. Mus. Novitates No. 526, p. 1.

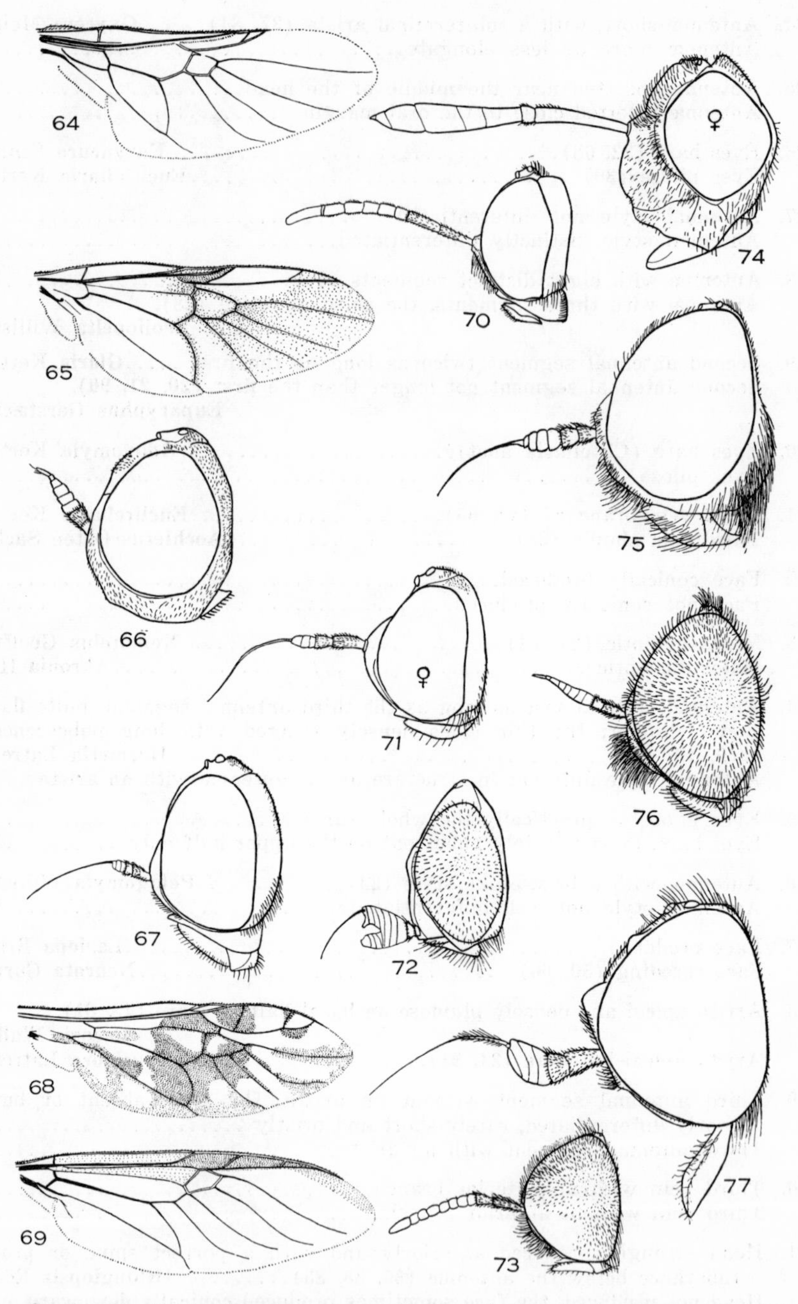

Stratiomyidæ V.—64, **Nemotelus arator**; 65, **Euclitellaria subulata**; 66, **Neurota tricolor**; 67, **Rhaphiocera armata**; 68, **Euryneura panamensis**, n. sp.; 69, **Promeranisa nasuta**; 70, **Analcocerus**; 71, **Histiodroma inermis**; 72, **Neochauna**; 73, **Chordonota**; 74, **Stratiomys mutabilis**; 75, **Nothomyia calopus**; 76, **Gyneuryparea lasiophthalmus**; 77, **Aloipha cingulatus**.

42. Eyes bare 43
Eyes thickly pilose in the ♂, pilose on lower half in ♀ (59, 76).
Gyneuryparia Enderlein

43. Antennæ situated near the lowest level of the eyes (32).
***Myxosargus** Brauer
Antennæ situated near the middle of the eyes in profile (17, 47).
Cyphomyia Wiedemann

44. Scutellum without spines 45
Scutellum with spines..46

45. Third antennal segment with eight annuli (73, 80)..**Chordonota** Gerstæcker
Third antennal segment with five or six annuli (11, 12, 42).
Odontomyia Meigen

46. Costa not thickened distally 47
Costa strongly thickened distally (26, 70).............**Analcocerus** Loew

47. Third antennal segment composed of seven or eight annuli............50
Third segment composed of not more than six annuli.................48

48. Head very strongly produced forward, the face strongly receding (69, 85).
Promeranisa Walker
Head rarely produced forward, if so the antennal prominence not constricted 49

49. First antennal segment three times as long as the second (13, 74, 79).
†**Stratiomys** Geoffroy
First segment less than three times the length of the second (11, 12, 42).
Odontomyia Meigen

50. First antennal segment two or three times as long as the second.
Campeprosopa Macquart
First antennal segment but little longer than the second, the third terminating in a bristle (40)................**Neorondania** Osten Sacken

51. Scutellum with spines 52
Scutellum without spines 53

52. Third vein not furcate (75).........................**Nothomyia** Lœw
Third vein furcate (31, 67).......................**Raphiocera** Macquart

53. Space between the second vein and the costa chitinized, the costa expanded on the apical half (19, 71)...............**Histiodroma** Schiner
Wing normal 54

54. Arista terminal, thick and long pubescent on the basal fourth.
Acrochæta Wiedemann
Arista terminal or dorsal, normal in shape and practically bare.......55

55. Lower lobe of the squamæ with a strap-like prolongation near the outer end 58
Lower lobe of squamæ transverse apically...........................56

---

* Curran, 1929, Amer. Mus. Novitates No. 378.
† In a forthcoming contribution Mr. M. T. James will propose a new genus for *S. constans, mutabilis,* etc.

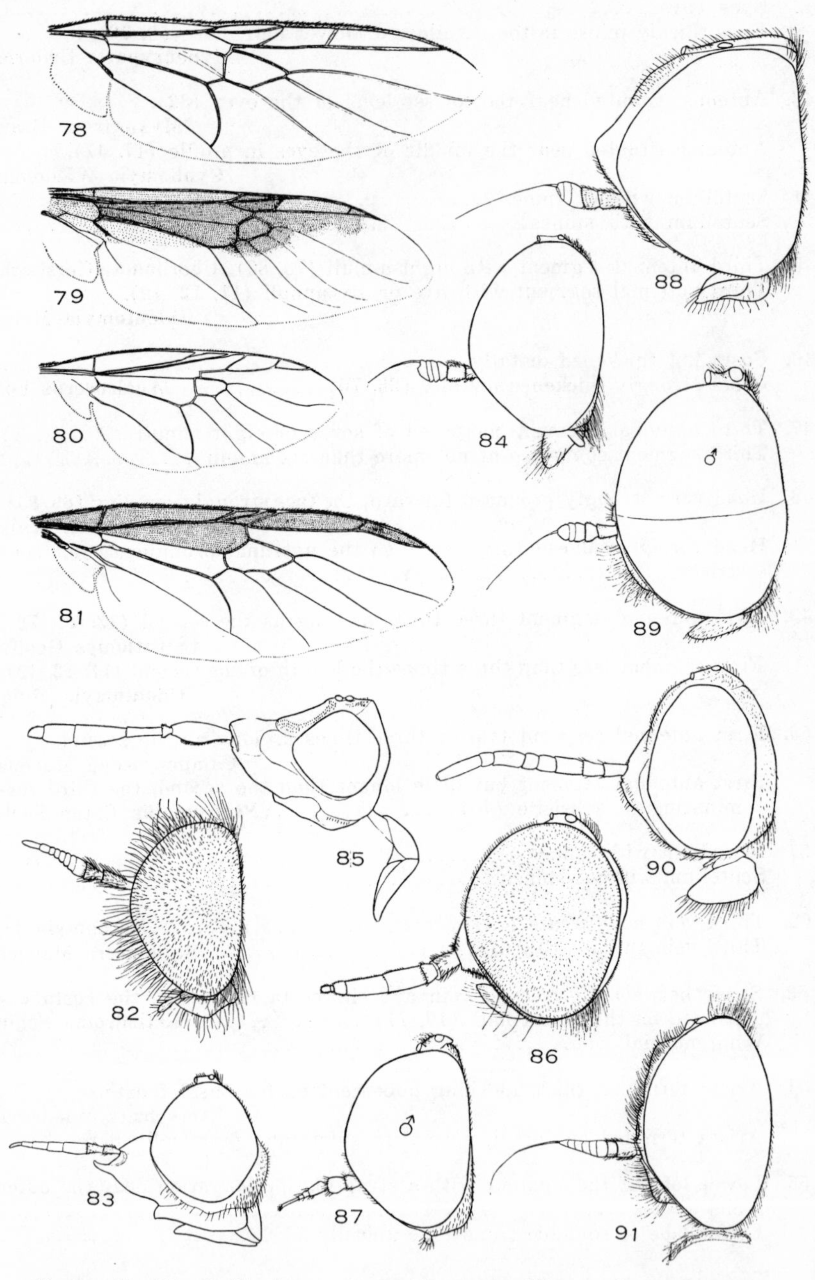

Stratiomyidæ VI.—78, **Neochauna**; 79, **Stratiomys mutabilis**; 80, **Chordonota carbonaria**; 81, **Cacosis nigra**; 82, **Actina viridis**; 83, **Rhingiopsis rostrata**; 84, **Oxycera albovittata**; 85, **Promeranisa nasuta**; 86, **Acanthinomyia**; 87, **Chiromyza**; 88, **Pedicella lucens**; 89, **Chrysochroma nigricornis**; 90, **Euparyphus**; 91, **Chrysochlora.**

56. Third vein with a branch near the end of the first vein...............57
Third vein without the basal branch (77)..............**Aloipha** Enderlein

57. Second antennal segment subtriangularly produced into the third on the inner side (15, 16, 39)..................................**Ptecticus** Lœw
Second antennal segment at most moderately convex on its inner end, never subtriangular (18, 63)........................*__Merosargus__ Lœw

58. Ocellar triangle situated far from the vertex and almost or quite twice as long as wide (14, 88)................................**Pedicella** Bigot
Ocellar triangle not or but little longer than wide, in the female partly behind the upper angles of the eyes, in the male usually somewhat in front of this point..59

59. Ocellar triangle in female lying almost all in front of the posterior angle of the eyes, the males without the eyes divided into definite zones of differently sized facets; anal cell much narrower than the combined basal cells (45, 89)...................**Chrysochroma** Williston
Ocellar triangle in female lying mostly behind the posterior angles of the eyes; males with the facets enlarged on the upper half; anal cell quite as wide as the combined basal cells (29, 48)....**Microchrysa** Lœw

* Curran, 1932, Amer. Mus. Novit. No. 534.

Family Cœnomyiidæ

Flies of medium to large size, the antennæ elongate, with the third segment annulate and more or less clearly subdivided.

Males holoptic or dichoptic. Antennæ never with a distinctly differentiated style although the terminal annulus may resemble one to a certain extent. Empodium developed pulvilliform, the pulvilli present. Squamæ small. Wing venation well developed, the discal cell always present, the fourth posterior cell sometimes closed.

As here defined this family includes insects of diverse structure but there seems to be no good character for their separation. The genus *Cœnomyia* has been placed in various families, including the Rhagionidæ, Tabanidæ and Stratiomyidæ. It appears, however, because of the facial structure, to be best placed between the two last mentioned families. Upon general structure alone *Cœnomyia* might well be isolated from the remainder of the other included genera except that *Arthropeas magnus* Johnson is very similar in appearance, differing only in having bare eyes and in lacking the scutellar spines.

The adults are found in woods, especially near moist places, while the larvæ mostly occur in decaying wood, under the bark of trees or in the soil and are carnivorous and predaceous. The opinion has been expressed that the larvæ of *Cœnomyia* may live upon the immature stages of Cicadas. A revision of the North American species will be found in Leonard* "Revision of the Rhagionidæ in the United States and Canada."

I might add that I cannot agree that the genus *Solva* Walker belongs to the Stratiomyidæ although there is no doubt that there is some relationship. Both the facial shape and wing venation exclude it from that family.

KEY TO GENERA

1. Eyes bare 2
   Eyes pilose (9, 11) ....**Cœnomyia** Latreille
2. Anterior tibiæ with one terminal spur.................................. 3
   Anterior tibiæ without terminal spur.................................. 4
3. Antennæ acute at the tip, the apical annulus elongate (1, 8).
   Arthropeas Lœw
   Antennæ obtuse at the tip, the apical annulus short and broad (3, 7).
   †**Xylophagus** Meigen
4. Fourth posterior cell open 5
   Fourth posterior cell closed (5, 12)........................**Solva** Walker
5. Face with a very large, prominent pilose swelling on either side (2, 10).
   Glutops Burgess
   Face not strongly swollen laterally, bare (4, 6).....**Arthroceras** Williston

---

* 1930. Mem. Amer. Ent. Soc., No. 7.

† Curran, 1933, Amer. Mus. Novitates No. 673, p. 1.

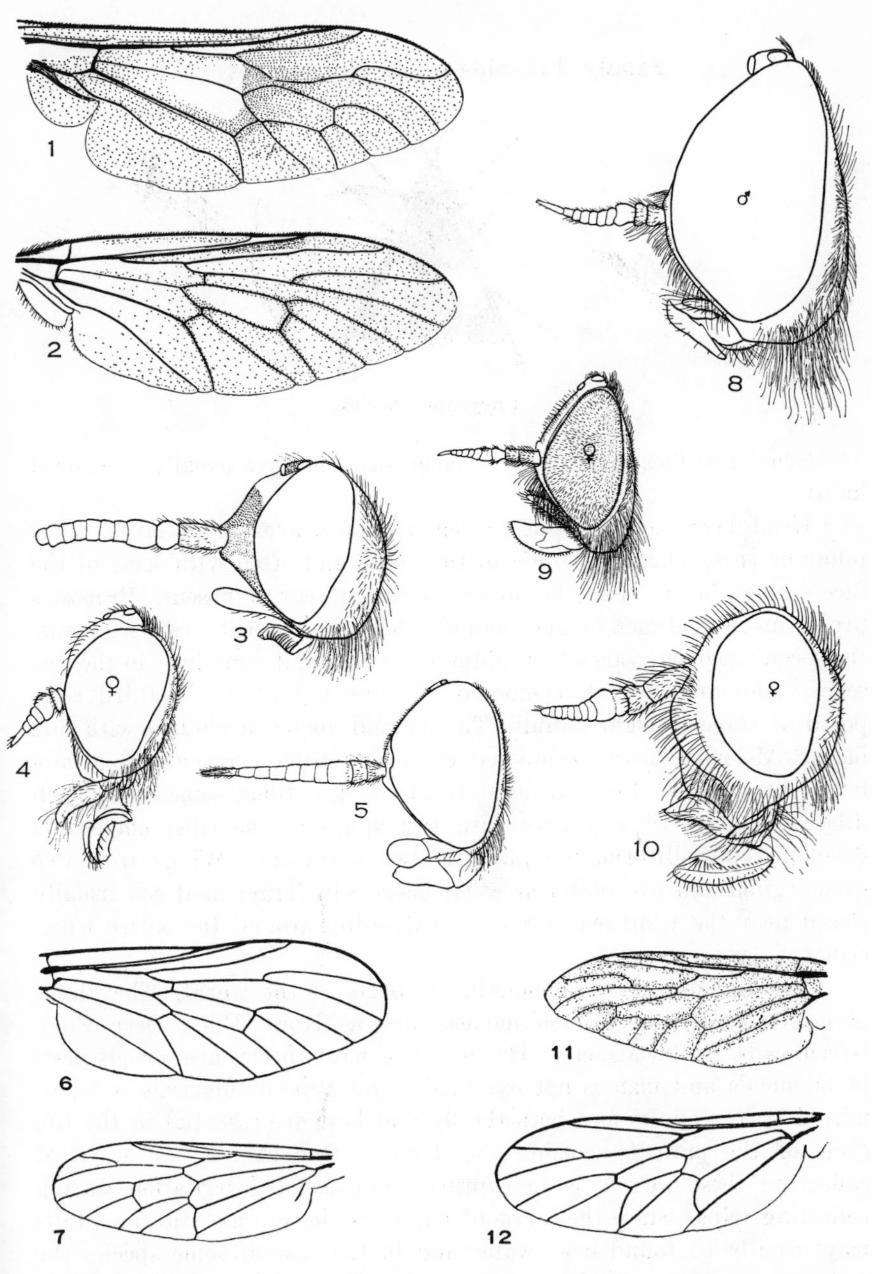

Cœnomyiidæ.—1, **Arthropeas magnus**; 2, **Glutops singularis**; 3, **Xylophagus laceyi**; 4, **Arthroceras leptis**; 5, **Solva aterrima**; 6, **Arthroceras**; 7, **Xylophagus**; 8, **Arthropeas magnus**; 9, **Cœnomyia pallida**; 10, **Glutops singularis**; 11, **Cœnomyia pallida**; 12, **Solva.**

Family Tabanidæ—The Horse Flies

Chrysops species.

Bristleless flies of medium to large size, the eyes usually bi-colored in life.

Head large, the occiput flattened or concave. Eyes large, short pilose or bare, usually holoptic in the males and often with some of the facets much larger than the others; ocelli present or absent. Proboscis projecting, sometimes longer than the body; palpi with two segments, the second segment variable in different genera and sometimes in the two sexes. Antennæ porrect, composed of three segments, the third composed of three to eight annuli. Thorax and abdomen clothed with fine hairs. Abdomen broad, composed of seven visible segments; genitalia never prominent. Legs moderately stout, the tibiæ sometimes much dilated; middle tibiæ always with two spurs at the tips; empodium developed pulvilliform, the pulvilli always present. Wings with two submarginal and five posterior cells; basal cells large; anal cell usually closed near the wing margin; costa extending around the entire wing. Squamæ large.

The Tabanids are common in all parts of the world. They have been given various common names, such as Horse Flies, Deer Flies, Greenheads, Bullheads, etc. The adults of most species are serious pests of mammals and man is not excepted. One type of filariasis is transmitted by the adults and both the fly and host are essential in the life cycle of the parasite causing the disease. One of the best ways of collecting these insects is to capture those causing irritation during collecting trips. Since the larvæ of many species are aquatic the adults may usually be found near water and in the case of some species the males are rare except adjacent to the breeding places, and, as this sex does not suck blood they must be looked for in places other than in the vicinity of warm blooded animals, the same being true for most of the genera of the Pangoniinæ, although the genus *Chrysops* of this subfamily contains some of the most serious pests of man. The males of some species feed upon pollen and nectar and may be found upon most melliferous flowers, hovering over streams or pools or even along paths. The sexes are frequently very different in appearance and difficult to associate.

The transmittal of disease by Tabanids may be a purely mechanical operation or the flies may serve as intermediate hosts of the parasitic organisms causing disease. *Tularæmia* is spread mechanically and is transmitted by *Chrysops discalis* Williston. Normally it is a disease of rodents (particularly rabbits) but man sometimes develops the disease after being bitten by the fly. It has also been demonstrated that *Anthrax* may be carried on the proboscis of Tabanids and cause infection as a result of the bite of the fly and various species of trypanosomes are transmitted. In Africa a filarial disease caused by *Loa loa* Cobbald, and known by that name, is transmitted by two species of *Chrysops*. The details have been worked out by A. and S. A. Connal (Trans. Roy. Soc. Trop. Med. Hyg., xv, pp. 131-134, 1913).

The eggs are laid, as a rule, in large masses on leaves and stems of plants overhanging water and are usually brown or black in color. They show characteristic generic arrangement and sometimes specific characters but too little is known about them to permit of their identification. The larvæ are predaceous. Larvæ have been found in rotten wood, under stones, in mud, etc. Pupation takes places near the surface of the soil. There are many papers dealing with the biology of North American Tabanidæ, but most of them are quite short. Papers by Cameron* and Marchand† on the immature stages are the most comprehensive.

The number of species of Tabanidæ is large, the genus *Tabanus* alone containing about 1200 described species. The first (and only) North American monograph of the family was published by Osten Sacken in 1875 and 1878. Since that time the number of species has greatly increased and the difficulty of identifying specimens is relatively greater. Hine has published on the Tabanidæ of Ohio‡, while there are numerous short papers scattered through the literature.

Fascicle 175 of ''Genera Insectorum'', by Dr. J. Surcouf, deals with this family but the treatment has been rather unfavorably criticized by other workers in the field. Several American students are now studying the family and excellent revisions of the nearctic species may be expected to appear in the near future.

---

* Cameron, 1926, Bull. Ent. Res., xvii, pp. 1-42, 5 plates.
† Marchand, 1920, Mon. Rockefeller Inst. Med. Res., No. 13, pp. 1-203, 15 plates.
‡ Hine, 1903, Ohio State University Bulletin, Ser. 7, No. 19.

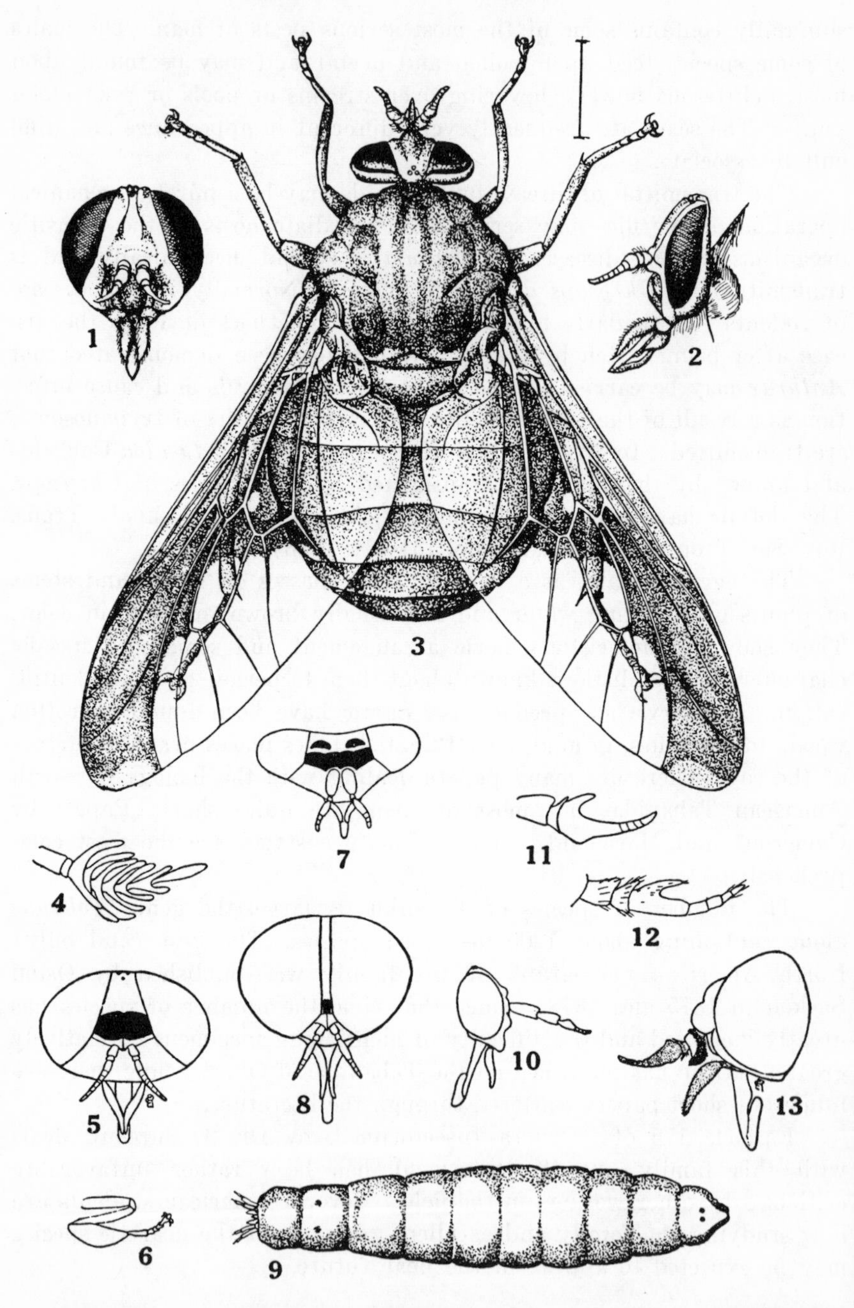

Tabanidæ I.—1, 2, 3, **Goniops chrysochroma**; 4, **Pityocera, antenna**; 5, **Apatolestes**; 6, **Lepiselaga crassipes**; 7, **Hæmatopota punctulata**; 8, **Diachlorus**; 9, **Goniops chrysochroma,** larva; 10, **Chrysops**; 11, 12, **Tabanus**, antenna; 13, **Snowiellus.**

KEY TO GENERA*

1. Hind tibiæ with apical spurs, which may be quite small (Pangoniinæ) 2
   Hind tibiæ without apical spurs (Tabaninæ) 15

2. Eyes with distinct pile 3
   Eyes bare 9

3. First posterior cell open.. 4
   First posterior cell closed....................................... 5

4. Face not produced, at most slightly convex (**Osca** Walker) (**22**). **Scaptia** Walker
   Face much produced, snout-like ....**Neopangonia** Ad. Lutz

5. Fourth posterior cell closed (**15, 20**)......................**Scione** Walker
   Fourth posterior cell open.. 6

6. Third antennal segment furcate.................................. 7
   Third antennal segment not branched.............................. 8

7. Third antennal segment branched dorsally and ventrally (**4**). **Pityocera** Giglio-Tos
   Third antennal segment branched only dorsally..........**Elaphella** Bezzi

8. Coxæ and femora slightly hairy..........................**Fidena** Walker
   Coxæ and femora densely covered with long pile (**Erephopsis** Rondani) (**34, 35**) ....**Melpia** Walker

9. First posterior cell closed; face merely convex, not snout-like; ocelli present; palpi long, sabre-shaped (**25, 29**).........**Esenbeckia** Rondani
   First posterior cell open.. 10

10. Third antennal segment composed of at least seven annuli.......... 11
    Third antennal segment composed of not more than five annuli; proboscis short 13

11. Posterior border of eye acutely angulate in female; proboscis very short; fork of third longitudinal vein without appendix; wings brownish in front, hyaline behind (**1, 2, 3, 9**)..........**Goniops** Aldrich
    Eyes of female not acutely angulate above; wings not so marked.... 12

12. Proboscis but little longer than palpi; frons of female very wide below; fork of third longitudinal vein with appendix (**5**)....**Apatolestes** Williston
    Proboscis much longer than palpi; frons of female narrow and almost parallel-sided (**31, 33**) ....**Buplex** Austen

13. Second antennal segment only half as long as the first (**16, 26**). **Silvius** Meigen
    Second antennal segment much more than half as long as the first.... 14

14. Abdomen inflated, much wider than thorax; fork of third longitudinal vein with long appendix..........................**Neochrysops** Walton
    Abdomen normal, depressed, not much wider than thorax; fork of third longitudinal vein without appendix (**10, 19**).........†**Chrysops** Meigen

---

* Checked by Dr. J. Bequaert.

† Kröber, 1926, Stett. Ent. Zeitung, lxxxvii, pp. 211-353, two plates; and, Neotropical, 1925, Konowia, iv, pp. 210-375, five plates.

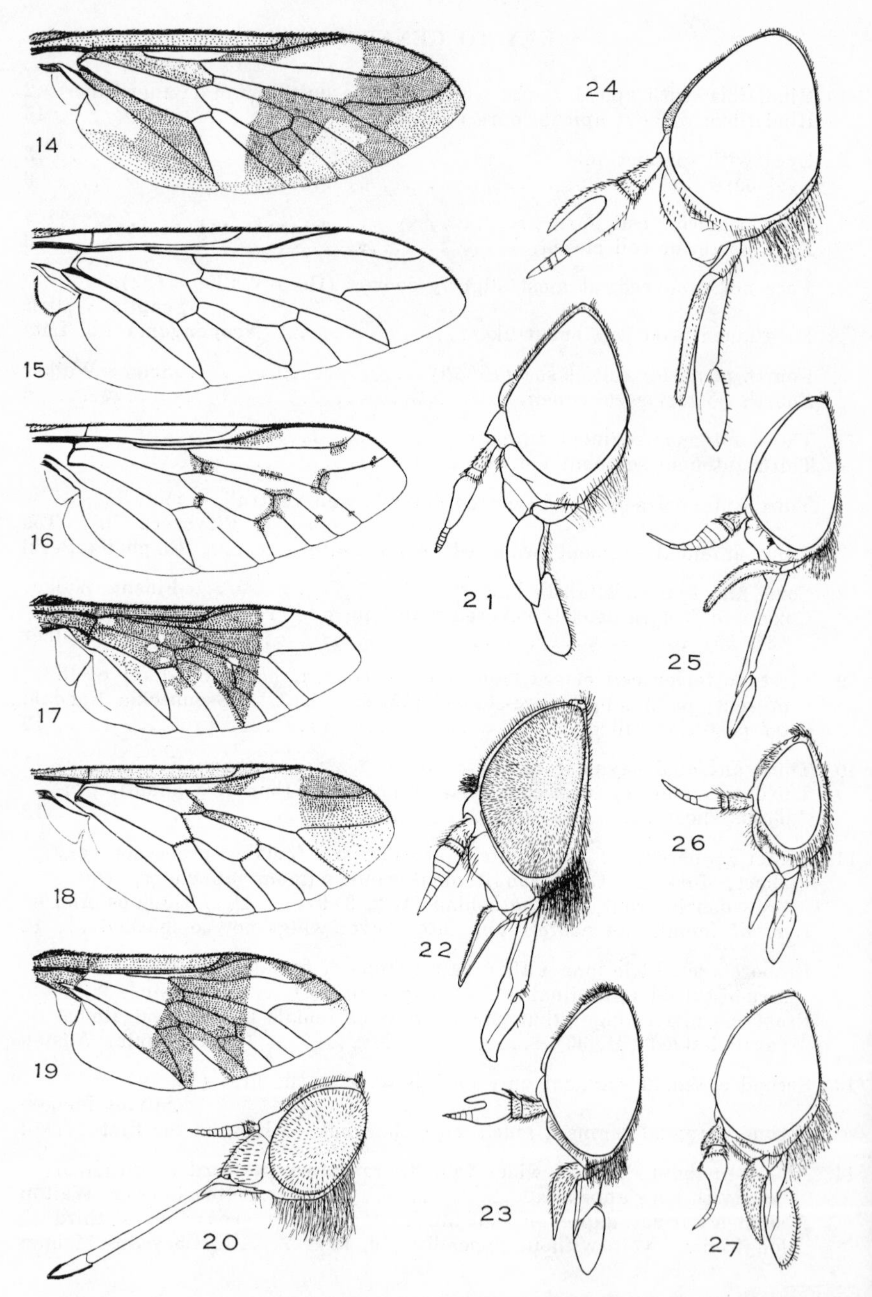

Tabanidæ II.—14, **Dichelacera analis**; 15, **Scione aurulans**; 16, **Silvius pollinosus**; 17, **Lepiselaga crassipes**; 18, **Diachlorus ferrugatus**; 19, **Chrysops melæna**; 20, **Scione aurulans**; 21, **Lepiselaga crassipes**; 22, **Scaptia**; 23, **Stibasoma theotænia panamensis**; 24, **Dichelacera analis**; 25, **Esenbeckia prasiniventris**; 26, **Silvius gigantulus**; 27, **Tabanus albocirculus**.

15. Third antennal segment with four annuli; frons of female wide; fork of third longitudinal vein with appendix (7, 28)...**Hæmatopota** Meigen
 Third antennal segment usually with five annuli; when with less the frons of female is narrow and the fork of third longitudinal vein bears no appendix 16

16. Third antennal segment not at all or barely angulated above........ 17
 Third antennal segment with distinct angle or process near the base above; ocelli rudimentary or absent.......................... 20

17. Ocelli present and of normal size; all tibiæ not or hardly swollen. **Merycomyia** Hine
 Ocelli absent; at least fore tibiæ swollen......................... 18

18. Fore tibiæ swollen; mid and hind tibiæ normal; palpi swollen at base, pointed at apex (8, 18).....................**Diachlorus** Osten Sacken
 All tibiæ swollen, the fore pair most; palpi flat and broad.......... 19

19. Third antennal segment broad and flat; subcallus divided by a median line ....**Selasoma** Macquart
 Third antennal segment narrow and slender; subcallus not divided medially (6, 17, 21) ....**Lepiselaga** Macquart

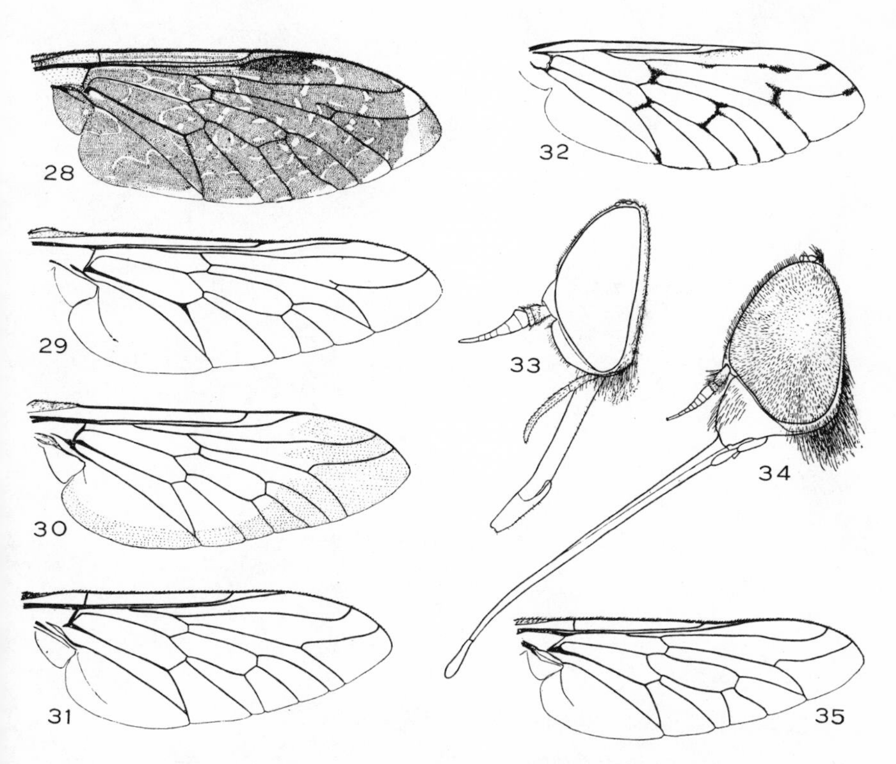

Tabanidæ III.—28, **Hæmatopota punctulata**; 29, **Esenbeckia prasiniventris**; 30, **Stibasoma fulvohirtum**; 31, **Buplex rasa**; 32, **Tabanus nervosus**; 33, **Buplex rasa**; 34, **Melpia venosa**; 35, **Melpia.**

20. Dorsal process of third antennal segment unusually long, extending to third annulus 21
Dorsal process moderately long or forming a tooth, sharp edge, or weak angle 22

21. Fore tibiæ strongly swollen; hind tibiæ ciliate with long hairs (**23, 30**).
Stibasoma Schiner
Fore tibiæ not or hardly swollen; hind tibiæ not ciliate (**14, 24**).
Dichelacera Macquart

22. Subcallus strongly swollen; first antennal segment much enlarged.... 23
Subcallus normal; first antennal segment not or slightly enlarged (**11, 12, 27, 32**)............ **Tabanus** Linnæus

23. First antennal segment subglobular as well from above as from the sides; all tibiæ strongly swollen............ **Bolbodimyia** Bigot
First antennal segment much produced downward (in side view), but not widened seen from above; tibiæ not or hardly swollen (**13**).
Snowiellus Hine

Family Pantophthalmidæ

Pantophthalmus sp., natural size.

Very large, usually broad, bristleless flies.

Eyes large, contiguous above the antennæ in the male; face rather short but often produced below into a distinct beak. Proboscis short, not adapted for piercing, with fleshy labellæ; palpi three-segmented, the basal segment short; ocelli present. Antennæ elongate, the third segment annulate and with a style-like apical section which may or may not be well differentiated. Squamæ small. Wings with two submarginal and five posterior cells, the fourth posterior cell and the anal cell closed. Tibiæ without apical spurs; posterior femora usually with a strong spur on the under surface beyond the middle; empodia pad-like.

The three genera placed in this family are closely related and there has always been much doubt concerning the validity of *Rhaphiorhynchus* which is undoubtedly but poorly separated from *Pantophthalmus* (*Acanthomera* Wiedemann). The genus *Atopomyia* Austen contains one species which is readily recognized by its slender, *Mydas*-like form. Austen* has revised the family but does not present keys to the species.

The Pantophthalmidæ occur only in the American tropics. The larvæ bore in solid wood (often in living trees) and the rasping sound made by them may be audible for a distance of several feet.

* 1923, Proc. Zool. Soc. London, pp. 551-598.

KEY TO GENERA

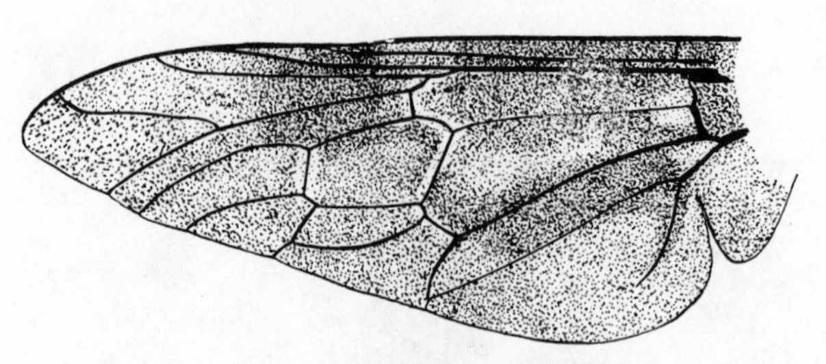

Pantophthalmus species.

1. Abdomen not or scarcely more than twice as long as wide, short and broad 2
   Abdomen three times as long as wide, long and narrow; **Mydas-like** species ....**Atopomyia** Austen

2. Third palpal segment almost always cylindrical, even when somewhat swollen and more or less pointed below, usually obtuse apically; facial beak, if present and fairly long, strongly tapering and the ventral spur on the posterior femora greatly reduced or almost absent.
   Pantophthalmus Thunberg
   Third palpal segment broadened and laterally compressed, especially in the female, pointed below; face with a long, narrow beak and the posterior femora with a strong ventral spur.
   Rhaphiorhynchus Wiedemann

Family Rhagionidæ—The Snipe Flies

Rhagio mystacea.

Small to medium sized, nearly bare or thinly pilose flies.

Face very strongly receding, the middle convex but lying much below the level of the eyes in profile; males holoptic or the eyes very narrowly separated. Antennæ composed of three segments, the third bearing a terminal or dorsal arista or rather slender style. Scutellum unarmed. Legs long; empodium developed pulvilliform (but slightly developed in *Hilarimorpha*). Wing venation strong; four or five posterior cells, the discal cell absent only in *Hilarimorpha*. Abdomen long and usually tapering.

The Snipe Flies are common in woods, especially near moist places and may be found on foliage, in long grass and on tree trunks. They are predaceous in both the adult and larval stages. Leonard* has revised the Nearctic species.

There has been much confusion in regard to the limits of this family, those genera which I have placed in the Cœnomyiidæ being included by Williston. *Hilarimorpha* has been placed in the Empidæ, and Bombyliidæ but from its general structure I feel certain that it belongs here, despite the poorly developed empodium. The shape of the face excludes it from both families mentioned and the wing venation cannot be considered of prime importance.

---

* 1930. Mem. Amer. Ent. Soc. No. 7.

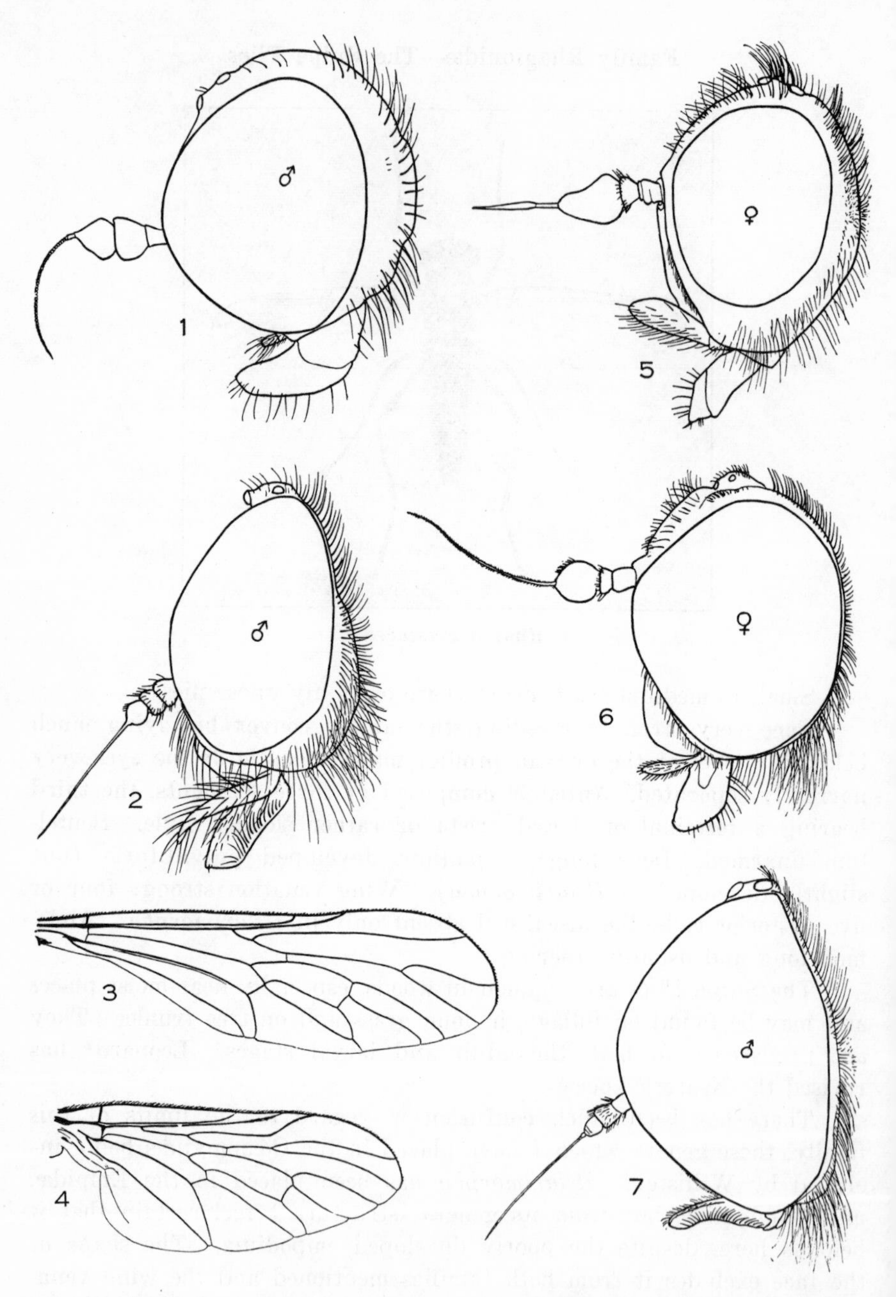

Rhagionidæ I.—1, **Vermileo**; 2, **Rhagio punctipennis**; 3, **Vermileo**; 4, **Symphoromyia pleuralis**; 5, **Ptiolina majuscula**; 6, **Chrysopilus quadratus**; 7, **Dialysis elongata.**

KEY TO GENERA

1. Anterior tibiæ without terminal spur.................................... 4
   Anterior tibiæ with one or two terminal spurs.......................... 2
2. Antennæ with a long terminal arista or style which is very much longer than the antenna proper (1); alula present or absent.... 3
   Antennæ with a short, thick terminal style; alula present.
   Bolbomyia Lœw
3. Alula present; scutellum haired; males holoptic (7, 14) (**Triptotricha** Lœw)..**Dialysis** Walker
   Alula absent; scutellum bare; males dichoptic (1, 3) (**Pheneus** Walker).
   Vermileo Macquart
4. Discal cell present; five posterior cells.................................. 5
   Discal cell absent; four posterior cells (11)... ....**Hilarimorpha** Schiner

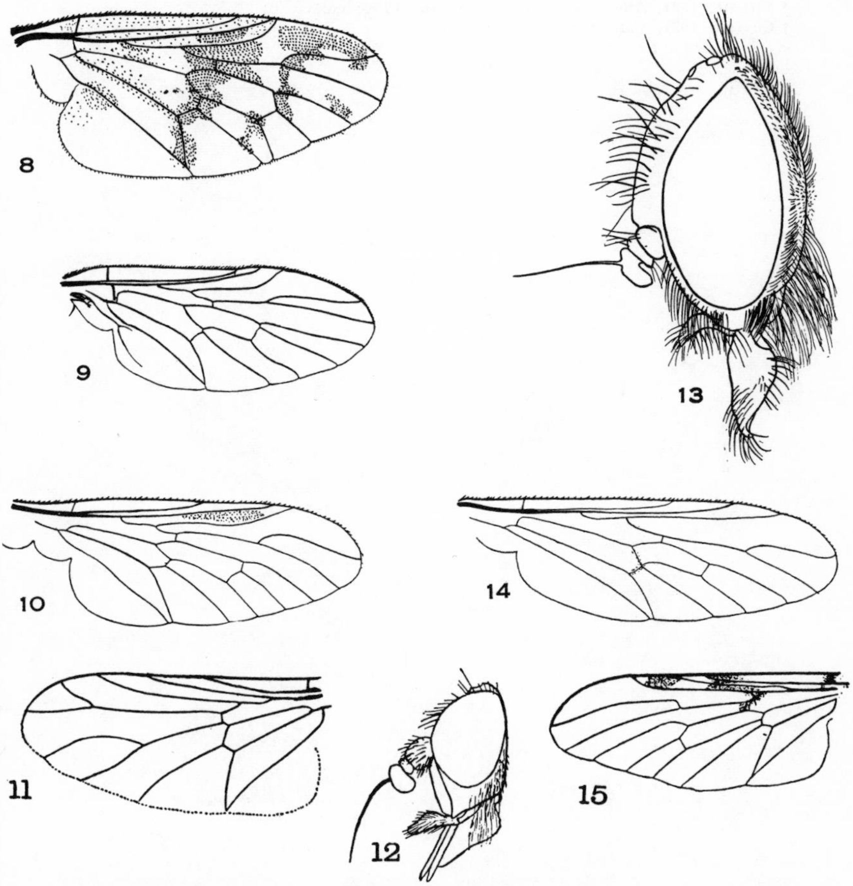

Rhagionidæ II.—8, **Atherix variegatus**; 9, **Ptiolina majuscula**; 10, **Rhagio incisus**; 11, **Hilarimorpha**; 12, **Symphoromyia**; 13, **Atherix variegtaus**; 14, **Dialysis elongata**; 15, **Chrysopilus**.

5. Third antennal segment round, oval or conical........................ 7
Third antennal segment kidney-shaped, with dorsal or subdorsal arista. 6

6. Posterior tibiæ with two terminal spurs (8, 13)..........**Atherix** Meigen
Posterior tibiæ with one terminal spur (4, 12)..**Symphoromyia** Frauenfeld

7. Posterior tibiæ with one terminal spur 8
Posterior tibiæ with two terminal spurs (2, 10)........**Rhagio** Fabricius

8. Antennæ bearing a terminal style.................................. 9
Antennæ with a long, slender terminal arista which is decidedly longer than the basal three segments combined (6, 15)..***Chrysopilus** Macquart

9. Style situated near the middle of the third antennal segment (5, 9).
†**Ptiolina** Zetterstedt
Style situated at the lower end of the third antennal segment.
Spania Meigen.

---

* Curran, 1931, Amer. Mus. Novit. No. 462 (Tropical).
† Curran, 1931, Can. Ent., lxiii, p. 249.

Family Scenopinidæ—The Window Flies

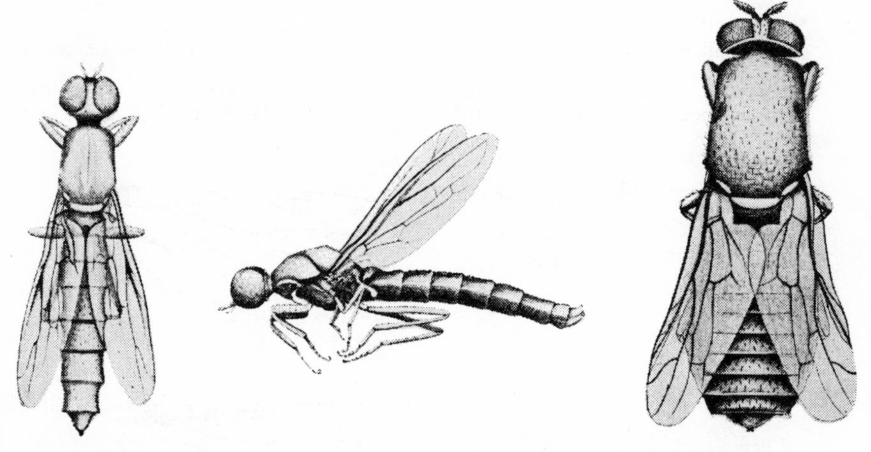

Pseudatrichia longurio, dorsal and lateral view, and **Scenopinus fenestralis** (right), dorsal view.

Flies of moderate or small size, usually blackish in color.

Front not excavated; face bare, short and broad; ocelli present; males usually holoptic; proboscis concealed; palpi cylindrical, bristly at the apex. Antennæ approximated at the base, the basal two segments short, the third elongate, simple, without style or arista. Thorax rather long, moderately convex above, the head situated low on the thorax; scutellum broad and short, convex apically and unarmed. Abdomen flattened or cylindrical, composed of seven segments. Legs short; empodia absent. Wing venation simple, the third vein branched; apical cell open or closed; basal cells long, the first much longer than the second.

The adults, with the exception of *Scenopinus fenestralis* Linnæus, are not common in collections. The larvæ have been recorded as living in decaying fungi and wood and under carpets. *S. fenestralis* is sometimes common on windows and is said to live upon carpet beetle larvæ, being predaceous. The common name of the family is derived from the window-frequenting habit.

Some authors have used the name *Omphrale* Meigen instead of *Scenopinus* Latreille, but I do not recognize Meigen's "1800" names. The family has been treated by Kröber in Genera Insectorum* and keys to the species are given.

* Fascicle 161. 1914.

KEY TO GENERA

1. Antennæ longer than the width of the head (Brazil)..**Cerocatus** Rondani
   Antennæ at most half as long as the width of the head............. 2

2. Apical cell closed and petiolate 3
   Apical cell open (1, 2)..............................**Scenopinus** Latreille

3. Body with metallic scales (3, 4)..................**Metatrichia** Coquillett
   Body without metallic scales (5)...........**Pseudatrichia** Osten Sacken

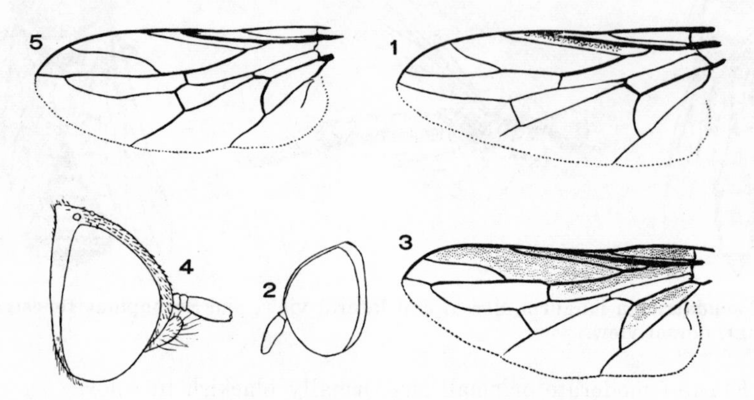

Scenopinidæ.—1, 2, **Scenopinus fenestralis**; 3, 4, **Metatrichia**; 5, **Pseudatrichia.**

Family Mydaidæ—The Mydas Flies

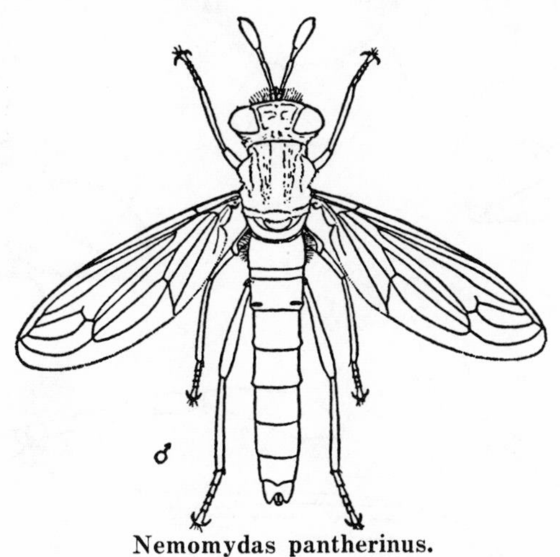

Nemomydas pantherinus.

Large to very large, thinly haired or nearly bare, elongated flies. Venation complicated, the basal cells long, the fourth vein always ending at or before the tip of the wing. Antennæ composed of four segments, the fourth always elongate. Both sexes dichoptic, the front excavated between the eyes; ocelli, except the anterior one, absent. Proboscis with fleshy labellæ, or rudimentary; palpi usually absent or extremely small, rarely long and slender. Empodia not developed pulvilliform.

The Mydas flies are easily recognized by the shape of the head, four-segmented antennæ and peculiar venation. The majority of the species are tropical in distribution and it is probable that the larvæ of all live in decaying wood.

The generic limits in the family are but poorly understood and only an abundance of material will enable one to properly limit the genera. Johnson* has dealt with the Nearctic forms, while papers by Bezzi† and Seguy‡ must receive attention in any attempt to deal with the family.

---

* Johnson, 1926, Proc. Bost. Soc. Nat. Hist., xxxviii, pp. 131-145.
† Bezzi, 1924, Ann. S. Afr. Mus., xix, pp. 191-234.
‡ Seguy, 1928, Encycl. Ent., Diptera, iv, pp. 129-156.

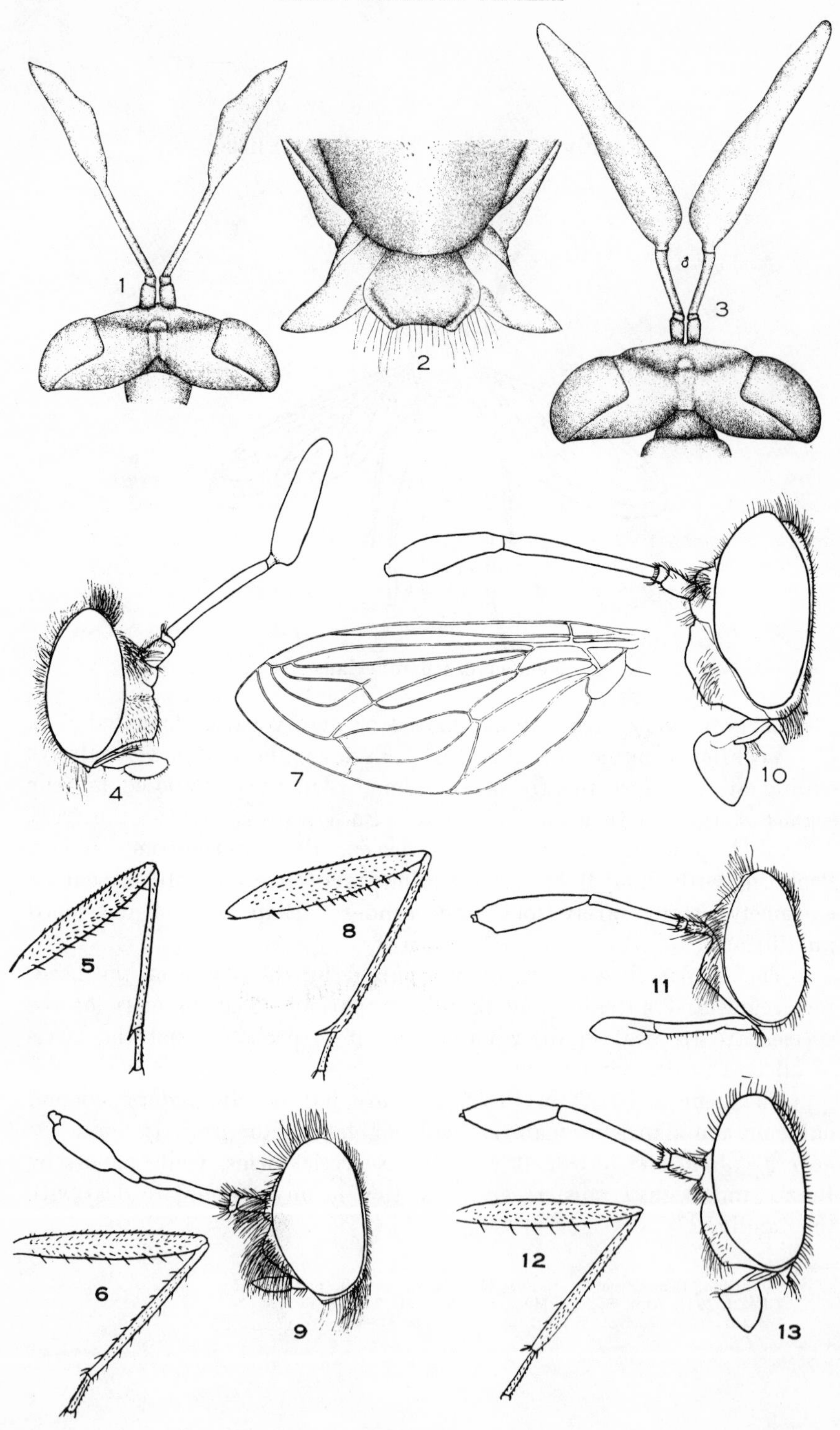

Mydiadæ.

KEY TO GENERA

1. Posterior tibiæ ending in a spur (5, 8) 2
   Posterior tibiæ without spur (6) 5

2. Spur of the posterior tibiæ longer than the width of the first tarsal segment, giving the tibiæ an arcuate appearance, the terminal bristle shorter than the spur; antennæ (always?) similar in both sexes.... 3
   Spur small and straight, shorter than the tarsal thickness or the terminal bristle; antennæ differing in the two sexes; palpi absent (1, 2, 3, 5, 7) ....**Phyllomydas** Bigot

3. Palpi wholly absent or represented by a bulbous swelling (8, 10; see colored plate)..................................**Mydas** Fabricius
   Palpi well developed, slender and sometimes half as long as the proboscis 4

4. Posterior femora rather strongly swollen; posterior trochanters without bristles (13)..............................***Lampromydas** Seguy
   Posterior femora not swollen; posterior trochanters bearing short, stout bristles (4, 12)............................†**Opomydas,** n. g.

5. No vein reaching the posterior border between the anal cell and tip of the wing 6
   A vein (the fifth) extends to the wing margin (4, 12)....†**Opomydas,** n. g.

6. Proboscis extending well beyond the oral opening (6, 11). ‡**Nomoneura** Bezzi
   Proboscis small, not extending beyond the oral opening (9). ‡**Nemomydas,** n. g.

---

* **Lampromydas** was based on specimens in which there is no vein extending to the wing margin between the anal vein and the tip of the wing but the character is not generic in this case. Of two specimens of (Mydas) **luteipennis** Lœw, one has a vein in one wing while the other specimen has none. This species and **maculiventris** Westwood, as well as two unidentified species before me, belong to **Lampromydas** unless the genotype of **Lampromydas** lacks palpi.

† **Ectyphus** Gerstæcker is not known from North America but apparently occurs in South America. The three described North American species belong to **Opomydas** of which **E. limbatus** Williston is the genotype.

‡ **Leptomydas** Gerstæcker is not known from America. The genus is distinguished by the hairy pleura, both the above genera having pile only on the pteropleura and supraspiracular convexities. The genotype of **Nemomydas** is **Leptomydas pantherinus** Gerstæcker.

Mydaidæ.—1, **Phyllomydas phyllocerus,** ♀; 2, **Phyllomydas phyllocerus,** ♀ genitalia from below; 3, **Phyllomydas phyllocerus;** ♂; 4, **Opomydas limbatus;** 5, **Phyllomydas phyllocerus,** hind leg; 6, **Nomoneura,** hind leg; 7, **Phyllomydas phyllocerus;** 8, **Mydas clavatus,** hind leg; 9, **Nemomydas pantherimus;** 10, **Mydas clavatus;** 11, **Nomoneura panamensis;** 12, **Opomydas townsendi,** hind leg; 13, **Lampromydas maculiventris.**

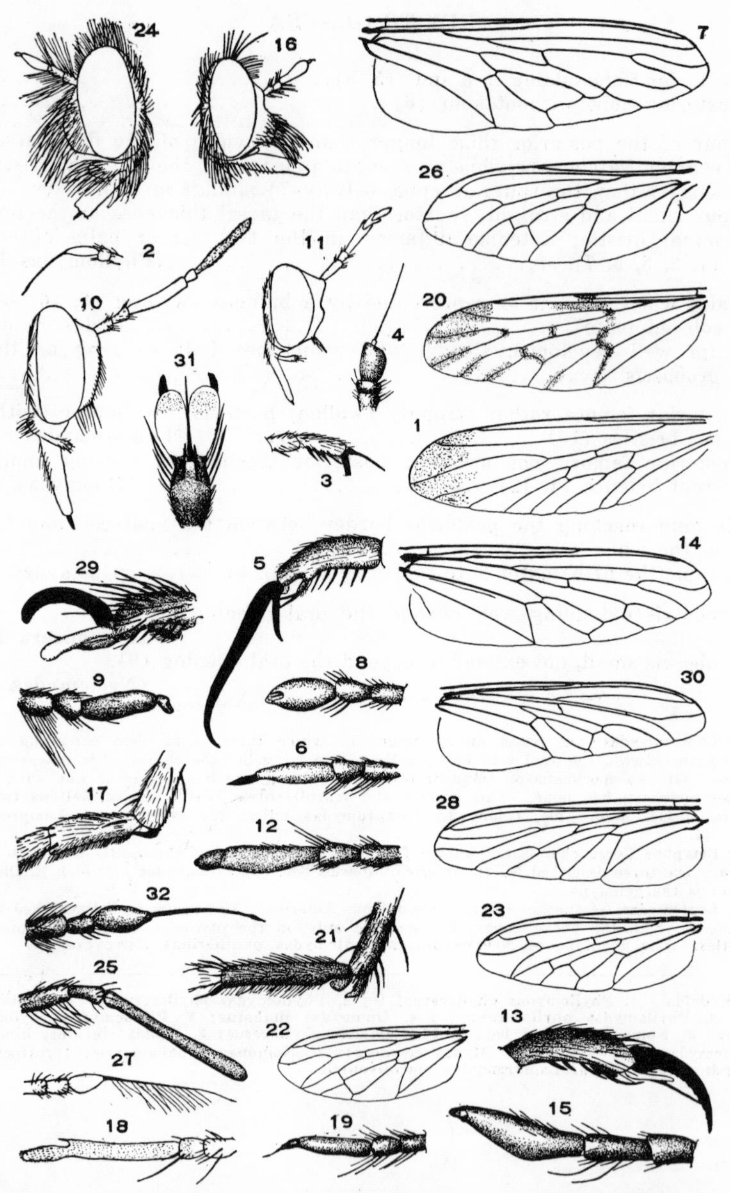

Asilidæ I.—1, **Leptogaster**; 2, **Leptogaster**, antenna; 3, **Leptogaster**, end of tarsus; 4, **Damalis**, antenna; 5, **Dicranus**, claw; 6, **Scleropegon**, antenna; 7, **Microstylum galactoides**; 8, **Psilocurus**, antenna; 9, **Laphystia**, antenna; 10, **Ceraturgus cruciatus**; 11, **Myelaphus melas**; 12, **Dioctria, antenna**; 13, **Blepharepium coarctatum, claw**; 14, **Diogmites winthemia**; 15, **Diogmites**, antenna; 16, **Lestomyia fraudigera**; 17, **Taracticus**, end of tibia; 18, **Taracticus**, antenna; 19, **Buckellia**, antenna; 20, **Nicocles rufus**; 21, **Pseudorus**, tibial spur; 22, **Atomosia puella**; 23, **Pogonosoma dorsata**; 24, **Dasylechia atrox**; 25, **Bombomima, antenna**; 26, **Laphria, Lampria**; 27, **Ommatius**, antenna; 28, **Eccritosia**; 29, **Mallophora**, claw; 30, **Promachus**; 31, **Promachus**, claws; 32, **Promachus**, antenna.

Family Asilidæ—The Assassin Flies

Species of moderate to large size, rarely small, usually rather elongate in form, often thickly hairy and always with bristles, entirely predaceous in habit.

Head flattened, broad and short, separated from the thorax by a neck (the prothorax) and freely movable. Front excavated above, usually broad in both sexes, rarely narrow. Ocelli present, usually situated upon a rounded tubercle; front with bristles. Antennæ porrect, usually composed of three simple segments, the third more or less elongate and with or without a terminal style or arista, the latter very rarely pectinate, the style rarely strongly thickened and forming one or two additional segments. Proboscis of moderate length, horny and adapted for piercing, directed downward or forward; labellæ never fleshy; palpi composed of two segments, the basal one often small and not freely articulated with the second. Thorax variable in shape, convex, usually bearing bristles. Abdomen composed of eight segments, the hypopygium and ovipositor usually prominent. Legs strong, usually bristly, of moderate length, the femora often, the posterior tibiæ sometimes thickened, the legs sometimes very long and rather slender; empodium present or absent; the puvilli rarely absent or greatly reduced. Wings lying parallel over the abdomen when at rest; basal cells long; two or three submarginal cells, five posterior cells (four in a very few genera); first and fourth posterior cells and the anal cell either open or closed.

The members of this family have usually been termed "Robber Flies" but I adopt "Assassin Flies" as much more suitable as a common name. All the Asilidæ are predaceous in the adult and probably in the larval stages. The adults are found everywhere but many groups of genera are restricted in habitat. Some will be found in clearings in and around the edges of woods, some on sand near water, others in open fields or on fallen trees or fenceposts. Some of the species are found almost entirely on tree trunks while others sit on the tips of dead branches of trees or the tops of dead weeds. The species of *Leptogaster* prefer long grass, particularly in moist places. Sandy beaches will usually yield a few species. The species of *Laphria* and *Bombomima* will usually be found resting upon leaves in the sun in or at the edges of woods while the genera related to *Asilus* mostly frequent open fields.

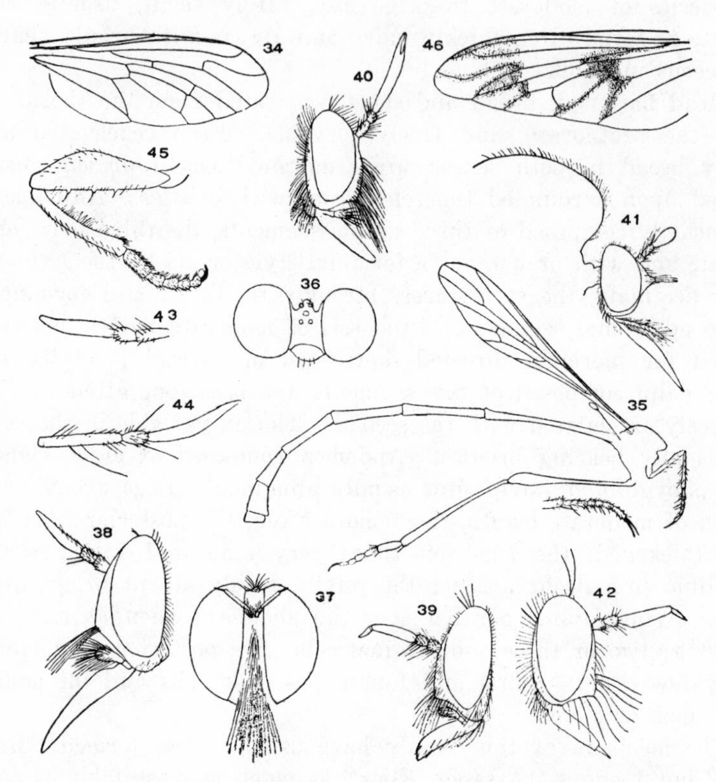

Asilidæ II.—34, **Psilocurus caudatus**; 35, **Leptopteromyia gracilis** (Brazil); 36, **Holcocephala**, head from in front; 37, **Scleropogon turquii**; 38, **Archilestris magnificus**; 39, **Chrysoceria picitarsis**; 40, **Dizonias**; 41, **Pseudorus bicolor**; 42, **Atonia mikii**; 43, **Atomosia macquartii**, antenna; 44, **Cerotainia**, antenna; 45, **Lampria**, hind leg; 46, **Andrenosoma.**

Many of the Asilids resemble bees and are quite powerful. They devour insects of all kinds, catching them during flight, and bees form the principal article of diet of some species although the variety of food is usually limited only by the intended victim's ability to escape. The prey is pierced by the powerful proboscis and the juices sucked out, the digestion taking place by the injection into the victim of a powerful "enzyme" which breaks down the muscular tissue. The collector should be careful in handling the larger species as they not infrequently bite, resulting in a painful, if not serious, wound.

The family is a large and popular one and includes many fine species. For the most part the classification is simple but in some genera it is difficult to separate the species by means of the available literature. There has been no monograph of the Nearctic species although Back* has dealt with about half the family. However, since the appearance of his contribution very many additional species have been described. Otherwise the literature is scattered although not difficult to obtain.

In the key will be found many references to keys to species which should prove very helpful in tracing out the species. I have not followed the practice of recognizing subfamilies as the characters previously used obviously separate related genera and some genera are difficult to place where the system is followed. For Cuban species see Bromley "The Asilidæ of Cuba," (Ann. Ent. Soc. Amer., xxii, pp. 272-294); also Texas Asilidæ by the same author.†

KEY TO GENERA

1. Anterior tibiæ with a terminal, sharply curved, ventral spur 2
   Anterior tibiæ with only straight or gently curving apical bristles 17

2. Marginal cell closed and petiolate **(121)** 3
   Marginal cell open 4

3. Face bare except for a very few hairs on the oral margin **(121, 122)**. **Doryclus** Jaennicke
   Face with strong hairs and many on the oral margin **(21, 41)**. **Pseudorus** Walker

4. Middle of mesonotum raised and bearing a crest of long, dense hairs **(50, 86)** ....‡**Comantella** Curran
   Mesonotum never with crest of dense hair 5

5. Antennæ with distinct, two-segmented apical style 13
   Antennæ either with a short, broad, one-segmented style bearing a spine in the depression, without style, or excised and bearing a spine above 6

* 1909, Tr. Amer. Ent. Soc., xxxv, pp. 137-400, plates II-XII.
† Bromley, 1934, Ann. Ent. Soc. Amer., xxvii, pp. 74-114.
‡ Curran, 1926, Can. Ent., lviii, p. 311.

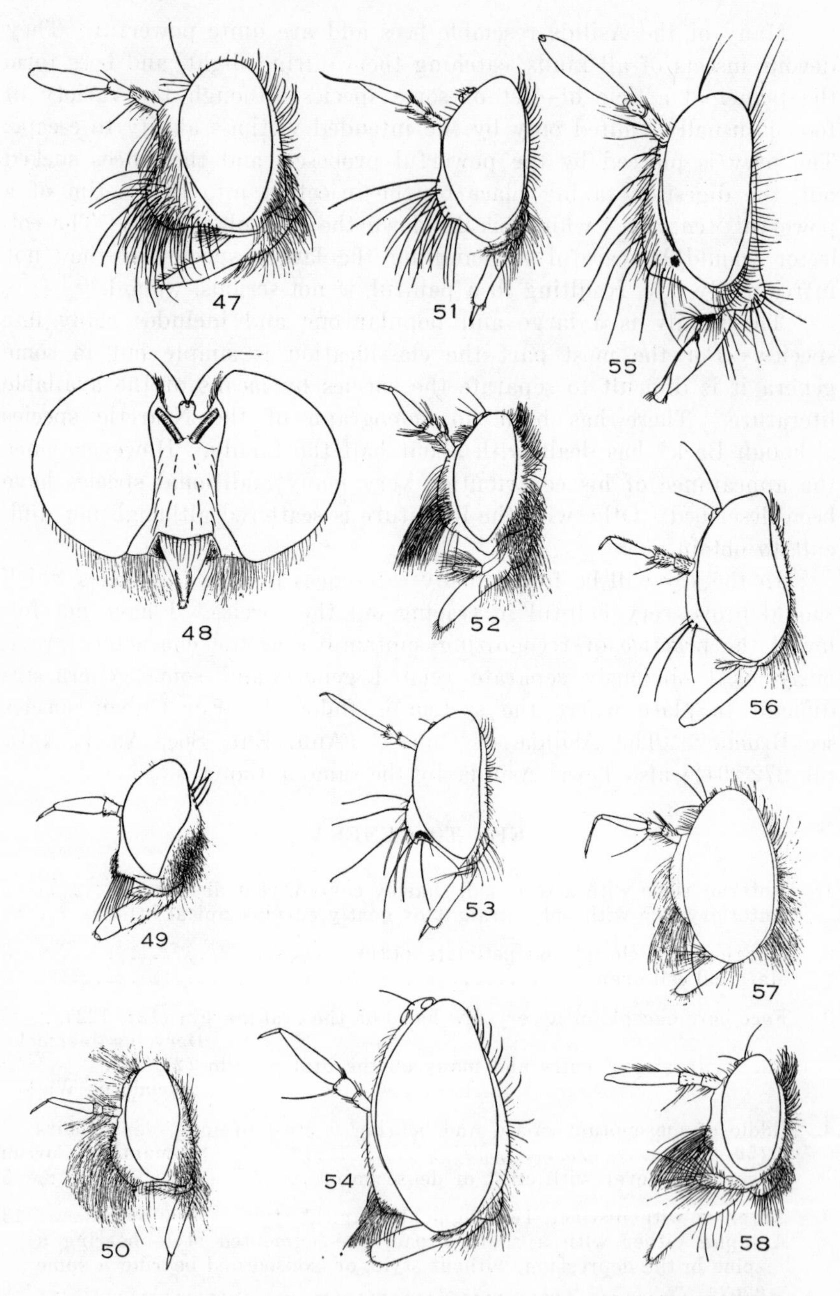

Asilidæ III.—47, **Pilica** sp. (Panama); 48, **Atomosia tibialis**, head from in front; 49, **Neopogon**; 50, **Comantella fallei**; 51, **Cerdistus dolichomerus**; 52, **Callinicus calanus**; 53, **Senoprosopis** (Panama); 54, **Hodophylax aridus**; 55, **Panamasilus xylota**; 56, **Plesioma**; 57, **Heteropogon macerinus**; 58, **Lastaurus**.

6. Third antennal segment with an apical depression or style in which is inserted a small short spine 8
Third antennal segment excised above beyond the middle and bearing a short spine 7

7. Pulvilli present and large (17, 18, 71, 142) .... *Taracticus Lœw
Pulvilli absent .... Parataracticus Cole

8. Posterior pulvilli not more than one-third as long as the claws, (13, 96, 123) .... Blepharepium Rondani
Posterior pulvilli more than half as long as the claws 9

9. Abdomen thickly pilose, at least laterally 10
Abdomen almost bare 11

10. Face convex, pilose on lower two-thirds (Brazil) .... Lastaurina, n. g.
Face flat above, pilose on less than lower half (58, 95) .. Lastaurus Lœw

11. Fourth posterior cell closed and petiolate at apex 12
Fourth posterior cell open or closed in the wing margin (88, 102). †Saropogon Lœw

12. Abdomen clavate; scutellum without bristles (138, 153) Senobasis Macquart
Abdomen not clavate; scutellum with bristles (14, 15, 150). Diogmites Lœw

13. Face gibbous in the middle, leaving a flattened space immediately below the antennæ (16, 94) .... ‡Lestomyia Williston
Face evenly convex or prominent below 14

14. The dense mystax occupies the lower half of the face (81, 87). Aphamartania Schiner
The dense mystax is limited to the lowest fourth 15

15. Scutellum without bristles or hair .... Cophura Osten Sacken
Scutellum with bristles or hair 16

16. Scutellum with fine hair on the disc (20, 97) .... Nicocles Jænnicke
Scutellum with bristles only (19, 83, 98) .... §Buckellia Curran

17. Marginal cell open or closed in the costa 18
Marginal cell closed and petiolate 59

18. Pulvilli vestigial or wanting 19
Pulvilli normal, the posterior pair sometimes shortened 25

19. Third antennal segment with a terminal arista or arista-like style, very slender species 22
Third antennal segment with or without terminal style, if stylate the abdomen robust 20

20. Claws very long and with an elongated tooth at the base of each claw (5) .... Dicranus Lœw
Claws normal 21

---

* Curran, 1930, Amer. Mus. Novit. No. 425, p. 4.
† Curran, 1931, Amer. Mus. Novit. No. 487, p. 1.
‡ Curran, 1931, Amer. Mus. Novit. No. 487, p. 3.
§ Curran, 1931, (Cophura), Amer. Mus. Novit. No. 487, p. 5; Melander, 1923, (Cophura), Psyche, xxx, p. 208 (includes Cophura).

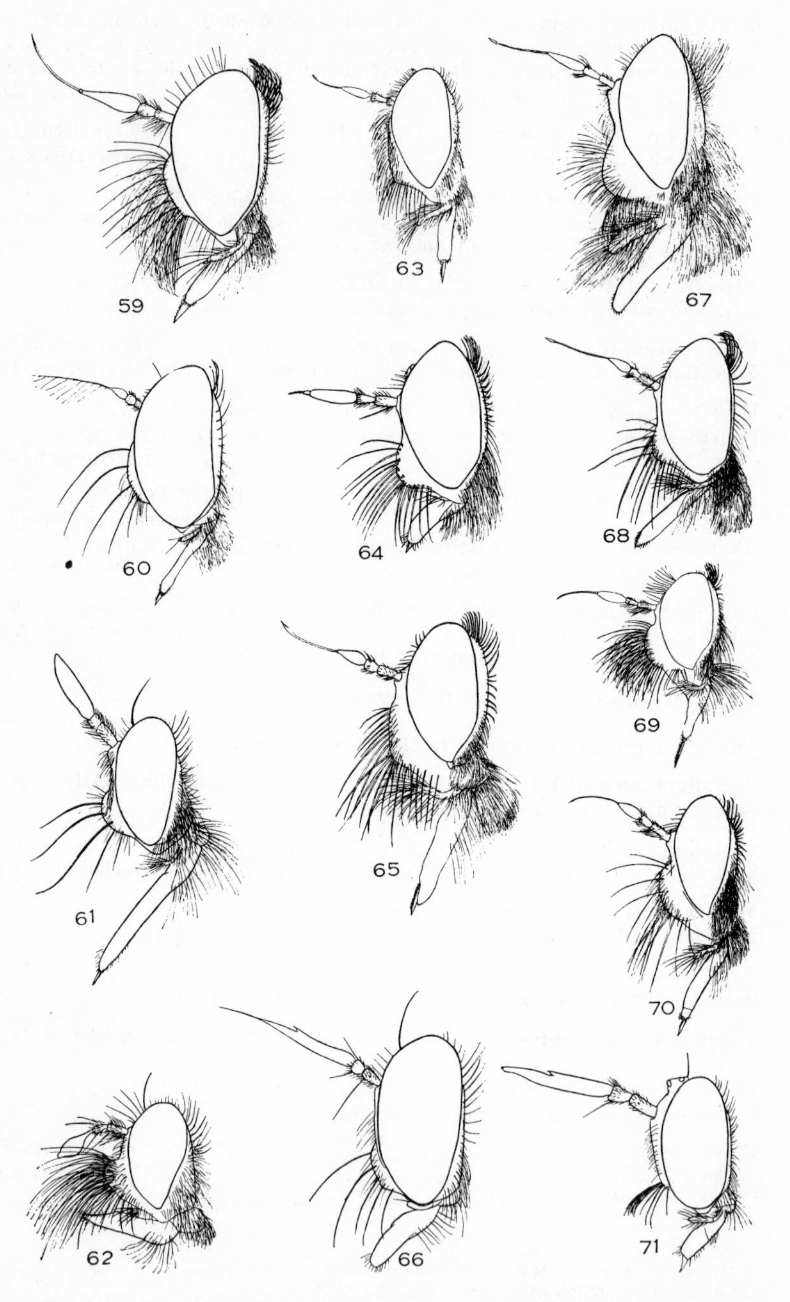

Asilidæ IV.—59, **Neoitamus flavofemoratus**; 60, **Ommatius**; 61, **Lampria mexicana**; 62, **Pogonosoma melanoptera**; 63, **Mallophorina clausicella**; 64, **Negasilus belli**; 65, **Proctacanthus micans**; 66, **Atractia dispar**; 67, **Mallophora orcina**; 68, **Pachychœta copulata**; 69, **Machimus occidentalis**; 70, **Erax** (Panama); 71, **Taracticus octopunctatus**.

21. Face wholly thickly pilose .... **Ablautus** Lœw
Mystax limited to the lowest fourth of the face, the face sparsely haired above (54, 100) .... **Hodophylax** James

22. Anal cell absent, the wings extremely narrow at the base (140).
Eurhabdus Aldrich
Anal, cell present 23

23. Mesonotum without dorsocentrals in front of the middle............ 24
Mesonotum with a pair of dorsocentrals in front of the middle.
Schildia Aldrich

24. Empodia entirely absent (147) .... **Psilonyx** Aldrich
Empodia present, about half as long as the claws (1, 2, 3, 148, 149).
Leptogaster Meigen

25. Antennæ with a slender terminal arista (4, 89)........ ***Damalis** Fabricius
Antennæ with or without a terminal style 26

26. Only four posterior cells (93) .... **Townsendia** Williston
Five posterior cells 27

27. Head slightly higher than broad; face narrow above, swollen and broadened below 28
Head obviously broader than high 30

28. Antennæ with a terminal style 29
Antennæ without visible style; fourth posterior cell closed before the border of the wing (118)......................... **Ospriocerus** Lœw

29. Metapleura bare (6, 37, 130)........................ †**Stenopogon** Lœw
Metapleura with hair or bristles (6, 37, 130).......... †**Scleropogon** Lœw

30. Antennæ apparently five segmented, the segments of the style simulating antennal segments 31
Antennal style usually strongly differentiated from the third antennal segment, absent, or the fifth segment longer than the second...... 33

31. Third and fourth antennal segments very deeply emarginate apically (11) .... **Myelaphus Bigot**
Third and fourth segments not concave apically 32

32. Fifth antennal segment not longer than the second (103).
Ceraturgopsis Johnson
Fifth antennal segment about as long as the third (10, 132).
Ceraturgus Wiedemann

33. Fourth posterior cell closed 34
Fourth posterior cell open, rarely almost closed.................. 40

34. Face haired above the mystax 36
Face bare except along the oral margin............................ 35

35. Metanotal callosities bare (38, 136) .... **Archilestris** Lœw
Metanotal callosities with hair or short bristles (7, 101)
Microstylum Macquart

36. First posterior cell closed and long petiolate (109).......... **Triclis** Lœw
First posterior cell open or closed in the wing margin.............. 37

* Curran, 1930, Amer. Mus. Novit. No. 425, p. 5.
† Bromley, 1931, Amer. Ent. Soc. Amer., xxiv, pp. 427-428.

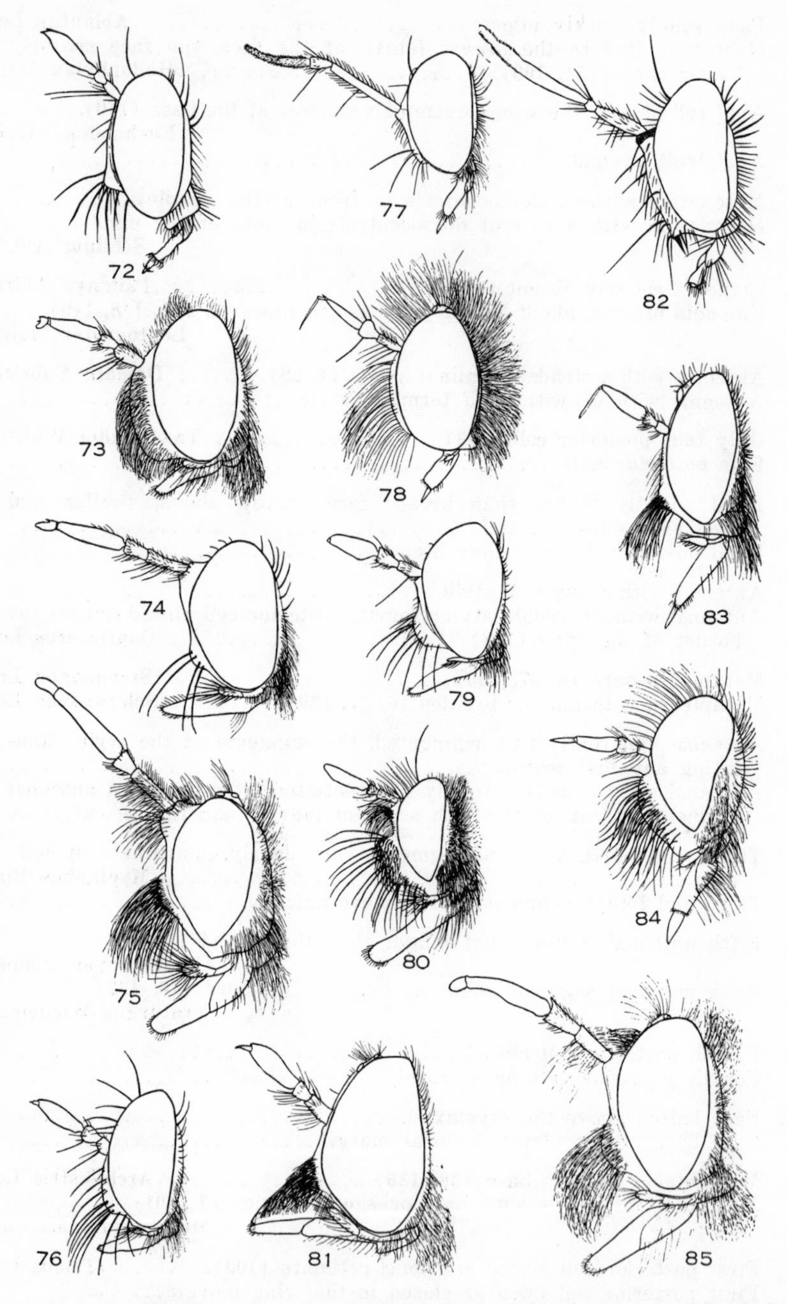

Asilidæ V.—72, **Eumecosoma shropshirei**; 73, **Laphystia sexfasciata**; 74, **Dioctria baumhaueri**; 75, **Dicolonus simplex**; 76, **Metapogon**; 77, **Cerotainia propinqua**; 78, **Holopogon guttula**; 79, **Psilocurus birdi**; 80, **Bombomima flavicollis**; 81, **Aphamartania**; 82, **Bathropsis basalis**; 83, **Buckellia stylosa**; 84, **Laisopogon opaculus**; 85, **Echthodopa**.

37. Antennæ without distinct style 38
    Antennæ with the style short and broad, two-segmented, easily distinguishable **(9, 73, 92)**..............................‡**Laphystia** Lœw

38. Anterior femora on the basal half of the under side with a large patch of dense, very short bristles..........................**Sphageus** Lœw
    Anterior femora without such bristles.. 39

39. Third antennal segment very much longer than the basal two combined **(40, 124)** ....**Dizonias** Lœw
    Third antennal segment not or scarcely longer than the basal two combined, elongate oval, swollen **(8, 34, 79)**..........***Psilocurus** Lœw

40. Antennal style as broad as the third antennal segment and simulating a segment, sometimes closely appressed and not easily differentiated. 41
    Antennal style narrower than the third segment or absent............ 44

41. Lateral slopes of the metanotum bare.. 42
    Lateral slopes of the metanotum with pile **(75, 91)**.......**Dicolonus** Lœw

42. Face bare except below... 43
    Face haired between mystax and antennæ **(103)**....**Ceraturgopsis** Johnson

43. Posterior femora with very short, stout bristles below on the apical half **(85)** ....**Ecthodopa** Lœw
    Posterior femora without short, stout bristles below, but with short, erect pile on the whole length **(12, 74, 90)**...........†**Dioctria** Meigen

44. Front narrowed posteriorly 45
    Front not narrowed posteriorly.. 46

45. Ocelli situated far forward on the front **(56, 133)**......**Plesioma** Macquart
    Ocelli situated near the vertex......................**Dolichodes** Macquart

46. Face bare except on the oral margin (cf. **Holcocephala**)............. 47
    Face with hair between the mystax and antennæ, or evenly haired.... 49

47. Third antennal segment swollen, about twice as wide as the second.
    Willistonina Back
    Third antennal segment elongate, more or less tapering from the base or only slightly wider than the second.......................... 48

48. Third antennal segment elongate, longer than the basal two combined **(49)** ....**Neopogon** Bezzi
    Third antennal segment oval, not as long as the basal two combined.
    Lissoteles Bezzi

49. Head very wide, the face with a deep, transverse groove above the oral margin and with only two to six hairs above the mystax **(36, 141)**.
    Holcocephala Jænnicke
    Head narrower, the face without the transverse depression.......... 50

50. Mesonotum with the dorsocentral bristles strong and extending in front of the suture, if rather weak anteriorly there are no acrostical hairs 51
    Dorsocentrals absent or not strongly differentiated; mesonotum hairy, the acrostical hair always present... 52

---

* Curran, 1931, Amer. Mus. Novit. No. 487, p. 8.

† Melander, 1923, Psyche, xxx, p. 212.

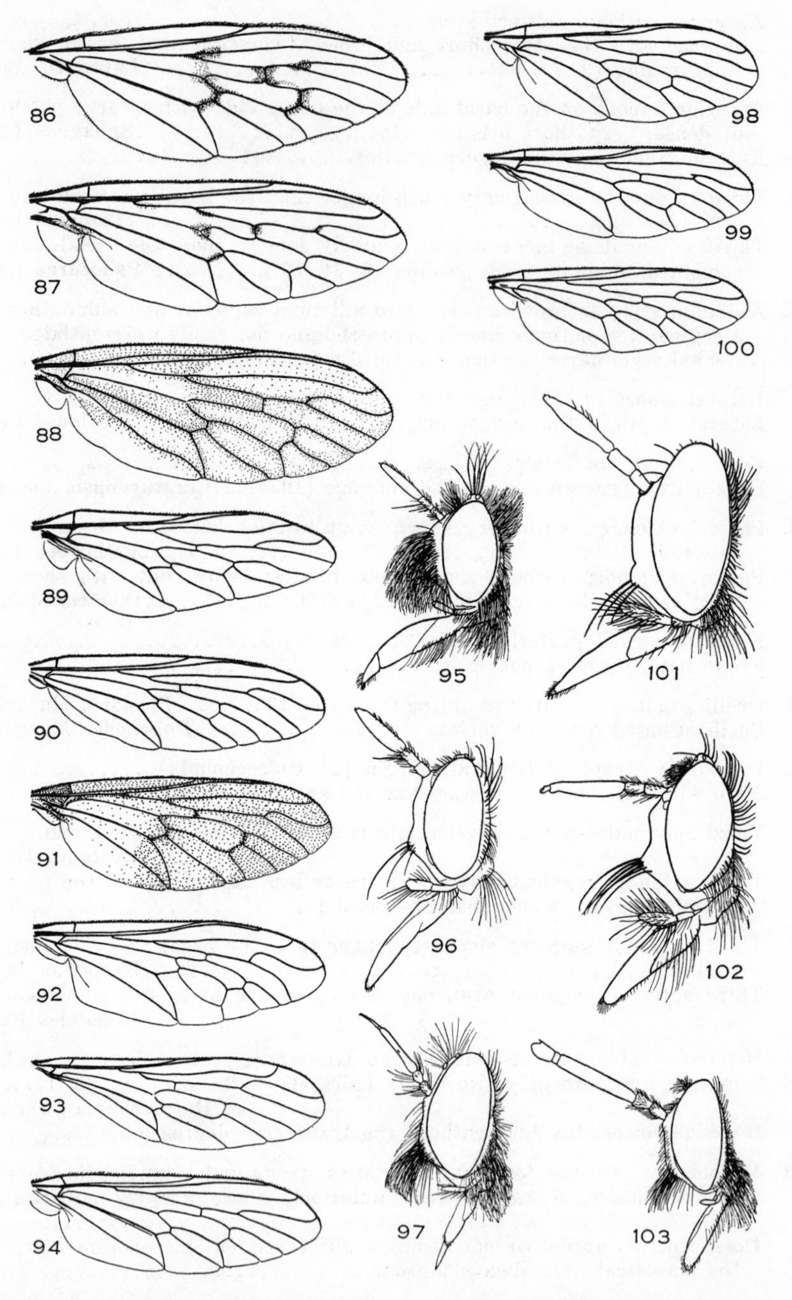

Asilidæ VI.—86, **Comantella fallei**; 87, **Aphamartania murina**; 88, **Saropogon luteus**; 89, **Damalis**; 90, **Dioctria baumhaueri**; 91, **Dicolonus simplex**; 92, **Laphystia sexfasciata**; 93, **Townsendia argyrata**; 94, **Lestomyia sabulonum**; 95, **Lastaurus**; 96, **Blepharepium secabilis**; 97, **Nicocles politus**; 98, **Buckellia pollinosa**; 99, **Lasiopogon tetragrammus**; 100, **Hodophylax aridus**; 101, **Microstylum galactoides**; 102, **Saropogon birdi**; 103, **Ceraturgopsis cornutus**.

51. No acrostical hairs **(76, 112)**..........................***Metapogon** Coquillett
Acrostical hairs present, usually abundant but short **(84, 99)**.
†**Lasiopogon** Lœw

52. Mesonotum with the hair appressed and usually with distinct, subappressed dorsocentral bristles posteriorly.......................... 53
Mesonotal hair erect, the bristles, if present, very fine and erect...... 56

53. No trace of dorsocentral bristles (type **Lasiopogon terricola** Johnson) **(84, 99)** ....**Alexiopogon**, n. g.
Distinct, though weak dorsocentrals posteriorly.................... 54

54. Abdomen elongate, more or less narrowed basally in the males........ 55
Abdomen short and broad, rather strongly tapering in both sexes; hair rather abundant but short..........................**Pycnopogon** Lœw

55. Disc of scutellum with hairs toward either side **(52, 126)**..**Callinicus** Lœw
Scutellum with marginal bristles and hairs only **(39)**.
Chrysoceria Williston

56. Face decidedly gibbous, the swelling clearly limited above........... 57
Face flat or evenly, gently convex.................................. 58

57. The third vein branches before the apex of the discal cell; style long **(129, 151)**..................................‡**Eucyrtopogon** Curran
The third vein branches conspicuously beyond the apex of the discal cell; style short **(128, 152)**........................§**Cyrtopogon** Lœw

58. Posterior tibiæ strongly swollen, about twice as large as the anterior ones **(78, 143)**..**Holopogon** Lœw
Posterior tibiæ not enlarged **(57, 127)**...............**Heteropogon** Lœw

59. Antennæ with a terminal arista.................................. 77
Antennæ with or without a terminal style which is never bristle-like.. 60

60. Wing with only two submarginal cells............................. 61
Wing with three submarginal cells **(23, 62)**..........**Pogonosoma** Rondani

61. Third antennal segment with an apical style, which is rarely difficult to discern 62
Third antennal segment without style.............................. 66

62. Third antennal segment excised and bearing a very short bristle beyond the middle on the upper side, the style slender **(66, 108)**.
Atractia Macquart
Third antennal segment not excised above.......................... 63

63. Face with strong, isolated bristles and short, fine hair............. 65
Face with soft hair, which may be long and contain some coarse ones.. 64

64. Face perpendicular, more prominent above or almost evenly convex; mesonotum not with dense, long yellow pile **(9, 73, 92)**.
¶**Laphystia** Lœw
Face most prominent below the middle, strongly convex; mesonotum with dense, long yellow pile **(24)**................**Dasylechia** Williston

---

* Melander, 1923, Psyche, xxx, p. 210.
† Melander, 1923, Psyche, xxx, p. 136.
‡ Curran, 1923, Can. Ent. lv, p. 95.
§ Curran, 1923, Can. Ent. lv, p. 123; Melander, 1923, Psyche, xxx, p. 102.
¶ Curran, 1931, Amer. Mus. Novit. No. 487, p. 11.

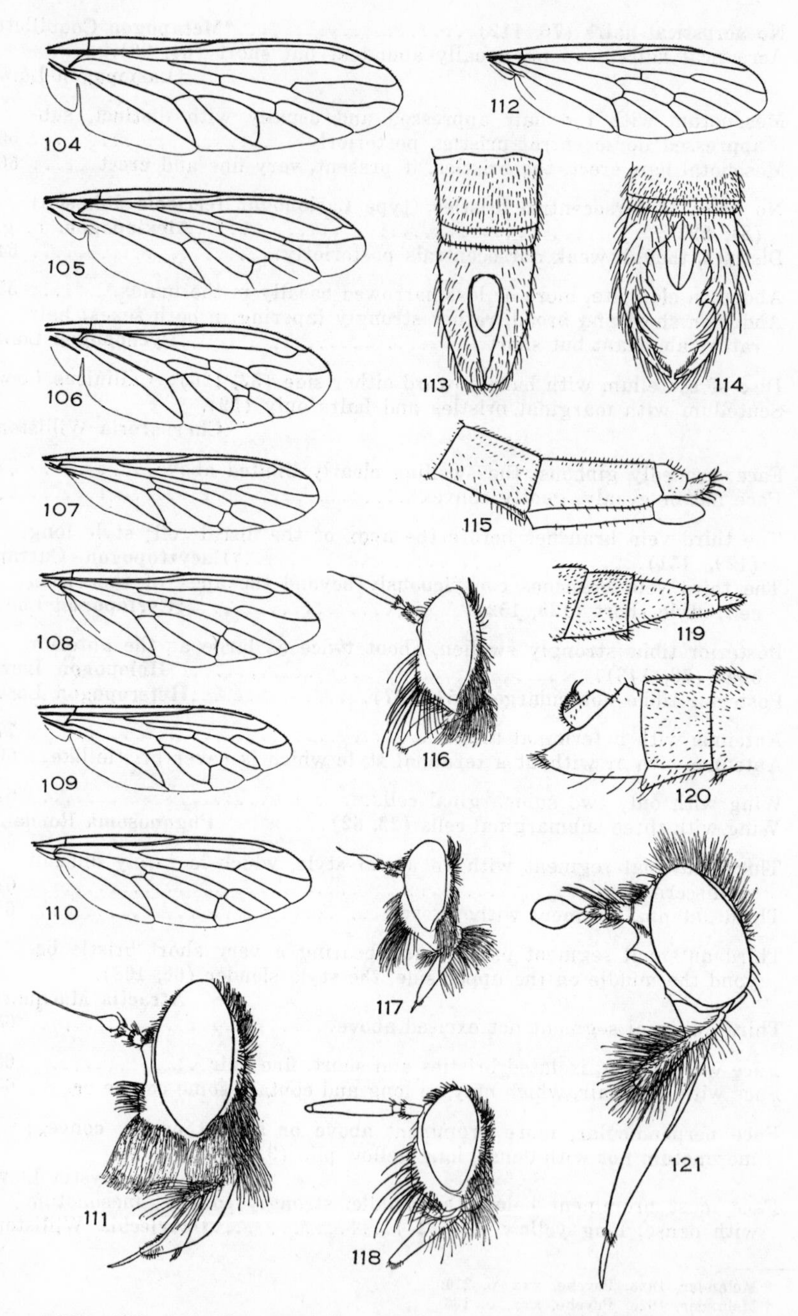

Asilidæ VII.—104, **Proctacanthella cacopilogus**; 105, **Mallophorina laphroides**; 106, **Negasilus belli**; 107, **Protichisma albibarbis**; 108, **Atractia dispar**; 109, **Triclis tagax**; 110, **Atonia** (n. sp. Brazil); 111, **Eccritosia barbata**; 112, **Metapogon**; 113, **Heligmoneura**; 114, **Philonicus albiceps**; 115, **Proctacanthella cacopilogus**; 116, **Asilus sericeus**; 117, **Proctacanthella cacopilogus**; 118, **Ospriocerus abdominalis**; 119, **Heligmoneura rubicunda**; 120, **Philonicus fuscus**; 121, **Doryclus distendens**.

65. First antennal segment less than twice as long as the second; style strongly differentiated (42, 110)....................**Atonia** Williston
First antennal segment more than three times as long as the second; style poorly differentiated (82, 145).............**Bathropsis** Hermann

66. Third antennal segment at least three times as long as the basal two combined ....**Aphestia** Schiner
Third antennal segment not more than twice as long as the first two combined 67

67. Metanotal slopes or callosities bearing pile or short, stout bristles.... 68
Metanotal callosities without pile or bristles........................ 73

68. Mesonotum evenly clothed with dense pile, most of which is yellow, some erect and some appressed; no bare areas outside the dorso-central area; large species (25, 80)............***Bombomima** Enderlein
Mesonotum without dense hair concealing the ground color.......... 69

69. Front at least slightly widening above, never narrowed.............. 70
Front narrowed above (22, 43, 48)...............†**Atomosia** Macquart

70. First antennal segment at least three times as long as the second.... 71
First antennal segment not twice as long as the second............. 72

71. Seventh abdominal segment elongate (107).........**Protichisma** Hermann
Seventh abdominal segment short, three or four times as wide as long, or apparently absent (44, 77, 146).................‡**Cerotainia** Schiner

72. Face strongly gibbous below and with rather abundant hair above (47) ....**Pilica** Curran
Face weakly gibbous below and with only a row of hairs on either side (72, 144)..............................§**Eumecosoma** Schiner

73. Face with a strong swelling occupying the lower half, most prominent in the middle.. 75
Face very gently convex or concave and most prominent just above the oral margin.. 74

74. Scutellum with long marginal bristles; large, elongate species (55). **Panamasilus** Curran
Scutellum with extremely short, upturned marginal hair; smaller, robust species (135).........................**Cerotainiops** Curran

75. Proboscis laterally compressed.. 76
Proboscis dorsoventrally compressed (46).........¶**Andrenosoma** Rondani

76. Metasternum with long hairs (26, 45, 61)...........**Lampria** Macquart
Metasternum bare (26)..............................‖**Laphria** Meigen

77. Arista pectinate below (27, 60)................°**Ommatius** Wiedemann
Arista not pectinate... 78

---

* This name replaces **Dasyllis**, a strictly South American genus. Unless the presence of metanotal hairs is a valid character the genus does not differ from **Laphria**. For key see Banks, 1917 (**Dasyllis**) Bull. Brooklyn Ent. Soc., xii, p. 52.

† Curran, 1930, Amer. Mus. Novit. No. 425, p. 15.

‡ Curran, 1930, Amer. Mus. Novit. No. 425, p. 11.

§ Curran, 1930, Amer. Mus. Novit. No. 425, p. 8.

¶ Curran, 1931, Amer. Mus. Novit. No. 487, p. 19.

‖ McAtee, 1918, Ohio Journ. Sci., xix, p. 143.

° Curran, 1928, Amer. Mus. Novit. No. 327.

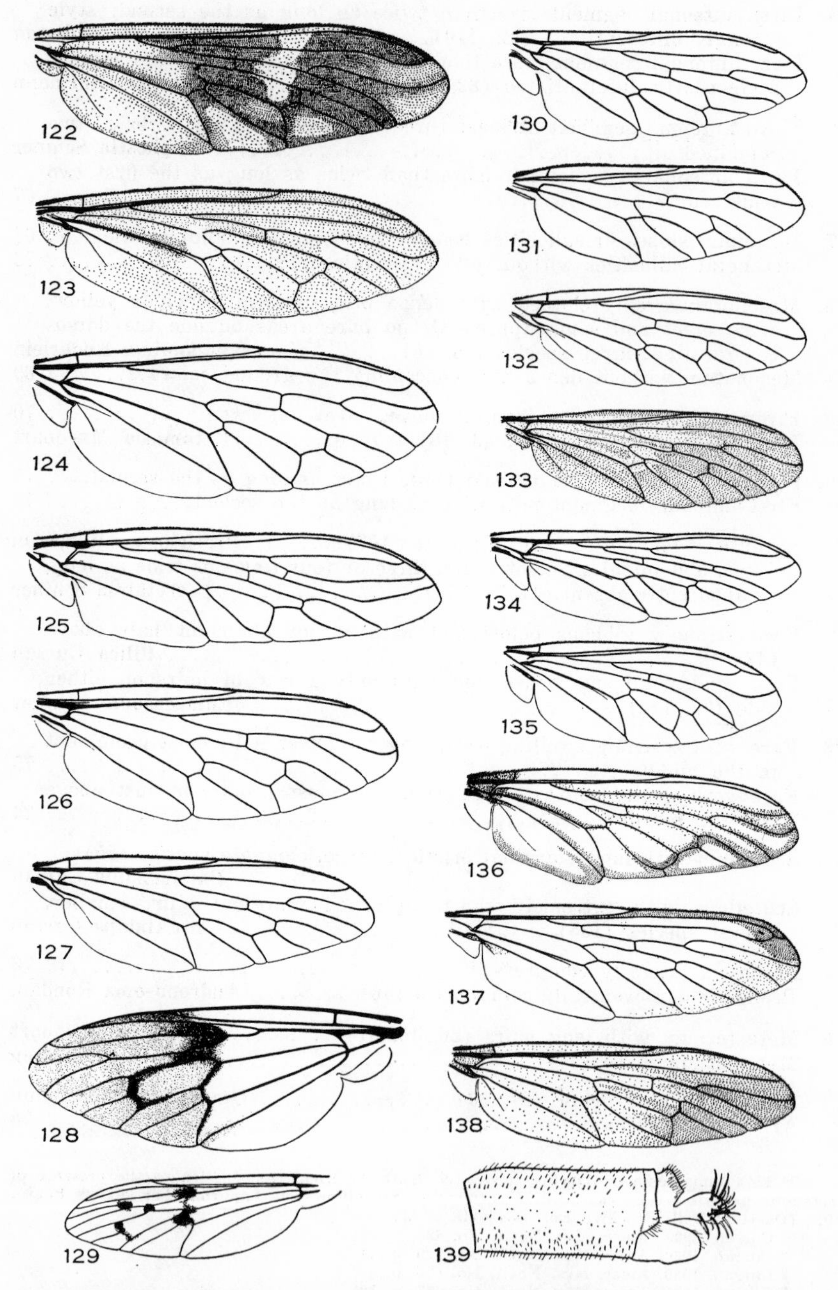

Asilidæ VIII.—122, **Doryclus** (n. sp.); 123, **Blepharepium secabilis**; 124, **Dizonias lucasi**; 125, **Erax anomalus**; 126, **Callinicus calanus**; 127, **Heteropogon** sp. (Utah); 128, **Cyrtopogon curtistylus**; 129, **Eucyrtopogon**; 130, **Scleropogon**; 131, **Neopogon**; 132, **Ceraturgus nigripes**; 133, **Plesioma lineata**; 134, **Promachina nimius**; 135, **Cerotainiops**; 136, **Archilestris magnificus**; 137, **Senoprosopis**; 138, **Senobasis mendax**; 139, **Proctacanthus micans.**

78. Third antennal segment long, with a bristle-bearing excision above (66, 108) .... **Atractia** Macquart
Third antennal segment usually short, never with a bristle-bearing concavity above 79

79. Slopes or lateral swellings of the metanotum pilose 92
Slopes or lateral swellings of the metanotum bare 80

80. Third antennal segment very long and narrow, tapering, with a short, thick arista; face very narrow (53, 137) ...... **Senoprosopis** Macquart
Third antennal segment short, with long arista; face not unusually narrow 81

81. Claws acute apically 84
Claws obtuse apically, thick almost to the apex 82

82. Front and face wide; space between antennæ and posterior ocelli strongly transverse 83
Front and face narrow; space between the antennæ and posterior ocelli as great as the width or practically so (134) ...... **Promachina** Bromley

83. Face evenly, gently convex, evenly pilose, the oral margin with bristles (63, 105) .... ***Mallophorina,** n. g.
Face more or less strongly gibbous below, not uniformly pilose (29, 67).
†**Mallophora** Macquart

84. Third antennal segment strikingly haired above ...... **Anarmostus** Lœw
Third antennal segment bare or with only a few short hairs above 85

85. Three submarginal cells 86
Two submarginal cells 87

86. The crossvein separating the second and third submarginal cells is situated well beyond the apex of the discal cell (30, 31, 32).
Promachus Lœw
This crossvein is situated well before the apex of the discal cell (70, 125)
‡**Erax** Scopoli

87. The posterior branch of the third vein meets the costa before the apex of the wing 88
The posterior branch of the third vein reaches the wing margin behind the apex of the wing 90

88. The ♀ ovipositor ends in a circlet of spines; abdomen of males longer than the wings (65, 139) .... **Proctacanthus** Macquart
The ♀ ovipositor is laterally compressed or bears many short spines above; wings reaching beyond the tip of the abdomen in males 89

89. Female ovipositor with many short, stout spines above; upper ocelli situated on the front slopes of the ocellar swelling (28, 111).
Eccritosia Schiner
Female ovipositor laterally compressed; upper ocelli on the top of the ocellar swelling (70, 125) .... ‡**Erax** Scopoli

---

* See page 183. Key, Curran, 1931, (Mallophora), Amer. Mus. Novit. No. 487, p. 21.
† Curran, 1930, Amer. Mus. Novit. No. 415, p. 12.
‡ Hine, 1919, Ann. Ent. Soc. Amer., xii, pp. 103-154.

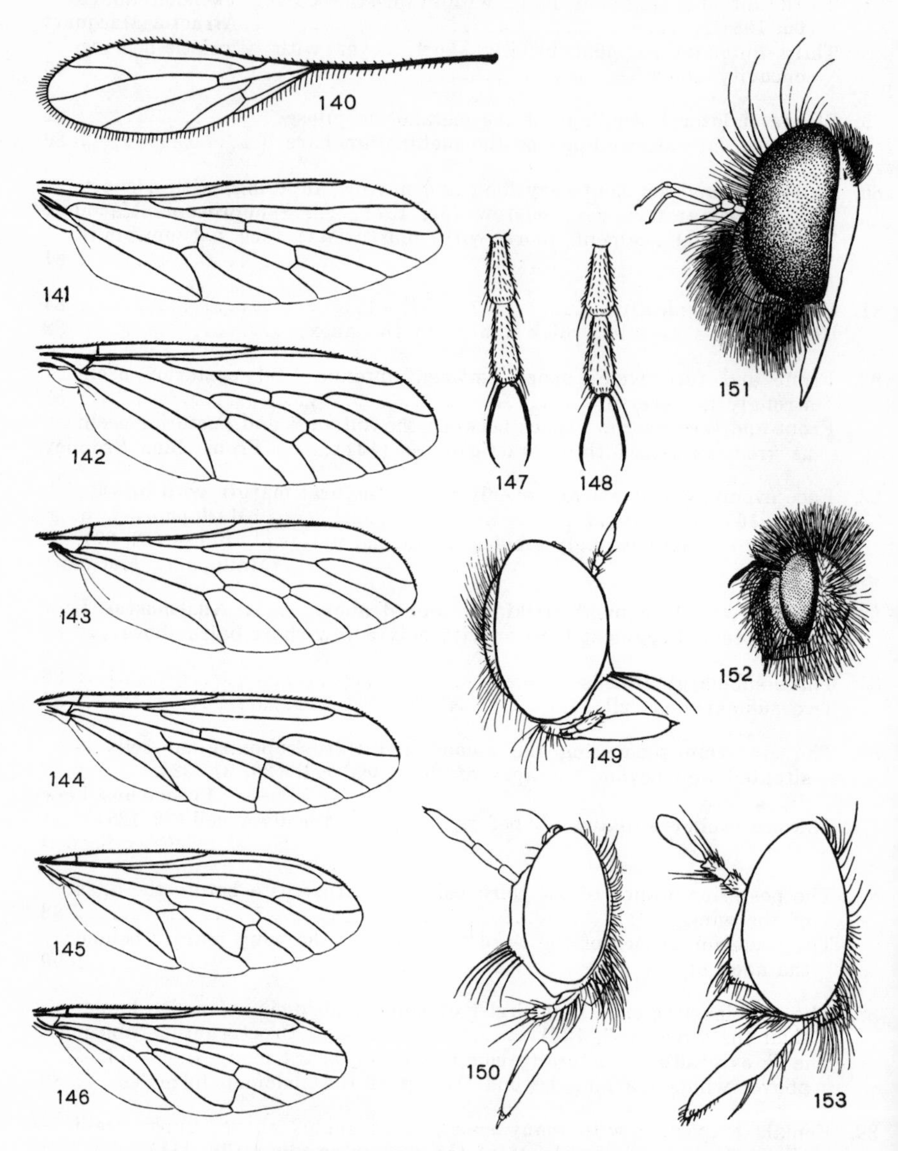

Asilidæ IX.—140, **Eurhabdus zephyrea**; 141, **Holcocephala calva**; 142. **Taracticus octopunctatus**; 143, **Holopogon guttula**; 114, **Eumecosoma gibbus**; 145, **Bathropsis basalis**; 146, **Cerotainia propinqua**; 147, **Psilonyx**, front tarsal claws; 148, **Leptogaster**, front tarsal claws; 149, **Leptogaster**; 150, **Deromyia litoralis**; 151, **Eucyrtopogon varipennis**; 152, **Cyrtopogon willistoni**; 153 **Senobasis analis.**

90. Face with a strong gibbosity occupying the lower half or more (**70, 125**)..***Erax** Scopoli
Face only weakly gibbous.. 91

91. Mystax dense, extending to above the middle of the face (**104, 115, 117**).
Proctacanthella Bromley
Mystax sparse, composed of bristles (**68**)............**Pachychœta** Bigot

92. Abdomen without bristles 93
Abdomen with bristles laterally before the segmental apices.......... 96

93. Facial gibbosity shining black........................**Rhadiurgus** Lœw
Facial gibbosity pollinose, weakly developed........................ 94

94. Scutellum with at least two bristles.................................. 95
Scutellum without bristles (**64, 106**).....................**Negasilus**, n. g.

95. Mystax composed of bristles only (**116**)................†**Asilus** Linnæus
Mystax composed mostly of very fine hair.............**Antiphrisson** Lœw

96. Occipital cilia abundant, rather long and curved at almost right angle at or near the apical third (**59**)..............†**Neoitamus** Osten Sacken
Occipital cilia shorter and stouter, not strongly curved.............. 97

97. Facial gibbosity strongly developed and reaching at least to slightly above the middle of the face (**Tolmerus** Lœw) (**69**)....†**Machimus** Lœw
Facial gibbosity weakly developed, not extending above the lower third of the face 98

98. Dorsocentrals extending in front of the suture (**51**).......†**Cerdistus** Lœw
Dorsocentrals not extending in front of the suture.................. 99

99. Female ovipositor armed at the apex with four or six stout, short bristles; forceps of male genitalia strongly curved and leaving a large open space on the apical half (**114, 120**)........†**Philonicus** Lœw
Female ovipositor without bristles; male genitalia compact, never leaving a large open space from dorsal view (**113, 119**).
†**Heligmoneura** Bigot

Alexiopogon, new genus

Distinguished from *Lasiopogon* Lœw by the absence of dorsocentral bristles. The figures of *Lasiopogon* will serve also for this genus. Genotype:—*Lasiopogon terricola* Johnson.

Mallophorina, new genus

Claws robust, obtuse apically; marginal cell closed and petiolate, the first posterior cell open or closed; antennæ with long, terminal arista-like style; face evenly gently convex or almost flat, and with almost uniform hair; front and face wide; body rather thickly pilose. Genotype,

* Hine, 1919, Ann. Ent. Soc. Amer. xii, pp. 103-154.
† Hine, 1909, (Asilus), Ann. Ent. Soc. Amer., ii, pp. 136-170.

—*Mallophora guildiana* Williston. Species included: *laphroides* Wiedemann, *clausicella* Macquart, *acra* Curran, all previously placed in *Mallophora.*

Negasilus, new genus

Related to *Asilus* Linnæus but at once distinguished by the absence of scutellar bristles. Artista short and style-like; face moderately convex on the lower half, the mystax composed of bristles only; occipital bristles straight; four pairs of dorsocentrals on the posterior half of the mesonotum; mesonotal hair all short and appressed; abdomen elongate and without bristles on the second and following segments. Genotype:—*N. belli,* n. sp.

N. belli is black, cinerous-yellowish pollinose, the male genitalia, apices of the femora and the tibiæ reddish.

Family Therevidæ—The Stilleto Flies

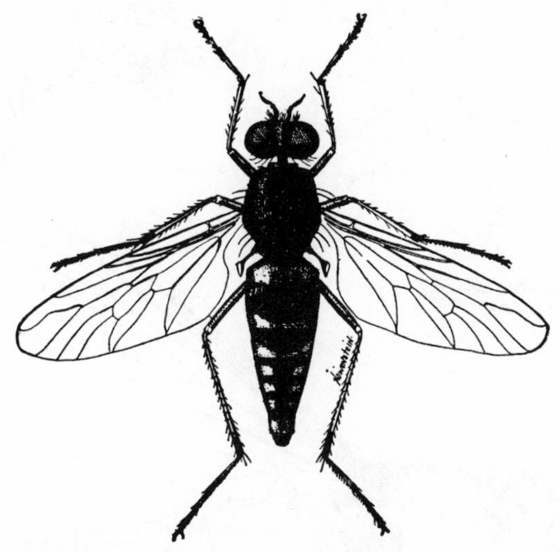

Thereva species.

Flies of moderate size, more or less bristly and often pilose, with predaceous habits.

Front not excavated, the eyes of the males usually holoptic or nearly so; proboscis projecting, the labellæ broad; palpi two-segmented; ocelli present. Antennæ with three segments and usually a sharp terminal style. Abdomen elongate, the genitalia small but exposed, the ovipositor with a circlet of spines. Legs with bristles; empodia absent; pulvilli usually present. Third vein furcate; five posterior cells, the fourth sometimes closed; anal cell closed toward the margin of the wing or narrowly open.

The adults are found in various places but are most abundant in dry areas, such as meadows, pastures and along sandy beaches. They often occur in considerable numbers in burnt-over areas and are always most abundant during hot weather. Cole* has revised the family and given keys to the North American species. A number of species have been described during recent years but most of the species will be found in Cole's paper.

The larvæ are not well known but are all believed to be predaceous and they may prove to be of considerable importance in the control of certain insects.

---

* 1923. Proc. U. S. N. M., lxii, Art. 4, pp. 1-140.

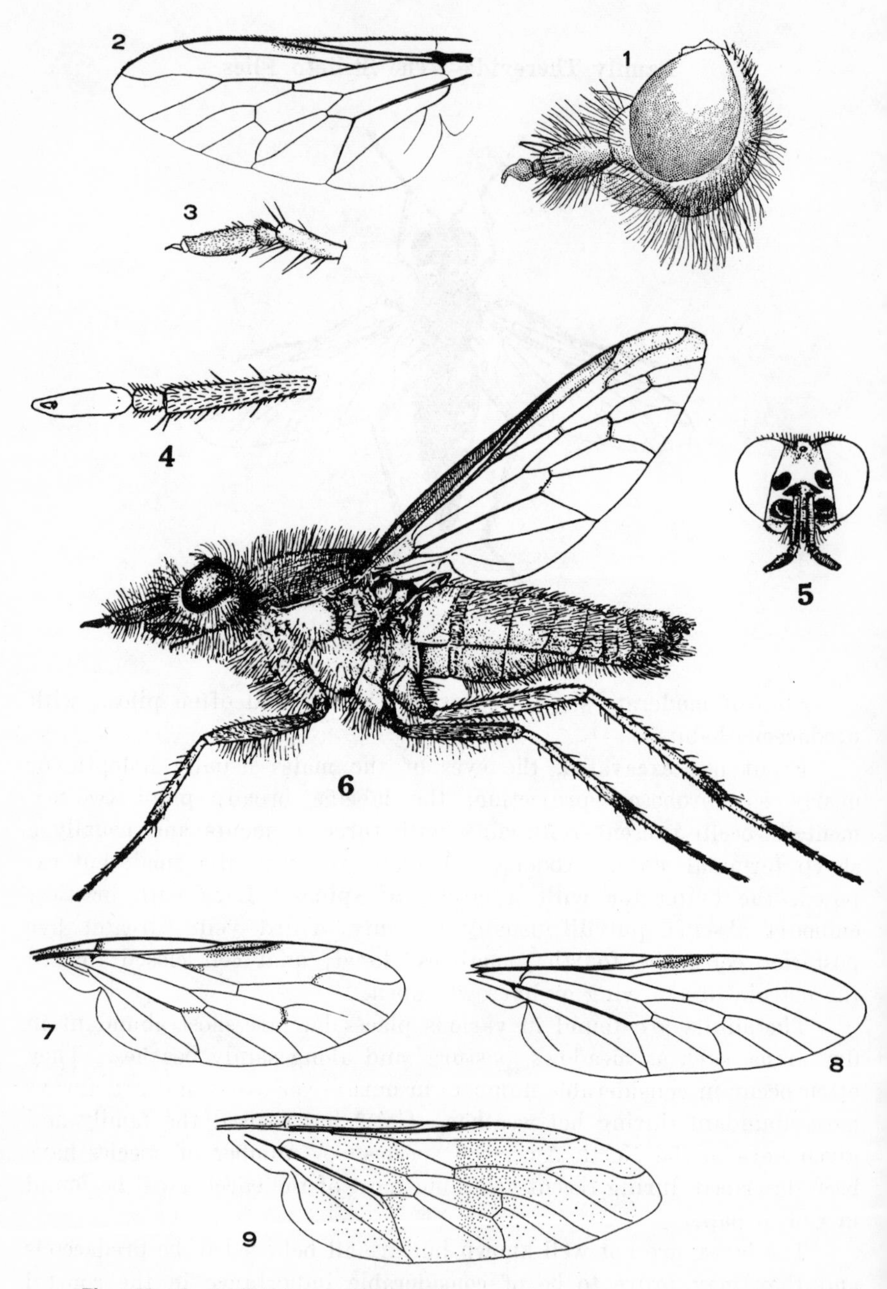

Therevidæ I.—1, **Tabuda**; 2, **Psilocephala**; 3, **Psilocephala**, antenna; 4, **Chromolepida bella**, antenna; 5, **Chrmomolepida bella**, head from above; 6, **Metaphragma planiceps**; 7, **Tabuda fulvipes**; 8, **Thereva melaneura**; 9, **Epomyia sumichrasti.**

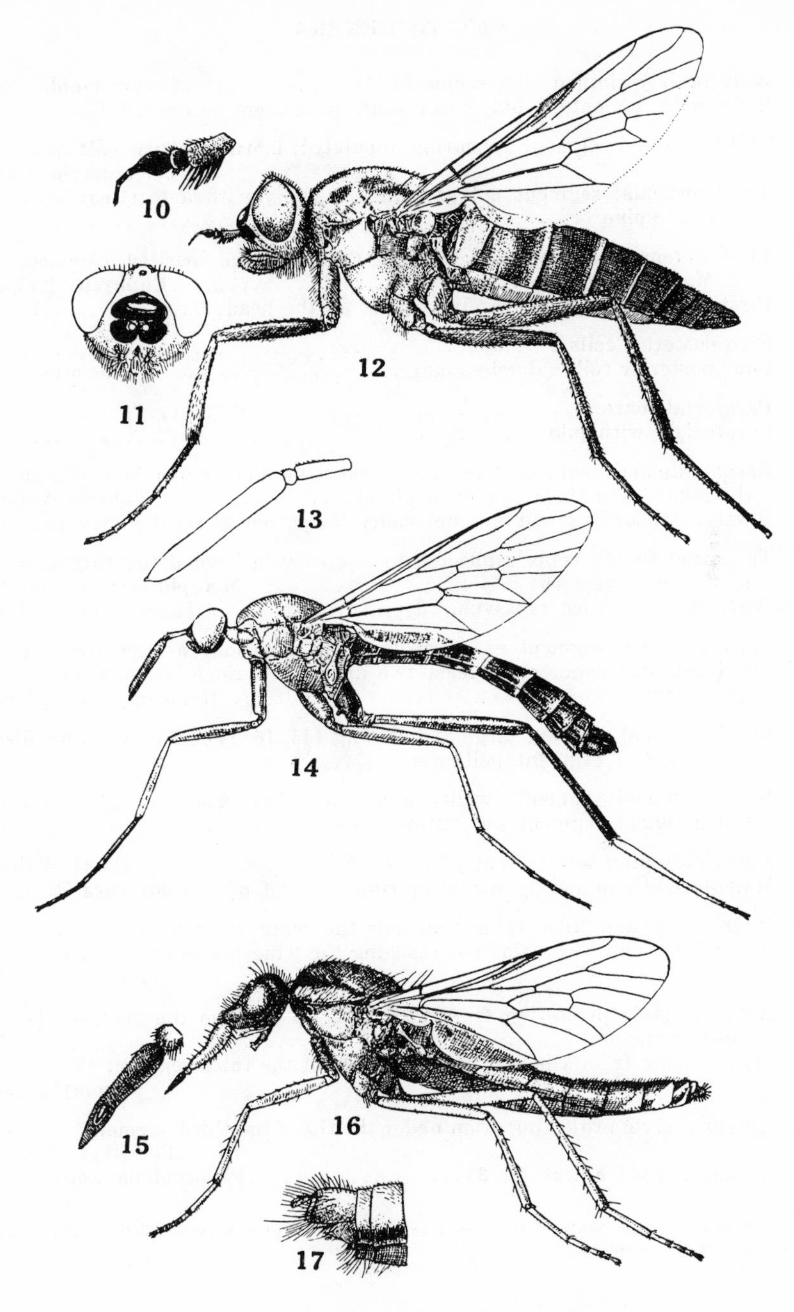

Therevidæ II.—10, 11, 12, **Pherocera signatifrons**; 13, 14, **Henicomyia hubbardi**; 15, 16, **Nebritus pellucidus**; 17, **Nebritus pellucidus**, ♂ genitalia.

KEY TO GENERA

1. Body largely clothed with scales (4, 5)................**Chromolepida** Cole
   Body with tomentum but never with irridescent scales............ 2

2. Third antennal segment appearing annulated; labrum narrow (Mexico). **Ozodiceromyia** Bigot
   Third antennal segment not annulated, usually with a terminal style or short spine 3

3. First antennal segment longer than the head and bristled (Mexico; cf. **Metaphragma** Coq.) ....**Euphycus** Kröber
   First antennal segment rarely as long as the head................. 4

4. Five posterior cells 5
   Four posterior cells (Bombyliidæ) ....**Cænotus** Cole

5. Parafacials bare 8
   Parafacials with pile 6

6. Basal antennal segment long and greatly swollen, much larger than the second and third combined (1, 7).................***Tabuda** Walker
   Basal antennal segment not unusually large, never greatly swollen.. 7

7. Third and fourth veins connected by a crossvein beyond the furcation of the third vein (6) ....**Metaphragma** Coquillett
   Wings without such crossvein (8) ....**Thereva** Zetterstedt

8. Third antennal segment not more than twice as long as the first.... 9
   Third antennal segment at least two and a half times as long as the first (Southern) (13, 14) ....**Henicomyia** Coquillett

9. Basal antennal segment large and shining (15, 16, 17)..**Nebritis** Coquillett
   Basal antennal segment pollinose 10

10. Basal antennal segment swollen and hairy (1).................... 11
    Basal antennal segment not strongly swollen...................... 12

11. Males dichoptic; lower front pilose (1, 7)...............***Tabuda** Walker
    Males holoptic or nearly so; lower front bare of pile..**Dialineura** Rondani

12. Intercallary and fifth veins reaching the wing margin............ 13
    Intercallary and fifth veins not reaching the wing margin (10, 11, 12). **Pherocera** Cole

13. Antennal style projecting from under the tip or from the apex of the third segment 14
    Style arising from a hollow near the apex of the third segment (9). **Epomyia** Cole

14. Antennal style projecting from under the tip of the third segment. **Furcifera** Kröber
    Antennal style apical (2, 3) ....**Psilocephala** Zetterstedt

---

* **Tabuda fulvipes** Walker, 1852, is a synonym of **Thereva nervosa** Walker, 1848. The latter becomes the genotype.

Family Apioceridæ

Apiocera species.

Large, elongate flies, with three-segmented antennæ and rather thinly pilose.

Antennæ with or without a short, terminal style. Front not excavated, wider in the female; ocelli present; face short; proboscis longer than the length of the head, not adapted for piercing, the labellæ not horny. Empodia wanting. Third vein usually furcate; basal cells long; five posterior cells, the fourth closed. Male forceps enlarged.

These flies are apparently restricted to arid or semi-arid regions and are not at all common in collections. Like the Nemestrids they are great hoverers and make a loud noise while in flight. The immature stages are unknown.

KEY TO GENERA

1. Proboscis more than twice as long as the head-height 2
   Proboscis not longer than the head-height **(1, 2)**...* **Apiocera** Westwood.
2. Anal cell closed before the wing margin (3, 4).
   Rhaphiomidas Osten Sacken
   Anal cell open....................................**Apomidas** Coquillett

* Painter, 1932, Ann. Ent. Soc. Amer., xxv, p. 351.

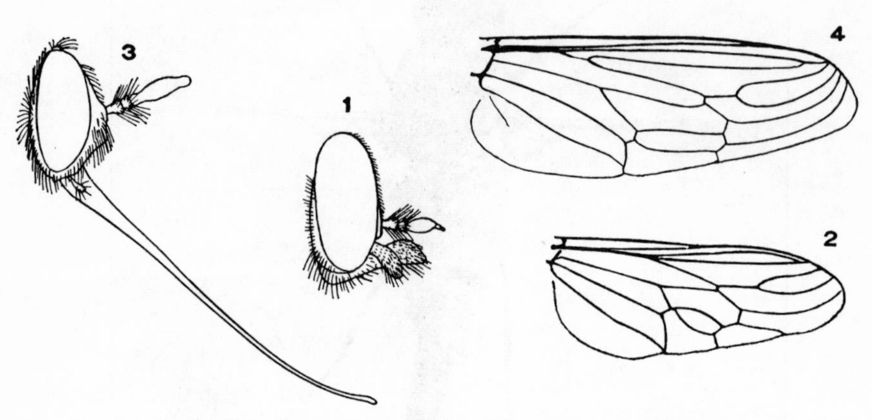

Apioceridæ.—1, 2, **Apiocera haruspex**; 3, 4, **Rhaphiomydas acton.**

Family Bombyliidæ—The Bee Flies

Small to moderately large flies, often with pictured wings and frequently clothed with abundant, delicate hairs or scales which are easily abraded, rarely with conspicuous bristles.

Head narrower than or as broad as the thorax, more or less hemispherical in shape; usually closely applied to the thorax. Face variable, usually short, often prominent below. Eyes large, often contiguous in the male, rarely so in the female. Antennæ three-segmented, porrect, rarely long, usually of moderate length, sometimes small; third segment simple; style usually small, never more than two-segmented, sometimes absent. Ocelli present. Proboscis sometimes short and with broad labellæ, usually more or less elongate and projecting from the oral cavity. Thorax convex above, sometimes strongly so, usually with bristles. Abdomen composed of six to eight segments, slender in a few genera, usually depressed but often cylindrical and more or less tapering. Legs moderately long and weak, usually with short, weak bristles or spines; pulvilli sometimes rudimentary, the empodia usually absent. Squamæ small. Wings often pictured; two to four submarginal cells (rarely with only one) discal cell almost always present (absent in some genera occurring outside North America); anal cell closed or narrowly open.

The family comprises almost two thousand described species and occurs throughout the world, being most abundantly represented in the tropical and subtropical regions. They are found particularly in warm spots, a relatively small number occurring in woods, and I have taken none in heavy shade. They like the warmest time of the day and most of them rest upon the dry soil, dried grass or upon grass in sandy places when not visiting flowers. Some species are found mostly at bloom, others but rarely. They are (mostly) great hoverers and generally very rapid fliers although they frequently fly but a short distance when disturbed. In the tropics I found many species in sunny places near the trees at the edge of the beach and along the trails in the forest, and similar places are productive in the north. Many of the species buzz persistently when captured.

Taxonomically the family is (in North America) in almost hopeless condition, the literature being extremely scattered. Only a few of the described species have been properly figured and without illustrations and usable keys the student is greatly handicapped. In addition to this unfortunate state of affairs the flies themselves present an obstacle, as the hairs are easily abraded and great care must be exercised in collecting them. Only a very few specimens should be placed

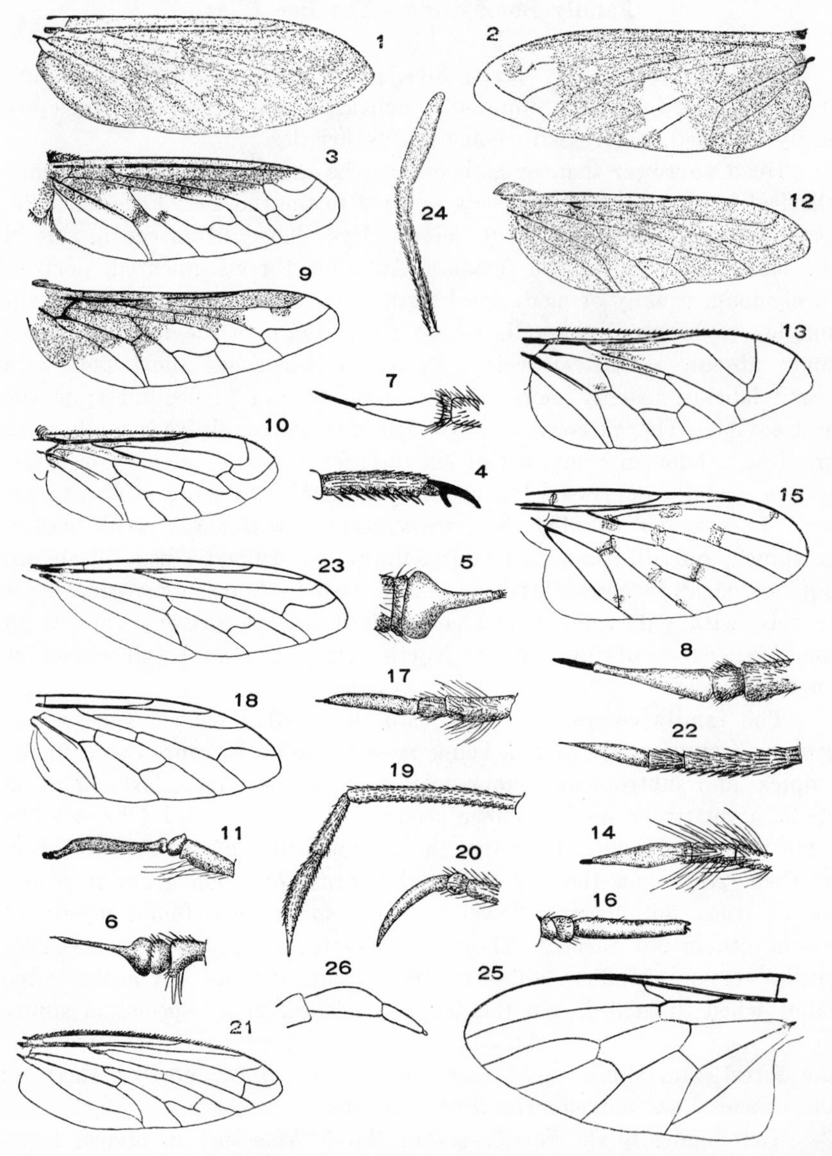

Bombyliidæ I.—1, Genus incertæ; 2, **Hyperalonia;** 3, **Litorhynchus;** 4, **Exoprosopa,** hind claw; 5, Anthrax, antenna; 6, **Villa,** antenna; 7, 8, **Exoprosopa,** antenna; 9, **Bombylius major;** 10, **Pantarbes;** 11, **Pantarbes,** antenna; 12, **Systœchus;** 13, **Lordotus;** 14, **Lordotus,** antenna; 15, **Phthiria;** 16, **Phthiria,** antenna; 17, **Sparnopolius,** antenna; 18, **Geron;** 19, 20, **Geron,** antenna; 21, **Toxophora;** 22, **Toxophora,** antenna; 23, **Systropus;** 24, **Systropus,** antenna; 25, **Mythicomyia,** wing; 26, **Mythicomyia,** antenna.

in the killing bottle and they must never be placed with other insects else they be ruined for all practical purposes. Without the hairs they are of no value and cannot be properly identified.

The larvæ are parasitic upon bees, wasps, grasshoppers and certain Lepidoptera, but not a great deal is known about most of the genera.

KEY TO GENERA

1. The second vein arises transversely opposite or almost opposite the anterior crossvein 2
   The second vein arises at an angle at a considerable distance from the anterior crossvein 19
2. Antennal style separated from the third segment by a distinct suture, sometimes short 3
   Antennal style not separated from the third segment 7
3. Antennal style terminating in a pencil of hairs (5, 54, 64). * **Anthrax** Scopoli
   Antennal style not terminating in a pencil of hairs 4
4. Pulvilli vestigial or absent 5
   Pulvilli large (49, 52) .... **Aldrichia** Coquillett
5. Four submarginal cells (2) .... **Hyperalonia** Rondani
   Three submarginal cells 6
6. Proboscis projecting more than the length of the labellæ beyond the anterior oral margin (3) .... † **Litorhynchus** Macquart
   Proboscis projecting less than the length of the labellæ (4, 7, 8, 57). † **Exoprosopa** Macquart
7. Anal cell open; eyes of ♂ not contiguous 8
   Anal cell closed; eyes of ♂ contiguous at the vertex. **Astrophanes** Osten Sacken
8. Anal cell widest at the middle 9
   Anal cell widest at the wing margin (36) .... **Mancia** Coquillett
9. Second vein strongly contorted and ⌐—⌐ shaped at the apex 10
   Second vein not strongly contorted 11
10. Three submarginal cells .... **Dipalta** Osten Sacken
    Two submarginal cells .... **Neodiplocampta,** n. g.
11. Two submarginal cells 13
    Three submarginal cells 12
12. Proboscis extending but little beyond the oral opening (6) .... **Villa** Lioy
    Proboscis extending far beyond the anterior oral margin (34, 51). **Stonyx** Osten Sacken
13. Face wholly without scales; labellæ long and narrow. **Pœcilanthrax** Osten Sacken
    Face with scales 14
14. Anterior tibiæ with spicules in regular rows 16
    Anterior tibiæ with at most two or three very small spicules 15

* Curran, 1927, Can. Ent. lix, p. 84 (partial key).
† Curran, 1930, Amer. Mus. Novit. No. 415, p. 2.

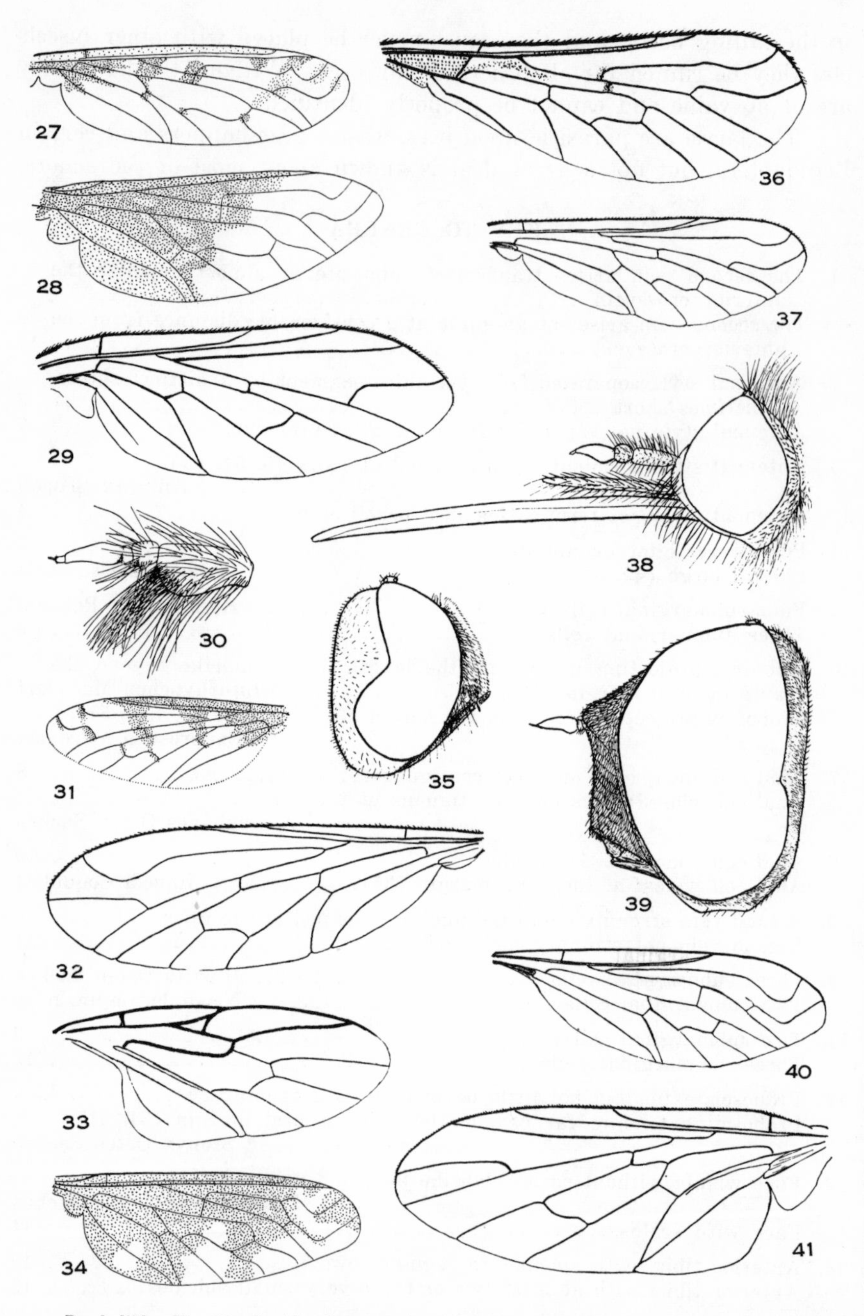

Bombyliidæ II.—27, **Lepidanthrax proboscidea**; 28, **Thyridanthrax selene**; 29, **Geron**; 30, **Calopelta fallax**, antenna; 31, **Sphenoidoptera varipennis**; 32, **Metacosmus mancipennis**; 33, **Glabellula crassicornis**; 34, **Stonyx clelia**; 35, **Ogcodocera**; 36, **Mancia nana**; 37, **Eucessia**, n. sp.; 38, **Geminaria canalis**; 39, **Eucessia**, n. sp.; 40 **Paracosmus morrisonia**; 41 **Rhabdoselaphus sigma.**

15. Face acute, strongly projecting..............**Chrysanthrax** Osten Sacken
Face not strongly projecting, the oral margin rounded (**28**).
Thyridanthrax Osten Sacken

16. Proboscis projecting far beyond the anterior oral margin............ 17
Proboscis projecting but little beyond the oral margin............... 18

17. Abdomen with broad scales on basal half (**27**).
* **Lepidanthrax** Osten Sacken
Abdomen without broad scales on basal half......**Rhynchanthrax** Painter

18. Face conical, acute at oral margin...................**Paravilla** Painter
Face obtuse below, the oral margin rounded.................**Villa** Lioy

19. With four posterior cells.. 24
With only three posterior cells.................................... 20

20. Slender, elongate species, with long, slender legs.................... 21
Shorter, more thick-set species, the abdomen tapering apically....... 22

21. Abdomen enlarged apically; eyes holoptic (**23, 24**)...**Systropus** Wiedemann
Abdomen not enlarged apically, cylindrical; males only holoptic.
Dolichomyia Wiedemann

22. Three submarginal cells or the third antennal segment obtuse........ 23
But two submarginal cells; third antennal segment acute (**18, 19, 20, 29**).
†**Geron** Meigen

23. Body clothed mostly with scales, the thorax with bristles; abdomen decumbent; antennæ long (**21, 22**).................**Toxophora** Meigen
Body clothed chiefly with hair; abdomen not decumbent (**41, 66**).
Rhabdopselaphus Bigot

24. Apical (first posterior) cell open or closed in the wing margin..... 31
Apical cell closed before the margin of the wing and petiolate........ 25

25. Two submarginal cells 27
Three submarginal cells 26

26. Head broader than the thorax; posterior orbits not excised (**10, 11**).
Pantarbes Osten Sacken
Head narrower than the thorax; posterior orbits excised...**Triplasius** Lœw

27. Proboscis protruding far beyond the anterior oral margin........... 28
Proboscis not protruding beyond the oral margin....**Anisotamia** Macquart

28. First basal cell much longer than the second........................ 29
First basal cell not longer than the second.......................... 30

29. Posterior orbits of the eyes convex or only slightly emarginate in the middle; head small (**9, 63**)..................**Bombylius** Linnaeus
Posterior orbits broadly and deeply emarginate; head as wide as the thorax ....‡**Heterostylum** Macquart

30. Shape of the face concealed by dense hair; vein closing the discal cell anteriorly half as long as the ultimate section of the vein behind it.
Anastœchus Osten Sacken
Shape of the face plainly visible; vein closing the discal cell anteriorly not nearly half as long as the ultimate section of the vein behind it (**12**) ....**Systœchus** Lœw

---

* Curran, 1930, Amer. Mus. Novit. No. 409, p. 1.
† Painter, 1932, Tr. Amer. Ent. Soc., lviii, pp. 139-167.
‡ Painter, 1930, J. Kans. Ent. Soc., iii, p. 1.

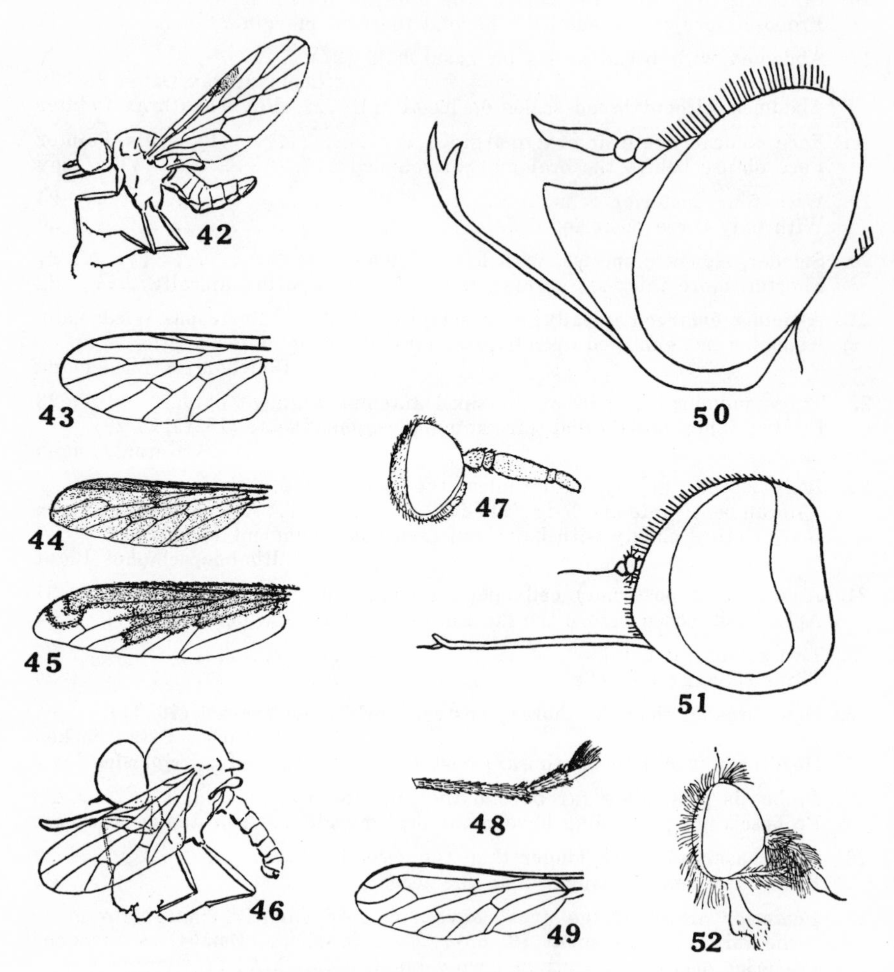

Bombyliidæ III.—42, **Prorates**; 43, **Desmatomyia**; 44, **Eclimus**; 45, **Lepidophora vetusta**; 46, **Mythicomyia**; 47, **Desmatomyia**; 48, **Lepidophora vetusta**; 49, **Aldrichia**; 50, **Amphicosmus cincturus**; 51, **Stonyx clelia**; 52, **Aldrichia.**

31. Two submarginal cells 36
Three submarginal cells 32

32. Abdomen very elongate, slender and almost bare; tibiæ without spicules (**50, 53**) ....**Amphicosmus** Coquillett
Abdomen robust and short; pilose species; tibiæ with spicules......... 33

33. Antennæ as long as the head, the third segment not longer than the basal two together 34
Antennæ shorter than the head, the third segment twice as long as the basal two combined ....**Exepacmus** Coquillett

34. Scutellum deeply sulcate longitudinally (**38**)........**Geminaria** Coquillett
Scutellum not sulcate 35

35. First antennal segment greatly swollen (**Ploas** Latreille) (**60**). **Conophorus** Meigen
First antennal segment not thickened (**13, 14**).............**Lordotus** Lœw

36. Anal cell closed 37
Anal cell open 41

37. Proboscis projecting beyond the anterior oral margin............... 39
Proboscis short, not projecting beyond the anterior oral margin..... 38

38. Abdomen elongate and tapering.........................**Cænotus** Cole
Abdomen short and broad, thickly pilose (**35**) ....**Ogcodocera** Macquart

39. The intercallary vein between the fourth and fifth vein arises from the discal cell 40
The intercallary vein arises from the fourth vein (**42** Empidæ **5, 10**). **Prorates** Melander

40. Face bare or short pilose; third antennal segment bare or with short, bristly hairs above (**15, 16**) ....**Phthiria** Meigen
Face with long hair; third antennal segment with long, bristly hairs. **Neacreotrichus** Cockerell

41. The second vein ends in the first vein............................. 42
The second vein ends in the costa 43

42. Discal and second basal cells united (**33**) (**Pachyneres** Greene). **Glabellula** Bezzi
Discal and second basal cells separated (**25, 26, 46**). **Mythicomyia** Coquillett

43. Body clothed chiefly with scales 43a
Body clothed with hair or nearly bare, sometimes with some scales.. 44

43a. First antennal segment at least as long as the third, densely clothed with scales; abdomen elongate (**45, 48**).......***Lepidophora** Westwood
First antennal segment not half as long as the third, without scales; abdomen short ....**Neodischistus** Painter

44. First basal cell much longer than the second...................... 46
First basal cell only slightly longer than the second................ 45

45. First antennal segment greatly swollen, widest apically (**30**). **Calopelta** Green
First antennal segment only a little swollen, widest in the middle. **Sparnopolius** Lœw

* Painter, 1925, Tr. Amer. Ent. Soc., li, p. 120.

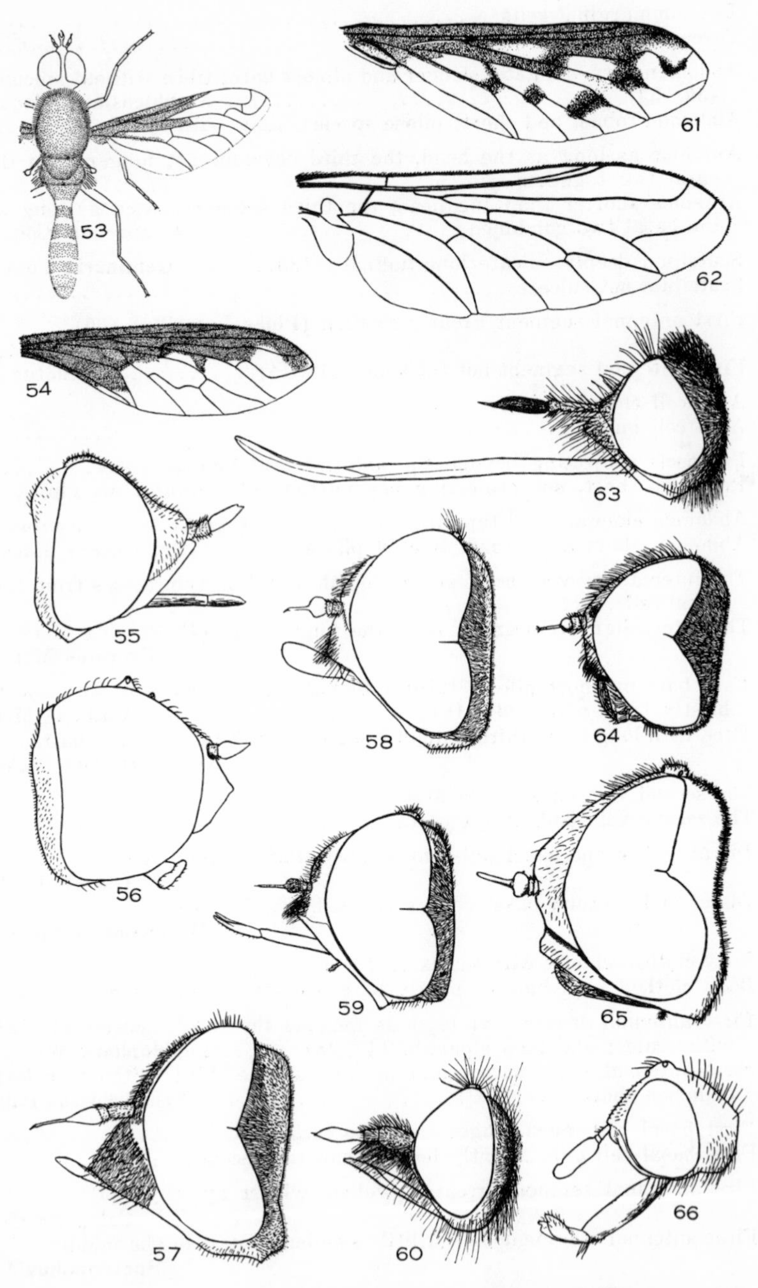

Bombyliidæ IV.—53, **Amphicosmus cincturus**; 54, **Anthrax**; 55, **Paracosmus morrisoni**; 56, **Metacosmus mancipennis**; 57, **Exoprosopa**; 58, **Aphæbantus cervinus**; 59, **Epacmus modestus**; 60, **Conophoras**; 61, **Neodiplocampta rœderi**; 62, **Parabombylius**; 63, **Bombylius**; 64, **Anthrax irroratus**; 65, **Desmatoneura argentifrons**; 66, **Rhabdoselaphus sigma**.

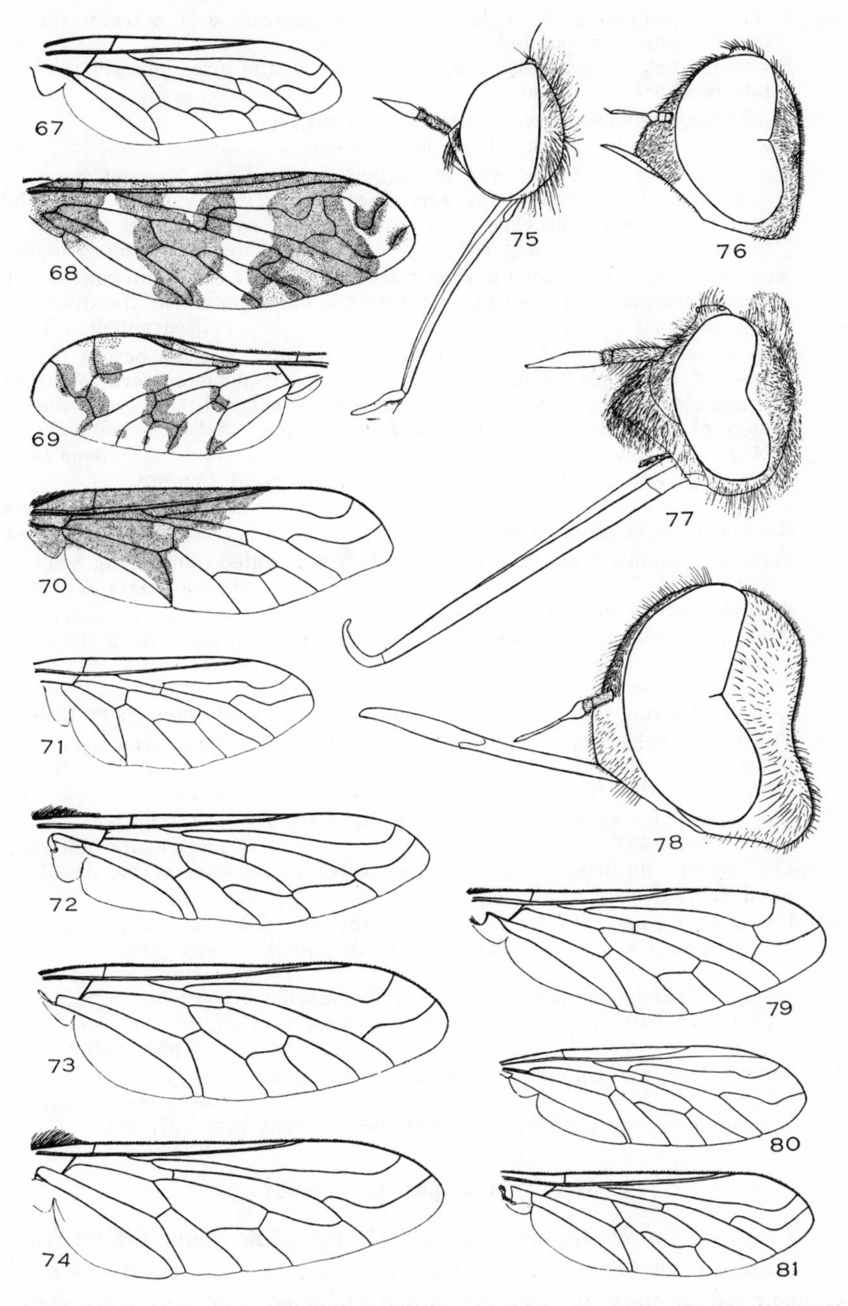

Bombyliidæ V.—67, **Anisotamia**; 68, **Dipalta**; 69, **Geminaria canalis**; 70, **Ogcodocera**; 71, **Astrophanes**; 72, **Heterostylum**; 73, **Sparnopolius**; 74, **Anastœchus**; 75, **Geron**; 76, **Mancia nana**; 77, **Heterostylum**; 78, **Litorhynchus**; 79, **Conophorus**; 80, **Desmatoneura**; 81, **Epacmus, Aphæbantus.**

46. Proboscis projecting strongly beyond the anterior oral margin, the labellæ long and pointed 47
Proboscis not or scarcely projecting beyond the oral margin, the labellæ short and broad 51
47. Face bare, the sides above, or the clypeus with hair 49
Face with hair in the middle at least below 48
48. Posterior border of the eyes emarginate, the facets bisected by a short bare line opposite the emargination 53
Posterior border of the eyes not emarginate, the eyes without a bare, bisecting line posteriorly (62) ....***Parabombylius** Williston
49. Anterior crossvein situated beyond the basal third of the discal cell.... 50
Anterior crossvein situated at or before the basal fourth of the discal cell (17) ....**Sparnopolius** Lœw
50. The anterior branch of the third vein arises only a little before the apex of the second vein (31) ....**Sphenoidoptera** Williston
The anterior branch of the third vein originates only a little beyond the apex of the discal cell and far before the apex of the second vein (44) ....**Eclimus** Lœw
51. Ocellar tubercle situated near the middle of the front (**32, 56**).
Metacosmus Coquillett
Ocellar tubercle situated near the vertex 52
52. Style of antennæ broad and flattened, two segmented, simulating segments (**43, 47**) ....**Desmatomyia** Williston
Style not broad and flattened 53
53. Posterior border of the eyes at least weakly indented and with a short, unfacetted stripe 54
Posterior border of the eyes not at all indented and without any unfacetted stripe (**40, 55**) ....**Paracosmus** Osten Sacken
54. Third antennal segment bulbous basally and with a long, almost parallel-sided apical part 55
Third antennal segment sub-triangular, tapering 57
55. The second vein arises at an almost right angle beyond the base of the discal cell (**65**) ....**Desmatoneura** Williston
The second vein arises at an acute angle before the base of the discal cell 56
56. Proboscis strongly projecting beyond the anterior oral margin, the labellæ long and narrow; face produced; pulvilli absent (**59**).
Epacmus Osten Sacken
Proboscis rarely strongly projecting, the labellæ broad; face usually receding; pulvilli present if the face projects (**58**).
Aphœbantus Lœw
57. Anterior oral margin close to the base of the antennæ.
Anisotamia Macquart
Anterior oral margin very far from the antennal base (**37, 39**).
Eucessia Coquillett

Neodiplocampta, new genus

Proposed for *Diplocampta rœderi* Curran. The genus differs from *Diplocampta* Schiner in having the face produced, the third antennal segment rather long and conical, broad abdomen, different wing venation, etc. *Anthrax paradoxa* Jænnicke also belongs to this genus.

---

* Painter, 1926, Ent. News, xxxvii, p. 74; Curran, 1930, Amer. Mus. Novit. No. 404, p. 7.

Family Nemestrinidæ

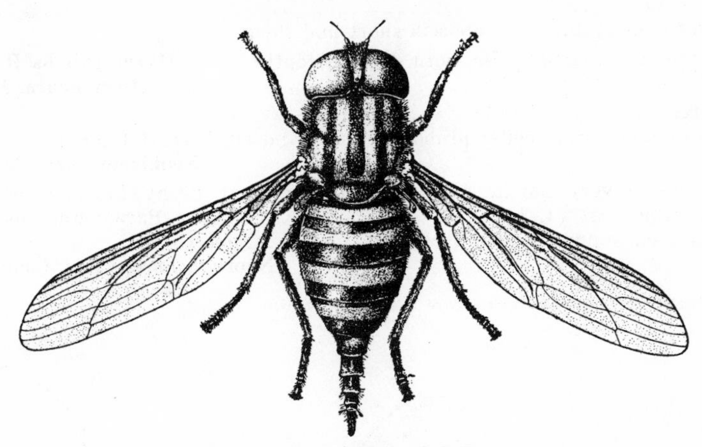

Neohirmoneura bradleyi Bequært.

Flies of moderate size, rather stout and compact in appearance, with many veins; thinly or densely pilose.

Head moderate in size, narrower or slightly wider than the thorax; eyes holoptic or dichoptic in the males, females dichoptic except in *Hyrmophlœba;* proboscis long to rudimentary. Antennæ short and small, three segmented, and with a stout, jointed terminal arista. Tibiæ without spurs; empodia pulvilliform but the pulvilli often minute. Venation complicated, the fourth and fifth veins curving forward to terminate before the apex of the wing; anterior crossvein very oblique and simulating a longitudinal vein, the basal cells both long; five or six posterior cells and two or three submarginals.

The Nemestrinids are not numerous in collections and are usually difficult to catch. I have found them only in open fields in which the vegetation is of considerable height and have observed them in considerable numbers. They hover persistently and dart quickly away at the least motion; when present in numbers their "buzz" is very obvious and they may be heard at a considerable distance. Those with long proboscis often visit flowers. In the American species the venation is relatively simple but in some species of the genus *Nemestrinus* there are numerous crossveins in the wings, and some of them have the proboscis greatly elongated. The genus *Hirmoneura* is known to live upon root feeding beetle larvæ in the larval stage and it is probable that all the species are parasitic.

Three papers by Bequaert* cover the North American species, of which there are about a dozen.

---

* Bequaert, 1919, Journ. N. Y. Ent. Soc., xxvii, pp. 301-307; 1930, Psyche, pp. 286-297; 1934, Journ. N. Y. Ent. Soc. xlii, pp. 163-184.

KEY TO GENERA

1. Eyes bare 3
   Eyes densely pilose; proboscis short and thick 2
2. Three submarginal cells, both sexes holoptic (3, 4). **Hyrmophlœba** Rondani
   Two submarginal cells .... ***Hirmoneura** Meigen
3. Three submarginal cells 4
   Two submarginal cells; proboscis short and thick (**text figure**).
   Neohirmoneura Bequaert
4. Proboscis very small, hardly visible, without fleshy labellae; alula rudimentary (**1, 2**) .... **Parasymmictus** Bigot
   Proboscis elongate and protruding; alula broad (**5 6**).
   Neorhynchocephalus Lichtwardt

* No North American species are at present known.

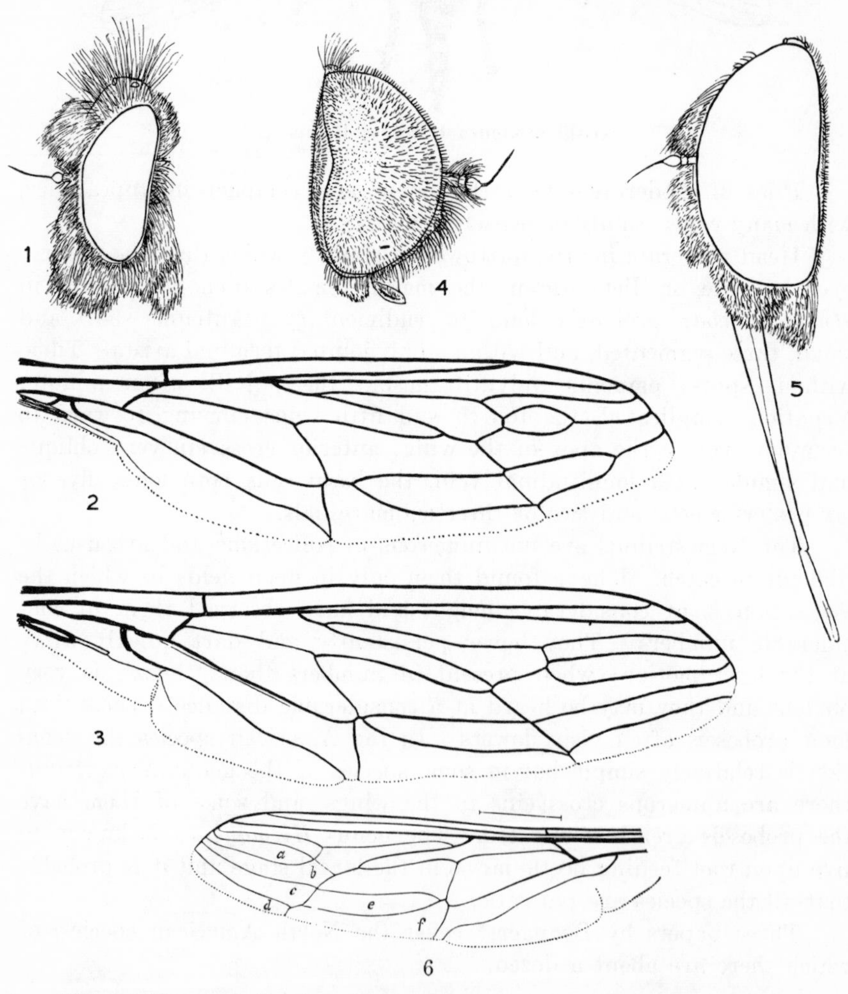

Nemestrinidæ.—1, 2, **Parasymmyctus clausa** O. S.; 3, 4, **Hirmophlœba texana**; 5, 6, **Neorhynchocephalus volaticus**, a third submarginal cell, **b-f** posterior cells.

Family Cyrtidæ

Opsebius pterodontinus.

Small to moderately large flies, never elongate, pilose or nearly bare.

Head small to very small, composed chiefly of the compound eyes which are usually contiguous in both sexes, the front, face or both obliterated; none, two or three ocelli present. Antennæ composed of two or three segments, with or without an apical arista, the third segment sometimes with apical bristles. Proboscis rudimentary or long, sometimes greatly exceeding the length of the body. Thorax large and convex, the squamæ and scutellum large. Abdomen inflated, convex, rather orbicular. Legs moderately stout, the empodia and pulvilli pad-like. Venation variable, the veins sometimes weak and indistinct; often a supernumerary crossvein between the third and fourth veins.

This family contains a small number of species and may be recognized by the swollen thorax, inflated abdomen and small head. Ten genera are known to occur in North America. Cole* has revised the family. Insofar as known the members of the family are parasitic on spiders.

KEY TO GENERA

1. Prothoracic lobes greatly enlarged and meeting in front of the mesonotum; proboscis elongate (3, 4) .... **Philopota** Wiedemann
   Prothoracic lobes not forming a shield in front of the mesonotum... 2
2. Proboscis small and aborted 4
   Proboscis elongate 3
3. Palpi absent; usually two ocelli (**13, 14**) .... **Lasia** Wiedemann
   Palpi present; three ocelli situated on a more or less prominent tubercle (**11, 12**) .... **Eulonchus** Gerstæcker

* 1919. Trans. Amer. Ent. Soc., xlv, pp. 1-79, plates I-XV.

4. Antennæ elongate, the third segment large 5
Antennæ short, the third segment small 7
5. Eyes pilose or pubescent 6
Eyes bare ....**Apelleia** Bellardi
6. Third antennal segment without terminal bristles **(9, 10)**
*Ocnæa Erickson
Third antennal segment with terminal bristly hairs..**Pialeoidea** Westwood
7. Antennæ inserted below the middle of the head 8
Antennæ inserted above the middle of the head 9
8. Third antennal segment with three terminal setæ **(7, 8)**.
Pterodontia Gray
Third antennal segment with an apical arista **(5, 6)**.....**Ogcodes** Latreille
9. Eyes pilose **(text figure)** ....**Opsebius** Costa
Eyes bare **(1, 2)** ....**Acrocera** Meigen

* Aldrich, 1932, Proc. U. S. N. M., lxxxi, Art. 9, p. 3.

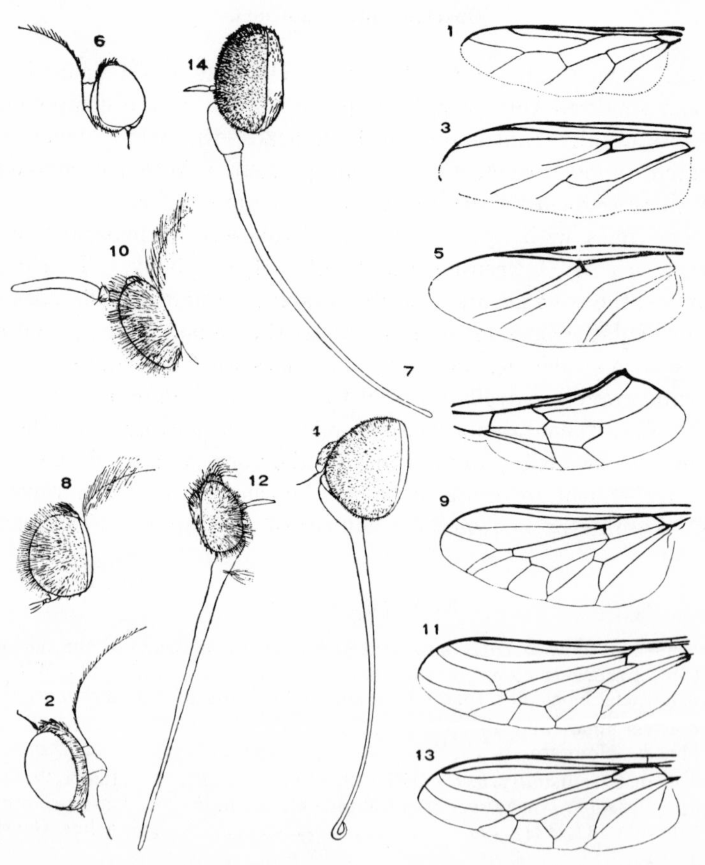

Crytidæ.—1, 2, **Acrocera**; 3, 4, **Philopota**; 5, 6, **Ogcodes**; 7, 8, **Pterodontia**; 9, 10, **Ocnæa**; 11, 12, **Eulonchus**; 13, 14, **Lasia**.

Family Empidæ—The Dance Flies

Flies of small to medium size, though rarely over 10 mm. in length.

Head more or less spherical, loosely connected with the thorax; males holoptic or dichoptic, the face sometimes almost obliterated by the approximate eyes; ocelli present. Antennæ porrect, composed of two or three segments, with or without an apical style or arista, or with dorsal arista; face receding or slightly prominent below, never with a strong mystax. Proboscis short or long, usually rigid. Thorax sometimes long and narrow, usually short, often strongly convex above. Male genitalia generally of complicated structure, often large or very large; ovipositor sometimes long and chitinized. Wing venation simple, the wings rarely absent or reduced in size; squamæ small; anal and second basal cell sometimes absent or incomplete. Legs usually slender, sometimes with structural peculiarities such as elongated coxæ or femora, the femora or tibiæ often thickened and with spines or tubercles or with processes or fringes of scales; pulvilli distinct; empodia usually membranous and linear.

The adults are found almost everywhere but the Empids are rare in arid regions. They are most abundant in moist places, especially in woods, along streams and on the shores of ponds and lakes. All are predaceous, feeding upon smaller insects, mites, etc. As a general rule they are observed upon foliage and grass but many of them are confined to restricted habitats and others appear to be very local in distribution. Certain genera are found almost entirely on the trunks of trees and may be collected most easily by placing the mouth of the killing bottle over them, while others occur in large numbers on small flowers, notably *Prunus virginiana.* A few genera are found only along the seashore where they dart about among the pebbles, feeding upon small insects or upon freshly killed invertebrates.

The mating habits of the Empidæ are extremely interesting, but no more than mention of them can be made here. In some cases the males capture prey and use this food as a lure to attract the females. Sometimes the females devour the offering or it may be discarded as soon as the mating is completed. In other cases the male provides a balloon like bubble to attract the female. In some cases it is believed that copulation cannot be completed unless food is provided.

The immature stages are not well known but the larvæ live in decaying vegetation, under bark, and in streams.

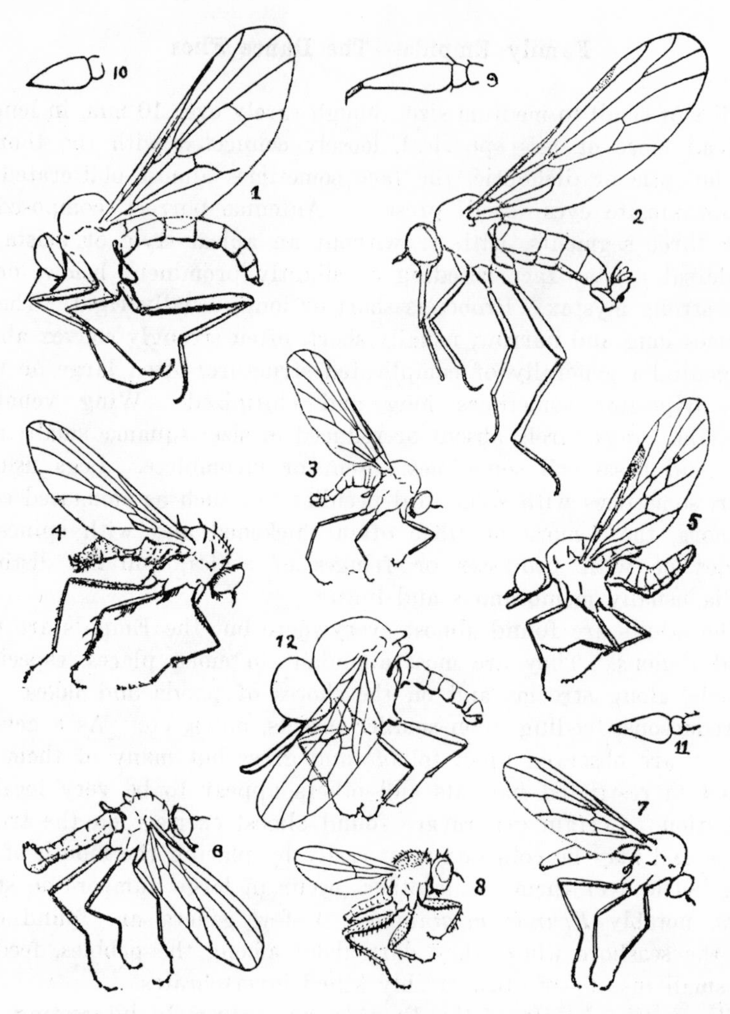

Empidæ I.—1, **Hybos**; 2, **Toreus**; 3, **Hesperempis**; 4, **Oreogeton**; 5, **Prorates** (Bombyliidæ); 6, **Heleodromia**; 7, **Ocydromia**; 8, **Coloboneura**; 9, **Toreus**, antenna; 10, **Prorates** (Bombyliidæ); 11, **Hesperempis**, 12; **Mythicomyia** (Bombyliidæ).

Melander has covered this family in Genera Insectorum* describing many new North American genera and species and presenting keys. Unfortunately the price of this work is prohibitive to the average worker so the family will no doubt receive little attention until a more readily accessible work is available.

KEY TO GENERA

1. Discal cell always united with the second basal, the anal cell always incomplete 55
   Second basal closed apically or the anal cell complete 2
2. Mesopleura obliquely longer than high 3
   Mesopleura distinctly higher than long.... 4
3. Anterior pair of legs far from the middle pair, raptorial.... 52
   Anterior legs not distant from the middle pair and not raptorial... 43
4. Auxiliary vein distinct and separated from the first vein.... 5
   Auxiliary vein weak and lying close to the first vein.... 13
5. Anal cell very much longer anteriorly 22
   Anal cell longest posteriorly, transverse apically or but little longer in front than at the middle 6
6. Costa ending at the third or fourth vein; two veins emitted by the discal cell 8
   Costa continuing around the wing; three veins emitted by the discal cell 7
7. Third vein forked (14) ....**Brachystoma** Meigen
   Third vein simple (28) ....**Anomalempis** Melander
8. Fourth vein not forked 9
   Fourth vein forked (30) ....**Meghyperus** Lœw
9. Pedicel of the second and third veins arising beyond the middle of the second basal cell 10
   Pedicel arising near the basal fourth of the second basal cell (25). **Syneches** Walker
10. Vein between the first and second basal cells distinct, the first basal cell not much wider than the second.... 11
    Vein between the first and second basal cells very weak, the first basal very much wider than the second (31)....**Syndyas** Lœw
11. Third and fourth veins convergent apically 12
    Third and fourth veins parallel or diverging (1, 21)....**Hybos** Meigen
12. Disc of mesonotum without pile; palpi elongate (35). **Lactistomyia** Melander
    Disc of mesonotum more or less densely pilose; palpi short. **Eubybos** Coquillett
13. Discal cell present 15
    Discal cell absent 14

* Fascicle 185, 1927.

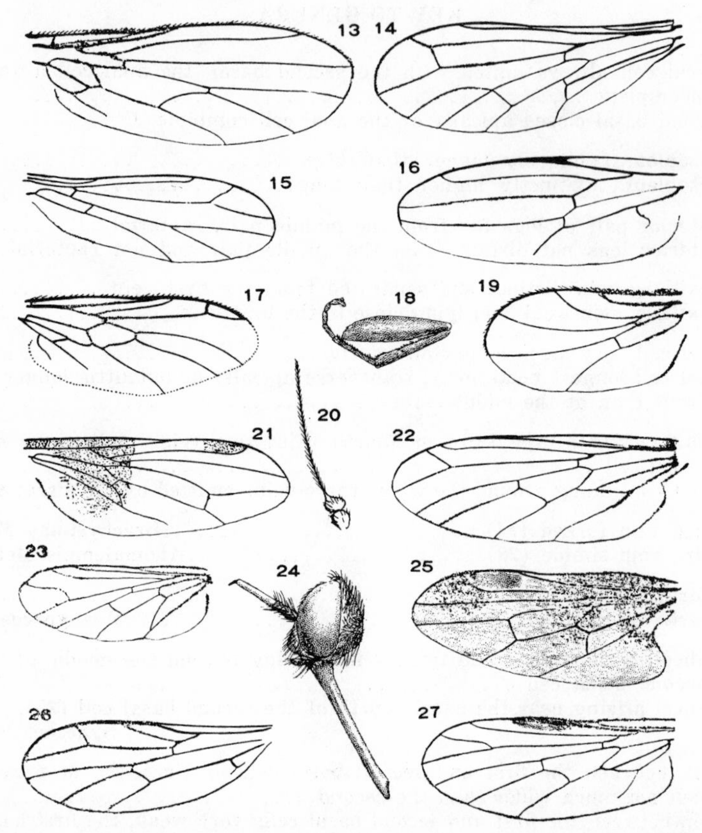

Empidæ II.—13, **Oreothalia**; 14, **Brachystoma**; 15, **Hemerodromia**; 16, **Tachypeza**; 17, **Lampremis**; 18, **Tachypeza**, front leg; 19, **Drapetis**; 20, **Drapetis**, antenna; 21, **Hybos**; 22, **Empis**; 23, **Geron** (Bombyliidæ); 24, **Empimorpha**; 25, **Syneches**; 26, **Chelifera**; 27, **Hilara.**

14. Posterior legs simple (41) .... **Bicellaria** Macquart
Posterior femora much enlarged and spinose ..... **Hoplocyrtoma** Melander

15. Discal cell emitting three veins apically or, if open, the fourth vein branched 17
Discal cell emitting two veins apically 16

16. Third antennal segment conical, the arista apical; middle tibiæ with several sets of bristles .... **Leptopeza** Macquart
Third antennal segment oval; the arista sub-dorsal; middle tibiæ with only apical bristles (7) .... **Ocydromia** Meigen

17. Posterior femora enlarged and spinose beneath (53, 57) .. **Œdalia** Meigen
Posterior femora not swollen 18

18. Posthumeral bristles present; antennæ apparently two segmented 19
Posthumeral bristles usually absent, the antennæ with three segments. **Euthyneura** Macquart

19. Antennæ ending in a style 20
Antennæ without style or arista (51, 59) .... **Allanthalia** Melander

20. Antennæ situated near the middle of the head, the third segment elongate 21
Antennæ situated much below the middle of the head, the third segment broad (60, 63) .... **Anthalia** Zetterstedt

21. Third antennal segment extremely long (45, 52) ..... **Axelempis** Curran
Third antennal segment normal .... **Trichina** Meigen

22. Basal and anal cells very small; third vein never forked; abdomen shorter than the robust thorax 23
Basal and anal cells not unusually short; third vein often furcate; abdomen as long or longer than the thorax 25

23. Eyes pubescent 24
Eyes bare (37) .... **Microphorus** Macquart

24. Face broadened below and more or less hairy; costa continuing around the wing (48, 55) .... **Parathalassius** Mik
Face not broadened below and with only oral hairs .. **Microphorella** Becker

25. Antennæ with three segments 26
Antennæ apparently two-segmented .... **Hormopeza** Zetterstedt

26. Proboscis directed obliquely forward or horizontal, the face broad, convex and short 27
Proboscis normally vertical, if more or less oblique the face is long and narrow 31

27. Auxiliary vein entire, ending in the costa 28
Auxiliary vein obsolete apically .... **Brochella** Melander

28. Third vein furcate 29
Third vein simple .... **Anthepiscopus** Becker

29. Arista terminal, sometimes style-like 30
Arista dorsal (34) .... **Gloma** Meigen

30. Hypopleura bare (38) .... **Iteaphila** Macquart
Hypopleura haired (4) .... **Oreogeton** Schiner

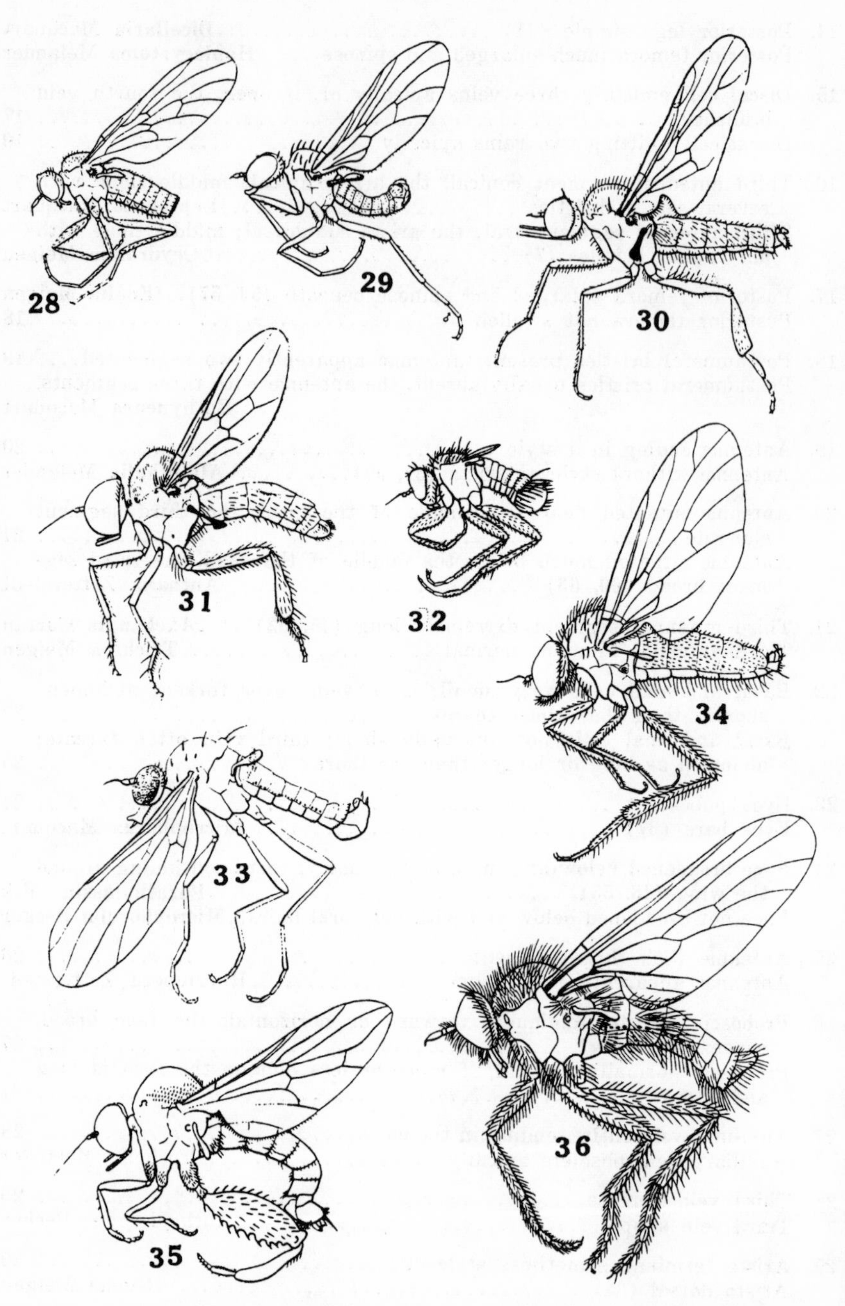

Empidæ III.—28, **Anomalempis tacomæ**; 29, **Philetus memorandus**; 30, **Meghyperus occidens**; 31, **Syndyas polita**; 32, **Thinodromia inchoata**; 33, **Heleodromia pullata**; 34, **Gloma fuscipennis**; 35, **Lactistomyia insolita**; 36, **Neocota weedii**.

31. Metapleura with hairs or bristles in front of the halteres............ 35
Metapleura bare 32

32. Auxiliary vein ending in the costa.................................. 33
Auxiliary vein obsolete apically (**2, 9**)................**Toreus** Melander

33. Auxiliary vein bending apically to meet the costa; anal angle prominent (**27, 39**)..................................**Hilara** Meigen
Auxiliary vein almost straight, the anal angle broadly rounded........ 34

34. Thoracic bristles strong; antennæ below the middle of the head (**29**). **Philetus** Melander
Thoracic bristles almost absent; antennæ at the middle of the head (**3, 11**)..................................**Hesperempis** Melander

35. Style three times the length of the third antennal segment. **Opeatocerata** Melander
Style not longer than the third segment........................... 36

36. First antennal segment nearly or quite as long as the third, the antennæ situated high upon the head.......................... 37
First segment much shorter than the third, situated at most a little above the middle of the head.............................. 38

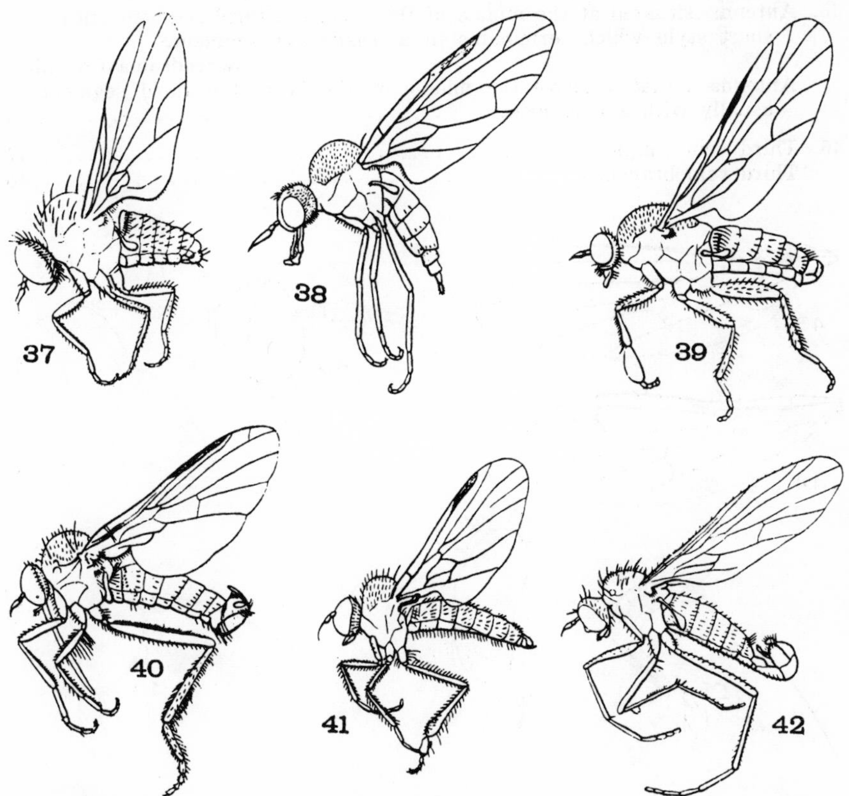

Empidæ IV.—37, **Microphorus velutinus**; 38, **Iteaphila macquarti**; 39, **Hilara**; 40, **Empis**; 41, **Bicellaria**; 42, **Proclinopyga amplectans**.

37. Arista much shorter than the third antennal segment (17).
Lamprempis Wheeler and Melander
Arista much longer than the third segment......**Porphyrochroa** Melander

38. Face hairy 39
Face bare 40

39. Third vein furcate (24)........................**Empimorpha** Coquillett
Third vein simple (36)..............................**Neocota** Coquillett

40. Third vein furcate (22, 40)..............................**Empis** Linnæus
Third vein simple.. 41

41. Third antennal segment many times longer than wide (45, 52).
.. **Axelempis** Curran
Third antennal segment normal..................**Rhamphomyia** Meigen

43. Third antennal segment remarkably lengthened, strap-like, and without evident style 44
Third antennal segment not remarkably long........................ 45

44. Antennæ inserted above the middle of the head.....**Niphogenia** Melander
Antennæ inserted below the middle of the head.....**Ceratempis** Melander

45. Antennæ situated at the middle of the head, the third segment with a short style which terminates in a bristle-like segment.
Boreodroma Coquillett
Antennæ situated above the middle of the head, the third segment usually with a long arista.. 46

46. Third vein simple 47
Third vein branched 48

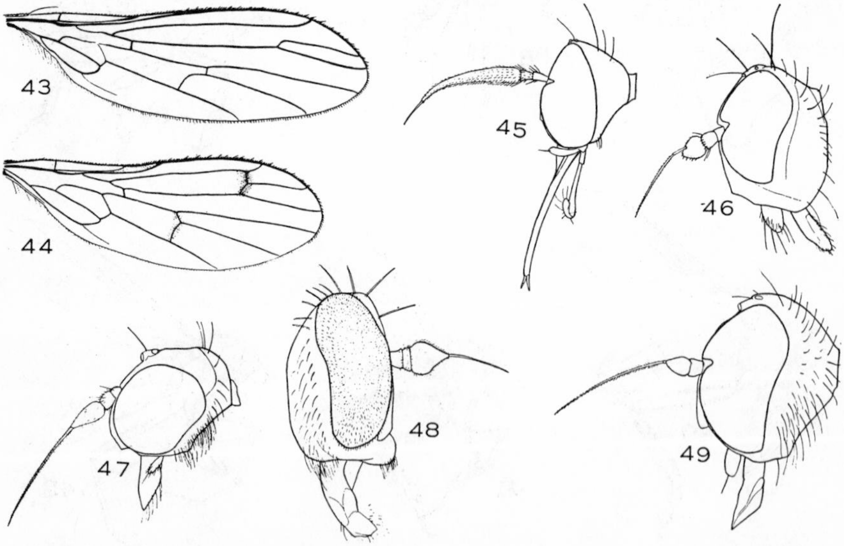

43 44 45 46 47 48 49

Empidæ V.—43 **Wiedemannia hamifera**; 44, **Clinocera binotata**; 45, **Axelempis fulvithorax**; 46, **Chersodromia houghi**; 47, **Chelipoda elongata**; 48, **Parathallasius aldrichi**; 49, **Platypalpus coquilletti.**

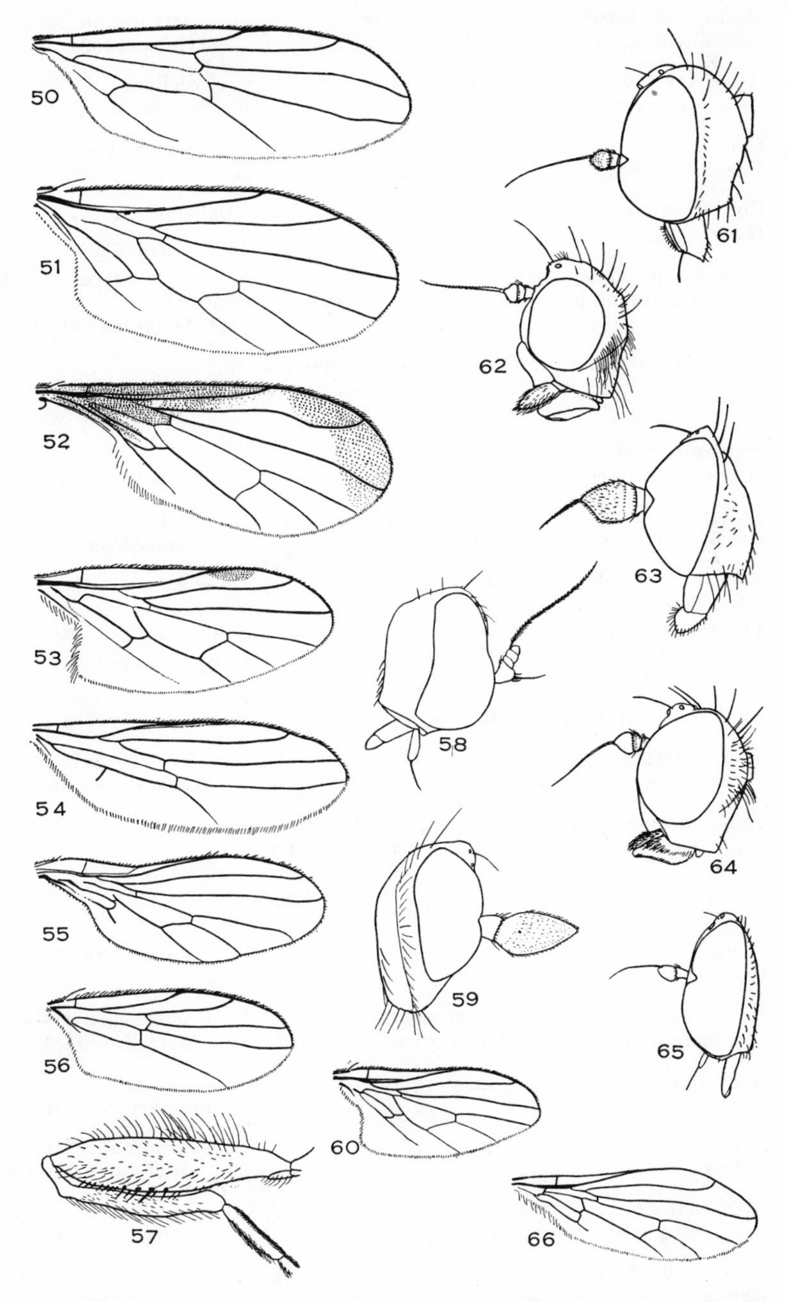

Empidæ VI.—50, **Platypalpus coquilletti;** 51, **Allanthalia pallida;** 52, **Axelempis fulvithorax;** 53, **Œdalia ohicensis;** 54, **Tachydromia postica;** 55, **Parathallasius aldrichi;** 56 **Chersodromia houghi;** 57, **Œdalia ohioensis;** 58, **Stilpon pectiniger;** 59, **Allanthalia pallida;** 60, **Anthalia bulbosa;** 61, **Tachydromia pusilla;** 62, **Wiedemannia hamifera;** 63, **Anthalia lacteipennis;** 64, **Clinocera taos;** 65, **Tachyempis simplicior;** 66, **Chelipoda elongata.**

47. Costa with setulæ (13)............................**Oreothalia** Melander
Costa without setulæ (6, 33)......................**Heleodromia** Haliday

48. Auxiliary vein obsolete apically (42).............**Proclinopyga** Melander
Auxiliary vein ending in the costa.................................. 49

49. Cheeks very wide ....**Rœderioides** Coquillett
Cheeks narrow 50

50. Body shining or sub-shining...................**Dolichocephala** Macquart
Body opaque 51

51. Face not prominent below; no acrostical setæ (44, 64)...**Clinocera** Meigen
Face prominent below; acrosticals present or absent (43, 62)
Wiedemannia Zetterstedt

52. Style shorter than the third antennal segment...................... 53
Arista more than twice as long as the third antennal segment (47, 66).
Chelipoda Macquart

53. Humeral crossvein absent.. 54
Humeral crossvein present (26)...................**Chelifera** Macquart

54. Discal cell closed apically............................**Colabris** Melander
Discal cell open apically (15)...................**Hemerodromia** Meigen

55. Thorax very elongate, the humeri large; proboscis slender and not tapering 56
Thorax more robust, the humeri rarely large; proboscis thick basally and more or less strongly tapering............................. 58

56. Anal crossvein completely absent................................ 57
Anal crossvein present (16, 18)......................**Tachypeza** Meigen

57. Front narrow, its sides nearly parallel (54, 61)......**Tachydromia** Meigen
Front V-shaped, wide above (65)..................**Tachyempis** Melander

58. First basal cell equal to or longer than the second................. 59
First basal cell decidedly shorter than the second.................. 64

59. Legs with strong bristles.. 60
Legs without conspicuous bristles............................... 62

60. Wings about one-third normal length (32).........**Thinodromia** Melander
Wings as long as the abdomen.................................... 61

61. Two pairs of presutural dorsocentrals (8).........**Coloboneura** Melander
One pair of presutural dorsocentrals (46, 56)......**Chersodromia** Walker

62. Eyes bare 63
Eyes pubescent ....**Megagrapha** Melander

63. Arista apical ....**Charadrodromia** Melander
Arista dorsal ....**Micrempis** Melander

64. Anal cell entirely absent.. 65
Anal cell partly formed (49, 50).................**Platypalpus** Macquart

65. Arista dorsal (58)......................................**Stilpon** Lœw
Arista apical or subapical (19, 20).......................**Drapetis** Meigen

Family Dolichopidæ—The Long-headed Flies

Small flies rarely exceeding 10 mm. in length, usually metallic green or blue, partly dusted with whitish, brownish or grayish, rarely yellow or blackish. Discal cell united with the second basal cell.

Head about as wide as the thorax, sometimes a little wider, usually a little higher than wide; face variable in width, sometimes practically eliminated by the approximation of the eyes, generally wider in the females than in the males; front usually wide and widening above, rarely obliterated by the approximation of the eyes in the males; with bristles above. Posterior orbits usually with orbital cilia which may be replaced below by fine hair. Proboscis fleshy, short, usually retracted; palpi flat, usually reposing on the proboscis, sometimes modified and highly ornamental. Antennæ composed of three segments, bearing a dorsal or apical arista; third segment usually more or less oval, sometimes elongated, especially in the males. Thorax convex above, sometimes with a conspicuous depression before the scutellum. Abdomen with five or six segments, conical, cylindrical, flattened, laterally compressed or more or less laterally compressed apically; hypopygium large, or small and concealed. Coxæ usually short, rarely a little elongate, the legs of moderate length, the femora usually somewhat enlarged, the tarsi of the males frequently beautifully modified, the tibiæ rarely so although sometimes brightly colored. Wings hyaline or with dark markings, sometimes ornamented with black and white or of peculiar shape. Second basal and discal cells united, the anal cell short, the sixth vein short or absent, the fourth vein usually straight or only gently curved forward, rarely forming a crossvein.

The adults occur everywhere in the vicinity of water and are particularly abundant in swamps and along lightly shaded streams where they occur on mud or sand; on foliage, usually in the sun; on stones in streams; on the trunks of trees and on fallen logs. Species of *Medeterus* and *Neurigona* are normally found on tree trunks, especially those having smooth bark; *Hydrophorus* and *Campsicnemus* occur on the surface of small pools; most genera occur on mud along water, some only on sand; *Diaphorus, Chrysotus* and *Hercostomus* occur chiefly on foliage and the same is true of *Condylostylus*, etc. Many of the species are extremely local in habitat, occurring only where conditions are perfectly suitable. The adults are all predaceous, feeding upon smaller insects and mites. I have frequently observed them devouring midges and also small larvæ occurring in the mud.

Many of the adults have very unusual mating dances which may be observed without difficulty as the species are common and soon return to their "mud flats" if disturbed. An excellent account of several of the species is given in the revision of *Dolichopus* by Van Duzee, Cole and Aldrich.

Little is known about the immature stages which are passed, for the most part, in mud, although some species live in the stems of grass and those of *Medeterus* live under the bark of trees and are definitely predaceous. Some species are said to feed upon decaying vegetation but they are probably predaceous.

The males are easily determined but the females are often difficult to name as they present less striking characters than the males. The American species were revised by Becker* but so many new forms have been described since that this work will furnish only a basis for the study of the family. The females present few structural characters and it is difficult to separate a few of the genera except by association and familiarity with the group. Several characters not previously used are employed in the key presented and most of the females are keyed out separately. With a little experience this sex should be as easily located in the correct genus as is the opposite sex and the males will trace out quite readily in this section of the key, although two or three genera are omitted as females are not available.

KEY TO GENERA†

1. Fourth vein with a widely divergent fork beyond the posterior cross-vein and with an appendage at the bend (16); mesonotum scarcely longer than wide 2
   Fourth vein without such fork though often with strong curvature; mesonotum usually conspicuously longer than wide 8
2. Front scarcely excavated above from anterior view 3
   Front strongly excavated above from anterior view 4
3. Sixth (anal) vein present .... **Psilopiella** Van Duzee
   Sixth vein absent .... **Leptorhethum** Aldrich
4. Arista not differentiated from the third antennal segment which is produced style-like and extremely long .... **Megistostylus** Bigot
   Arista clearly differentiated 5
5. Arista apical .... **Chrysosoma** Guerin
   Arista dorsal, rarely sub-apical 6
6. Lower part of the face with hairs (83) .... **Laxina,** n. g.
   Lower part of the face without hair 7
7. Scutellum with four bristles (16, 85) .... **Condylostylus** Bigot
   Scutellum with a pair of strong bristles and sometimes a weak basal hair on either side (17, 71) .... **Sciapus** Zeller

* 1922 (1921). Abh. Zool.-bot., Gesselsch., Wien, xiii, pp. 1-395.

† **Syntormon** Lœw appears to be distinct from **Synarthrus** to which our American species belong.

8. Thorax almost as broad as long; head wider than high; the front deeply excavated from anterior view; face wide (**48, 51**). * **Mesorhaga** Schiner
   Thorax and head different.. 9
9. Basal segment of the posterior tarsi with stout bristles above (**24, 42, 57**)..† **Dolichopus** Latreille
   Basal segment of the posterior tarsi without bristles above.......... 10
10. Mesopleura produced as a finger-like strip along the posterior edge of the anterior coxæ (**20**)..........................‡ **Liancalus** Lœw
    Mesopleura normal, not produced as above......................... 11
11. Males 12
    Females 64
12. Hypopygium long, extending forward under the venter............. 13
    Hypopygium short, only the lamellæ sometimes extending forward... 25
13. Arista long pubescent, sub-plumose.............................. 14
    Arista quite short pubescent or bare............................. 16
14. Third antennal segment very large, acuminate.....**Leptocorypha** Aldrich
    Third antennal segment normal, short and somewhat pointed........ 15
15. Face wide below, roof-like over the mouth, concave in the middle (**22, 25, 46, 77**)..............................§ **Pelastoneurus** Lœw
    Face narrow, especially below (**66, 79**)...............**Sarcionus** Aldrich
16. About the posterior third of the mesonotum concave or flattened..... 17
    Mesonotum flattened only immediately before the scutellum.......... 20
17. Second antennal segment prolonged along the inner side of the third (**67, 73**)...................................**Cœloglutus** Aldrich
    Second antennal segment not prolonged along the third............ 18
18. Hypopygium pedunculate, at least not sessile, reaching almost to the base of the abdomen 19
    Hypopygium sessile, the basal part not reaching half way to the base of the abdomen although the lamellæ may do so (**45, 81**). ¶**Paraphrosylus** Becker
19. Third and fourth veins strongly converging apically, the distance between them at their apices not more than half as great as opposite the posterior crossvein; bristles rarely yellow (**63, 86**). ‖**Medeterus** Fischer
    Third and fourth veins separated apically by at least two-thirds the distance separating them opposite the anterior crossvein; hair and bristles yellow (**31, 59**).....................°**Thrypticus** Gerstæcker
20. The face hangs down apron-like below the eyes (**15, 38**). ø**Polymedon** Osten Sacken
    The face is not produced as a long, thin ribbon.................. 21

* Van Duzee, 1917, Ent. News, xxviii, p. 123.
† Van Duzee, Cole and Aldrich, 1921, Bull. 116, U. S. N. Mus.; Van Duzee and Curran, 1934, Amer. Mus. Novit. Nos. 683, 684.
‡ Van Duzee, 1917, Ent. News, xxviii, p. 126.
§ Van Duzee, 1923, Ann. Ent. Soc. Amer., xvi, p. 30.
¶ Van Duzee, 1924, Pan-Pac. Ent., i, p. 73.
‖ Van Duzee, 1928, Psyche, xxxv, p. 38.
° Van Duzee, 1921, Psyche, xxviii, p. 124.
ø Van Duzee, 1927, Ann. Ent. Soc. Amer., xx, p. 123.

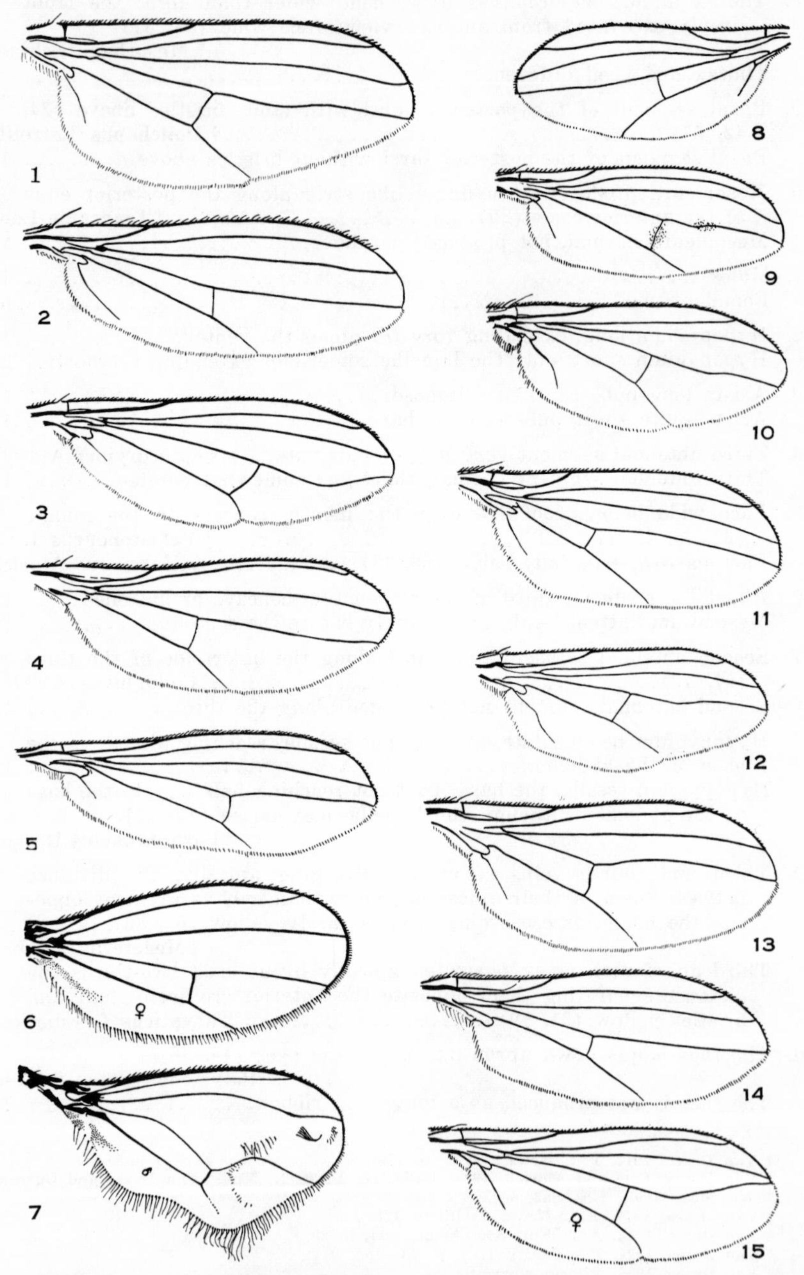

Dolichopidæ I.—1, **Anepsiomyia linearis**; 2, **Campsicnemus latipes**; 3, **Stolidosoma permutatum**; 4, **Xanthina nigromacula**; 5, **Diostracus prasinus**; 6, 7, **Collinellula magistri**; 8, **Peloropeodes brevis**; 9, **Synarthrus tricoloripes**; 10, **Keirosoma albicinctum**; 11, **Chrysotimus luteus**; 12, **Nematoproctus flavicauda**; 13, **Chrysotus discolor**; 14, **Thinophilus ochreifacies**; 15, **Polymedon dilaticosta.**

21. Third and fourth veins parallel apically.......................... 22
    Third and fourth veins strongly converging apically or the fourth strongly curved forward 23

22. First antennal segment bare above (8, 33)....... * **Peloropeodes** Wheeler
    First antennal segment haired above at apex (55, 70). †**Gymnopternus** Lœw

23. Fourth vein with a rather sharply rounded curvature and parallel with the third at the tip (46).....................**Paracleius** Bigot
    Fourth vein straight beyond the crossvein or with a gentle curvature (44, 61) 24

24. Head conspicuously higher than wide, the face extending to the lower edge of the eyes; fourth vein curved beyond the posterior crossvein (29, 44)...............................‡**Tachytrechus** Walker
    Head but little higher than wide, the face not reaching the lower edge of the eyes; fourth vein straight beyond the crossvein (61, 76). **Hercostomus** Lœw

25. Costa reaching to the fourth vein................................ 26
    Costa ending at the third vein (58).................§**Asyndetus** Lœw

26. First antennal segment bare above.............................. 34
    First antennal segment haired above, at least apically............. 27

27. Arista dorsal, rarely subapical.................................. 29
    Arista apical or practically so.................................. 28

28. Third antennal segment bilobed or with a strong anuglar projection below on the basal third (30, 40)................**Hypocharassus** Mik
    Third antennal segment triangular or subtriangular (18, 74). ¶**Argyra** Macquart

29. Acrostical setæ absent 31
    Acrostical setæ present, two-rowed.............................. 30

30. Fourth vein doubly bent at nearly right angles (68, 82). **Syntomoneurum** Becker
    Fourth vein not sharply curved (3, 37).............**Stolidosoma** Becker

31. Arista long pubescent or plumose................................ 32
    Arista very short pubescent or bare............................. 33

32. Third and fourth veins parallel or only a little convergent. **Phylarchus** Aldrich
    Fourth vein strongly curved forward, very close to the third at its apex; (Some species of **Sarcionus** and **Pelastoneurus** might come here as a few have short genitalia).

33. Palpi very small; face very narrow (1).............**Anepsiomyia** Bezzi
    Palpi larger; lower section of face twice as wide as long (5, 34). **Diostracus** Lœw

34. Mesonotum with an elongate, longitudinal depression on the posterior third or slightly less.. 35

---

* Van Duzee, 1926, Tr. Amer. Ent. Soc., liii, pp. 39-46 (Kophosoma).
† Curran, 1933, Amer. Mus. Novit. No. 682, p. 2.
‡ Green, 1922, Proc. U. S. N. M., lx, Article 17.
§ Van Duzee, 1919, Ent. News, xxx, p. 248.
¶ Van Duzee, 1925, Proc. U. S. N. M., lxvi, Art. 23.

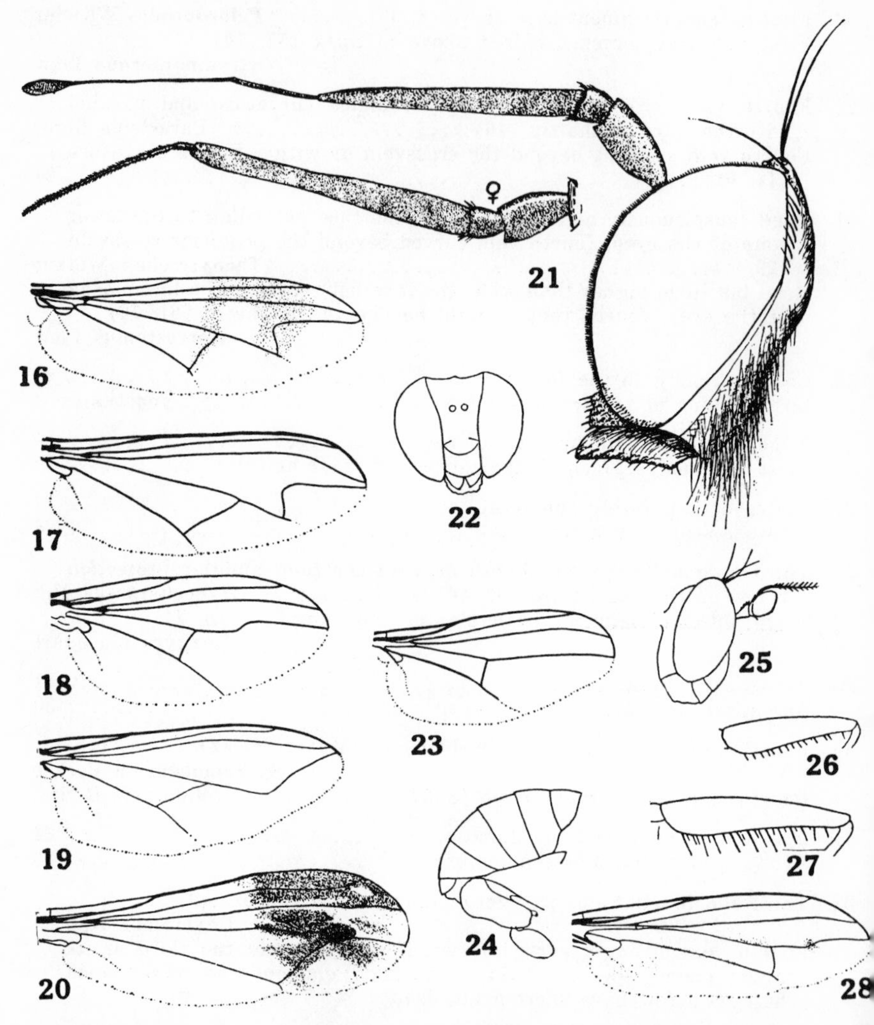

Dolichopidæ II.—16, **Condylostylus sipho**; 17, **Sciapus unifasciatus**; 18, **Argyra**; 19, **Plagioneurus univittatus**; 20, **Liancalus similis**; 21, **Rhaphphium**; 22, **Pelastoneurus vagans**; 23, **Diaphorus**; 24, **Dolichopus**, ♂ abdomen; 25, **Pelastoneurus vagans**; 26, **Hydrophorus**, front femur; 27, **Scellus**, front femur; 28, **Scellus vigil**.

Mesonotum without such depression, usually with a slight, transverse depression 42

35. Acrostical setulæ present, at least at the anterior edge of the thorax. 36
Acrostical setulæ absent............................**Micromorphus** Mik

36. Third and fourth veins almost parallel beyond the crossvein......... 37
Third and fourth veins converging before the apex (52).
*__Neurigona__ Rondani

37. Acrostical setulæ present only on the anterior margin of the mesonotum (60) ....**Xanthochlorus** Lœw
Acrostical setulæ extending at least to the suture.................. 38

38. Sixth (anal) vein present... 39
Sixth (anal) vein absent.. 40

39. Hair and bristles wholly yellow (11)................**Chrysotimus** Lœw
Hair and bristles not yellow (52)..................*__Neurigona__ Rondani

40. Arista apical (36).. 41
Arista sub-apical; third antennal segment pointed (62)..†**Achalcus** Lœw

41. Pleura metallic (6, 7)...............................**Collinellula** Aldrich
Pleura yellow; third antennal segment rounded apically (4, 36).
†**Xanthina** Aldrich

42. Fourth vein ending well before the tip of the wing; posterior crossvein very oblique (19).. 43
Fourth vein ending but little before the tip of the wing, usually in or slightly behind it... 44

43. Dorsocentral bristles strong (19)..................**Plagioneurus** Lœw
Dorsocentral bristles hair-like..................**Œdematopus** Van Duzee

44. Posterior crossvein situated less than its own length from the wing margin along the fifth vein, the basal segment of the posterior tarsi longer than the second (43).. 45
Posterior crossvein much shorter than the ultimate section of the fifth vein, or the first segment of the posterior tarsi decidedly shorter than the second (9).. 49

45. Pteropleura haired in front of the posterior spiracle................ 46
Pteropleura bare 47

46. First antennal segment with stout setulæ below (72)..**Melanderia** Aldrich
First antennal segment bare below (**Hydrophorus** pt) (80).
Millardia, n. g.

47. Pteropleura produced to form a mammiform projection in front of the posterior spiracle (27, 28)..........................‡**Scellus** Lœw
Pteropleura plain 48

48. Middle of the propleura haired; third antennal segment subrectangular, the arista dorsal (26, 43, 56, 78)............§**Hydrophorus** Fallén

* Van Duzee, 1913, Ann. Ent. Soc. Amer., vi, pp. 22-61.

† The only difference in these two genera appears to be in the shape of the third antennal segment. They should probably be united.

‡ Greene, 1924, Proc. U. S. N. M., lxv, Art. 16.

§ Van Duzee, 1926, Pan.-Pac. Ent., iii, p. 5.

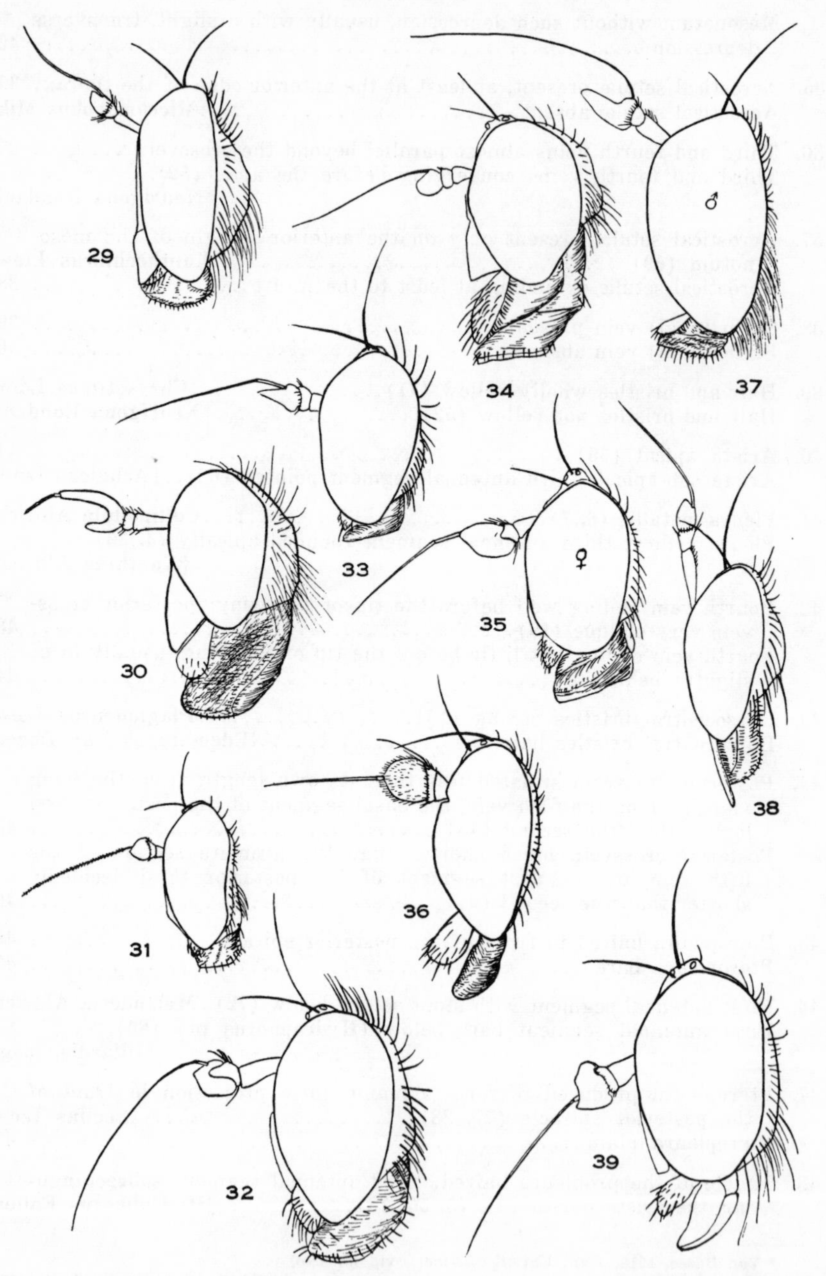

Dolichopidæ III.—29, **Tachytrechus**; 30, **Hypocharasus**; 31, **Thrypticus**; 32, **Neosyntormon**; 33, **Peloropeodes brevis**; 34, **Diostracus prasinus**; 35, **Parasyntormon asellus**; 36, **Xanthina subcurva**; 37, **Stolidosoma permutatum**; 38, **Polymedon dilaticosta**; 39, **Chrysotus discolor**.

Middle of propleura bare; third antennal segment rather triangular, the arista apical (45, 81)....................*Paraphrosylus Becker

49. Acrostical setulæ present, though weak.......................... 50
Acrostical setulæ absent (14)...............†Thinophilus Wahlberg

50. Arista apical or practically so, sometimes arising a little above the tip of the pointed third antennal segment...................... 51
Arista dorsal 58

51. Propleura bare or with a single bristly hair in the middle........... 53
Propleura haired in the middle.................................. 52

52. Second antennal segment produced thumb-like into the third on the inner surface (9, 84)............................‡Synarthrus Lœw
Second antennal segment not strongly convex apically (21, 47, 49). §Rhaphium Meigen

53. Second longitudinal vein very strongly sinuous (65) (**Eutarsus** Aldrich, Van Duzee, not Lœw).....................**Diaphorus** Meigen
Second vein at most gently undulate............................. 54

54. Second antennal segment produced thumb-like into the third; abdomen elongate and not tapering apically (35, 54). **Parasyntormon** Wheeler
Second antennal segment usually transverse, rarely strongly convex apically, if so the abdomen short, cylindrical and tapering from base to apex 55

55. Body silvery white pollinose; middle of propleura with a single bristle (64) ....**Leucostola** Lœw
Body rarely silvery pollinose; middle of propleura bare............. 56

56. Lower section of face not differentiated.......................... 57
Lower section of face strongly differentiated and large (45, 81). *Paraphrosylus Becker

57. Front narrow, if wide the apex of the abdomen with four bristles (23, 75)....................................¶Diaphorus Meigen
Front wide, the face usually very narrow, the apical abdominal segment without strong bristles (13, 39).............‖Chrysotus Meigen

58. Second antennal segment produced thumb-line into the third on the inner surface (32, 50, 69)......................**Neosyntormon, n. g.**
Second antennal segment transverse or gently convex apically....... 59

59. Middle of propleura bare.. 60
Middle of propleura haired....................................... 63

60. Abdomen flattened dorsoventrally (2)..........°Campsicnemus Walker
Abdomen not flattened dorsoventrally 61

* Van Duzee, 1924, Pan.-Pac. Ent., i, p. 73.
† Van Duzee, 1926, Ann. Ent. Soc. Amer. xix, p. 35.
‡ Van Duzee, 1925, Tr. Amer. Ent. Soc. l, pp. 257-287 (Syntormon).
§ Curran, 1926-1927, Tr. Roy. Can. Inst., xv, pt. 2, pp. 249-260; xvi, pt. 1, pp. 99-179.
¶ Van Duzee, 1922, Bull. Buff. Soc. Nat. Sci., xi, pp. 161-194.
‖ Van Duzee, 1924, Bull. Buff. Soc. Nat. Sci., xiii, pp. 1-53; 1931, Amer. Mus. Novit. No. 483 (Neotropical)
° Van Duzee, 1917, Ent. News, p. 124; Curran, 1933, Amer. Mus. Novit. No. 682, p. 5.

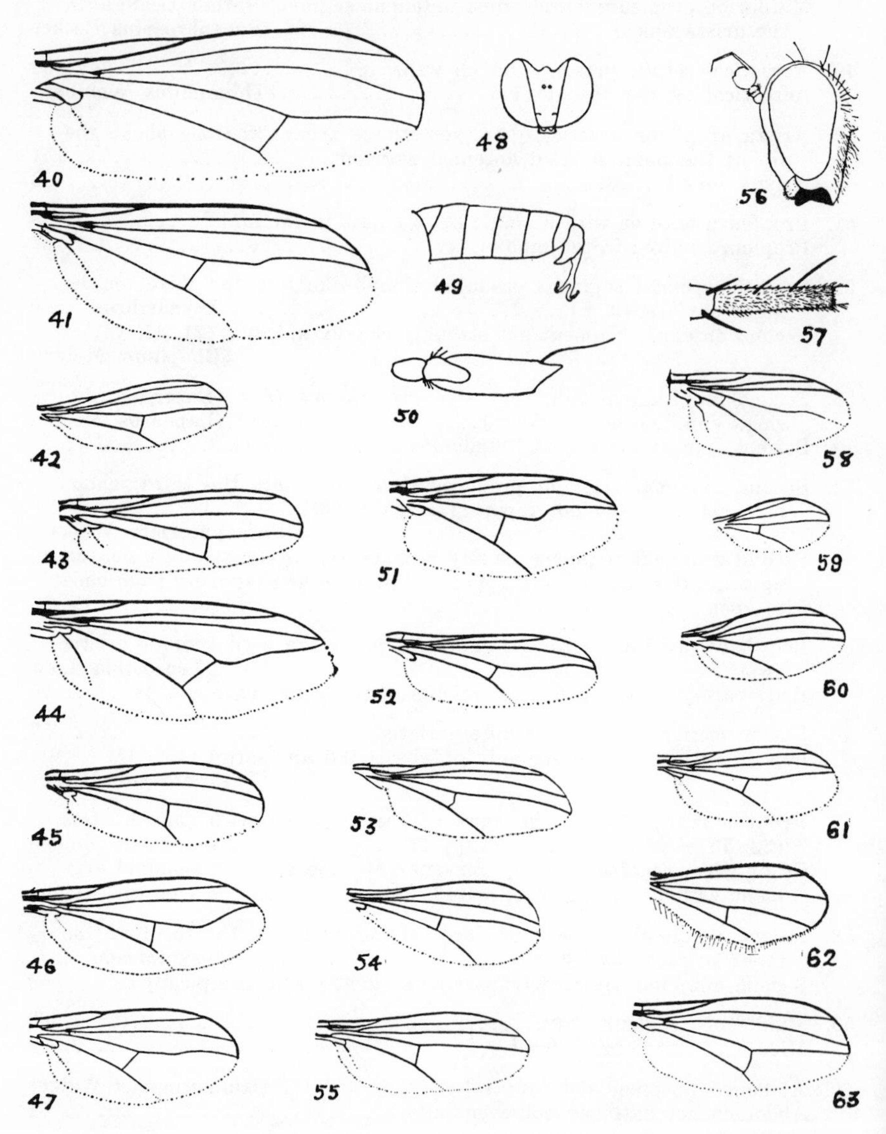

Dolichopidæ IV.—40, **Hypocharassus**; 41, **Dolichopus**; 42, **Sympycnus**; 43, **Hydrophorus**; 44, **Tachytrechus sanus**; 45, **Paraphrosylus**; 46, **Petastoneurus**; 47, **Rhaphium**; 48, **Mesorhaga**, head from in front; 49, **Rhaphium** abdomen from side; 50, **Neosyntormon**; 51, **Mesorhaga**; 52, **Neurigona**; 53, **Sympycnus**; 54, **Parasyntormon**; 55, **Gymnopternus**; 56, **Hydrophorus**; 57, **Dolichopus**, 1st segment of posterior tarsus; 58, **Asyndetus syntormoides**; 59, **Thrypticus**; 60, **Xanthochlorus**; 61, **Hercostomus**; 62, **Achalcus**; 63, **Medeterus.**

61. Abdomen long and slender, more or less cylindrical, the genitalia small (**42, 53**) ....*Sympycnus Lœw
Abdomen either tapering or short with large, asymetrical hypopygium 62

62. Abdomen tapering; genitalia small; scutellum without secondary basal bristles ....**Teuchophorus** Lœw
Abdomen short and chunky, the genitalia large, asymetrical (**Kophosoma** Van Duzee, **Pachypyga** Parent) (**8, 33**)...†**Peloropeodes** Wheeler

63. Third and fourth veins rather approximate apically (**12**).
‡**Nematoproctus** Lœw
Third and fourth veins almost parallel beyond the crossvein (**10**).
Keirosoma Van Duzee

Females

64. Costa continuing to the fourth vein.............................. 65
Costa ending at the third vein (**58**)..................§**Asyndetus** Lœw

65. Pteropleura produced to form a mammiform protuberance in front of the posterior spiracle (**27, 28**)..........................**Scellus** Lœw
Pteropleura not produced 66

66. First antennal segment haired above............................ 67
First Antennal segment bare above.............................. 80

67. Arista plumose or very long pubescent......................... 68
Arista short pubescent or bare.................................. 70

68. No acrostical setulæ.............................**Phylarchus** Aldrich
With acrostical setulæ... 69

69. Face wide, bulging below (**22, 25, 46, 77**)...........**Pelastoneurus** Lœw
Face narrower, never strongly bulging below the middle (**66, 79**).
Sarcionus Aldrich
¶**Leptocorypha** Aldrich

70. Arista dorsal 72
Arista apical 71

71. Third antennal segment subtriangular or triangular (**18, 74**).
Argyra Macquart
Third antennal segment either furcate or with a strong, angular projection basally (**30, 40**).........................**Hypocharassus** Mik

72. Propleura with hair or a single bristly hair on the median portion... 73
Propleura entirely bare on the median portion (**5, 34**)...**Diostracus** Lœw

73. Pteropleura with a small tuft of very fine short hairs in front of the posterior spiracle (these are sometimes difficult to discern in most views); fourth vein not curved forward near the apex (**55, 70**).
Gymnopternus Lœw
Without such hairs, or the fourth vein strongly curved forward apically 74

---

* Van Duzee, 1930, Pan-Pac. Ent., vii, pp. 35-36.
† Van Duzee, 1926, Tr. Amer. Ent. Soc., lii, pp. 39-46 (Kophosoma).
‡ Van Duzee, 1930, Psyche, xxxvii, p. 167.
§ Van Duzee, 1919, Ent. News, xxx, p. 248.
¶ Female unknown.

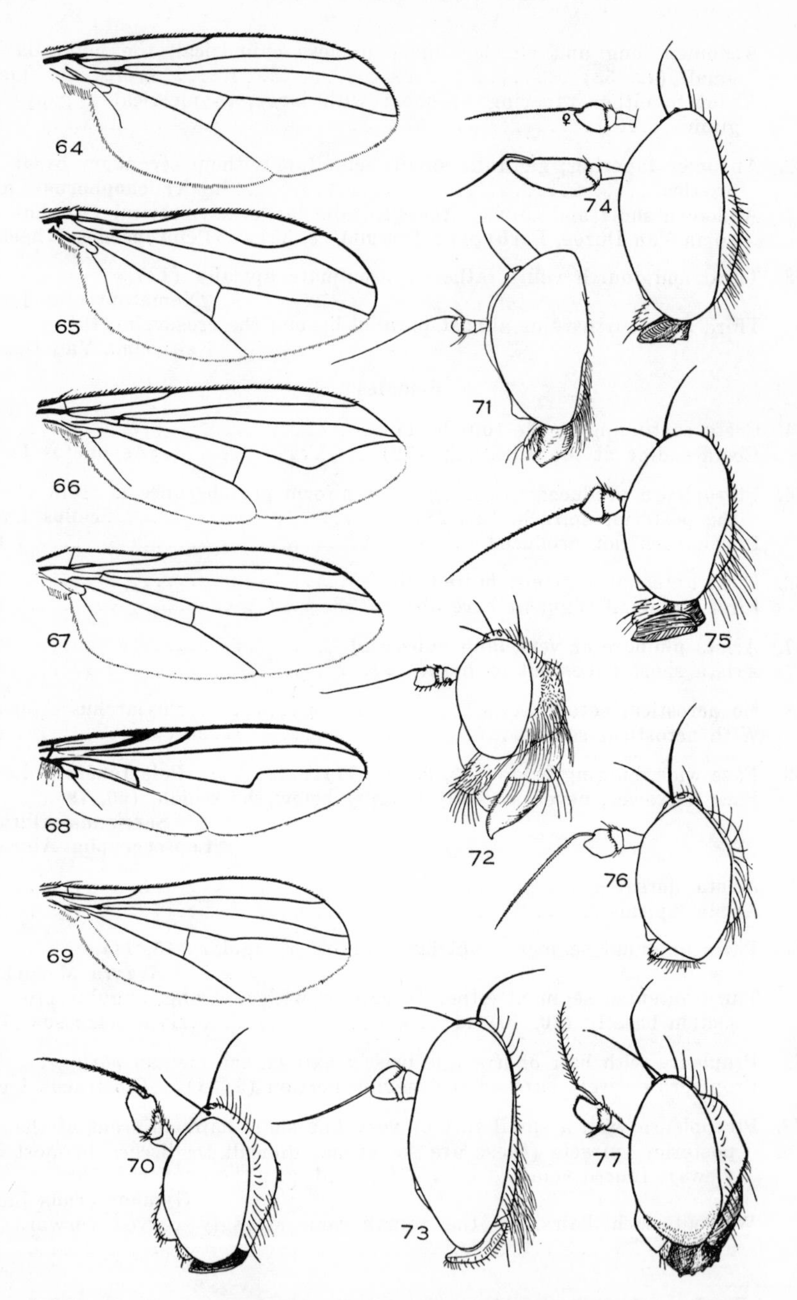

Dolichopidæ V.—64, **Leucostola cingulata**; 65, **Diaphorus nigripennis**; 66, **Sarcionus pectinatus**; 67, **Cœloglutus bicoloripes**; 68, **Syntomoneurum alatum**; 69, **Neosyntormon**; 70, **Gymnopternus**; 71, **Sciapus tener**; 72, **Melanderia mandibulata**; 73, **Cœloglutus bicoloripes**; 74, **Argyra**; 75, **Diaphorus**; 76, **Hercostomus**; 77, **Pelastoneurus abbreviatus.**

74. Third and fourth veins conspicuously converging apically or the fourth strongly curved 75
Third and fourth veins parallel beyond the posterior crossvein, or nearly so (1)................................**Anepsiomyia** Bezzi

75. Fourth vein approaching the third in a broad curve and running parallel with it at the apex..............................**Paracleius** Bigot
Fourth vein not so strongly approaching the third or not parallel with it apically (3).. 76

76. A second pair of weak scutellar bristles or hairs; metapleura bare; fourth vein sometimes angularly curved.......................... 77
A single pair of scutellar bristles; metasternum with two or three minute hairs in front of the posterior spiracle, visible only in some lights; fourth vein with single curve (3, 37).......**Stolidosoma** Becker

77. Fourth vein straight beyond the posterior crossvein, though approaching the third (61, 76)............................**Hercostomus** Lœw
Fourth vein curved beyond the crossvein.......................... 78

78. Sixth (anal) vein extending close to the margin of the wing (68).... 79
Sixth (anal) vein extending little more than half way to the margin of the wing beyond the anal cell (15, 38).....**Polymedon** Osten Sacken

79. Fourth vein bent twice in middle of apical section (68, 82).
Syntomoneurum Becker
Fourth vein not bent at nearly right angles (29, 44)..**Tachytrechus** Lœw

80. A longitudinal flat or slightly concave area on the posterior third of the mesonotum 81
No such area although there is usually a more or less distinct transverse depression immediately before the scutellum............... 91

81. Third and fourth veins parallel or almost so beyond the posterior crossvein 82
Fourth vein converging toward the third.......................... 86

82. Hair and bristles wholly yellow.................................. 85
Hair and bristles partly or wholly black or brown................. 83

83. Acrostical setulæ in two rows.................................... 88
Acrostical setulæ distinct only on the anterior border of the mesonotum, or absent 84

84. Yellowish species (60).........................**Xanthochlorus** Lœw
Black or green species.........................**Micromorphus** Mik

85. Sixth (anal) vein absent (31, 59)...............**Thrypticus** Gerstæcker
Sixth vein present (11)..........................**Chrysotimus** Lœw

86. Fourth vein conspicuously doubly curved forward beyond the crossvein; sixth (anal) vein reaching the wing margin or practically so, strong and curved backward at the tip; usually large species (52).
* **Neurigona** Rondani
Fourth vein straight beyond the posterior crossvein; sixth vein weak, sometimes represented by a fold and usually curving toward the apex of the wing before its end................................ 87

* Van Duzee, 1913, Ann. Ent. Soc. Amer., vi, pp. 22-61.

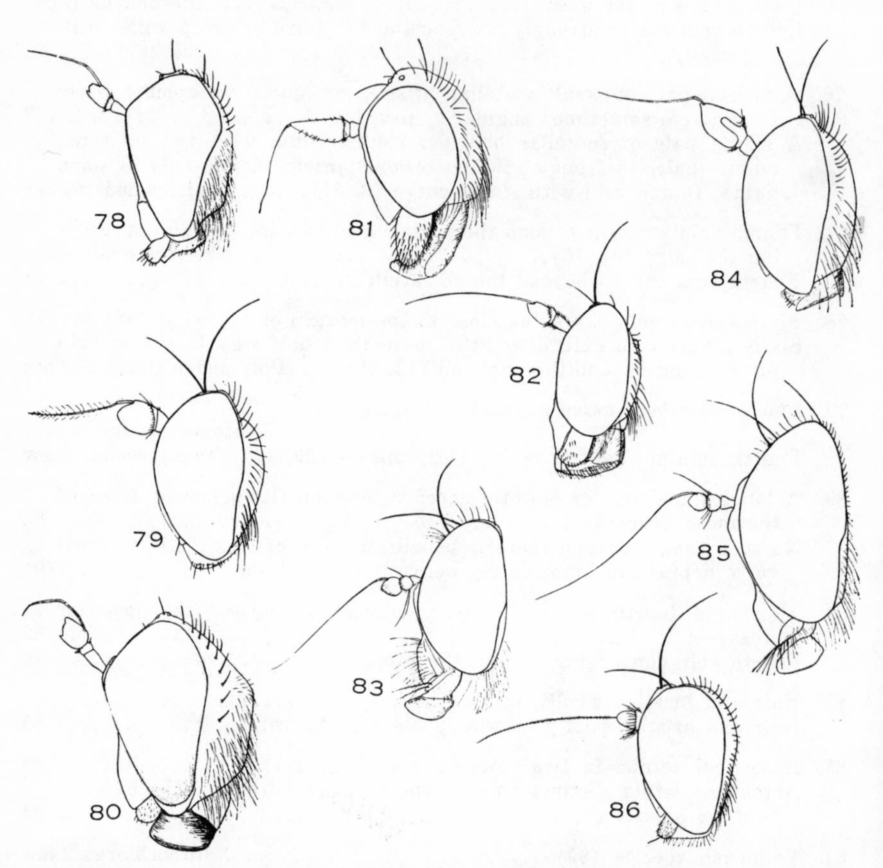

Dolichopidæ VI.—78, **Hydrophorus extrarius**; 79, **Sarcionus actutispina**; 80, **Millardia viridiflos**; 81, **Paraphrosylus prædator**; 82, **Syntomoneurum alatum**; 83, **Laxina caudatus**; 84, **Synarthrus tricoloripes**; 85, **Condylostylus sipho**; 86, **Medeterus nigrimana**.

87. Second antennal segment produced along the inner side of the third (67, 73) .... **Cœloglutus** Aldrich
Second antennal segment not produced along the third (63, 86). **Medeterus** Fischer

88. Sixth (anal) vein absent 89
Sixth (anal) vein extending almost to the wing margin (52). * **Neurigona** Lœw

89. Arista subapical (62) .... **Achalcus** Lœw
Arista apical 90

90. Pleura yellowish (4, 36) .... **Xanthina** Aldrich
Pleura metallic green (6, 7) .... † **Collinellula** Aldrich

91. Fourth vein ending well before the tip of the wing, its outer edge concave just beyond the bend 92
Fourth vein ending but little before the tip of the wing, if curved beyond the posterior crossvein there is no concavity on the outer side 93

92. Dorsocentral bristles strong (19) .... **Plagioneurus** Lœw
Dorsocentral bristles hair-like .... **Œdematopus** Van Duzee

93. Posterior crossvein as long or longer than the ultimate section of the fifth vein; basal segment of the posterior tarsi longer than the second 94
Posterior crossvein rarely as long as the ultimate section of the fifth vein, if so, the basal segment of the posterior tarsi shorter than the second 97

94. Pteropleura haired in front of the posterior spiracle 95
Pteropleura bare in front of the posterior spiracle 96

95. First antennal segment with stout setulæ below (72). **Melanderia** Aldrich
First antennal segment bare below (**Hydrophorus** pt) (80). **Millardia, n. g.**

96. Middle of the propleura haired (26, 43, 56, 78) ..... **Hydrophorus** Meigen
Middle of the propleura bare (45, 81) .... **Paraphrosylus** Becker

97. Acrostical setulæ present 98
Acrostical setulæ absent (14) .... **Thinophilus** Wahlberg

98. Arista apical or practically so, sometimes arising a little above the tip of the pointed third antennal segment 99
Arista dorsal, rarely arising a little beyond the middle of the third segment 105

99. Propleura bare or with a single bristle in the middle 101
Propleura haired in the middle 100

100. Second antennal segment projecting thumb-like into the third on the inner side (9, 84) .... **Synarthrus** Lœw
Second antennal segment transverse or only gently convex apically (21, 47, 49) .... ‡ **Rhaphium** Meigen

---

* Van Duzee, 1913, Ann. Ent. Soc. Amer., vi, pp. 22-61.

† I have not seen specimens of **Collinellula** but the genus is very close to **Xanthina** and no structural differences are mentioned in the description.

‡ Curran, 1926-1927, Tr. Roy. Can. Inst., xv, pt. 2, pp. 249-260; xvi, pt. 1, pp. 99-179.

101. Second antennal segment produced thumb-like into the third on the inner side (35, 54)..........................**Parasyntormon** Wheeler
Second antennal segment transverse or only gently convex apically...102

102. Middle of propleura wholly bare....................................103
Middle of propleura with a single bristly hair (64).....**Leucostola** Lœw

103. Lower section of the face not differentiated, the face short..........104
Lower section of the face strongly differentiated, the face reaching practically to the lower level of the eyes (45, 81).
Paraphrosylus Becker

104. **Diaphorus** Meigen and **Chrysotus** Meigen come here but there are no good characters for the separation of the females.

105. Second antennal segment produced thumb-like into the third on the inner side (32, 50, 69)........................**Neosyntormon,** n. g.
Second antennal segment with the apex at most a little convex on the inner side 106

106. Middle of propleura bare..107
Middle of propleura haired..109

107. Abdomen flattened dorsoventrally, rarely swollen; face narrowest in the middle (2).................................**Campsicnemus** Walker
Abdomen cylindrical or tapering.....................................108

108. Abdomen short and tapering...110
Abdomen long and slender, usually cylindrical or laterally compressed (42, 53)..**Sympycnus** Lœw

109. Third and fourth veins parallel or nearly so beyond the posterior crossvein (10)...............................**Keirosoma** Van Duzee
Third and fourth veins rather approximate apically (12).
Nematoproctus Lœw

110. Scutellum with a secondary pair of weak marginal scutellars situated between the base and the strong pair; sixth vein strongly developed; anal lobe distinct (8, 33)......................**Peloropeodes Wheeler**
Scutellum without secondary basals, but with a pair of apical hairs; sixth vein weakly developed; anal lobe very weak...**Teuchophorus** Lœw

Laxina, new genus

This genus is erected for those species, formerly placed in *Condylostylus, Sciapus* and *Psilopus,* in which the lower section of the face is hairy. The arista is dorsal; mesonotum rather square; scutellum with four bristles and the wings either hyaline or variegated with brown. Genotype:—*Dolichopus patibulatus* Say.

Neosyntormon, new genus

Differs from *Parasyntormon* Wheeler in having the arista dorsal, even though situated toward the apex of the third antennal segment. The propleura is bare and the hypopleura lacks hair. Both these characters are true of *Parasyntormon* also, but all the species of *Synarthrus* Loew have both the propleura and hypopleura haired. Genitalia small. Genotype:—*Parasyntormon montivagum* Wheeler.

P. asellus Wheeler is the only species I have seen belonging to *Parasyntormon.* The genus *Eutarsus* Loew is close to *Neosyntormon* but both the propleura and pteropleura bear fine hair, as in *Synarthrus. Eutarsus* does not occur in America.

Peloropeodes Wheeler

In his original description of this genus one might infer that the arista is apical, but I believe this is erroneous and that the arista is inserted toward the end of the third segment in the male. The type males of *salax* Wheeler, the genotype, all lack the third antennal segment so the point cannot be cleared up at present. Both females, however, are in excellent condition and since no type has been selected for the species, I now select one of the females. On general structure there can be no doubt that both *Pachypyga* Parent and *Kophosoma* Van Duzee are synonyms.

Teuchophorus Lœw

Wheeler has described a species from South Dakota which appears to have been correctly placed. The type is not in good condition, both wings being absent and part of the abdomen eaten away, but from what can be seen the specimen agrees well with European material taken near Leningrad. This genus is very close to *Peloropeodes* differing in having small genitalia, as in *Sympycnus,* less evident anal angle to the wings with less developed sixth vein, and the absence of a pair of small basal bristles on the scutellum in addition to the large pair. As a rule there is a pair of small hairs on the apical portion of the scutellum, absent in the species of *Peloropeodes* I have seen.

Millardia, new genus

This genus is proposed for the reception of species formerly placed in *Hydrophorus* Meigen in which the pteropleura bears conspicuous fine hairs and most, if not all of the species have several pairs of postvertical bristles instead of a single pair. Genotype:—*Hydrophorus viridiflos* Walker.

Family Lonchopteridæ—The Pointed-wing Flies

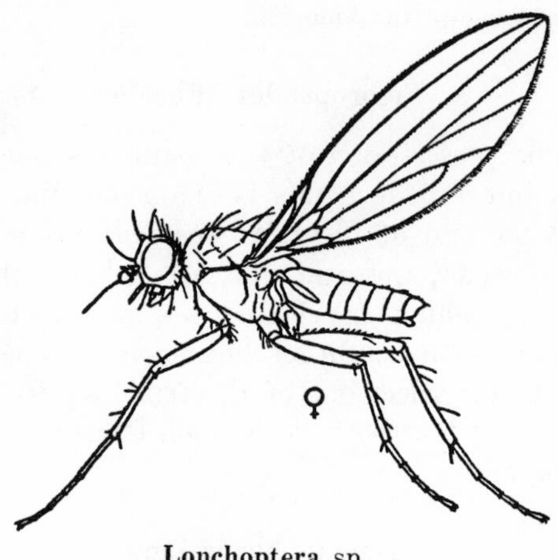

Lonchoptera sp.

Small, slender brownish or yellowish flies, the length 2 to 5 mm.

Head bristly; ocelli present; antennæ short, the third segment rounded, with a terminal arista. Legs moderately long, bristly, the pulvilli very small; empodia absent. Wings pointed apically, with only the basal crossveins, the anal cell closed; first vein very short, the fourth furcate.

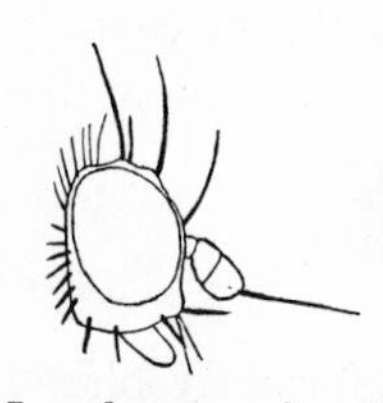

Lonchoptera, head

The adults are found in moist places and especially along shady brooks. The larvæ live under leaves and decaying vegetation; they are flat, with long bristles on the anterior two and apical segments; ten segments, the head not differentiated; posterior apiracles broadly separated on the apical segment. The larva transforms into a prepupa within the larval skin and later into a true pupa.

The family contains less than two dozen species, all belonging to the genus *Lonchoptera* Meigen. A key to the American species is given below. Descriptions of them are contained in American Museum Novitates No. 696.

TABLE OF SPECIES

1. Bristles of the vertex and the orbital cilia wholly yellowish 4
   At least several of the upper orbital cilia black 2
2. Bristles of the vertex black 3
   Bristles of the vertex yellowish; about half the orbital cilia black 4
3. Wings very sharply pointed, very slightly concave posteriorly toward the apex, or at any rate not generally convex .... **uniseta** Curran
   Wings broader and much less sharply pointed, gently convex before the apex .... **occidentalis** Curran
4. Anal vein widely removed from the border of the wing; base of fifth vein with four or five long bristles .... **borealis** Curran
   Anal vein fused with the posterior border of the wing; base of fifth vein with numerous setulæ .... **dubia** Curran

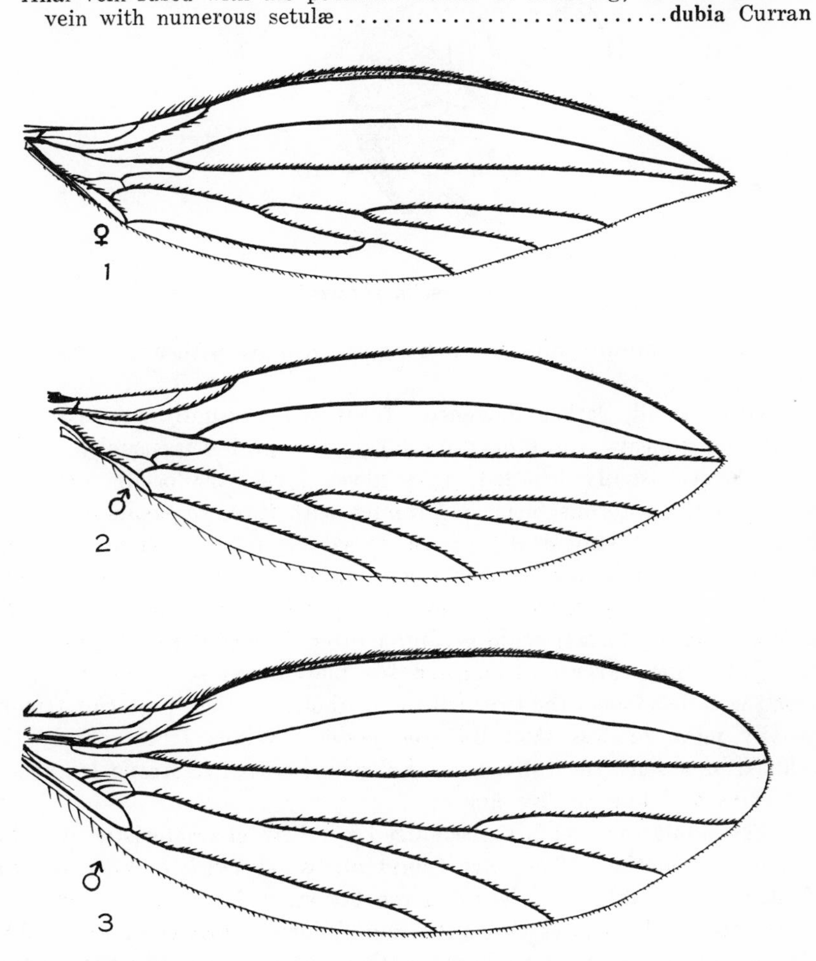

Wings of **Lonchoptera.**—1, **uniseta** Curran; 2, **occidentalis** Curran; 3, **borealis** Curran. (Courtesy American Museum of Natural History.)

Family Phoridæ

Megaselia species.

Small or minute flies, often wingless, usually with a hunch-backed appearance.

Head small, rather flattened; front wide, usually bristled; face short and concave; oral opening large, the proboscis usually fleshy; palpi large, usually bristled; eyes never large, the ocelli sometimes absent in the apterous forms. Antennæ with three segments, the third large, the basal two small; arista dorsal or apical. Thorax usually arched, the scutellum absent in some wingless forms. Abdomen short, usually tapering posteriorly, sometimes partly membranous, especially in the wingless forms; male genitalia often large, in the female small and projecting, large and adapted for piercing in some genera. Legs short, well developed, the tibæ with or without bristles; posterior femora usually more or less laterally compressed. Wings large, poorly developed or absent, the fully developed wings with two strong longitudinal veins and four or five fine ones.

The adults are readily recognized by their characteristic antennæ and wing venation. They are found almost everywhere but are particularly abundant about decaying vegetation, on leaves and windows or in the nests of termites and ants, and following armies of ants. The alate adults move about on leaves with a quick, jerky movement which is quite characteristic of the family.

The larval habits are diverse. Some are parasitic while others are unquestionably scavengers. The larva of *Apocephalus* lives in the heads of ants, the head dropping off when the larva is mature, while that of *Cataclinusa pachychondylæ* lives curled about the necks of ant larvæ and feeds upon the food proffered the latter by the ants. Some species live on decaying animal matter and at least one species has been reared from honey comb. The family is one of great interest and offers an excellent field of study for patient, careful students of animal behavior.

The latest revision of the North American species is by Malloch.* The following key is adapted from Schmitz† and may prove unsatisfactory in some respects, but as I lack very many of the genera I am unable to improve upon it. Some of the characters used appear to be of little value from a generic standpoint but the species included in the genera present differences in addition to those given. Despite the title, Schmitz' paper is little more than a generic revision insofar as the taxonomist is concerned but a complete bibliography is included.

KEY TO GENERA‡

1. Prothoracic spiracle lateral.. 2
   Prothoracic spiracle dorsal (18)..................**Ænigmatias** Meinert

2. Supra-antennal bristles proclinate, if absent the tibiæ lack isolated strong bristles 18
   Supra-antennal bristles erect, divergent or reclinate, if absent the tibiæ bear strong bristles; never wingless.............................. 3

3. Third vein with very evident branch..................................... 4
   Third vein not forked or only obscurely so.............................. 11

* 1912. Proc. U. S. N. M., xliii, pp. 411-529.
† 1929. Rev. der Phoriden, privately published (Dümmler, Berlin & Bonn).
‡ Checked by Dr. C. T. Brues.

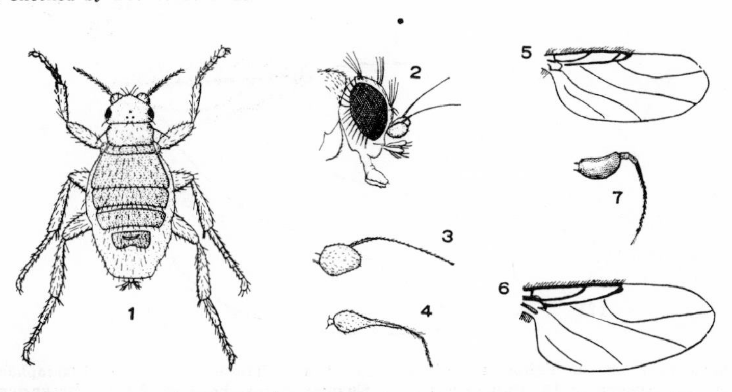

Phoridæ I.—1, **Pulicophora**; ♀; 2, **Megaselia**; 3, **Phora**, antenna; 4, **Conicera**, antenna; 5, **Megaselia**; 6, **Hypocera**; 7, **Apocephalus**, antenna.

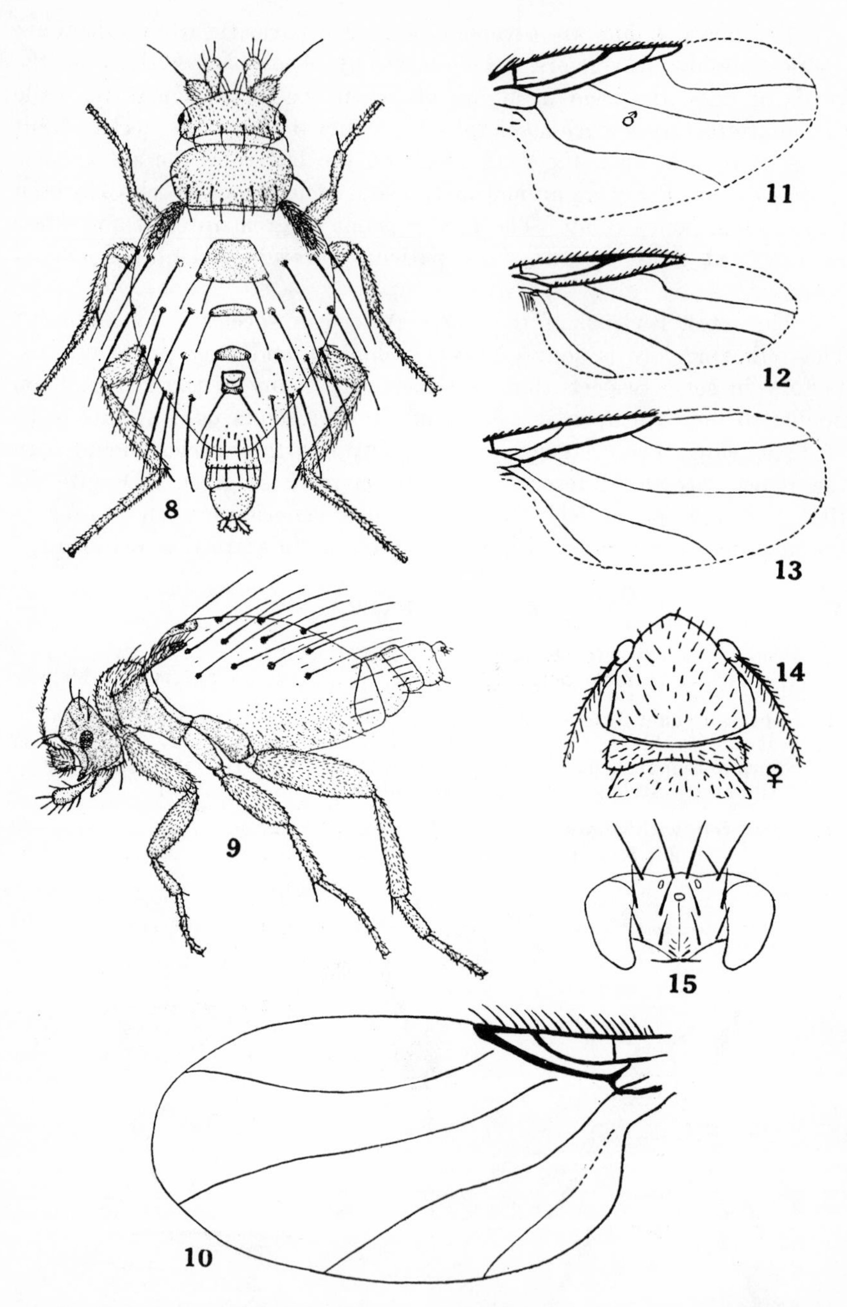

Phoridæ II.—8, 9, **Ecitomyia spinosa,** dorsal and lateral views; 10, **Plastophora;** 11, **Triphleba;** 12, **Aneurina;** 13, **Pulicophora;** 14, **Chonocephalus,** head of ♀; 15, **Beckerina,** head showing bristles.

4. At least the middle tibiæ with strong bristles........................ 5
   Tibiæ without conspicuous bristles (15, 21)...........**Beckerina** Malloch

5. Mesopleura haired, at least in front near the spiracle................ 6
   Mesopleura bare 8

6. Mesopleura with very long bristle............**Chætopleurophora** Schmitz
   Mesopleura without long bristle... 7

7. Posterior tibiæ with from one to three rows of closely placed short setulæ dorsally (19)................................**Dohrniphora** Dahl
   Posterior tibiæ without such ciliate rows..**Chætocnemistoptera** Borgmeier

8. Third vein with closely placed setulæ above (12)...........**Aneurina** Lioy
   Third vein bare or very sparsely setulose............................. 9

9. Middle tibiæ with a strong anterior bristle beyond the middle. **Paraspiniphora** Malloch
   Middle tibiæ with a very weak bristle beyond the middle, or bare.....10

10. Posterior tibiæ with one to three rows of conspicuous, short setulæ dorsally (25) ....**Diploneura** Lioy
    Posterior tibiæ without such setulæ (11).............**Triphleba** Rondani

11. Arista dorsal, at most sub-apical.................................... 12
    Arista apical 17

12. Middle tibiæ without dorsal bristles beyond the basal third........... 13
    Middle tibiæ with more than one pair of dorsal bristles.............. 14

13. Eyes bare (3)......................................**Phora** Latreille
    Eyes haired ....**Chætocnemistoptera** Borgmeier

14. Supra-antennal bristles present (6)....................**Hypocera** Lioy
    Supra-antennal bristles absent 15

15. Ocelli widely separated, their triangle separated from the front anteriorly by a three-ridged depression..............**Stichillus** Enderlein
    Ocelli normal, or the triangle forming a tubercle.................... 16

16. Eyes very large; front very narrow (26)........**Trineurocephala** Schmitz
    Eyes normal; front wide ....**Borophaga** Enderlein

17. Posterior tibiæ with a pair of bristles on the basal half (4, 24). **Conicera** Meigen
    Posterior tibiæ otherwise (22)................**Coniceromyia** Borgmeier

18. Wings entirely normal in size... 19
    Wings smaller than normal or absent.................................. 46

19. Third vein forked 20
    Third vein simple.. 32

20. Posterior tibiæ with a dorsal row of contiguous hairs and a postero-dorsal row of short cilia or at least one or two short bristles....... 23
    Posterior tibiæ without the dorsal row of setulæ and the postero-dorsal cilia 21

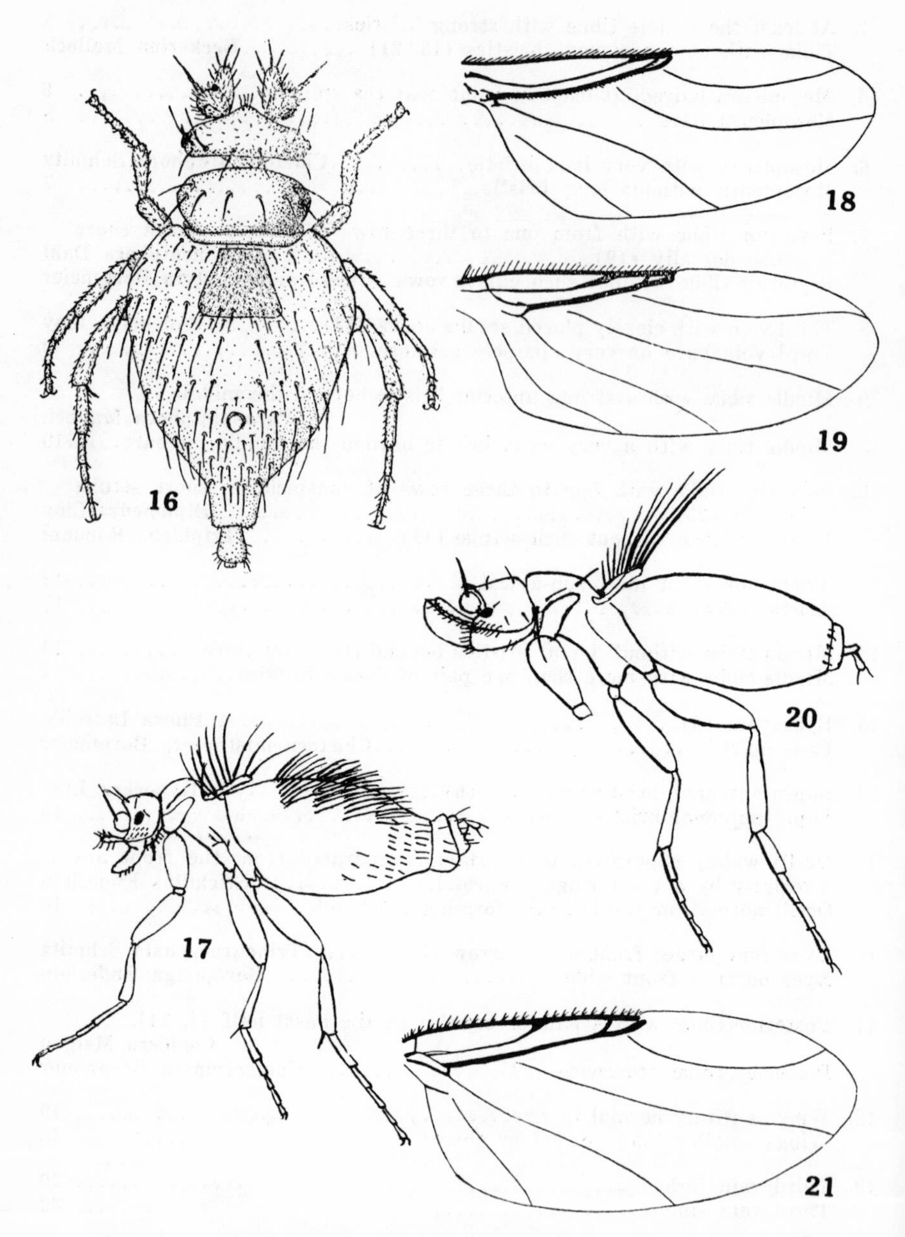

Phoridæ III.—16, **Ecituncula setosa**; 17, **Xanionotum**; 18, **Ænigmatias**, ♂; 19, **Dohrniphora alleni**; 20, **Acontistoptera melanderi**; 21, **Beckerina neotropica.**

21. Anterior orbital bristle present....................**Woodiphora** Schmitz
At least the anterior orbital bristle absent.......................... 22

22. All the bristles on the anterior half of the front missing (23).
Gymnophora Macquart
Median frontals present...........................**Metopina** Macquart

23. Supra-antennals entirely missing................................ 24
At least one pair of supra-antennals............................... 26

24. Arista apical or subapical.. 25
Arista dorsal ....**Cremersia** Schmitz

25. Hypopygium large; anal segment laterally compressed, the outline lancet-shaped; fifth sternite with long apical hairs.
Neodohrniphora Malloch
Hypopygium small, the anal segment long and linear; ovipositor of female chitinized and projecting..............**Apocephalus** Coquillett

26. Front with four rows of bristles.................................. 27
Bristling of the front incomplete; arista apical.
Acanthophorides Borgmeier

27. Upper pair of post-antennal bristles erect, directed more or less outward 28
Upper pair of post-antennals proclinate or reclinate, not directed outward 29

28. Upper post-antennals distinctly proclinate and directed a little outward ....**Pseudohypocera** Malloch
Upper post-antennals directed outward (7).......**Apocephalus** Coquillett

29. Weak vein beyond the third vein weak or absent..........**Syneura** Brues
This vein distinct... 30

30. Epistoma strongly produced, tube-like............**Trophithauma** Schmitz
Face normal, not produced... 31

31. Proboscis very long and thin (♂ unknown).....**Rhyncophoromyia** Malloch
Proboscis normal (**Phalocrotophora** Enderlein) (2, 5)...**Megaselia** Rondani

32. Bristling of the front complete (as in **Megaselia**) or with additional bristles 33
Bristling incomplete, the anterior orbital or other bristles absent..... 37

33. Front with additional bristles on the median area.
Pseudacteon Coquillett
Front with normal number of bristles.............................. 34

34. The weak vein lying parallel with the costa absent or indistinct...... 35
This vein distinct (2, 5)..............................**Megaselia** Rondani

35. Costa short, widened and almost filling the costal cell.
Parametopina Borgmeier
Costa short but not abnormally widened............................ 36

36. Apices of first and third veins approximate...............**Syneura** Brues
Apices of first and third veins not approximated (10).
Plastophora Brues

37. Bristles of the front normal except for the absence of the anterior pair of frontals 38
Bristles of the front differing in other ways 44

38. A weak vein lies parallel with the costa beyond the third vein 39
This vein absent 41

39. First vein wholly bare 40
First vein with one or two small bristles basally **(20)**.
Acontistoptera Brues

40. Third and fourth weak veins very strongly curved toward each other.
Metopina Macquart
Third and fourth veins normal **(1, 13)** .... **Pulicophora** Dahl

41. First vein present 42
First vein absent **(8, 9)** .... **Ecitomyia** Brues

42. Front with two pairs of post-antennal bristles 43
Front with one pair of post-antennal bristles **(17)** ..... **Xanionotum** Brues

43. Post-antennal bristles of equal size .... **Ecitophora** Schmitz
Post-antennal bristles of two sizes .. **Ecitoptera** Borgmeier and Schmitz

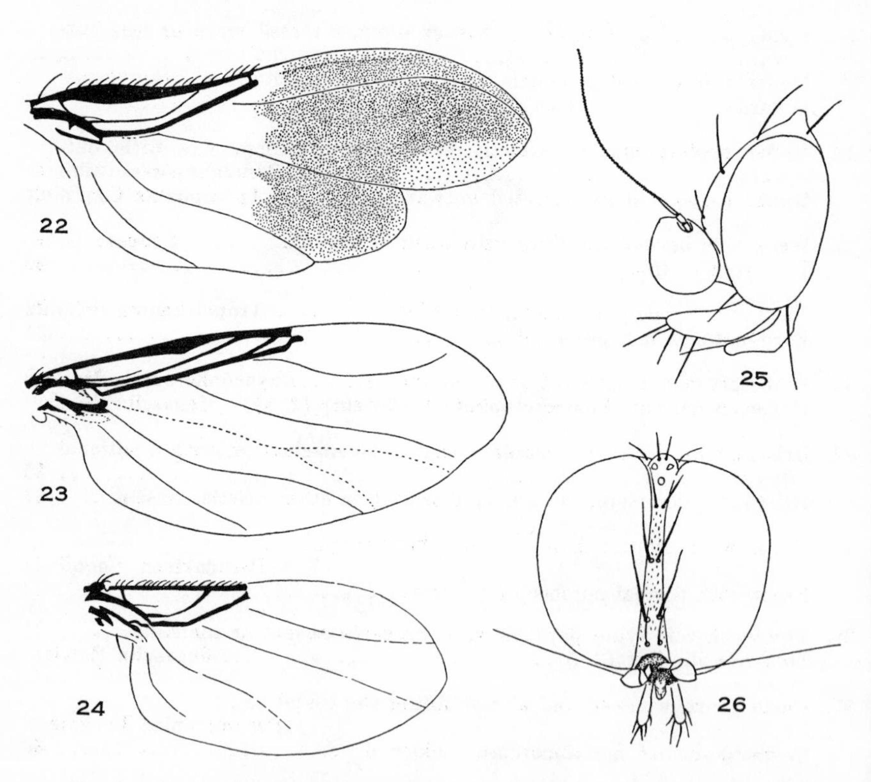

Phoridæ IV.—22, **Coniceromyia vespertilio**; 23, **Gymnophora verrucata**; 24, **Conicera**; 25, **Diploneura**; 26, **Trineurocephala.**

44. Post-antennal bristles not distinguishable from others along the anterior border of the front........................**Cataclinusa** Schmitz
Post-antennals absent 45

45. Front bristled only at the vertex and along the upper, inner margins of the antennal grooves which are narrower than the space between them; wings without basal transverse vein (**14**).
Chonocephalus Wandolleck
Front narrow, only the post-antennal and pre-ocellar bristles absent.
Melaloncha Brues

46. Wings wholly absent or microscopic.............................. 52
Wings distinctly developed though small........................... 47

47. Ocelli present 48
Ocelli absent 50

48. Wings with trace of several veins................................ 49
Wings with at most the costal vein visible; halteres absent.
Ecitophora Schmitz

49. Proboscis geniculate or bent, distinctly elongate.
Ecitoptera Borgmeier & Schmitz
Proboscis normal ....**Commoptera** Brues

50. Wing rudiments with long bristles................................ 51
Wing rudiments with hairs or cilia (**8, 9**)..............**Ecitomyia** Brues

51. Eyes situated well behind the front margin of the head in profile; halteres present, though small (**17**)................**Xanionotum** Brues
Eyes situated at the front margin of the head in profile; halteres absent (**20**) ....**Acontistoptera** Brues

52. Ocelli present (**1, 13**)..................................**Pulicophora** Dahl
Ocelli absent 53

53. Thorax without bristles (**14**)................**Chonocephalus** Wandolleck
Thorax with bristles (**16**)..........................**Ecituncula** Schmitz

Family Platypezidæ—The Flat-footed Flies

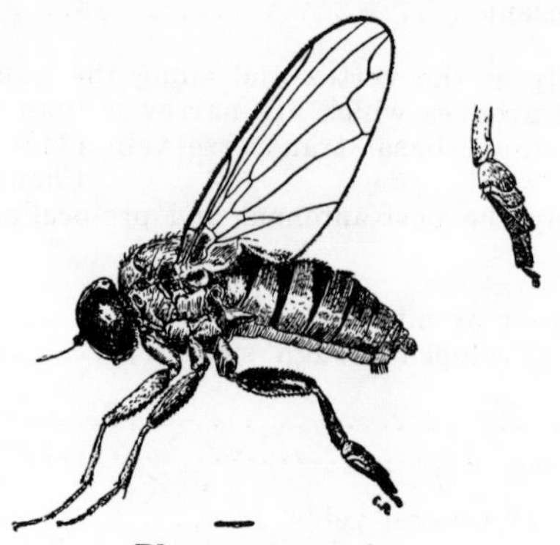

Platypeza species.

These are small flies with short hair and bristles, characterized by the wing venation and peculiarly shaped posterior tarsi, the basal segment being (usually) much flattened and sometimes strikingly ornamented.

Head hemispherical, as broad or broader than the thorax and closely applied to it; face depressed, short and broad; eyes bare, holoptic in the males and in some females; ocelli present. Antennæ porrect, the basal two segments short, the third more or less elongate-oval, pyriform or conical, with a terminal arista. Thorax rather stout, the mesonotum and scutellum with bristles. Legs short and strong, the posterior pair more or less thickened and at least the basal segment of their tarsi thickened or variously ornamented. Wings rather large; third vein simple, the fourth sometimes forked; apical cell open; basal cells rather small; posterior crossvein rarely absent. Abdomen rather short, broad and tapering or laterally compressed; hypopygium generally small.

The larvæ have been found in fungi and are flat, oval in outline, with jointed thread-like appendages on the sides of the segments. The puparia are rather similar to the larvæ in appearance.

For the most part the Platypezids are not common in collections nor are they often met with in the field. Williston states that they have been observed dancing in small swarms but they are usually found upon the leaves of bushes and low trees where they move about in a characteristic, jerky but remarkably agile manner. Mr. Johnson has obtained most of his specimens of *Agathomyia* by sweeping foliage. The species of *Callimyia* prefer moist woods. Fewer than thirty North American species are known.

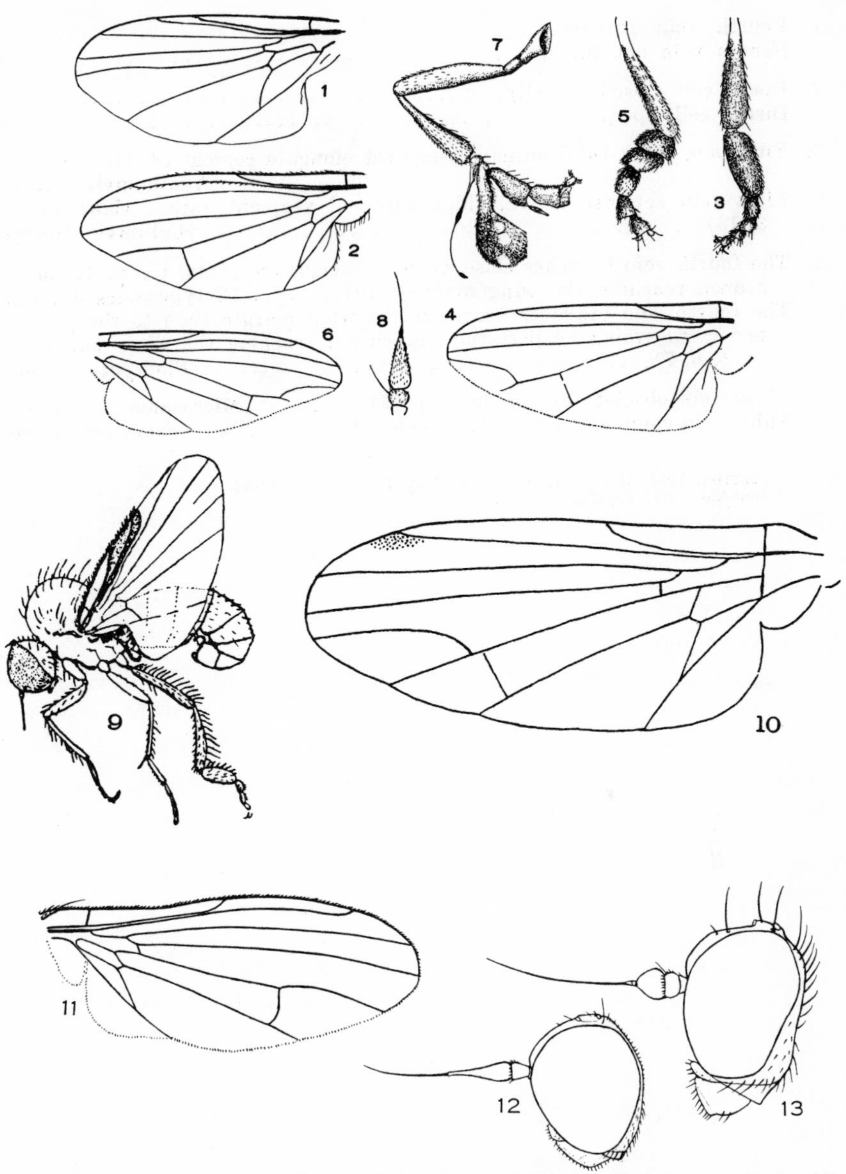

Platypezidæ.—1, **Platycnema;** 2, **Callimyia;** 3, **Callimyia,** hind tarsus of ♂; 4-7, **Platypeza,** wings and posterior legs; 8, **Agathomyia, antenna;** 9, **Microsania pectipennis;** 10, **Platypezoides diversa;** 11, 12, **Agathomyia;** 13, **Callimyia.**

KEY TO GENERA

1. Fourth vein furcate.. 4
   Fourth vein not furcate... 2

2. Discal cell closed apically.. 3
   Discal cell open... 5

3. First vein bare; third antennal segment elongate conical (**8, 11, 12**). *__Agathomyia__ Verrall
   First vein setulose above; third antennal segment rather short (**2, 3, 13**) ....†**Callimyia** Meigen

4. The fourth vein branches close to the posterior crossvein, the posterior branch reaching the wing margin (**10**).........**Platypezoides** Johnson
   The fourth vein branches nearer to the wing margin than to the posterior crossvein, the posterior branch not reaching the wing margin (**4, 5, 6, 7**)..*__Platypeza__ Meigen

5. Third vein obsolete except apically (**9**)...........**Microsania** Zetterstedt
   Third vein complete; three closed cells (**1**)........**Platycnema** Zetterstedt

---

* Johnson, 1923, Occ. Pap. Bost. Soc. Nat. Hist., v, pp. 51-58.
† Johnson, 1916, Psyche, xxiii, pp. 27-33.

Family Pipunculidæ—The Big-headed Flies

This family is characterized by the very large head and thinly pilose or practically bare body.

Head broader than the thorax, nearly spherical, composed chiefly of the large eyes; eyes of the male contiguous above the antennæ or closely approximated, in the female separated by a narrow front; face narrow. Antennæ small, three segmented, the third segment oval, reniform or aculeate below; arista dorsal. Ocelli present; proboscis small, usually concealed. Abdomen composed of six or seven segments, small, cylindrical; hypopygium conspicuous, often large; ovipositor usually elongate and extending forward under the abdomen. Legs simple; tarsi broad, the basal segment elongate; pulvilli present. Wings much longer than the abdomen; basal cells elongate; anal cell reaching close to the wing margin, rarely incomplete; apical cell narrowed apically but always open; three posterior cells; venation incomplete in *Chalarus* Walker. Squamæ vestigial. The wings are held flat over the abdomen when the insect is at rest.

The larvæ are parasitic on bugs of the families Cicadellidæ and Miridæ, and perhaps on other Homoptera and Heteroptera. The larvæ are elliptical, thick, depressed and narrowed at either end, naked and small. The oval, shining black puparia are obtuse at either end and somewhat smaller than the larvæ.

Pipunculidæ are found commonly wherever their hosts are to be found, but more especially near the edges of woods, in clearings and along shaded lanes. I have found them in large numbers in a small clearing in which the ground was kept constantly moist from a spring at one end and also along the edges of streams. Almost one hundred species are known from North America, most of which belong to the genus *Pipunculus*. Cresson* has monographed the family.

---

* Trans. Amer. Ent. Soc., xxxvi, pp. 267-329.

KEY TO GENERA

1. Discal cell closed 2
   Discal cell open apically the venation incomplete (3)......**Chalarus Walker**
2. Scutellar bristles present.. 3
   Scutellar bristles absent (1, 2)........................**Pipunculus Latreille**
3. Ocellar bristles absent; occiput widely visible from the side (6, 7).
   Nephrocerus Zetterstedt
   Ocellar bristles present; occiput narrow (4, 5)..............**Verrallia Mik**

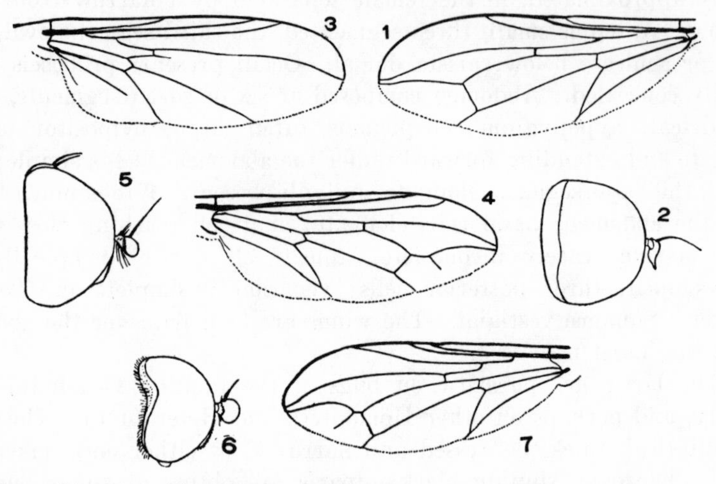

Pipunculidæ.—1, 2, **Pipunculus**; 3, **Chalarus**; 4, 5, **Verrallia**; 6, 7, **Nephrocerus.**

Family Syrphidæ—The Flower Flies

Small to large flies, the wing with a "spurious vein" lying between the third and fourth longitudinal veins.

Head variable, but never elongated, except rarely the produced epistoma. Face moderately wide to wide; eyes usually holoptic in the males, always dichoptic in the females. Oral opening large; proboscis usually short. Antennæ short or elongate, composed of three segments, usually with a dorsal arista, rarely with a terminal style. Ocelli present. Thorax rather large and robust, rarely with bristles. Abdomen composed of four to six visible segments; hypopygium rarely prominent, though often large. Legs variable but never elongate. Wings comparatively large; third vein never branched, straight or dipped into the apical cell, the apical cell closed; basal cells long; anal cell closed before the margin of the wing, always long; between the third and fourth veins a strong fold or "spurious vein", rarely absent, which is characteristic of the family.

The Syrphidæ comprise one of the largest and most popular groups of Diptera. They may be found anywhere and many species are very common. Most of them visit flowers but some occur only in woods, in moist places, in fields, or near ants' nests, depending upon their habits. The adults display great variation in habitus but may be recognized at once by their characteristic wing venation. Any locality with varied habitat should yield at least a hundred species and the general collector is certain to have many of them in his collection. Most of the common species are easily recognized by the use of "Williston's Synopsis" but on the whole the family is a difficult one, many of the genera and species being difficult to separate by means of keys and descriptions. Unfortunately there is no recent revision of the North American forms of which less than half are included in Williston's work. The number of short papers dealing with the family is very large and the literature scattered through numerous periodicals. Many attempts have been made to divide the Syrphidæ into subfamilies but with little success. Some of the groups may be well defined in one region but almost every character thus far used is found to lose its value when the study is extended to include the world fauna.

Almost all of the Syrphids are beneficial and they are second in importance only to the bees as pollinators of plants. Many of them live upon aphids, (plant lice) and mealy bugs in the larval stages. A few are known to be definitely injurious.

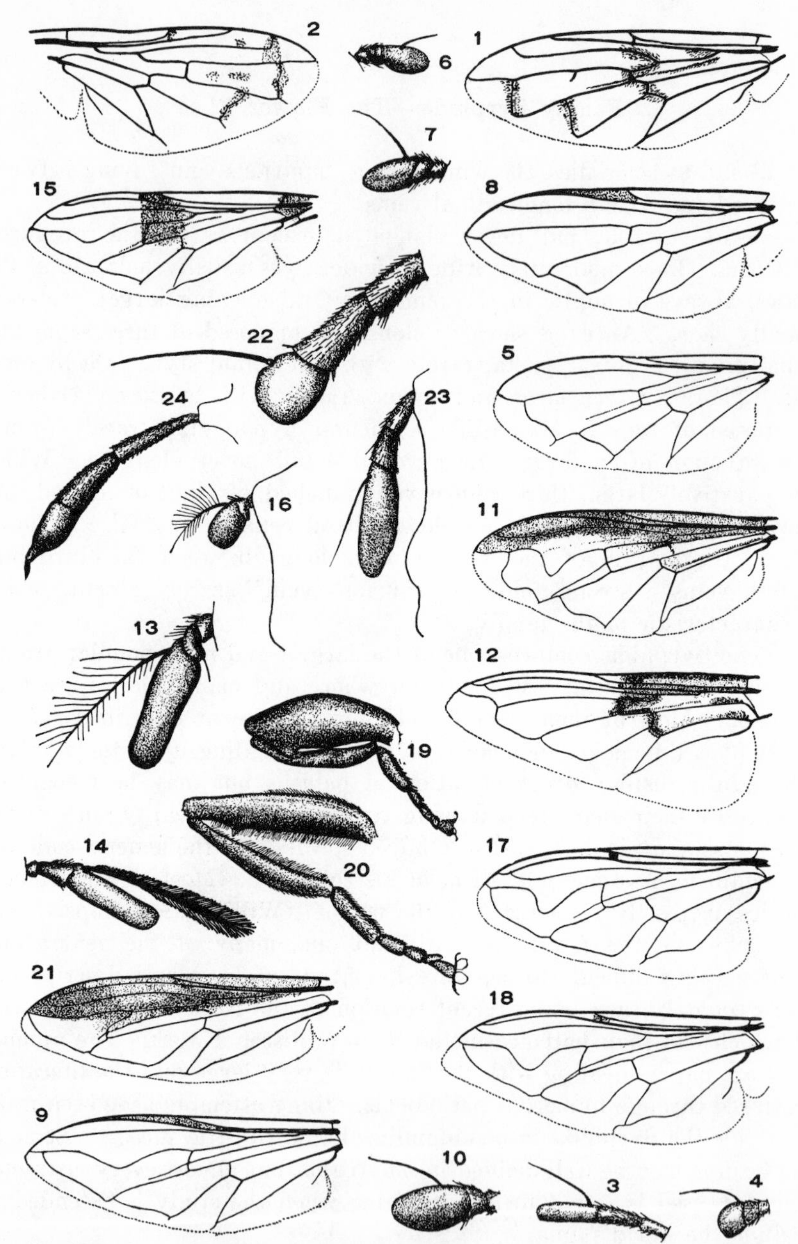

Syrphidæ I.—1, **Microdon**; 2, **Orthoneura nitida**; 3, **Orthoneura nitida,** antenna; 4, **Chrysogaster nigripes,** antenna; 5, **Paragus**; 6, **Pipizella,** antenna; 7, **Paragus,** antenna; 8, **Cheilosia**; 9, **Syrphus laxus**; 10, **Syrphus laxus,** antenna; 11, **Salpingogaster**; 12, **Volucella**; 13, **Volucella,** antenna; 14, **Copestylum marginatum,** antenna; 15, **Arctophila flagrans**; 16, **Sericomyia militaris,** antenna; 17, **Eristalis**; 18, **Elophilus fasciatus**; 19, **Tropidea quadrata,** hind leg; 20, **Milesia,** hind leg; 21, **Spilomyia longicornis**; 22, **Spilomyia longicornis,** antenna; 23, **Chrysotoxum,** antenna; 24, **Cerioides,** antenna.

The larvæ are variable in habits and form. Some live in the nests of ants, termites, bees, etc., but nothing is known regarding their relationship to their hosts. Most of them live in decaying vegetation, while a very few are injurious to growing plants and bulbs. Among the well-known larval forms are the rat-tailed maggots which may be found in liquid media containing decaying vegetation and very rarely in carrion. The larvæ may be divided into four types: the Microdon type, with an unusually hard, convex upper surface and flat, soft ventral surface; the Syrphus type, some of which approach the first group in appearance, living upon aphids, decaying vegetation and plants; the short-tailed maggots, living in decaying vegetation; and the rat-tailed maggots which live in liquid media.

In the key to the genera several minute characters are used. These may prove difficult at first but once the student is familiar with them they will be found to be most useful. In some cases there may be difficulty in deciding the genus to which a species belongs but comparison with specimens of known genera will aid in reaching a decision. The final recourse, after careful study, is to send the puzzle to a specialist and receive his opinion. Most of them will gladly tell you what it is and return the specimen.

KEY TO GENERA

1. Antennæ with a terminal style, the third antennal segment tapering.. 2
   Antennæ with a dorsal arista, if sub-apical the third segment is not tapering from the base.. 3

2. Eyes bare (24, 46, 51).......................... * **Cerioides** Rondani
   Eyes pilose ....**Callicera** Panzer

3. Arista bare; antennæ usually longer than the convex, pilose face; third vein usually with a stump of vein extending into the apical cell; anterior crossvein situated before the middle of the discal cell; apical crossvein often recurrent............................ 4
   Arista variable; antennæ usually shorter, if elongate the humeri are bare, or the arista plumose; face concave, tuberculate or carinate, never rather evenly convex 6

4. Third vein with a stump of vein extending into the apical cell....... 5
   Third vein without such stump but there may be one from the fourth vein and from the apical crossvein..............**Mixogaster** Macquart

5. Abdomen spatulate.......................**Rhopalosyrphus** Arribalzaga
   Abdomen not spatulate (1, 53, 59)................. † **Microdon** Meigen

6. Humeri pilose 7
   Humeri bare, often mostly concealed by the occiput................ 18

* Curran, 1925, Kans. Univ. Sci. Bull., xv, p. 25.
† Curran, 1925, Kans. Univ. Sci. Bull., xv, p. 48.

Syrphidæ II.—25, **Ferdinandea**; 26, **Volucella fasciata**; 27, **Eumyiolepta auricaudata**; 28, **Syritta pipiens**; 29, **Xylota pigra**; 30, **Pipizella**; 31, **Platycheirus erraticus**; 32, **Syrphus wiedemanni**; 33, **Sericomyia militaris**; 34, **Polydontomyia curvipes**; 35, **Scæva pyrastri**; 36, **Tropidea quadrata**; 37, **Baccha lemur**; 38, **Trichopsomyia**; 39, **Baccha**; 40, **Apophysophora** (S. Amer.); 41, **Chrysotoxum**.

7. Face perpendicular, with a swelling above; anterior crossvein at the basal fourth of the discal cell; antennæ elongate and porrect; abdomen strongly constricted basally............. **Mixogaster** Macquart
   Face more or less tuberculate or carinate or the oral margin at least slightly prominent 8

8. All the femora with a patch of black setulæ on their bases anteriorly; third vein strongly curved into the apical cell.................... 91
   Posterior femora never with such setulæ; third vein at most moderately curved 9

9. Arista plumose, rarely pectinate; legs never with bristles.......... 10
   Arista bare or pubescent, if short plumose the legs bear bristles..... 16

10. Apical crossvein recurrent.. 11
    Apical crossvein not recurrent, the apical cell never longest at its middle 15

11. Face with three strong tubercles, one on either side of the median tubercle (**76**)..................... ***Ornidia** St. Fargeau and Serville
    Face with only one tubercle or almost flat.......................... 12

12. Arista bushy plumose, appearing more or less strap-like (**14, 65, 75**). † **Copestylum** Macquart
    Arista loosely plumose or pectinate................................. 13

13. Arista pectinate, the upper rays long, the lower ones extremely short. **Volucellosia** Curran
    Arista plumose 14

14. Eyes of the male widely separated, the front much longer than the face .... **Megametopon** Giglio-Tos
    Eyes of male contiguous, the front at most slightly longer than the face (**12, 13, 26, 77**)........................... ‡ **Volucella** Geoffroy

15. Facial side margins very distinct and extending almost to the base of the antennæ 43
    Side margins not extending above the middle of the facial convexity.. 88

16. Apical crossvein strongly recurrent, the first posterior cell longest in the middle and usually with an appendage at this point (**66, 78**). **Citibæna** Walker
    First posterior cell not longest in the middle, the apical cell not strongly recurrent 17

17. Genitalia entirely concealed by the strongly convex abdomen when seen from the side; third antennal segment orbicular, very large; anterior crossvein situated before the middle of the discal cell (**67, 79**). **Nausigaster** Williston
    Genitalia visible from lateral view; third antennal segment never orbicular and abnormally large.................................. 42

18. Antennæ elongate and porrect; thorax and abdomen with bright yellow markings; wasp-like flies (**23, 41, 82**).......... §**Chrysotoxum** Meigen

---

* Curran, 1930, Amer. Mus. Novit. No. 413, p. 2.
† Curran, 1930, Amer. Mus. Novit. No. 413, p. 3.
‡ Curran, 1930, Amer. Mus. Novit. No. 413, p. 6.
§ Shannon, 1926, Pr. U. S. N. M., lxix, Art. 11, p. 3.

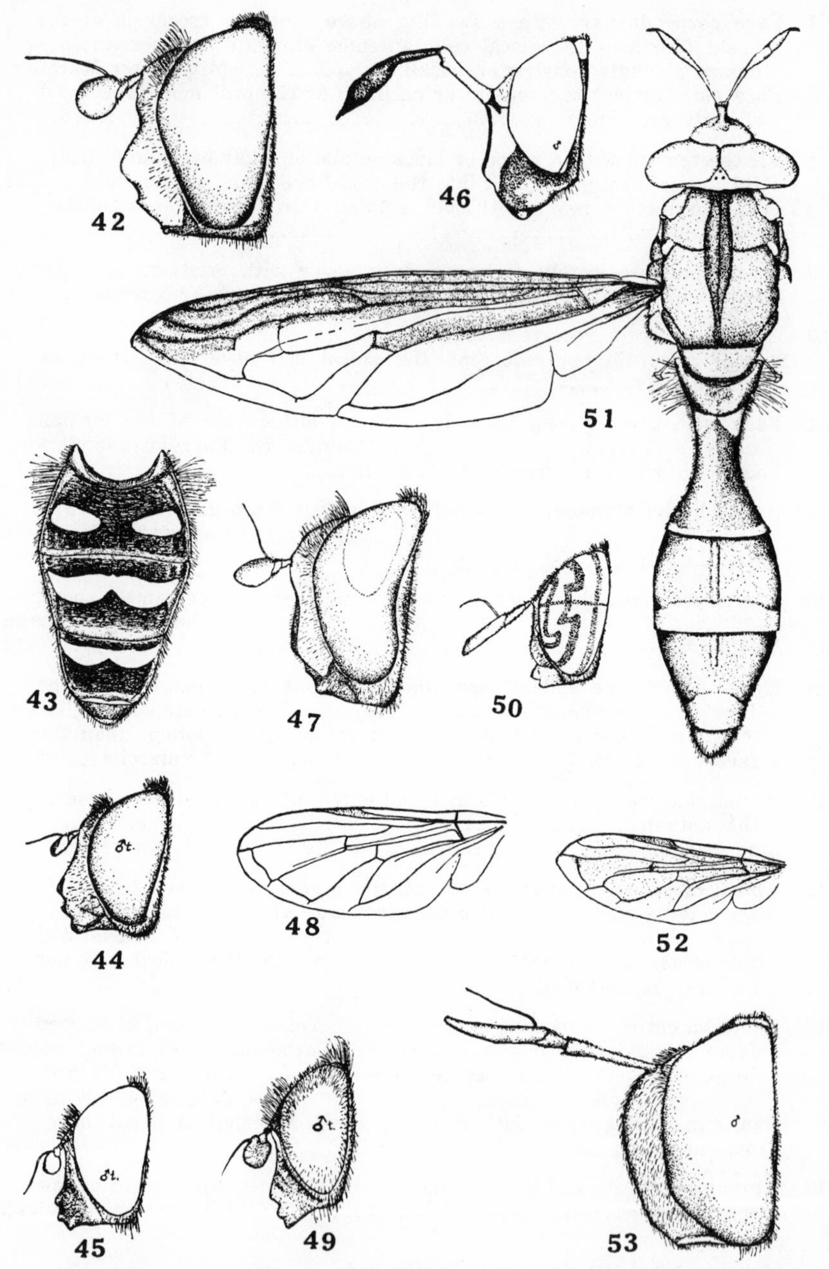

Syrphidæ III.—42, **Epistrophe submarginalis**; 43, **Syrphus aberrantis**; 44, **Melanostoma confusa**; 45, **Cartosyrphus tarda**; 46, **Ceriodes ancorata**; 47, **Syrphus aberrantis**; 48, **Melanostoma luteipennis**; 49, **Cheilosia ferruginea**; 50, **Orthoneura nitidula**; 51, **Cerioides abdominalis**; 52, **Chrysogaster ontario**; 53, **Microdon fulgens.**

Antennæ shorter, if somewhat elongate they are decumbent and the abdomen drooping or wholly black.............................. 19

19. Face and scutellum more or less yellowish or translucent (if the face is entirely black the abdomen is oval and little more than twice as long as wide)... 20
Face wholly black, the scutellum rarely with a yellow tip........... 38

20. Abdomen drooping, never with yellow fasciæ in American species though often largely reddish; third antennal segment more than twice as long as broad; small species (**7, 80**)........**Paragus** Latreille
Abdomen not normally drooping; antennæ usually short, the third segment rarely twice as long as wide, the abdomen usually with yellow spots or bands 21

21. Abdomen margined (the immediate lateral margins raised and not curving under) (**43**)... 22
Abdomen not margined, the thin side margins curving under........ 27

22. Species with long pile, the base of the abdomen broadly pale yellowish, the abdomen moderately broad; eyes pilose (**68, 81**).
Leucozona Schiner
Species with shorter pile and usually with yellow markings beyond the second segment 23

23. Pleura with very bright, sharply limited yellow markings; front long and narrow ....**Xanthogramma** Schiner
Pleura with diffuse yellowish markings or none; sides of mesonotum sometimes yellow 24

24. Third vein dipped into apical cell; third antennal segment long, robust, pointed; front not inflated; eyes bare; abdomen broad and flat, with wide fasciæ ....**Didea** Macquart
Third vein rarely dipped into apical cell, if so the eyes are pilose or the abdominal spots are arcuate and the front more or less inflated. 25

25. Male genitalia projecting, long and cylindrical; abdomen of female broadly oval, the fifth segment half as long as the fourth (**84, 85**).
Eupeodes Osten Sacken
Male genitalia normal; if the fifth segment of the female is about half as long as the fourth the abdomen has sub-parallel sides and the front is not whitish yellow immediately above the antennæ.... 26

26. Wings practically without villi; front very much swollen; apical cell much broadened on the apical half (**35, 86, 87**)........**Scæva** **Fabricius**
Wings largely villous; front seldom much swollen; apical cell widened in only a few species (**9, 10, 32, 43, 47**)...........***Syrphus** **Fabricius**

27. Pleura with sharply limited yellow markings; no yellow prescutellar spots; mesonotum without cinereous vitta; abdomen elliptical.
Xanthogramma Schiner
Pleura with or without sharply limited yellow markings, if present the abdomen is long and narrow or the mesonotum bears a cinerous median vitta 28

28. Abdomen dark except for a pair of large, basal yellowish spots; eyes pilose ....**Ischyrosyrphus** **Bigot**
Abdomen differently marked; eyes bare............................ 29

---

* Curran, 1930, Bull. Amer. Mus. Nat. Hist., lxi, p. 56; Fluke, 1933, Trans. Wisc. Acad. Sci., Arts & Letters, 28, pp. 63-126.

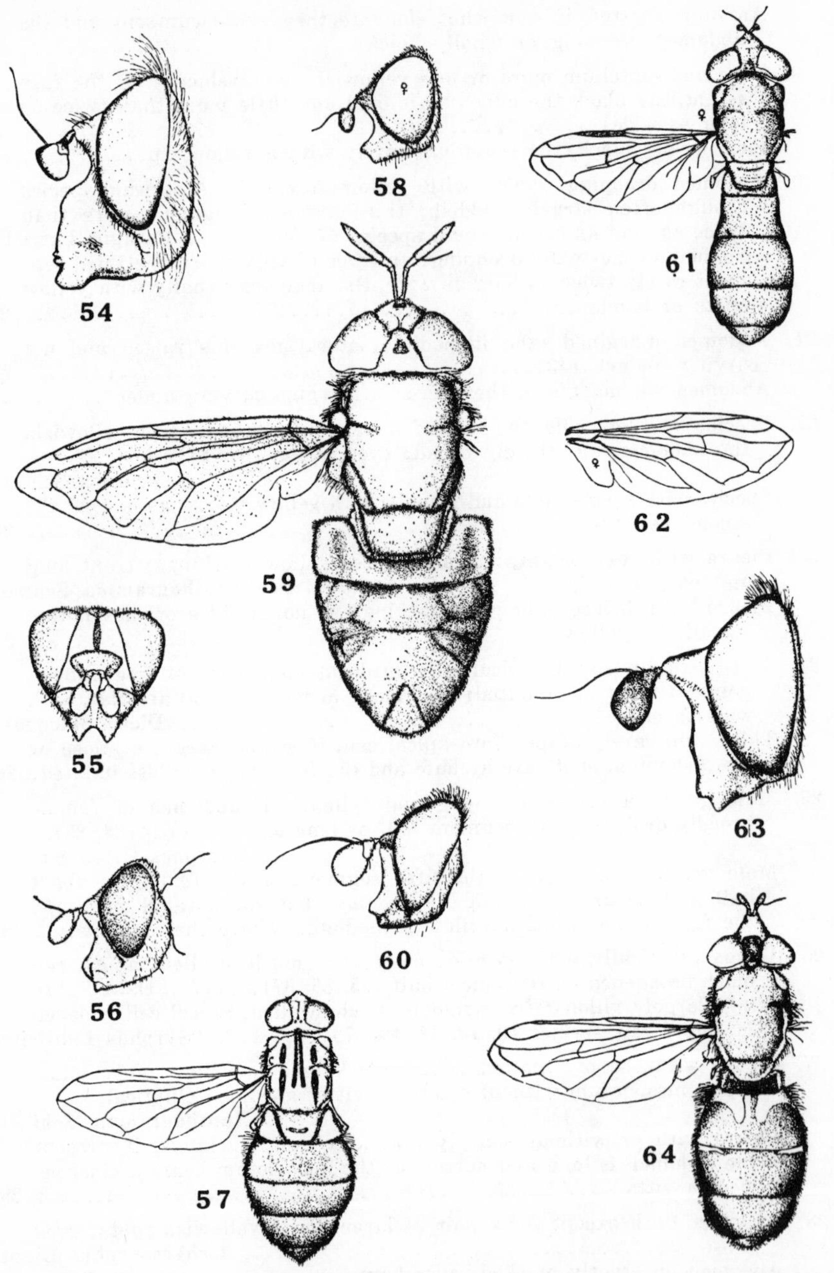

Syrphidæ IV.—54, **Criorrhina caudata**; 55, **Brachyopa basilaris**, head from in front; 56, **Brachyopa basilaris**; 57, **Brachyopa nigricauda**; 58, **Chalcosyrphus depressus**; 59, **Microdon fulgens**; 60, **Cynorhina nigripes**; 61, **Chalcosyrphus depressus**; 62, **Chalcomyia ærea**; 63, **Cynorhina metcalfi**; 64, **Cynorhina pictipes**.

29. Pleura with sharply limited yellow markings or largely yellow, or the abdomen very long and often spatulate........................ 31
Pleura blackish with at most diffuse yellow markings; rarely a pair of small yellow prescutellar spots; abdomen elliptical or with parallel sides 30

30. Abdomen very long, the face and front narrow, the former narrowed below **(37, 39, 71)**..............................*__Baccha__ Fabricius
Abdomen not remarkably long, the face not narrowed below **(42)**. †**Epistrophe** Walker

31. Abdomen very long, club-shaped, spatulate or with parallel sides; face strongly narrowed below; if the abdomen is rather short it is almost unicolorous 36
Abdomen of moderate length; never spatulate, if rather short and with parallel sides it bears bright yellow markings................ 32

32. Large wasp-like species; a pair of small yellow prescutellar spots **(83)** ....**Doros** Meigen
Smaller species, never over 10 mm. in length...................... 33

33. Mesonotum with a median cinereous or metallic vitta; abdomen usually short oval, always very much flattened..................... 34
Mesonotum without such vitta; abdomen with parallel sides or pointed apically in female... 35

34. Posterior femora strongly arcuate in male, the female abdomen tapering apically **(89, 90)**..........................**Toxomerus** Macquart
Posterior femora simple; female abdomen obtuse apically. ‡**Mesogramma** Lœw

35. Male hypopygium globosely enlarged; fifth abdominal segment of the female with fasciæ which may be broken into spots **(72, 88)**. §**Sphærophoria** St. Fargeau and Serville
Male genitalia small; fifth segment of female with four spots, the median pair longitudinally placed, the outer pair oblique. ¶**Allograpta** Osten Sacken

36. Third vein rather deeply looped into the apical cell (Tropical) **(11)**. ‖**Salpingogaster** Schiner
Third vein not deeply looped into the apical cell................... 37

37. Apical crossvein transverse ....**Calostigma** Shannon
Apical crossvein oblique, usually curved **(37, 39, 71)**..°**Baccha** Fabricius

38. Abdomen cylindrical basally **(37, 39, 71)**.............°**Baccha** Fabricius
Abdomen with parallel sides or elliptical......................... 39

39. Wings shorter than the abdomen **(69, 70, 73, 74)**.....**Pyrophæna** Schiner
Wings longer than the abdomen.................................. 40

---

* Curran, 1930, Amer. Mus. Novit. No. 403, p. 1.
† Curran, 1925, (Stenosyrphus). Kans. Univ. Sci. Bull., xv, p. 95.
‡ cf. **Calostigma** Shannon; Key, Curran, 1930, Amer. Mus. Novit. No. 405, p. 1.
§ Curran, 1930, Bull. Amer. Mus. Nat. Hist., lxi, p. 61.
¶ Curran, 1932, Amer. Mus. Novit. No. 519, p. 2.
‖ Curran, 1932, Amer. Mus. Novit. No. 519, p. 5.
° Curran, 1930, Amer. Mus. Novit. No. 403, p. 1.

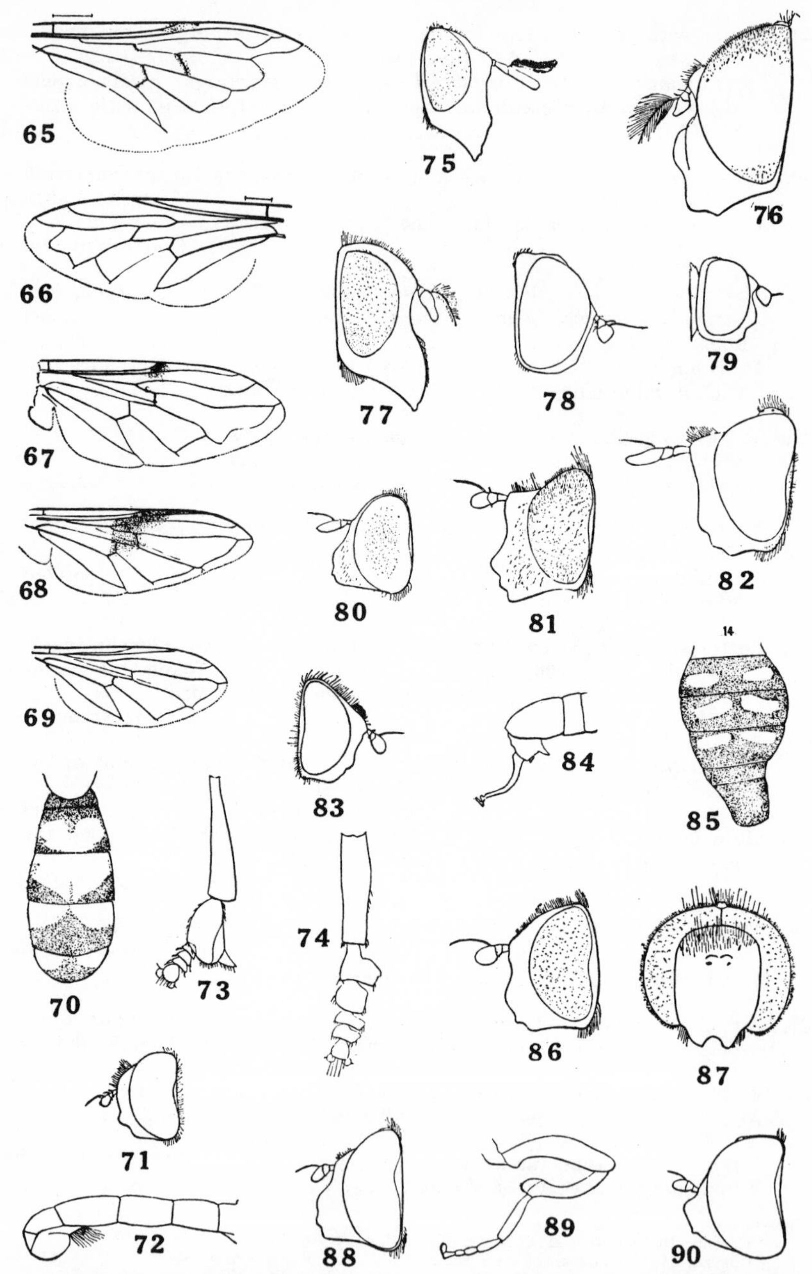

Syrphidæ V.—65, **Copestylum marginatum**; 66, **Citibæna**; 67, **Nausigaster punctulata**; 68, **Leucozona americanum**; 69, **Pyrophæna granditarsis**; 70, **Pyrophæna granditarsis**, abdomen; 71, **Baccha fuscipennis**; 72, **Sphærophoria cylindrica**, abdomen; 73, 74, **Pyrophæna granditarsis**, front and middle tibiæ and tarsi; 75, **Copestylum marginatum**; 76, **Ornidia obesa**; 77, **Volucella bombylans**; 78, **Citibæna**; 79, **Nausigaster**; 80, **Paragus tibialis**; 81, **Leucozona americanum**; 82, **Chrysotoxum**; 83, **Doros æqualis**; 84, 85, **Eupeodes volucris**, ♂ abdomen and genitalia; 86, 87, **Scæva pyrastri**; 88, **Sphærophoria cylindrica**; 89, 90, **Toxomerus geminatus**, hind leg and head.

40. Abdomen broad and flat; face narrowed below; tip of scutellum usually yellow .... **Xanthandrus** Verrall
Abdomen with parallel sides, less flattened; face at most parallel sided, usually widened below; scutellum wholly black........ 41

41. Male with the anterior tibiæ or tarsi, or both, dilated **(31, 100, 101)**. ***Platycheirus** St. Fargeau and Serville
Legs simple **(44, 48)**........ †**Melanostoma** Schiner

42. Anterior crossvein situated well before the middle of the discal cell, or the mesonotum with bristles **(91)**........ 43
Anterior crossvein situated at or beyond the middle of the discal cell, thorax rarely with short spines **(115)**........ 65

43. Eyes bare 44
Eyes pilose 45

44. Facial grooves extending almost to the antennæ; fourth vein joining the third well before the wing-tip; thorax often with bristles; anterior crossvein near the basal third of the discal cell; arista often plumose **(45, 91, 104)**........ ‡**Cartosyrphus** Bigot
Facial grooves less distinct or the anterior crossvein near the middle of the discal cell 50

45. Facial grooves distinct and extending almost to the antennæ **(8, 49)**. §**Cheilosia** Meigen
Facial grooves usually forming pits below and never extending distinctly to near the antennæ........ 46

46. Face evenly receding, the anterior oral margin projecting. **Psilota** Meigen
Face tuberculate, or the oral margin not conspicuously projecting... 47

47. Face widening below........ ¶**Pipiza** Fallen
Face not wider below than at the antennæ........ 48

48. Middle tibiæ slender, not convex anteriorly from dorsal view........ 49
Middle tibiæ in male conspicuously broadened, in the female slightly broadened and gently convex anteriorly from dorsal view; middle coxæ of male with small slender process near their inner end. ‖**Cnemodon** Egger

49. Fifth sternite only half as long as the fifth tergite in the male; antennæ of female elongate oval........ °**Heryngia** Rondani
Fifth sternite three-fourths as long as the tergite; antennæ of female more than twice as long as wide; eyes usually with an indistinct, transverse, less thickly pilose stripe **(6, 30)**........ ø**Pipizella** Rondani

50. Mesonotum with strong bristles, the legs never bristled; abdominal pile erect; face tuberculate **(25, 99)**........ **Ferdinandea** Scopoli
Mesonotum without bristles or the legs also with bristles........ 51

---

* Curran, 1927, Amer. Mus. Novit. No. 247, p. 1.
† Curran, 1930, Bull. Amer. Mus. Nat. Hist., lxi, p. 64.
‡ Shannon, 1922, Ins. Ins. Mens., x, p. 131.
§ Shannon, 1922, Ins. Ins. Mens., x, p. 127.
¶ Curran, 1921, Pr. Calif. Acad. Sci., xi, p. 374.
‖ Curran, 1921, Pr. Calif. Acad. Sci., xi, p. 358.
° Curran, 1921, Pr. Calif. Acad. Sci., xi, p. 354.
ø Curran, 1924, Tr. Amer. Ent. Soc., xlix, p. 340.

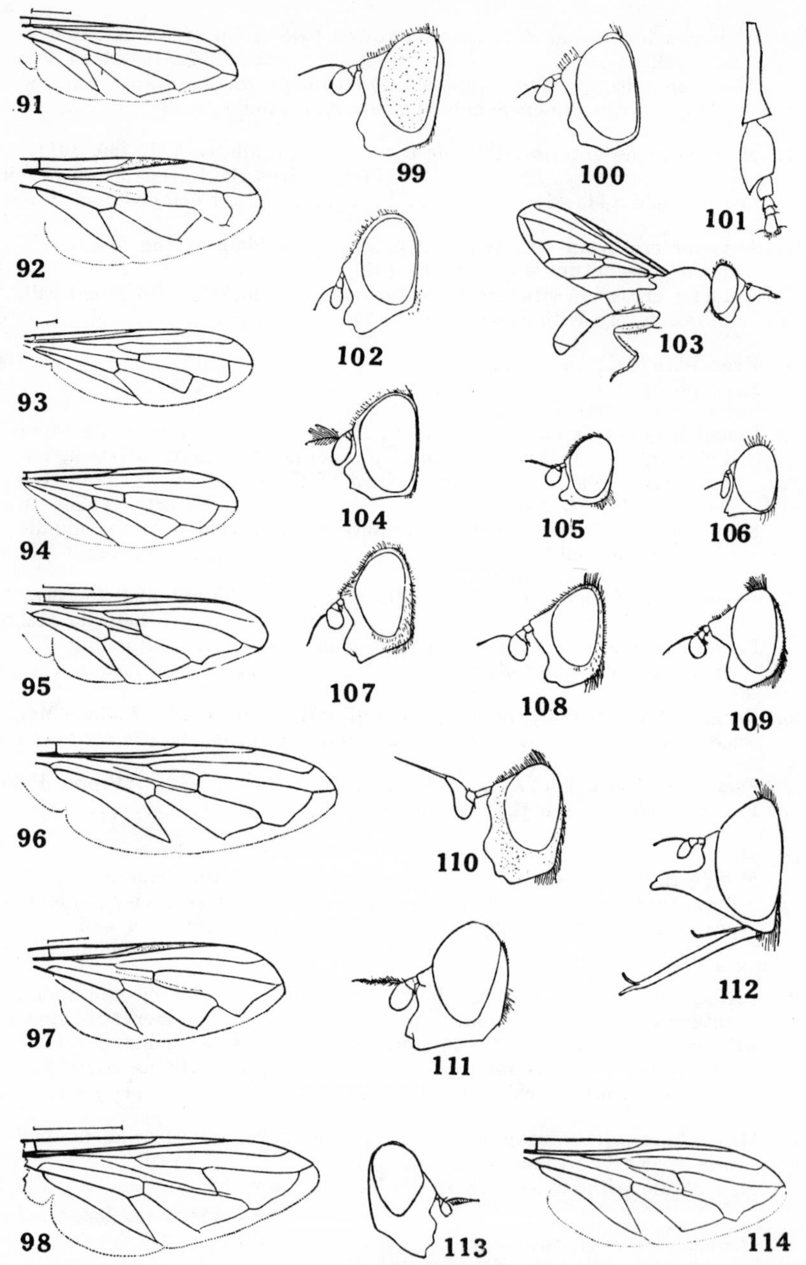

Syrphidæ V.—91, **Cartosyrphus**; 92, **Chrysogaster nigrovittata**; 93, **Neoascia globosa**; 94, **Sphegina infuscata**; 95, **Rhingia nasica**; 96, **Hammerschmidtia ferruginea**; 97, **Brachyopa notata**; 98, **Merapioidus villosus**; 99, **Ferdinandea crœsus**; 100, **Platycheirus quadratus**; 101, **Platycheirus peltatus**, front tibia and tarsus; 102, **Chrysogaster**; 103, **Pelecocera pergandei**; 104, **Cartosyrphus**; 105, **Sphegina infuscata**; 106, **Neoascia globosa**; 107, **Myiolepta nigra**; 108, 109, **Chalcomyia ærea**, ♀ ♂; 110, **Merapioidus villosus**; 111, **Brachyopa notata**; 112, **Rhingia nasica**; 113, **Hammerschmidtia**; 114, **Criorrhina.**

51. Third antennal segment elongate; apical crossvein more or less recurrent (2, 3, 50)....... **Orthoneura** Macquart
Third antennal segment never twice as long as wide....... 52

52. Disc of abdomen opaque black, the sides shining (4, 52, 92, 102). **Chrysogaster** Meigen
Disc of abdomen either wholly shining or with shining spots or bands. 53

53. Abdomen constricted basally or the third antennal segment very large 54
Abdomen broad; third antennal segment of normal size....... 57

54. Antennæ with a terminal arista on the produced upper angle (103). **Pelecocera** Meigen
Antennæ with dorsal arista, the third antennal segment not produced at point of its insertion....... 55

55. Abdomen not constricted basally....... **Chamæsyrphus** Mik
Abdomen petiolate 56

56. Third antennal segment longer than wide; arista shorter than antennæ (93, 106)....... ***Neoascia** Williston
Third segment at most slightly longer than wide, the arista longer than antenna (94, 105)....... †**Sphegina** Meigen

57. Face wholly black in ground color....... 58
Face partly yellow in ground color....... 61

58. Hair of the thorax and abdomen scale-like and appressed. **Lepidostola** Williston
Pile not scale-like, much of it erect....... 59

59. Scutellum large, subquadrate; male dichoptic....... 60
Scutellum rounded apically; male holoptic (107)....... **Myiolepta** Newman

60. Mesonotum with a large, flattened rectangle posteriorly (58, 61). **Chalcosyrphus** Curran
Mesonotum regularly convex (62, 108, 109)....... **Chalcomyia** Williston

61. Pile mostly scale-like and closely appressed (27, 124, 125). ‡**Eumyiolepta** Shannon
Pile normal 62

62. Legs bearing distinct bristles (96, 113)....... **Hammerschmidtia** Schummel
Legs without bristles....... 63

63. Epistoma produced into a long, porrect snout (95, 112).. **Rhingia** Scopoli
Epistoma not produced snout-like....... 64

64. The costal vein ends at the tip of the wing (55, 56, 57, 97, 111). §**Brachyopa** Meigen
The costal vein ends before the tip of the wing (60, 63, 64). ¶**Cynorhina** Williston

---

* Curran, 1925, Pr. Ent. Soc. Wash., xxvii, p. 51.
† Shannon, 1923, Bull. Brooklyn Ent. Soc., xviii, p. 19.
‡ Malloch, 1922, Ent. News, xxxiii, p. 267.
§ Curran, 1922, Ann. Ent. Soc. Amer., xv, p. 243.
¶ Curran, 1924, Can. Ent., lvi, p. 195.

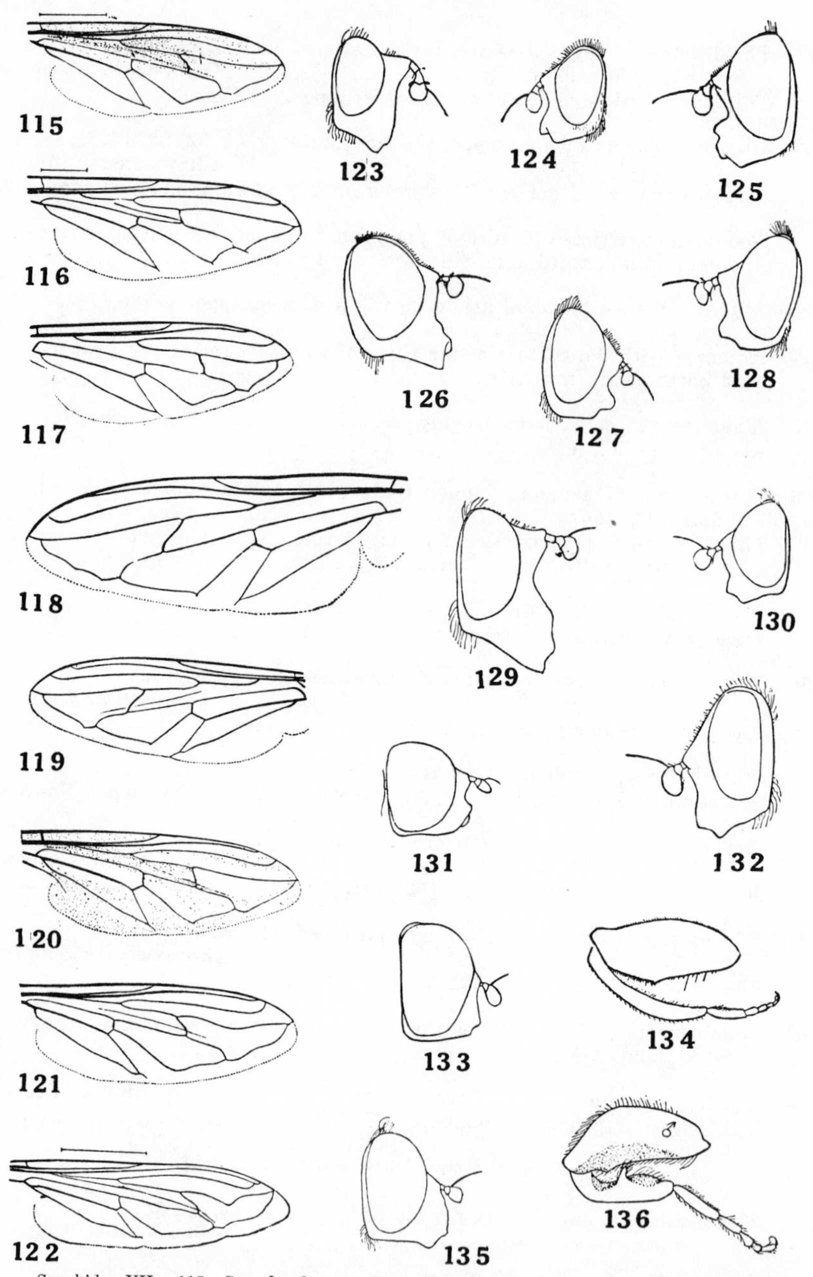

Syrphidæ VII.—115, **Somula decora**; 116, **Cynorhinella bella**; 117, **Crioprora cyanella**; 118, **Pocota grandis**; 119, **Chrysosomidia pulcher**; 120, **Sphecomyia pattoni**; 121, **Senogaster**; 122, **Milesia**; 123, **Somula decora**; 124, 125, **Eumyiolepta**, ♀, ♂, head; 126, **Cyniorhinella bella**; 127, **Pocota**; 128, **Chrysosomidia pulcher**; 129, **Sphecomyia pattoni**; 130, **Heliophilus pigra**; 131, **Senogaster**; 132, **Temnostoma alternans**; 133, 134, **Syritta pipiens**, head and hind leg; 135, **Tropidia quadrata**; 136, **Teuchocnemis**, hind leg.

65. Mesonotum with distinct yellow markings in addition to those on the humeri 78
Mesonotum without distinct yellow markings, although the humeri may be yellow, sometimes partly or wholly pollinose.............. 66

66. Third longitudinal vein moderately curved into the apical cell........ 83
Third longitudinal at most slightly curved into the apical cell........ 67

67. Face produced downward; usually an indication of facial tubercle.... 68
Face produced well forward and somewhat downward or evenly concave and not produced downward.................................. 72

68. Pile long and furry; flies bumble-bee-like in appearance.............. 69
Pile shorter; flies not bumble-bee-like.................................. 70

69. Arista placed at the tip of a conically produced third antennal segment (**98, 110**)..................................**Merapioidus** Bigot
Arista dorsal, not situated on a prominence (**54, 114**).*__Criorrhina__ Meigen

70. Antennæ inserted on a long, conical prominence; face retreating below (**115, 123**).................................**Somula** Macquart
Antennæ not situated on a strong prominence, inserted lower down on the head; abdomen shorter and broader.......................... 71

71. Posterior femora swollen and with an apical projection below; abdomen of the male rather slender, wholly black (**116, 126**).
Cynorhinella Curran
Posterior femora simple (**60, 63, 64**)..............†**Cynorhina** Williston

72. Epistoma produced forward and downward (**117, 152**).
Crioprora Osten Sacken
Epistoma not produced downward or forward beyond the antennal prominence 73

73. Bumble-bee-like flies, the pile very thick (**118, 127**).
Pocota St. Fargeau and Serville
Not bumble-bee-like, the pile rather thin.............................. 74

74. Face tuberculate..............................‡**Calliprobola** Rondani
Face concave or carinate.. 75

75. Face carinate; posterior femora greatly swollen.......§**Planes** Rondani
Face concave in profile... 76

76. Pile of the scutellum thick and rather long but not concealing the ground color; head quite flat or gently concave above from anterior view; posterior femora with small tubercles below.
Brachypalpus Macquart
Pile thinner and shorter, few of the hairs as long as the scutellum; head not quite flat above.. 77

77. Abdomen bright metallic æneous with opaque black bands and brassy or golden yellow pile; posterior femora slender and with black setæ beneath on almost the whole length; abdomen subcylindrical (Genotype, **Calliprobola crawfordi** Shannon) (**119, 128**).
¶**Chrysosomidia**, n. g.

---

* Curran, 1925, Kans. Univ. Sci. Bull., xv, p. 141.
† Curran, 1924, Can. Ent., lvi, p. 195.
‡ No North American specimens I have seen belong to this genus.
§ Shannon, 1926, Pr. U. S. N. M., lxix, Art. 9, p. 12.
¶ Shannon, 1916, (Calliprobola), Pr. Ent. Soc. Wash., xviii, p. 109.

Abdomen differently colored; posterior femora usually with low ridge on the apical fourth bearing stout, short, spinose setæ; head gently convex above from anterior view; abdomen not wholly pale pilose (**29, 130**) .... ***Heliophilus** Meigen

78. Face produced downward, longer than the front; pale mesonotal markings pollinose (**120, 129**) .... †**Sphecomyia** Latreille
Face not conpicuously produced, shorter than the front; if doubtful the pale mesonotal markings are of the ground color 79

* Shannon, 1926, Proc. U. S. N. M., lxix, Art. 9, pp. 16, 26 (**Xylotomima, Xylota**).
† Curran, 1932, Amer. Mus. Novit. No. 519, p. 8.

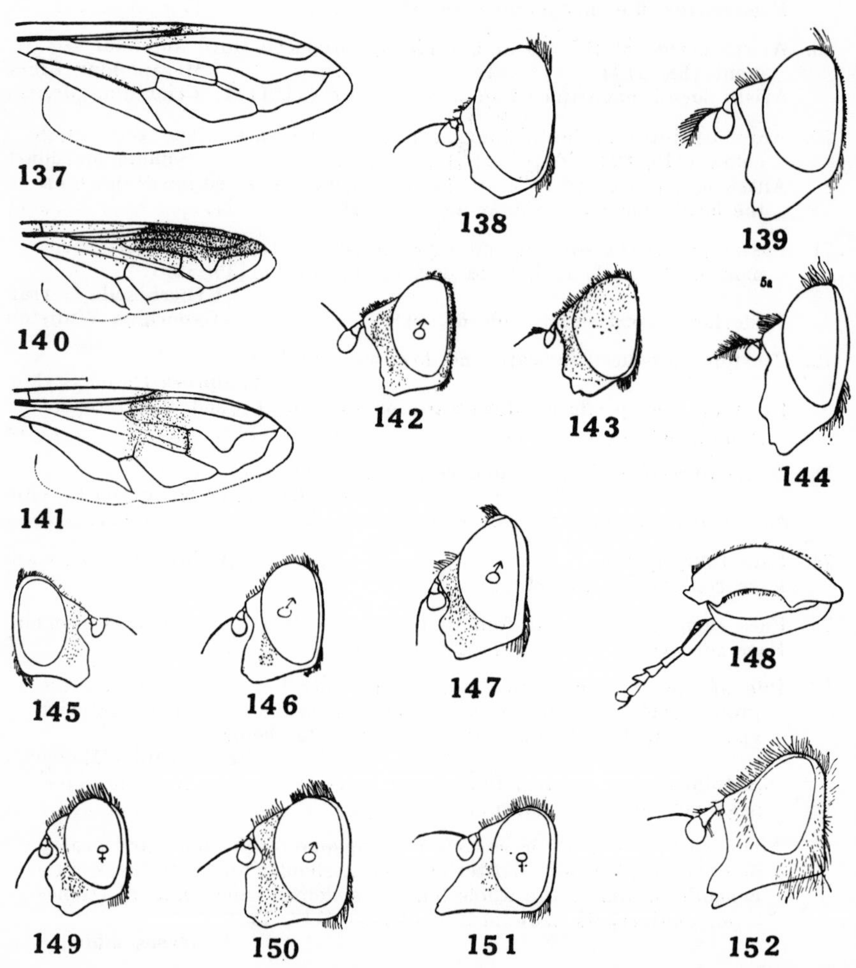

Syrphidæ VIII.—137, **Teuchocnemis lituratus**; 138, **Pterallastes thoracicus**; 139, **Sericomyia militaris**; 140, **Mecromacrus cinctus**; 141, **Mallota sackeni**; 142, **Mecromacrus cinctus**; 143; **Eristalis transversus**; 144, **Arctophila flagrans**; 145, **Polydontomyia curvipes**; 146, **Parhelophilus lætus**; 147, **Mallota cimbiciformis**; 148, **Polydontomyia**, hind leg; 149, **Lunomyia**; 150, **Asemosyrphus mexicanum**; 151, **Lejops stipatus**; 152, **Crioprora**.

79. Face broadly carinate, convex in profile..........**Ceriogaster** Williston
Face concave or more or less tuberculate 80

80. Face produced somewhat downward and weakly tuberculate (**60, 63, 64**) ....***Cynorhina** Williston
Face concave, not tuberculate.. 81

81. Abdomen with yellow pollinose fasciæ.............................. 82
Abdomen brassy, with opaque black fasciæ (**119, 128**).
†**Chrysosomidia**, n. g.

82. Posterior femora with a tooth-like projection below near the apical end ....**Spilomyia** Meigen
Posterior femora simple (**21, 22, 132**).
‡**Temnostoma** St. Fargeau and Serville

83. Posterior femora with a bifid spur below; face concave, subcarinate (**121, 131**)..................................**Senogaster** Macquart
Posterior femora without such spur................................ 84

84. Posterior femora very greatly swollen, never with a triangular preapical protuberance, though usually spinose; head almost circular, the cheeks linear (**28, 133, 134**)..**Syritta** St. Fargeau and Serville
Posterior femora much less swollen; head not globose............... 85

85. Posterior femora with a small, toothlike projection below toward the apex§ (**20, 122**) ....**Milesia** Latreille
Posterior femora not toothed, sometimes with a triangular process apically 86

86. Posterior femora with a triangular projection apically (**19, 36, 135**).
¶**Tropidia** Meigen
Posterior femora without such process............................ 87

87. Posterior femora strongly swollen and strongly arcuate, their tibiæ with a median internal spur in the male (**136, 137**).
Teuchocnemis Osten Sacken
Posterior femora much less swollen and but little curved; tibiæ simple; mesonotum ochraceous pollinose (**138**)......**Pterallastes** Lœw

88. Abdomen with pale spots or fasciæ................................ 89
Abdomen without pale spots or fasciæ, rarely reddish in ground color beneath thick reddish pile on the second segment................ 90

89. Posterior calli with short, stout bristles; abdominal spots more or less orbicular.....................................**Condidea** Coquillett
Posterior calli without bristles; abdomen with narrow pale fasciæ at least beyond the second segment (**16, 33, 139**)..‖**Sericomyia** Meigen

90. Face very broad and swollen; body pile almost unicolorous.
Pyritis Hunter
Face not unusually broad; pile bicolored (**15, 144**)....**Arctophila** Schiner

91. Marginal cell closed and petiolate................................ 92
Marginal cell open.. 95

---

* Curran, 1924, Can. Ent. lvi, p. 195.
† Shannon, 1916, (Calliprobola), Pr. Ent. Soc. Wash., xviii, p. 109.
‡ Curran, 1930, Bull. Amer. Mus. Nat. Hist., lxi, p. 72.
§ Absent in some Oriental species.
¶ Shannon, 1926, Pr. U. S. N. M., lxix, Art. 9, p. 9.
‖ Curran, 1934, Amer. Mus. Novit. No. 724, p. 6.

92. Epistoma produced into a long, porrect snout....**Lycastrirrhyncha** Bigot
Epistoma not produced.. 93

93. Eyes light brown with numerous small brown spots.
Lathyrophthalmus Mik
Eyes normally unicolorous.. 94

94. Thorax with yellow markings of short, squamose hairs **(140, 142)**.
Meromacrus Rondani
Hair of the thorax never squamose or forming dense yellow patches **(17, 143)** ....*__Eristalis__ Latreille

95. Posterior femora before the apex with a strongly raised, sub-triangular ridge, the base with a distinct spur................**Merodon** Meigen
Posterior femora variable, but never with a spur bearing triangular plate or strong ridge.. 96

96. Eyes pilose 97
Eyes bare 98

97. Third antennal segment not longer than wide **(141, 147)**.‡**Mallota** Meigen
Third antennal segment twice as long as wide..........**Quichuana** Knab

98. Mesonotum densely and evenly yellow pollinose, the ground color concealed; face concave in female; with a tubercle but receding below in the male **(138)**.................................**Pterallastes** Lœw
Mesonotum differently colored 99

99. Large robust species, the thorax thickly yellow or orange pilose, rarely whitish; posterior femora swollen and arcuate in both sexes; rather bumble-bee-like flies **(141, 147)** ....†**Mallota** Meigen
Usually smaller and always more slender; if the posterior femora are arcuate the tibiæ end in an apical spur..........................100

100. Posterior tibiæ ending in a spur or triangular production, never transverse on the ventral apex....................................101
Posterior tibiæ transverse or rounded apically, never produced.......102

101. Large species, at least 12 mm. in length, the mesonotum at most obscurely vittate **(34, 145, 148)**..............**Polydontomyia** Williston
Smaller, more slender species, the mesonotum usually with two or more cinereous or yellowish vitæ **(151)**................‡**Lejops** Rondani

102. Face entirely pollinose **(146)**................‡**Parhelophilus** Girschner
Face with a shining median vitta on at least the lower half.........103

103. Stigma simulating a crossvein.......................................104
Stigma at least twice as long as wide, although often paler apically, never simulating a crossvein **(18)** ....‡**Elophilus** Meigen

104. Ocellar triangle extremely large in both sexes, the outer ocelli lying very close to the eyes **(150)**..................‡**Asemosyrphus** Bigot
Ocellar triangle smaller **(149)** ....‡**Lunomyia** Curran and Fluke

---

* Curran, 1930, Amer. Mus. Novit. No. 411, p. 3.
† Curran, 1930, Bull. Amer. Mus. Nat. Hist., lxi, p. 74.
‡ Curran and Fluke, 1926, Trans-Wisconsin Acad. Sci., Arts & Letters, xxii, pp. 207-281.

Family Conopidæ—The Thick-headed flies

Rather thinly pilose or nearly bare, elongate flies of moderate size. Head broad, the front broad in both sexes; ocelli present or absent. Antennæ with three segments, the third bearing a dorsal arista or terminal style. Oral opening large, the proboscis long and slender, often geniculate. Abdomen often constricted basally, the genitalia of both sexes conspicuous, often large or greatly elongated in the females. Anal cell closed, the first basal cell always very long, the second moderately long; apical cell closed or much narrowed. Above the antennæ an inflatable ptilinum.

The Conopids are commonly found about flowers and are sluggish in flight. They occur from spring to autumn but are much more common during the spring and early summer. The species of *Stylogaster* are rapid in flight, the flies being great hoverers. I have found them in the tropics in rather large numbers hovering over ant armies where they usually remain a few inches above the ground, suddenly disappearing, only to reappear in another patch of sunlight. In the north I have found them only about flowers of the Labiateæ and have observed them hovering as they sucked the nectar. Many of the species resemble Hymenoptera.

The members of this family are parasitic, mostly upon bees and wasps, oviposition usually occurring during flight. There are also records of parasitism on Orthoptera and the species of *Stylogaster* are in some way connected with ants but the exact relationship is unknown.

The generic and specific limits in the family are, for the most part, not sharply drawn, and this is especially true in the case of *Conops* and *Physocephala*. There have been a number of papers published dealing with the family in whole or in part; the most important of these is referred to in the footnote.*

KEY TO GENERA

1. Antennæ with a terminal style.................................... 2
   Antennæ with a dorsal or subdorsal arista.......................... 4

2. Face with deep lateral grooves..................................... 3
   Face without lateral grooves, the median carina strong; ocelli vestigial (4)..**Tropidomyia** Williston

* Van Duzee, 1927, Proc. Calif. Acad. Sci., xvi, pp. 573-604.

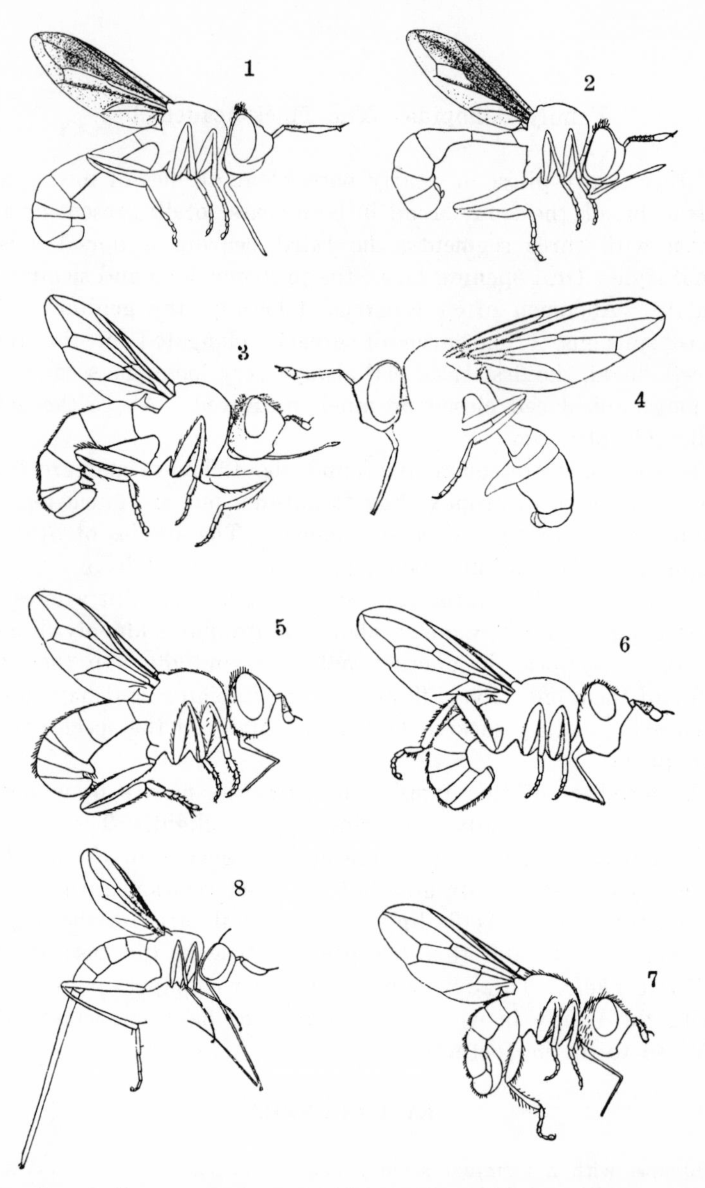

Conopidæ.—1, **Conops xanthopareus**; 2, **Physocephala furcillata**; 3, **Zodion fulvifrons**; 4, **Tropidomyia bimaculata**; 5, **Occemya modesta**; 6, **Myopa clausa**; 7, **Dalmannia picta**; 8, **Stylogaster neglecta.**

3. Anterior crossvein situated at most a little beyond the middle of the discal cell; femora regular in outline 9
   Anterior crossvein situated well beyond the middle of the discal cell; femora swollen basally, narrowed on the apical half or more (2). *__Physocephala__ Schiner

4. Proboscis geniculate 5
   Proboscis straight, directed forward (3)................**Zodion** Latreille

5. Vertex and tibiæ without bristles; face grooved...................... 6
   Vertex and the apex of the tibiæ with bristles; face not grooved (8). †**Stylogaster** Macquart

6. Anal cell much longer than the second basal....................... 7
   Anal cell but little longer than the second basal (7)..**Dalmannia** Desvoidy

7. Cheeks narrower than the eye-height.............................. 8
   Cheeks at least as wide as the eye-height (6)...........**Myopa** Fabricius

8. Antennæ longer than the front; propleura haired (5)...**Occemya** Desvoidy
   Antennæ shorter than the front; propleura bare............**Sicus** Scopoli

9. Third antennal segment much longer than either the first or second. **Aconops** Krœber
   Third antennal segment at most slightly longer than the first or second (1)....................................‡**Conops** Linnæus

* Van Duzee, 1934, Ann. Ent. Soc. Amer., xxvii, p. 320.
† Aldrich, 1930, Proc. U. S. N. M., lxxviii, Art. 9, pp. 1-27.
‡ Kröber, 1927, Konowia, vi, p. 139.

Family Pyrgotidæ

Elongate flies of moderate size, the ocelli absent in the North American genera, present only in *Teretrura* Bigot of the American forms; wings long, the legs somewhat elongate.

Head large, the front more or less produced, without frontal bristles; ocelli absent (present in only one American genus); cheeks wide; proboscis thick, the labellæ well developed; palpi large, flattened, or the proboscis narrow and short without labellæ and the palpi narrow; antennæ short to moderately long, the second segment without a dorsal excision, the third usually larger than the second, rarely minute. Legs moderately long. Wings long; auxiliary vein long, ending free or in the costa; apical cell widely open, not narrowed apically; anal cell usually triangular apically. Abdomen long, sometimes clavate in the males; female genitalia large, more or less cylindrical.

Species of the genus *Pyrgota* are parasitic in the larval stage on June beetles (Scarabæidæ) and the flies are sometimes common in the vicinity of badly infested fields. I suspect that *Pyrgotella chagnoni* Johnson is parasitic on species of *Dichelonyx* but my suspicion is based merely upon the fact that I have observed this species commonly in an open woods where the adult beetles were very common. The flies apparently are most active on dark days, in the evening or at night and they frequently are attracted to light. They are nocturnal and *P. undata* Wiedemann has been observed ovipositing on adult June beetles during flight. The flies select the soft part of the abdomen beneath the opened elytra in order to lay their eggs and the beetles have been observed on the ground making a loud noise as they struggled to escape the fly.

The exact limits of this family have not been definitely determined, and it is not certain that the species possessing ocelli should be retained in the family. Nothing of a definite nature is known of the immature stages of any of the American genera other than *Pyrgota*. There are two North American genera and three from South America that have been assigned to the family.

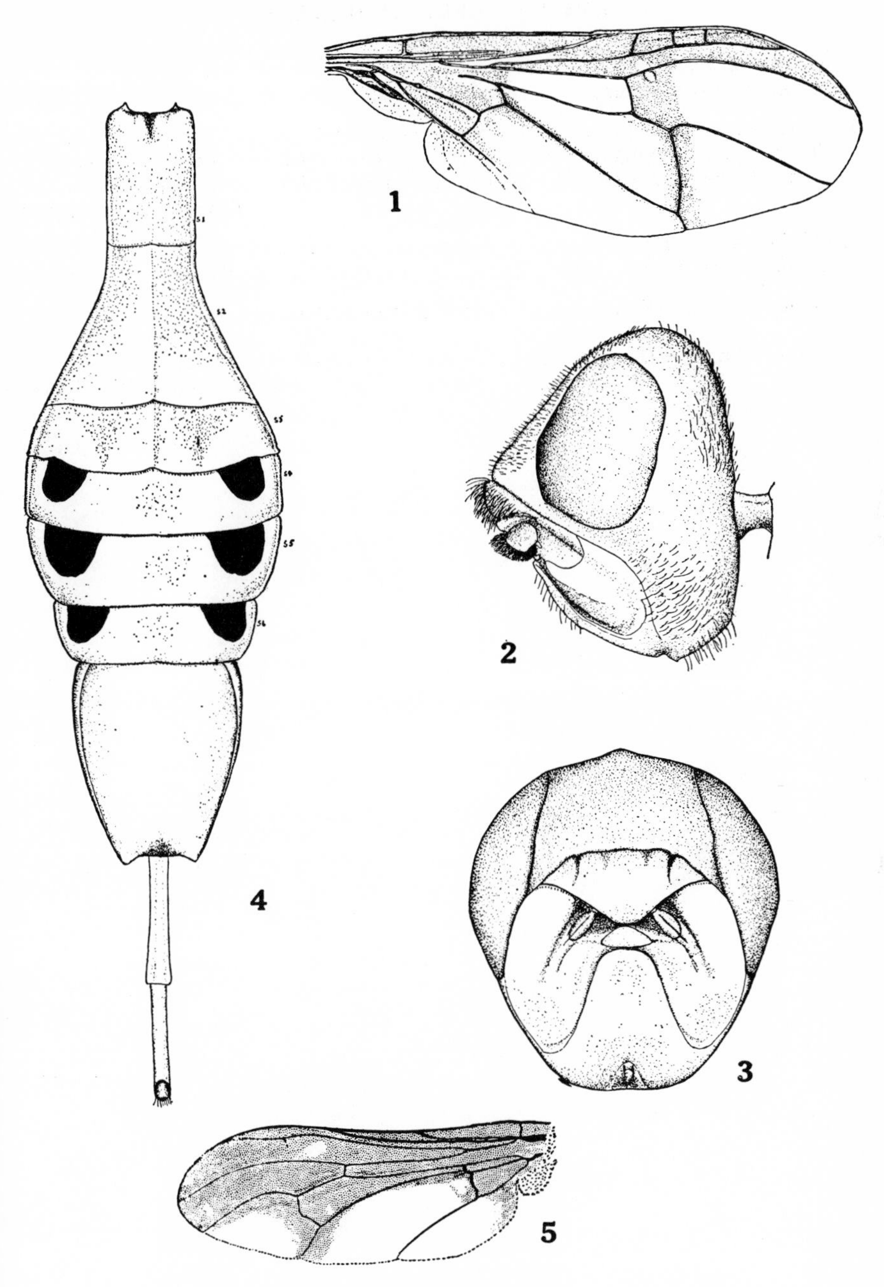

Pyrgotidæ.—Figures 1-4, **Tauroscypson guiana**; 5, **Pyrgota undata.**

KEY TO AMERICAN GENERA

1. Ocelli absent 2
   Ocelli present (Chile) .... **Teretrura** Bigot

2. Third antennal segment as large as the second 3
   Third antennal segment minute, the arista curved over the second segment and with long rays on the free side (British Guiana) (1-4).
   Tauroscypson Curran

3. Alula very narrow 4
   Alula large, convex behind (5) .... **Pyrgota** Wiedemann

4. Apex of anal cell transverse (Type: **Pyrgota chagnoni** Johnson).
   Pyrgotella, n. g.
   Apex of anal cell with triangular production behind (Bolivia).
   Leptopyrgota Hendel

Family Otitidæ—The Pictured-wing Flies

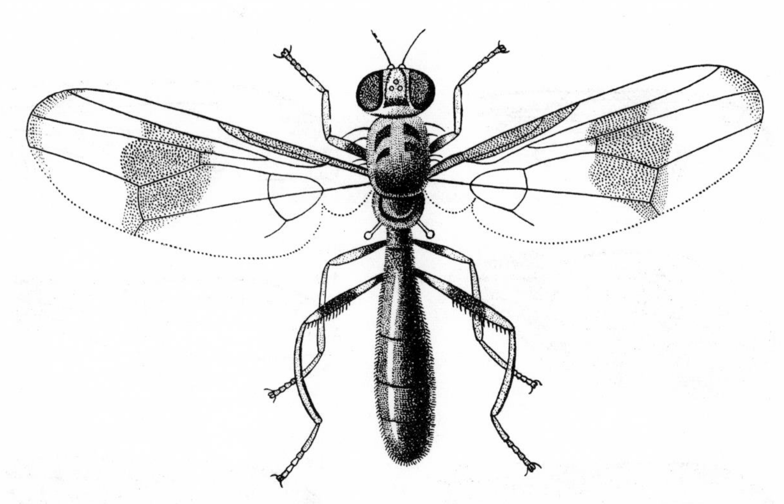

Paneryma elongata.

Rather small to moderately large flies, the wings usually marked with brown, black or yellowish.

Eyes separated in both sexes; frontals usually limited to the upper part; face variable, the oral vibrissæ always absent; clypeus usually well developed; proboscis short and stout; palpi large. Abdomen with five or six segments, the basal two more or less coalescent; male with long, curled penis, the female with a flattened, three segmented ovipositor. Legs short and stout or moderately long, the preapical tibial bristle present or absent. Wing venation usually complete, the anal cell absent in one genus; auxiliary vein separated from the first vein though often approximated to it, second basal and anal cells of moderate size.

The adults are usually found in moist places and many of the species are very common. This family is cosmopolitan but the species are most numerous in the tropics, particularly in South and Central America. Several of the species have the head strongly produced laterally and one fairly common species of *Richardia* has the eyes situated on long stalks, but this is a male character only.

Little is known about the immature stages although the larvæ of *Tritoxa* are said to damage onions and others have been reared from decaying plant products.

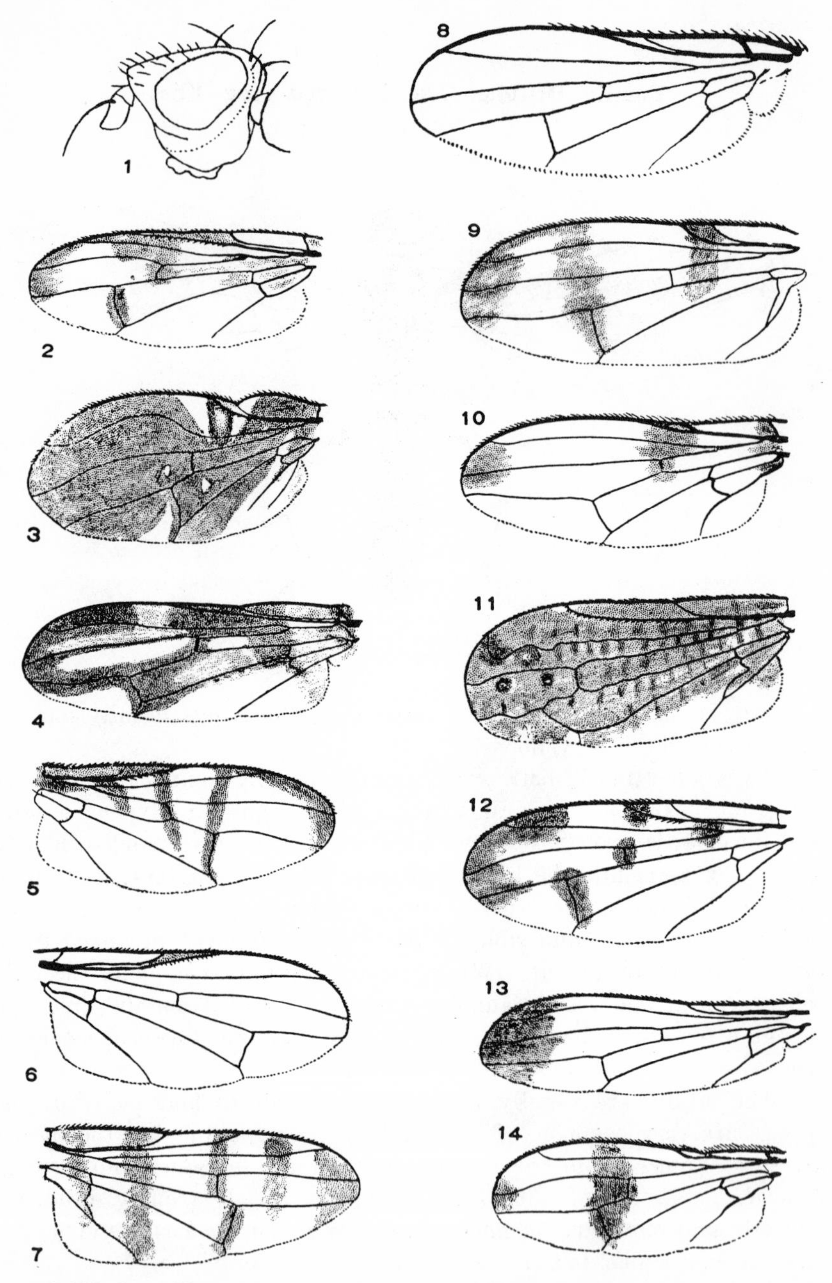

Otitidæ I.—1, **Macrostenomyia**; 2, **Senopterina**; 3, **Delphinia picta**; 4, **Idana**; 5, **Rivellia**; 6, **Tetanops**; 7, **Pseudotephritis**; 8, **Psairopterella macrocephala**; 9, **Chætopsis**; 10, **Coilometopia**; 11, **Pterocalla**; 12, **Melieria**; 13, **Eumetopiella**; 14, **Richardia**.

In the following key I have not followed the usual practice of recognizing the subfamilies, which Hendel has raised to family rank, for the very good reason that I do not believe the characters used are of much importance. The subfamily "Ortalinæ" (the name *Ortalis* is preoccupied in Ornithology and is not available) is distinguished by the presence of a propleural bristle, yet this is present, though less developed, in the Pterocallinæ, which is distinguished by its long stigmatal cell, a character which is also subject to variation. As in the Trupaneidæ several of the genera in this family have been based upon wing pattern. The characters at present in use are undoubtedly fairly stable but some of the generic characters are admittedly weak inasmuch as the differences in venation might easily be connected by the discovery of new forms. Hendel has published several papers dealing with the family and has treated all but the "Ortalinæ" in Genera Insectorum (fascicles 96, 106, 113, 157).

The genus *Otites* was established by Latreille in 1804 (Nouv. Dict. d'Hist. Nat., xxiv, p. 196) and not in 1805 as given in catalogues. The type named was *musca porcus*, credited to Bosc, but this species is the same as *formosa* Panzer. Platystomidæ cannot be used for the family name as *Platystoma* is preoccupied in Mollusca.

KEY TO GENERA*

1. First vein bare 2
   First vein with dorsal setulæ at least on the apical third............ 34

2. Costa greatly weakened or broken at end of the auxiliary vein (Richardinæ) 3
   Costa not weakened or broken (Ulidinæ).......................... 17

3. Posterior femora with short spines below.......................... 5
   Femora without spines below.................................... 4

4. Head about twice as long as high (56)..................**Coniceps** Lœw
   Head not as long as high (38, 92)......................**Epiplatea** Lœw

5. Posterior femora swollen, much larger than the others; eyes sometimes stalked (14)..............................**Richardia** Desvoidy
   Posterior femora not conspicuously swollen.......................... 6

6. Anal vein reaching the wing margin, at least as a fold.............. 9
   Anal vein not nearly reaching the wing margin...................... 7

7. Occiput very strongly narrowed at the upper third (80, 97). **Odontomera** Macquart
   Occiput regular in outline.. 8

* **Pareuxesta** Coquillett is omitted.

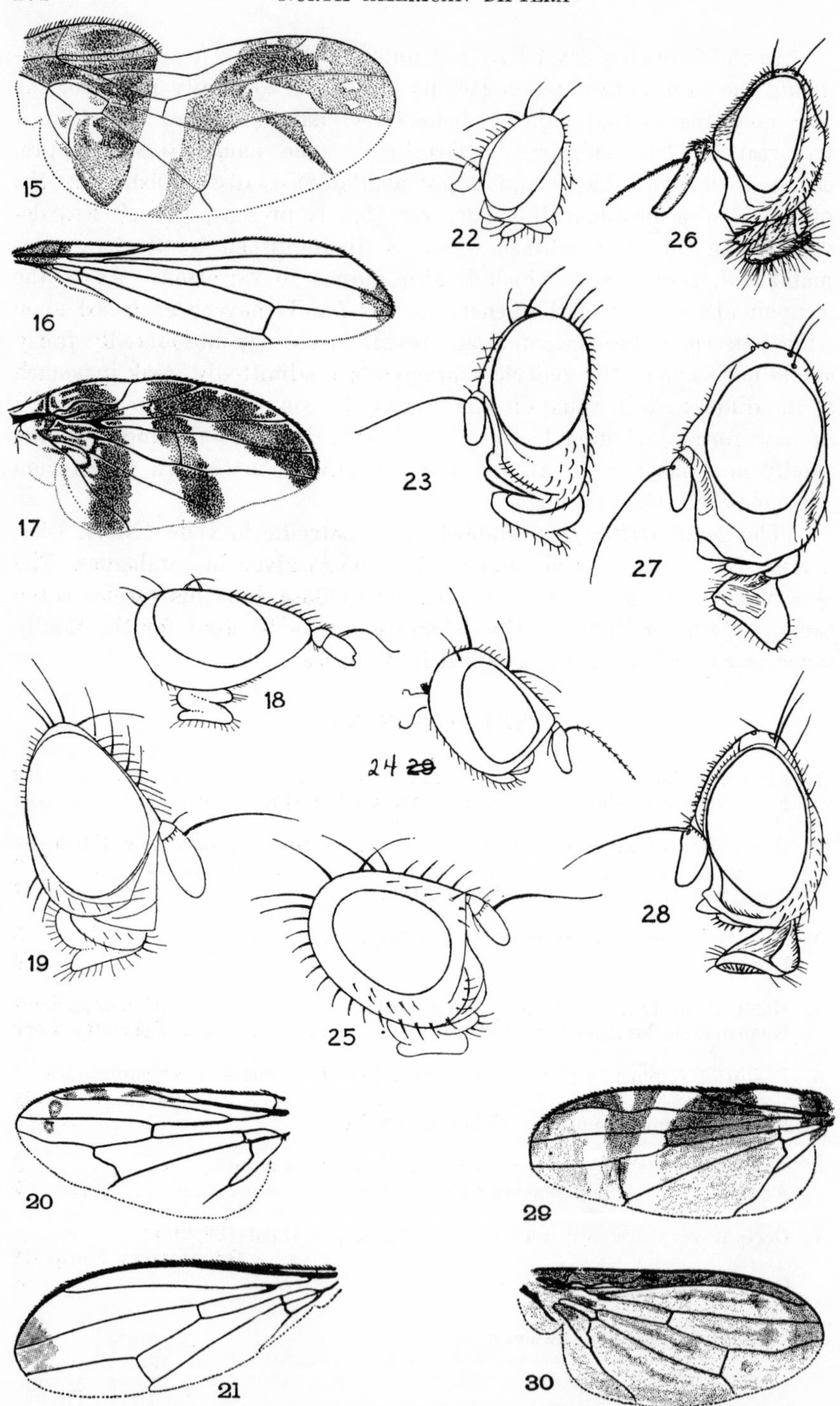

Otitidæ II.—15, **Ostracocœlia mirabilis**; 16, **Myrmecothea**; 17, **Dyscrasis hendeli**; 18, **Eumetopiella rufipes**; 19, **Acrosticta foveolata**; 20, **Œdopa**; 21, **Macrostenomyia**; 22, **Eumecosomyia gracilis**; 23, **Paragorgopsis maculata**; 24, **Sepsisoma sepsioides**; 25, **Steneretma**; 26, **Rivellia**; 27, **Chrysomyza**; 28, **Xanthacrona bipustulata**; 29, **Euphara**; 30, **Notogramma**.

8. Occiput, from lateral view, strongly convex above the neck (**24**). **Sepsisoma** Johnson
   Occiput flat or slightly concave above the neck (**1, 21**). **Macrostenomyia** Hendel

9. Anterior crossvein situated farther from the posterior crossvein than the length of the latter.... 10
   Crossveins situated closer to each other than the length of the posterior crossvein (**100**) ....**Hemixantha** Lœw

10. Abdomen with almost parallel sides or coarctate basally.... 11
    Abdomen tapering to the base.... 13

11. Anterior crossvein situated before the middle of the discal cell (**31, 68**). **Setellida** Hendel
    Anterior crossvein situated beyond the middle of the discal cell.... 12

12. Anterior femora without spines beneath (**78, 96**). **Neoidiotypa** Osten Sacken
    All the femora with spines beneath....**Paneryma** Wulp

13. First antennal segment short.... 14
    First antennal segment as long as the second (**49, 93**)..**Pœcilomyia** Hendel

14. Anterior crossvein situated at or before the middle of the discal cell; front concave above from anterior view (**10, 73**). **Coilometopia** Macquart
    Anterior crossvein situated well beyond the middle of the discal cell.. 15

15. Two pairs of scutellars.... 16
    Only one pair of scutellars (**63, 76, 98, 107**)....**Melanoloma** Lœw

16. Front much wider than either eye (**42, 105**)....**Zetekomyia,** n. g.
    Front narrower than either eye....**Melanolomina,** n. g.

17. Antennæ widely separated, situated in deep grooves, the face strongly convex in profile (**50**)....**Ulidia** Meigen
    Antennæ not situated in deep grooves or the face not strongly convex.. 18

18. Anal vein absent or not extending beyond the anal cell.... 19
    Anal vein extending well beyond the anal cell.... 20

19. Anal cell absent, the wings very narrow (**25, 36**)....**Steneretma** Lœw
    Anal cell present (**22, 45**)....**Eumecosomyia** Hendel

20. Front with large rather deep pits or with strong transverse ridges or grooves 21
    Front normal, sometimes with four longitudinal grooves above.... 22

21. Auxiliary vein forming a rather acute angle with the costa (**19, 37**). **Acrosticta** Lœw
    Auxiliary vein forming an obtuse angle with the costa (**30, 89**). **Notogramma** Lœw

22. Antennæ as long as the head, the third segment four times as long as wide (**51, 74**)....**Stictomyia** Bigot
    Antennæ much shorter, the third segment never three times as long as wide 23

23. Face convex in the middle in profile.... 24
    Face concave in profile.... 25

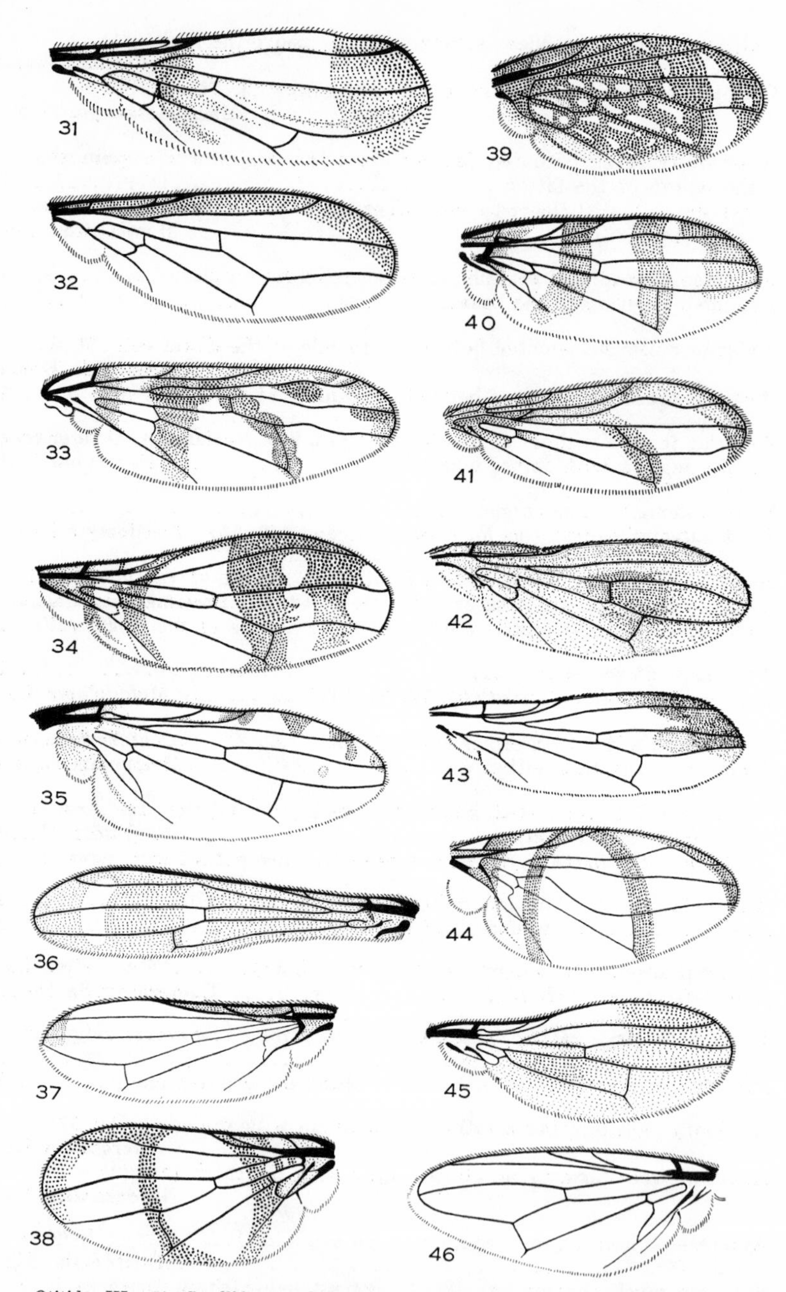

Otitidæ III.—31, **Setellida cœrulescens**; 32, **Setellia costalis**; 33, **Myennis**; 34, **Automola automaria**; 35, **Parœdopa punctigera**; 36, **Steneretma**; 37, **Acrosticta foveolata**; 38, **Epiplatea arcuata**; 39, **Amphicnephes pullus**; 40, **Pareuxesta latifasciata**; 41, **Xanthacrona bipustulata**; 42, **Zetekomyia banksi**; 43, **Stenomyia**; 44, **Axiologina ferrum-equinum**; 45, **Eumecosomyia gracilis**; 46, **Chrysomyza ænea**.

24. Eyes conspicuously higher than long, the face gently concave above (35, 67) .... **Parœdopa** Coquillett
Eyes about as long as high, the face not concave above (20, 69). **Œdopa** Lœw

25. Head not or scarcely longer than high.............................. 26
Head nearly twice as long as high (13, 18).........**Eumetopiella** Hendel

26. Third antennal segment with the apex rounded above............... 27
Third antennal segment with the apex angulate above................ 32

27. Anterior crossvein situated near or beyond the middle of the discal cell 28
Anterior crossvein situated near the basal sixth of the discal cell (44, 82)..**Axiologina** Hendel

28. Mesopleura bare; two sternopleurals (84, 102)...........**Seioptera** Kirby
Mesopleura haired; one sternopleural............................... 29

29. Frontal vitta with hairs or bristles................................. 30
Frontal vitta bare (27, 46).........................*__Chrysomyza__ Fallén

30. Prescutellar acrosticals absent ....**Zacompsia** Coquillett
Prescutellar acrosticals present...................................... 31

31. Bristles arising from black spots (29)...................**Euphara** Lœw
Frontals not arising from conspicuous black spots (64, 85).†**Euxesta** Lœw

32. Frontal vitta with at most two pairs of cruciate bristles or the face strongly receding.. 33
Frontal vitta with hairs or several bristles (64, 85)........**Euxesta** Lœw

33. Face strongly receding (43, 104)........................**Stenomyia** Lœw
Face perpendicular below (9, 83).........................**Chætopsis** Lœw

34. Costa fractured or greatly weakened at the end of the auxiliary vein.. 35
Costa entire 36

35. Abdomen petiolate (32, 72)............................**Setellia** Desvoidy
Abdomen oval, not narrowed sub-basally.................**Epiplatea** Lœw

36. Propleural bristle weak or absent.................................... 37
Propleural bristle strong... 59

37. Three supra-alar bristles... 38
Four supra-alar bristles..............................Family Tanypezidæ

38. Subcostal (stigmatal) cell usually extremely large; antennal grooves absent (Pterocallinæ) 39
Subcostal cell usually normal; antennal grooves well developed, often deep (Platystominæ auct.).. 48

39. Posterior crossvein more or less recurrent, never forming a sharp angle with the fourth vein.. 40
Posterior crossvein not recurrent, forming less than a right angle with the fourth vein.. 43

40. Anterior crossvein situated beyond the middle of the discal cell...... 41
Anterior crossvein situated before the middle of the discal cell (58). **Megalæmyia** Hendel

---

* Hendel, 1909, Zool. Anzeiger, xxxiv, pp. 612-622.
† Hendel, 1909, Ann. Mus. Nat. Hung., ix, p. 151.

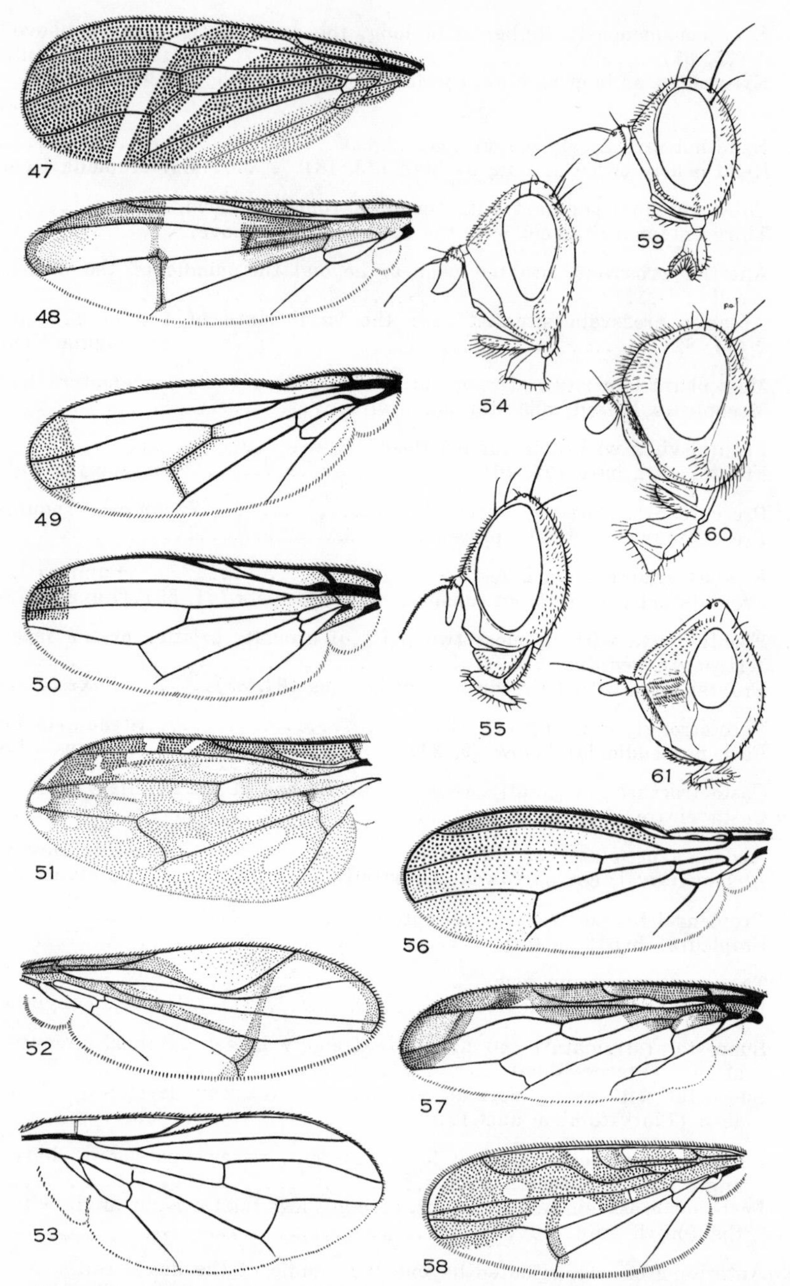

Otitidæ IV.—47, **Tritoxa flexa**; 48, **Himeroessa pretiosa**; 49, **Pœcilomyia longicornis**; 50, **Ulidia apicalis**; 51, **Stictomyia punctata**; 52; **Dasymetopa stigma**; 53, **Califortalis hirsutifrons**; 54, **Ortalimyia aldrichi**; 55, **Delphinia**; 56, **Coniceps niger**; 57, **Diacrita costatis**; 58, **Megalæmyia**; 59, **Melieria similis**; 60, **Califortalis hirsutifrons**; 61, **Tetanops luridipennis.**

41. Tip of the anal cell extending beyond the apex of the second basal cell 42
    Tip of the anal cell not produced beyond the apex of the second basal cell (28, 41)..................................**Xanthacrona** Wulp

42. Five pairs of dorsocentrals and acrosticals (17, 90)....**Dyscrasis** Aldrich
    Two pairs of dorsocentrals (33).......................**Myennis** Desvoidy

43. Triangle of the anal cell almost as long as the basal section.......... 44
    Triangle much shorter than the basal part.......................... 45

44. Wings with parallel sides (11, 108).................**Pterocalla** Rondani
    Wings widest sub-basally (99, 106).............**Callopistromyia** Hendel

45. Anal cell convex apically, sometimes transverse on the posterior third, but never with a produced angle (23, 101)....**Paragorgopsis** Giglio-Tos
    Anal cell at least somewhat produced posteriorly.................. 46

46. Second vein almost straight.. 47
    Second vein strongly sinuous apically (91, 103)..**Pseudopterocalla** Hendel

47. Anterior crossvein situated at or before the middle of the discal cell (52, 87)......................................**Dasymetopa** Lœw
    Anterior crossvein situated beyond the middle of the discal cell (7, 109) ....**Pseudotephritis** Johnson

48. Occiput very broad and convex from lateral view.................... 49
    Occiput narrow, usually flattened.................................. 52

49. Without sternopleurals (16, 75)..................**Myrmecothea** Hendel
    With one sternopleural... 50

50. Posterior crossvein situated more than its own length beyond the anterior crossvein (62, 79)...................**Myrmecomya** Desvoidy
    Posterior crossvein situated less than its length beyond the anterior crossvein 51

51. Costal cell wide, convex anteriorly (3, 55)............**Delphinia** Desvoidy
    Costal cell narrow, its anterior edge straight (47, 70).......**Tritoxa** Lœw

52. Abdomen somewhat laterally compressed; one pair of weak frontal bristles above; third antennal segment elongate; arista bare (2). **Senopterina** Macquart
    Abdomen cylindrical or flattened, if slender the arista is plumose, the antennæ are short or there are two pairs of frontals.............. 53

53. Abdomen elongate, more or less cylindrical basally................. 55
    Abdomen short and rather flattened................................. 54

54. Costal cell widened, anal cell angled posteriorly (15). **Ostracocœlia** Giglio-Tos
    Costal cell normal; anal cell rounded posteriorly (39, 65). **Amphicnephes** Lœw

55. Sternopleural bristle absent....................................... 57
    Sternopleural bristle present...................................... 56

56. Anal cell rounded apically (4, 71)..........................**Idana** Lœw
    Anal cell angulate posteriorly (57, 66)............**Diacrita** Gerstæcker

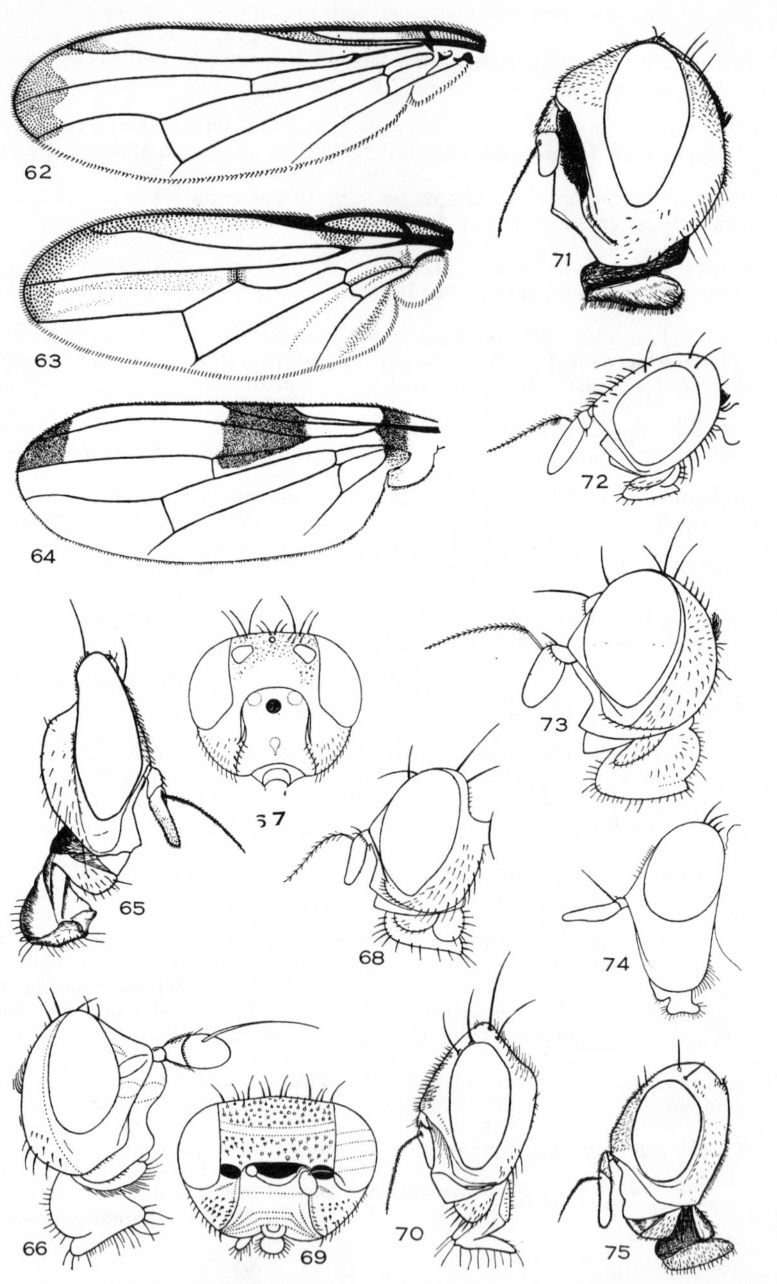

Otitidæ V.—62, **Myrmecomya**; 63, **Melanoloma affinis**; 64, **Euxesta mitis**; 65, **Amphicnephes**; 66, **Diacrita costalis**; 67, **Parœdopa punctigera**; 68, **Setellida cœrulescens**; 69, **Œdopa**; 70, **Tritoxa incurva**; 71, **Idana**; 72, **Setellia**; 73, **Coilometopia**; 74, **Stictomyia**; 75, **Myrmecothea**.

57. Discal cell conspicuously widened before the anterior crossvein (**5, 26**). **Rivellia** Desvoidy
Discal cell not conspicuously widened, rarely widest at the middle..... 58

58. Anterior crossvein oblique, at the middle of the discal cell (**48, 86**). **Himeroëssa** Lœw
Anterior crossvein transverse, well beyond the middle of the discal cell ....**Acrostictella** Hendel

59. Face sharply carinate.. 60
Face not sharply carinate... 62

60. Third antennal segment angulate above or elongate................ 61
Third antennal segment orbicular..................**Tetropismenus** Lœw

61. Third antennal segment angulate at upper apex.........**Tephronota** Lœw
Third segment elongate...............................**Hiatus** Cresson

62. Mesonotum with presutural bristles (**12, 59**)..........**Melieria** Desvoidy
Mesonotum without presutural bristles............................. 63

63. Front widening anteriorly.. 64
Front narrowed anteriorly (**34**)........................**Automola** Lœw

64. Three or four pairs of scutellar bristles; postocellars long and fine; hair of front long and rather abundant (**53, 60**).......**Califortalis,** n. g.
Two pairs of scutellars; postocellars short; hair of front short, sparse and rather coarse.. 65

65. Verticals long and strong; cheeks much narrower than the eye-height (**Ortalis** auct) 66
Verticals short; cheeks almost or quite as wide as the eye-height (**6, 61**)...**Tetanops** Fallén

66. Two pairs of well developed frontals; lunule haired (**77, 95**). **Ceratoxys** Rondani
Only one pair of well developed frontals; lunule bare (**54, 94**). **Ortalimyia,** n. g.

Melanolomina, new genus

Differs from *Melanoloma* Loew in possessing two pairs of scutellar bristles. In the two species before me the mesonotum is more or less reddish and not metallic. Genotype:—*Odontomera varians* Schiner.

Zetekomyia, new genus

Differs from *Melanolomina* in having the front more than twice as wide as the eyes (from dorsal view) and a somewhat more elongate and more distinctly clavate abdomen. The head bears only four pairs of bristles: a pair of frontals, pair of ocellars, situated behind the anterior ocellus, and inner and outer verticals; hair very short; antennæ sepa-

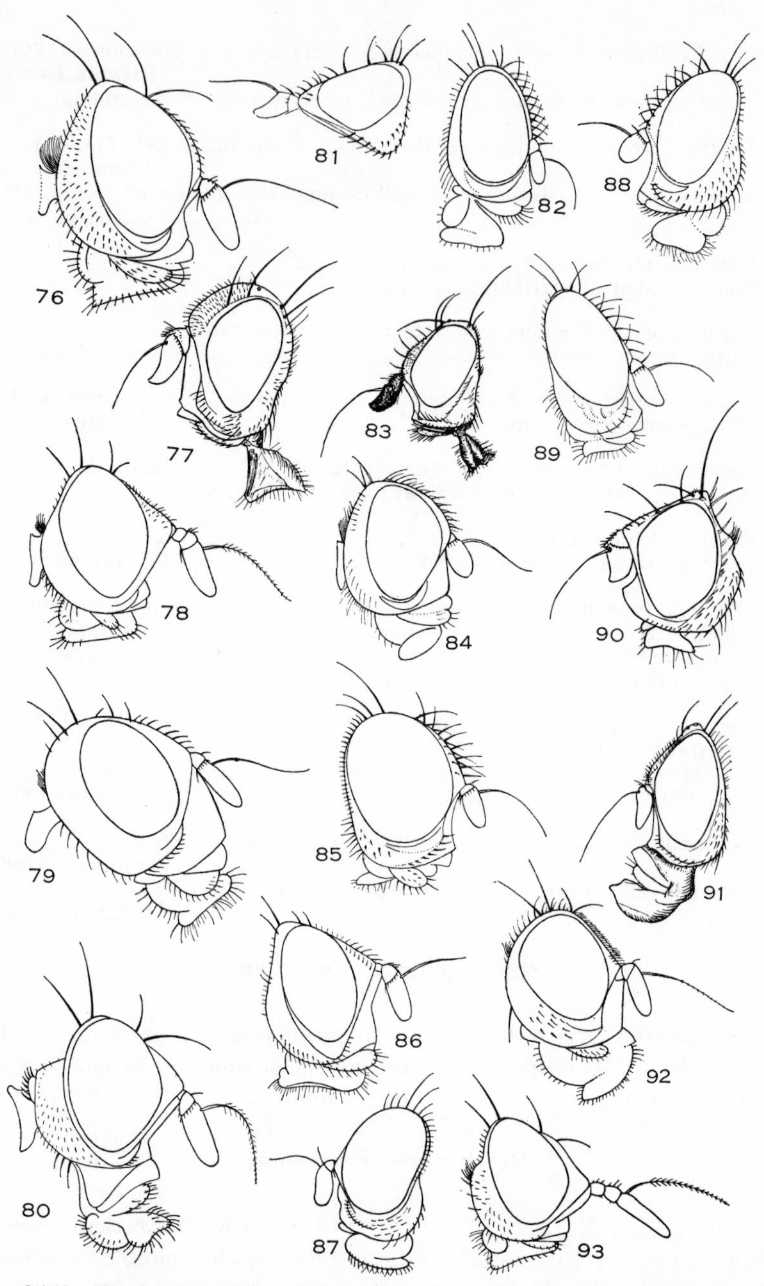

Otitidæ VI.—76, **Melanoloma affinis**; 77, **Ceratoxys latiuscula**; 78, **Neoidiotypa appendiculata**; 79, **Myrmecomya**; 80, **Odontomera nitens**; 81, **Acrometopia** (Chamæmyidæ); 82, **Axiologina ferrum-equinum**; 83, **Chætopsis ænea**; 84, **Seioptera vibrans**; 85, **Euxesta annonæ**; 86, **Himeroëssa pretiosa**; 87, **Dasymetopa**; 88, **Pareuxesta latifasciata**; 89, **Notogramma stigma**; 90, **Dyscrasis**; 91, **Pseudopterocalla**; 92, **Epiplatea arcuata**; 93, **Pœcilomyia longicornis**.

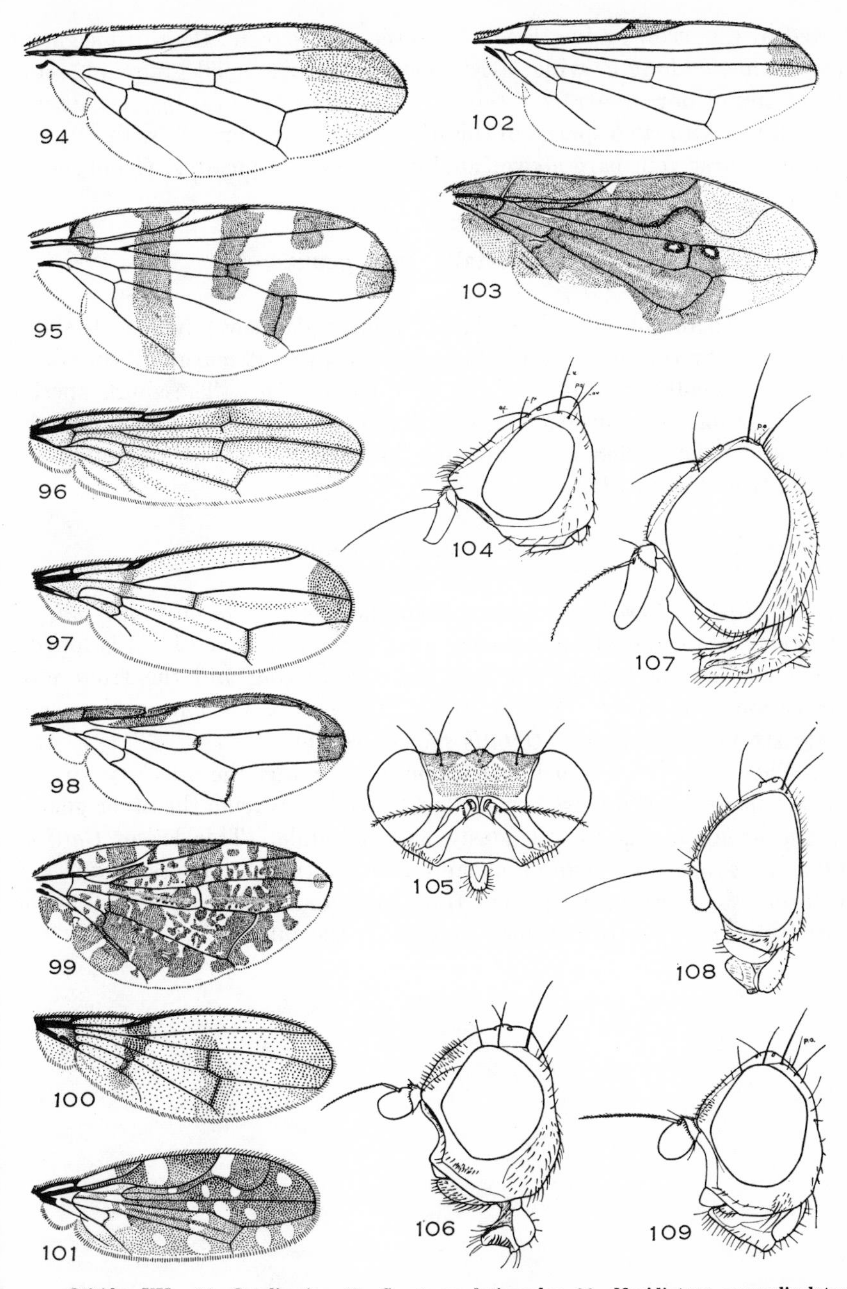

Otitidæ VII.—94, **Ortalimyia**; 95, **Ceratoxys latiuscula**; 96, **Neoidiotypa appendiculata**; 97, **Odontomera nitens**; 98, **Melanoloma decrepita**; 99, **Callopistromyia annulipes**; 100, **Hemixantha spinipes**; 101, **Paragorgopsis maculata**; 102, **Seioptera vibrans**; 103, **Pseudopterocalla**; 104, **Stenomyia**; 105, **Zetekomyia banksi**; 106, **Callopistromyia annulipes**; 107, **Melanoloma decrepita**; 108, **Pterocalla**; 109, **Pseudotephritis vau.**

rated by a narrow carina, reaching to the oral margin, the third segment three times as long as wide; arista short plumose; facial grooves absent; two pairs of dorsocentrals; propleural and sternopleural bristles absent; scutellum with two pairs of bristles; posterior femora with bristles beneath; first vein bare above; anal cell rounded apically. Genotype:—*Z. banksi,* n. sp.

Califortalis, new genus

Related to *Ceratoxys* Rondani (*Anacampta* Lœw) but readily distinguished by the presence of three or four pairs of marginal scutellars, a single, hair-like frontal and the very hairy front. The single species has somewhat the aspect of certain species of *Tetanops* Fallén but the bristles of the vertex are long and fine. Genotype:—*C. hirsutifrons,* n. sp., from California.

Ortalimyia, new genus

Related to *Ceratoxys* Rondani but the front bears only one pair of strong frontals and at most a very weak second pair, the head is longer, the facial carina higher, the face more retreating and the front narrower and less hairy. The bristles of the vertex are long and moderately strong. Genotype:—*Ortalis snowi* Cresson.

There has been much confusion concerning the identity of the genera mentioned in these notes. *Ceratoxys* differs from the other genera in the group by its conspicuously haired lunule. This leaves *Califortalis, Tetanops* and *Ortalimyia* and I think the characters in the key will serve to separate them. The front in *Tetanops* is always wrinkled or pitted and frequently pollinose except for the pits.

Family Trupaneidæ—The Fruit Flies

Mostly rather small flies, usually with pictured wings, the auxiliary vein curving forward at a right angle.

Head hemispherical, usually short; oral vibrissæ not distinct, the face vertical or somewhat retreating. Front broad, with bristles laterally, the anterior orbitals situated close to the orbits. Antennæ decumbent, short, rarely elongated. Proboscis of moderate length, rarely elongate and with the labellæ folding back, the labellæ usually broad and fleshy. Thorax with bristles although the anterior ones may be absent. Legs of moderate length, the tibiæ without preapical bristles. Wings large, usually with dark pattern, the auxiliary vein curving forward at right angles and sometimes evanescent at the tip; basal cells and anal cell always present, the latter often drawn out posteriorly into a long point or triangle. Abdomen composed of four or five segments; male genitalia small and only partly exposed; ovipositor segmented, usually exposed.

The adults are found in various habitats, often upon flowers. The larvæ live in the seeds and fruits of plants of various kinds or form galls. One of our commonest species lives in the heads of thistles, several make galls on golden rod, while others, like the fruit maggots, live in apples, cherries, citrus fruits, etc. Still others are leaf miners. The family is of considerable economic importance and has received a great deal of attention during recent years.

Among the papers essential to a study of the family are those listed below.* Other references will be found given in the key. Unfortunately the classification of this family is extremely artificial, being based largely upon the type of wing markings. In the key I have, in places, ignored the classification based upon wing maculation and a number of species must be shifted to genera in which they belong structurally, although differing to a certain degree, in wing pattern. Only the fact that I do not have access to all the North American genera prevents a more thorough revision of the genera. Recognition of many of the described species is difficult because they are not illustrated.

For many suggestions and the generous loan of material in this family I am greatly indebted to Mr. Marston Bates.

---

* Loew, 1873, Mon. N. A. Dipt., iii, pp. 211-351. Phillips, 1923, Rev. Trypet. N. E. Amer., Journ. N. Y. Ent. Soc., xxxi, pp. 119-155. Hendel, 1927, Flieg. Palæarkt. Reg.—Trypetidæ.

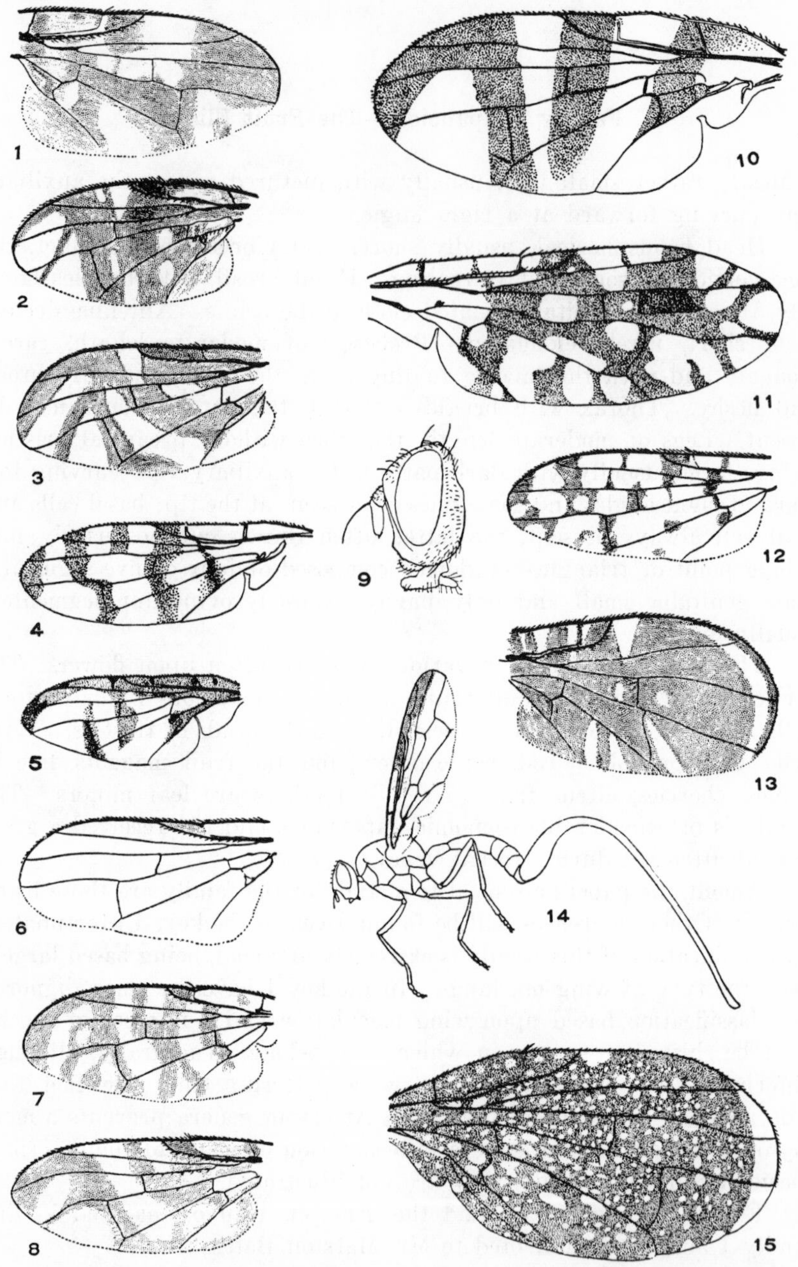

Trypaneidæ I.—1, **Xenochæta**; 2, **Hexachæta**; 3, **Anastrepha**; 4, **Euribia rufipes**; 5, **Acidia versatilis**; 6, **Neaspilota**; 7, **Œdicarena**; 8, **Straussia**; 9, **Anastrepha**; 10, **Rhagoletis indifferens**; 11, **Tephritis jonesi**; 12, **Tephritis** sp.; 13, **Polymorphomyia basilica**; 14, **Toxotrypanea curvicauda**; 15, **Eutreta pacifica**.

KEY TO GENERA*

1. Scutellum with six strong, regularly placed bristles.................. 2
   Scutellum with not more than two pairs of bristles or they are weak and not regularly placed, the apical pair being very widely separated 4

2. Front more than half as wide as the head (1)..........**Xenochæta** Snow
   Front decidedly less than half as wide as the head.................. 3

3. Triangle of the anal cell longer than the petiole (**46, 70**). **Blepharoneura** Lœw
   Triangle of the anal cell shorter than the petiole (**2, 69**)..**Hexachæta** Loew

4. Scutellum with two pairs of bristles, the apical pair strong........... 5
   Scutellum with one pair of strong bristles or if with two pairs the apical pair is absent and there are two pairs on the basal half...... 36

5. Fourth vein not or scarcely curved forward at the apex............. 6
   Fourth vein strongly curved forward at the apex (**3, 9**). **Anastrepha** Schiner

6. Anterior pair of dorsocentrals situated far in front of a line drawn between the anterior pair of supra-alars......................... 24
   Anterior dorsocentrals situated at most slightly in front of such a line, usually behind 7

7. Proboscis very long and slender, geniculate; (**Asimoneura** Czerny; **Rhynencina** Johnson; **Aleomyia** Phillips) (**4, 42**).......**Euribia** Latreille
   Proboscis short and thick, not geniculate in the middle.............. 8

8. Arista short plumose or bare...................................... 9
   Arista long plumose..........................**Molynocœlia** Giglio-Tos

9. Scutellum not mostly shining black or the apex yellow or sulcate..... 10
   Scutellum mostly shining black, the base narrowly yellow, the apex never sulcate (**29, 66**)..............................**Ceratitis** McLeay

10. Acrostical and dorsocentral bristles in an almost transverse row (**5, 60**). †**Acidia** Desvoidy
    Dorsocentrals placed far in front of the acrosticals so that there appear to be two pairs of dorsocentrals................................... 11

11. Notopleura with several setulæ near the posterior bristle (**24, 63**). **Epochra** Lœw
    Notopleura bare 12

12. Cheeks at most slightly more than one-fourth as wide as the eye-height, if doubtful the scutellum is sulcate....................... 13
    Cheeks at least two-fifths as wide as the eye-height; oral margin not strongly produced 22

13. Stigmatal cell long and narrow, four times as long as wide; wings reticulate (**21, 36**)...............................**Icterica** Lœw
    Stigmatal cell shorter and broader, not over three times as long as wide; wings not reticulate.................................... 14

---

* **Baryplegma** Wulp is omitted.

† **Trypeta versatilis** Curran is a true **Acidia** while **Acidia fratria** Lœw is a true **Trypeta.**

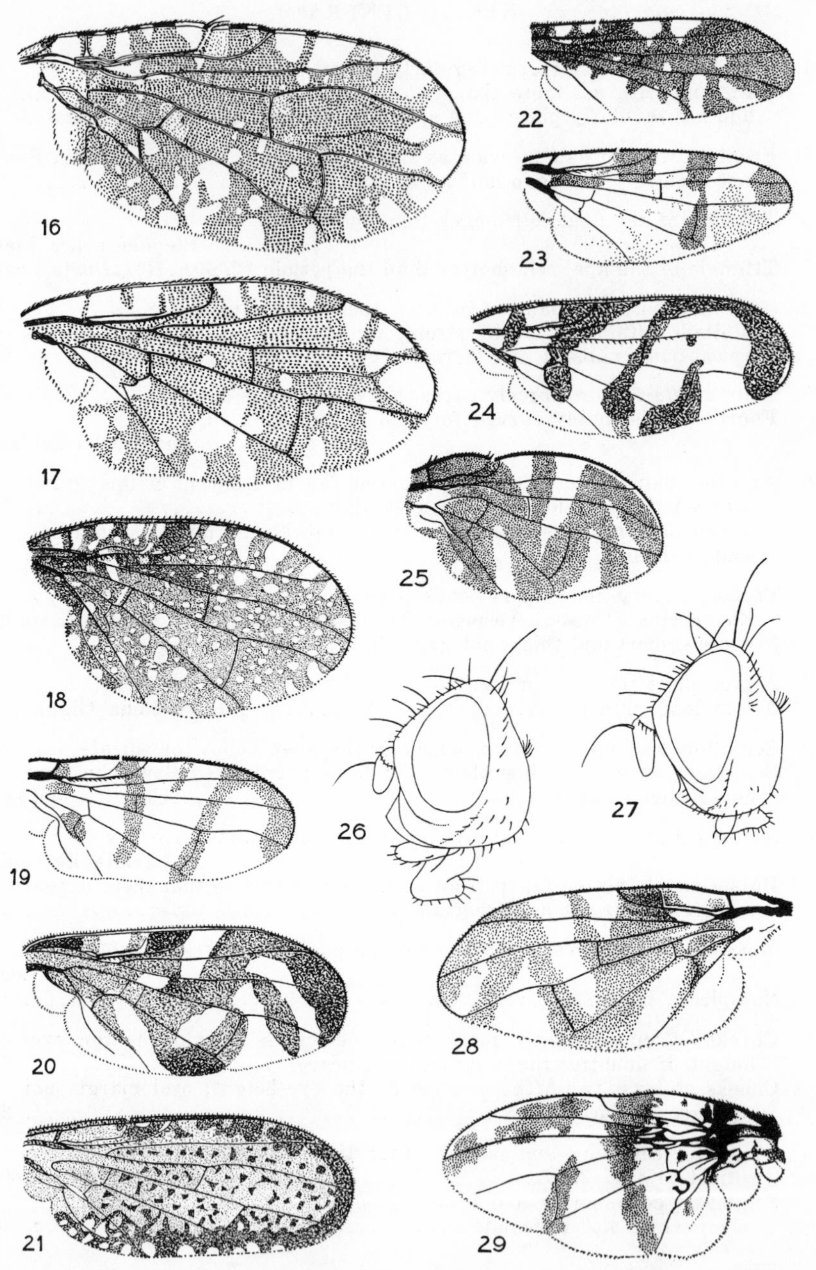

Trypaneidæ II.—16, **Eurostina confusa**; 17, **Tetreuaresta obscuriventris**; 18, **Xanthomyia platyptera**; 19, **Zonosema**; 20, **Trypeta fratria**; 21, **Icterica circinata**; 22, **Eucosmoptera tetraspina**; 23, **Terellia floriscentiæ**; 24, **Epochra canadensis**; 25, **Stenopa vulnerata**; 26, **Orellia**; 27, 28, **Myoleja cæsio**; 29, **Ceratitis capitata**.

14. Notopleura densely pollinose 20
    Notopleura not pollinose 15

15. Third antennal segment little longer than the basal two combined, never triangularly produced at the tip 18
    Third antennal segment elongate, usually produced as a sharp triangle at the upper apex 16

16. Postcallar (postalar) bristle situated far in front of the posterior intra-alar .... **Zonosemata** Benjamin
    Postcallar, intra-alar and acrostical bristles in almost straight line....16a

16a. Dorsocentral bristles situated well behind the supra-alar bristles **(19, 31)** .... **Zonosema** Lœw
    Dorsocentral bristles situated at most very slightly behind the supra-alars, usually slightly in front of them 17

17. Third longitudinal vein with at most two basal setulæ, usually bare; anterior crossvein situated but little beyond the middle of the discal cell **(10, 43)** .... *__Rhagoletis__ Lœw
    Third vein with several strong setulæ on basal part; anterior crossvein situated well beyond the middle of the discal cell (**Euleia** Walker) **(27, 28)** .... †**Myoleja** Rondani

18. Scutellum swollen, convex, more or less deeply longitudinally grooved apically (**Tomoplagina** Curran) **(58, 65)** .... **Peronyma** Lœw
    Scutellum flat dorsally, not at all grooved 19

19. Face more or less carinate, not concave in profile, the oral margin not produced **(20, 49)** .... ‡**Trypeta** Meigen
    Face concave in profile, the oral margin produced **(23, 62)**.
    Terellia Desvoidy

20. Costal spine not longer than the thickness of the costa; wings narrow. 21
    Costal spines more than twice as long as the costal thickness; wings very broad, reticulate **(18, 37)** .... **Xanthomyia** Phillips

21. Wings reticulate; abdomen with paired shining black spots; oral margin not produced **(47, 53)** .... **Acidogona** Lœw
    Wings hyaline, rarely banded; abdomen without paired black spots; oral margin conspicuously produced **(6, 34)**...§**Neaspilota** Osten Sacken

22. Scutellar bristles longer than the scutellum; antennal pits limited below, the head long 23
    Scutellar bristles very short; antennal pits almost obsolete; third antennal segment with several hairs above; tibiæ swollen **(40, 57)**.
    ¶**Pyrgotoides**, n. g.

23. Fourth vein ending at or near the tip of the wing **(7, 30)**.
    Œdicarena Snow

* Cresson, 1929, Tr. Amer. Ent. Soc., lv, pp. 401-414, 1 plate. Curran, 1932, Amer. Mus. Novit. No. 526, p. 5.

† **Euleia** Walker is the older name but there is considerable doubt about the identity of the genotype and I use **Myoleja** to avoid confusion.

‡ **Acidia fratria** Lœw belongs here.

§ Curran, 1932, Amer. Mus. Novit. No. 526, p. 3.

¶ A large species resembling the species of **Pyrgota** but distinguished by wing venation, presence of strong ocelli, shape of the head, etc. The genotype is **crassipes** n.sp. from Panama.

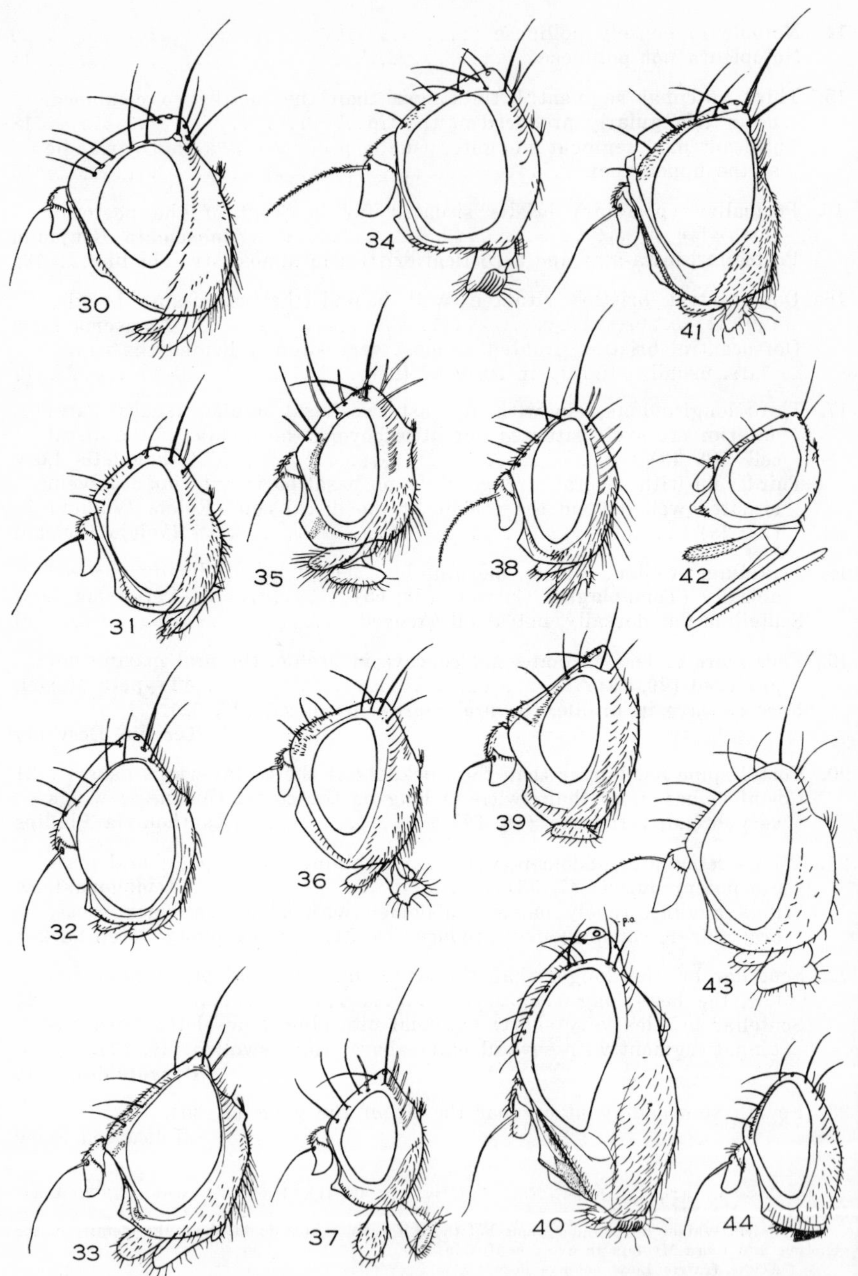

Trypaneidæ III.—30, **Œdicarena diffusa**; 31, **Zonosema electa**; 32, **Tomoplagia**; 33, **Eutreta**; 34, **Neaspilota albidipennis**; 35, **Paracantha**; 36, **Icterica sericata**; 37, **Xanthomyia platyptera**; 38, **Stenopa vulnerata**; 39, **Eurostina confusa**; 40, **Pyrgotoides clavipes**; 41, **Poliomota**; 42, **Euribia**; 43, **Rhagoletis cerasi**; 44, **Procecidochares**.

Fourth vein ending behind the tip of the wing, the wing-apex near the third vein; wings rather pointed (**8, 50, 51**).........**Straussia** Desvoidy

24. Anterior and posterior crossveins separated from each other by much less than half the length of the anterior crossvein; posterior crossvein very strongly recurrent (13)...............**Polymorphomyia** Snow
Crossveins much less approximate; posterior crossvein not strongly recurrent 25

25. Scuttellum strongly shining black, swollen and hemispherical......... 26
Scutellum more or less dull, more or less flattened or at most moderately convex 27

26. Parafacials bare (**44, 79**)......................**Procecidochares** Hendel
Parafacials with a row of rather long pale hairs (**61**)...**Callachna** Aldrich

27. Notopleura cinereous pollinose.................................... 28
Notopleura bare or rather thinly brownish pollinose.................. 31

28. Anal cell drawn out posteriorly into an elongate triangle............. 29
Anal cell not drawn out apically, or with a short, transverse triangle (**Euaresta** Lœw; **Urophora** Lœw) (**11, 12, 64**).......**Tephritis** Latreille

29. Antennal pits not deep, not separated and strongly marked........... 30
Antennal pits deep, separated and strongly defined (**41, 48**).
*__Polionota__ Wulp

30. Face and front rather strongly narrowed to the antennæ; oral margin with hair only on the anterior half (**17, 54**)......†**Tetreuaresta** Hendel
Face and front not strongly narrowed to the antennæ; oral margin with bristles almost to the oral angles (**45, 59**).............**Acrotænia** Lœw

31. Anterior crossvein situated not more than its own length from the posterior, both strongly oblique (**32, 72**).........**Tomoplagia** Coquillett
Anterior crossvein situated more than its length from the posterior, both never strongly oblique..................................... 32

32. Stigmal cell scarcely longer than wide (**25, 38**).............**Stenopa** Lœw
Stigmal cell usually twice as long as wide, always much longer....... 33

33. Front with two pairs of black reclinate bristles, none converging (**35, 73**) ....**Paracantha** Coquillett
Front with three pairs of convergent frontals....................... 34

34. Costal spines short and not very conspicuous....................... 35
Costal spines rather long and conspicuous (**15, 33**).........‡**Eutreta** Lœw

35. Wings with crossbands (**26**)..........................**Orellia** Desvoidy
Wings with a brown pattern containing hyaline indentations and spots (**22**) ....**Eucosmoptera** Phillips

* The single specimen I have before me is loaned by Dr. Aldrich and is determined as **mucida** Giglio-Tos. The figure by Giglio-Tos shows the anterior crossvein in the hyaline costal triangle and much farther from the posterior crossvein than I find it. The species I have illustrated may not be **mucida**, and may even belong to a different genus, depending upon the shape of the head. Mr. Van der Wulp's drawing is poor in regard to the anal cell.

† This genus is very doubtfully distinct from **Acrotænia.**

‡ Curran, 1932, Amer. Mus. Novit. No. 556.

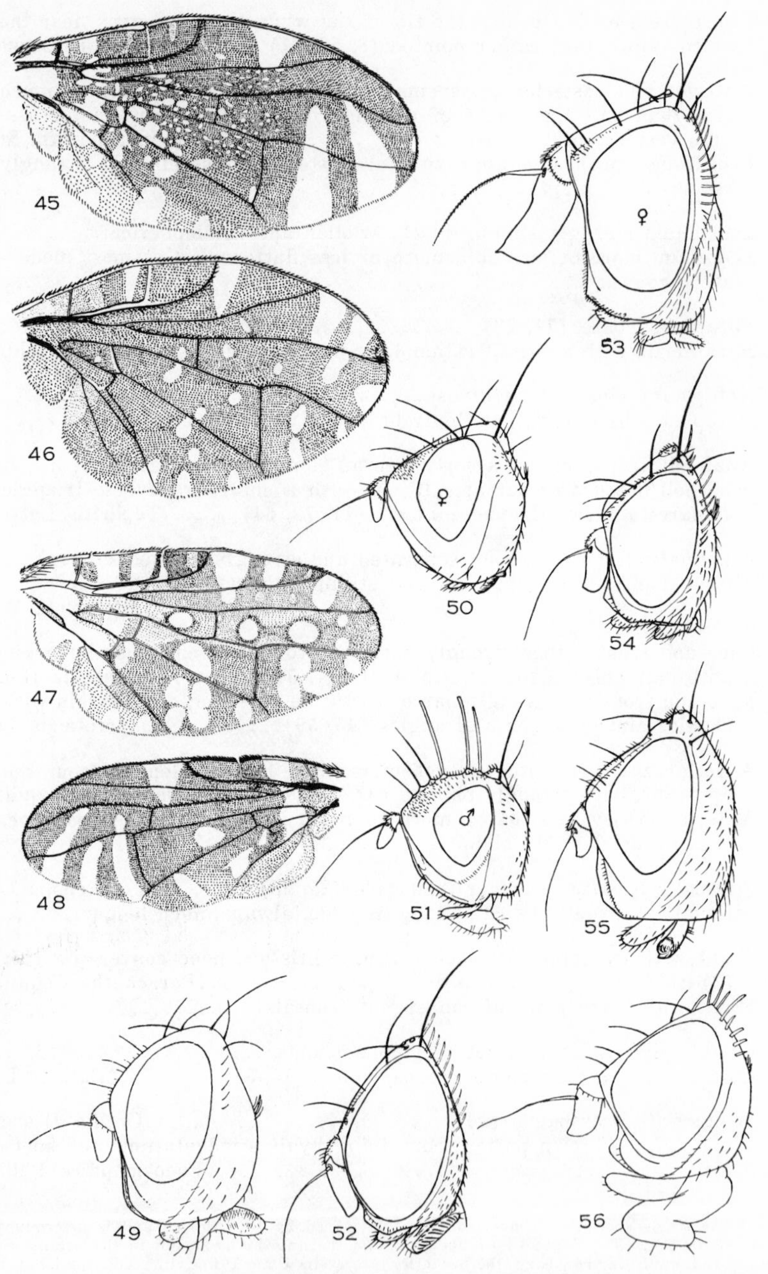

Trypaneidæ IV.—45, **Acrotænia**; 46, **Blepharoneura**; 47, **Acidogona**; 48, **Polionota**; 49, **Trypeta**; 50, 51, **Straussia longipennis**; 52, **Xanthaciura insecta**; 53, **Acidogona melaneura**; 54, **Tetreuaresta obscuriventris**; 55, **Eurosta comma**; 56, **Trypanea.**

36. Front bristles well developed; ocellars present...................... 37
Frontals weak; ocellars absent; ovipositor very long and cylindrical (14) ....**Toxotrypanea** Gerstæcker

37. Head higher than long.. 38
Head longer than high **(67)**.. 44

38. Scutellum without a deep longitudinal furrow......................... 39
Scutellum swollen and with a deep longitudinal furrow **(58, 65)**.
Peronyma Lœw

39. Front immediately above the antennæ almost half as wide as the head and very much wider than either eye.................................. 40
Front much less than half as wide as the head and, anteriorly, little if any wider than one eye from anterior view.................... 41

40. Anterior pair of dorsocentrals situated far in front of a line drawn between the anterior pair of supra-alar bristles **(16, 39)**.
***Eurostina** Curran
Anterior pair of dorsocentrals situated at most slightly in front of a line drawn between the anterior supra-alars or behind such a line **(55, 71)**...**Eurosta** Lœw

41. Front twice as long as the width at vertex **(52, 74)**...**Xanthaciura** Hendel
Front much less than twice as long as the width at vertex............ 42

42. Front with at least three pairs of convergent frontal bristles.......... 43
Front with two pairs of convergent frontals **(76)**.....**Dyseuaresta** Hendel

43. Head almost as long as high, the oral margin projecting; eyes oblique, broadly oval **(56, 75)**............................†**Trupanea** Schrank
Head much higher than long, the oral margin but little projecting; eyes perpendicular, rather narrowly oval **(68, 78)**..........‡**Aciurina** Curran

44. Third antennal segment short, the apex rounded (Europe) **(67)**.
Ensina Lœw
Third antennal segment rather long, the upper apex angulate **(77)**.
Paroxyna Hendel

The student will find it difficult to locate many species described in genera other than those to which they are now assigned. In the following list are given (1) the present genus and (2) in ( ) the genera in which species may be found.

Acidia (Spilographa).
Dyseuaresta (Euaresta, Tephritis).
Ensina (Tephritis).
Euribia (Aleomyia, Urophora, Tephritis Hendel, 1914).
Myoleja (Aciura, Acidia, Eucosmoptera).
Tephritis (Euaresta, Ensina, Trypanea, Urellia).
Terellia (Trypeta, Orellia).
Tetreuaresta (Euaresta, Tephritis).
Trypanea (Urellia, Tephritis).
Trypeta (Orellia, Terellia, etc.).
Zonosema (Spilographa, Acidia).

* Originally **Eurosta latifrons** Lœw was named as type of this genus but the species is a true **Eurosta** and does not possess the generic characters of **Eurostina.** The type of the genus should be known as **Eurostina confusa,** Slosson Collection, Delaware Water Gap.

† Curran, 1932, Amer. Mus. Novit. No. 556 (Trypanea).

‡ Curran, 1932, Amer. Mus. Novit. No. 556. In a letter to the author Dr. Hendel suggested the synonymy of this genus with **Tephrella** Bezzi and this is quite possible. However, I am retaining **Aciurina** on the suggestion of Mr. Bates, as a comparison of specimens with the genotype of **Tephrella**, a little known species, may prove that two genera exist.

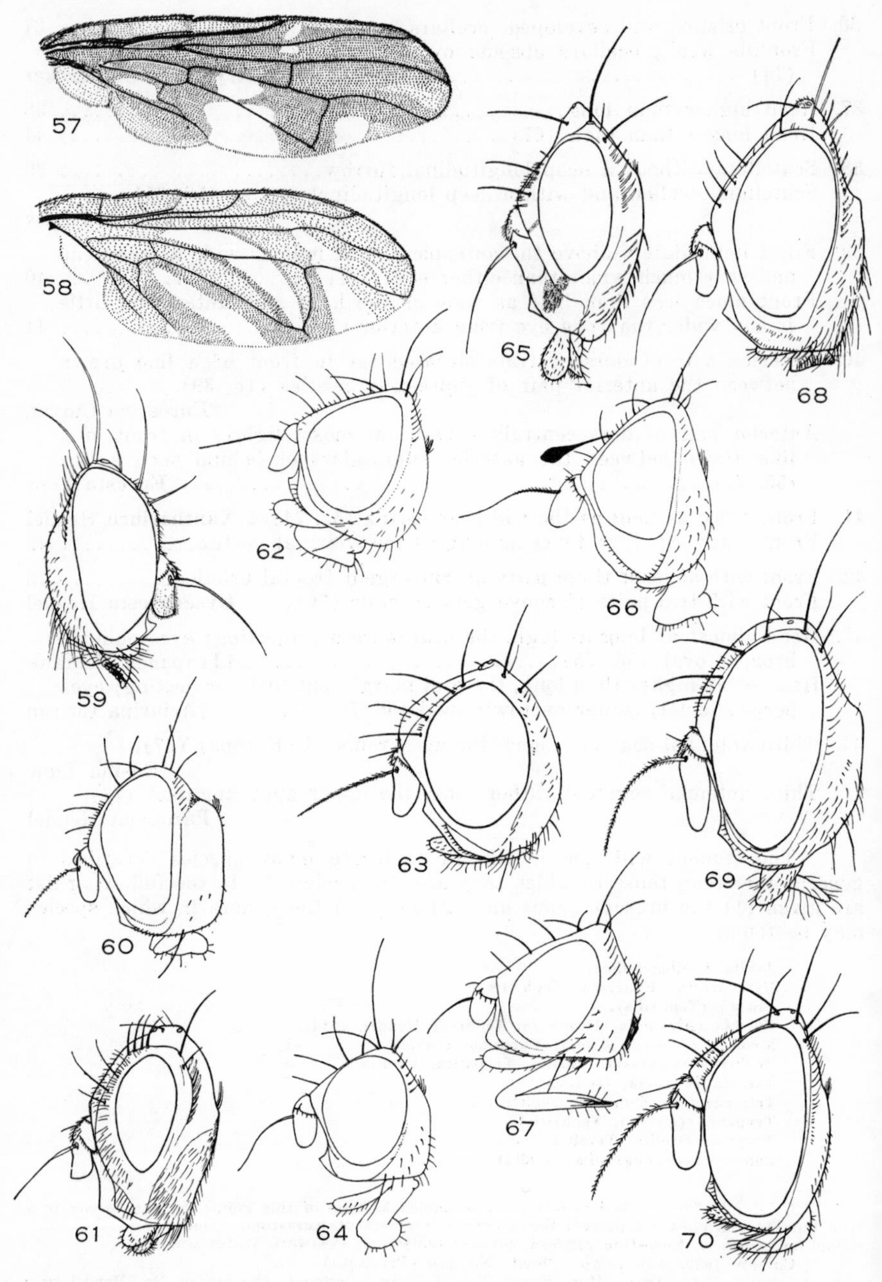

Trypaneidæ V.—57, **Pyrgotoides clavipes**; 58, **Peronyma**; 59, **Acrotænia**; 60, **Acidia**; 61, **Callachna**; 62, **Terellia**; 63, **Epochra canadensis**; 64, **Tephritis**; 65, **Peronyma maculata**; 66, **Ceratitis capitata**; 67, **Paroxyna**; 68, **Aciurina**; 69, **Hexachæta**; 70, **Blepharoneura** (sp. Panama).

Mr. Bates has furnished the following list of species giving the correct generic position according to our present concepts:

Acidia johnsoni Thomas = **Aciurina.**
Aciura limata Coquillett (**Eucosmoptera** Phillips) = **Myoleja.**
Aciura nigricornis Doane (**Eucosmoptera** Phillips) = **Myoleja.**
Rhagoletis formosa Coquillett = **Euribia.**
Rhagoletis grindeliæ Coquillett = **Euribia.**
Rhynencina longirostris Johnson = **Euribia.**
Trypeta baccharis Coquillett = probably **Tephritis.**
Trypeta bigeloviæ Cockerell (**Eurosta** Townsend) = **Aciurina.**

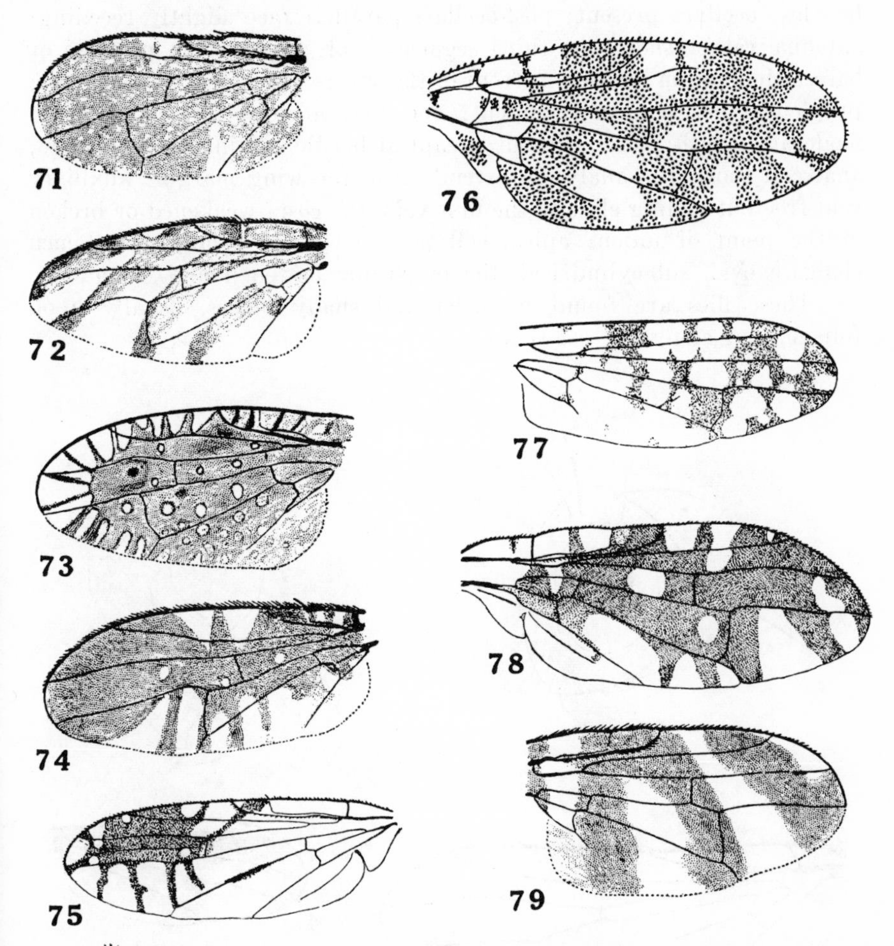

Trypaneidæ VI.—71, **Eurosta**; 72, **Tomoplagia**; 73, **Paracantha**; 74, **Xanthaciura insecta**; 75, **Trypanea wheeleri**; 76, **Dyseuaresta plesia**; 77, **Ensina**; 78, **Aciurina trixa**; 79, **Procecidochares.**

Family Pallopteridæ

Flies of medium size, usually with pictured wings, the auxiliary vein entire.

Head higher than long; oral vibrissæ absent; a single pair of frontal bristles; ocellars present; post-ocellars parallel; face slightly receding; antennæ rather short, the third segment oval; arista short plumose or bare. Mesonotum bristled in front of the suture (except in two species); propleural bristle usually absent; one sternopleural bristle. Legs of moderate length; tibiæ without preapical bristle. Wings rather large; anal cell short, the anal vein extending to the wing margin; auxiliary vein free but ending close to the first vein, the costa weakened or broken at the point of union; apical cell not narrowed apically. Abdomen elongate oval, sub-cylindrical, the ovipositor flattened and elongate.

These flies are found in moist and shady places, usually upon foliage, and along the sea-shore.

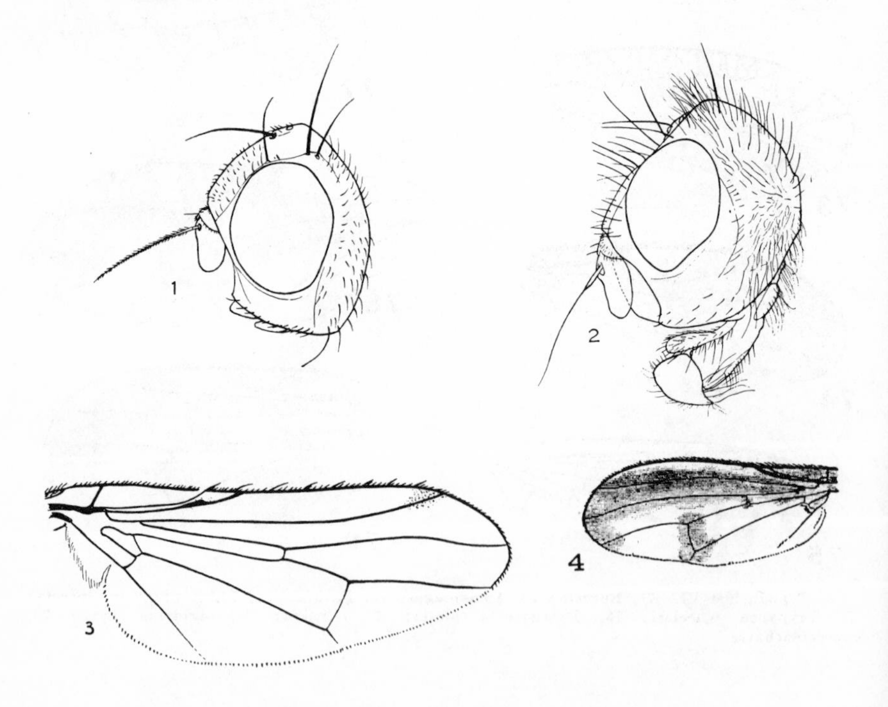

Pallopteridæ.—1, **Palloptera arcuata;** 2, 3, **Omomyia hirsuta;** 4, **Palloptera jucunda.**

Palloptera Fallén has been considered the only genus and has been reviewed by Malloch.* The genus has been placed in the Lauxaniidæ and Lonchæidæ. It differs from the former in lacking preapical tibial bristles and from the latter in having the front transverse anteriorly, the lunule being concealed. In many respects it shows a relationship to the Helomyzidæ but is excluded from the group by its flattened ovipositor and is, perhaps, more closely allied to the Otitidæ. The genus *Omomyia,* placed in the Cœlopidæ by Coquillett, belongs here. It shows a remarkable sexual dimorphism, the males bearing long, woolly pile while the females show little trace of it.

KEY TO GENERA

1. Facial carina strong, the antennal grooves deep; males densely pilose (2, 3) .... **Omomyia** Coquillett
   Facial carina quite weak; antennal grooves shallow; never densely pilose (1, 4) .... **Palloptera** Fallén

* 1924. Proc. U. S. N. M., lxv, Article 12, pp. 6-7.

Family Lonchæidæ

Small shining blackish flies, the auxiliary vein entire; the tibiæ without preapical bristles.

Head shorter than high; face and front moderately wide; oral vibrissæ absent; front with a single orbital, clothed with short hairs; ocellars present; postocellars divergent; antennæ elongate, decumbent. Thorax bristled posteriorly; mesopleura with bristles behind; one or two sternopleurals; propleural present, the propleura without hair. Legs short; tibiæ without preapical bristle. Wing venation complete; second basal and anal cells short, the anal vein reaching the wing margin faintly, and bisinuate. Abdomen oval, rather flat; ovipositor rather long and triangular.

The adults occur almost everywhere but prefer moist or shady places. The larvæ live in plants or decaying vegetation. They have been reared from under bark and may be predaceous.

This family is readily distinguished from the Periscelidæ by its entire auxiliary vein; from the Sapromyzidæ by the absence of preapical tibial bristles on at least the anterior and posterior tibiæ and from the Pallopteridæ by the presence of a propleural bristle and the exposed frontal lunule.

Lonchœa Fallén is the only genus recognized although *Earomyia* Zetterstedt may be distinguished by having the frontal lunule bare. Malloch* has reviewed the species. A few have been described since the publication of his paper.

* 1924. Proc. U. S. N. M., lxv, Art. 12, pp. 3-6.

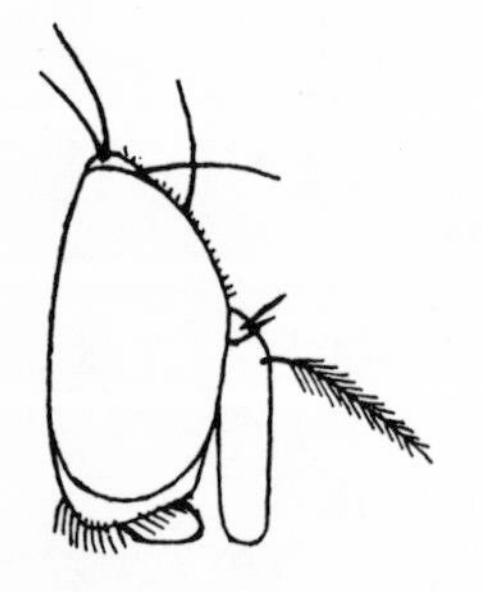

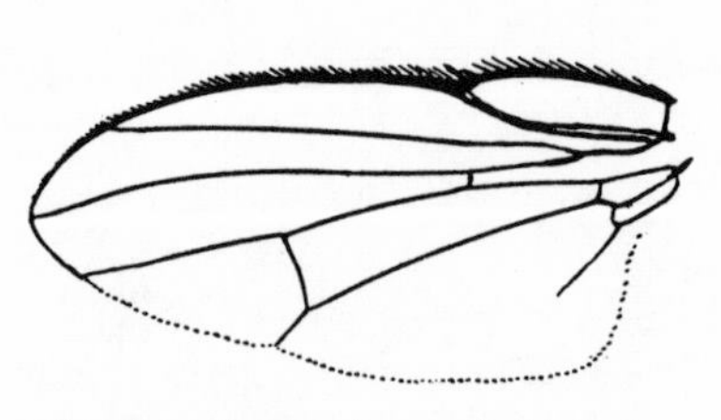

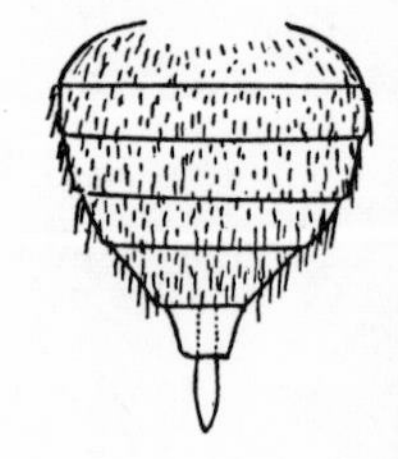

Lonchæa, head, wing and abdomen.

Family Ropalomeridæ

Moderately large tropical flies of a brownish and grayish color.

Front broad, excavated, with or without bristles; face broad, carinate, tuberculate or the oral margin prominent; cheeks broad, hairy; clypeus projecting; oral vibrissæ absent; proboscis short, the palpi slender or dilated; antennæ short; arista dorsal, bare or plumose. Thorax elongate; mesonotum with but few bristles, usually more or less mottled with gray and brown; scutellum often prominent and grooved. Abdomen shorter than the wings, flattened; hypopygium moderately large, largely concealed; ovipositor telescopic, projecting. Femora all

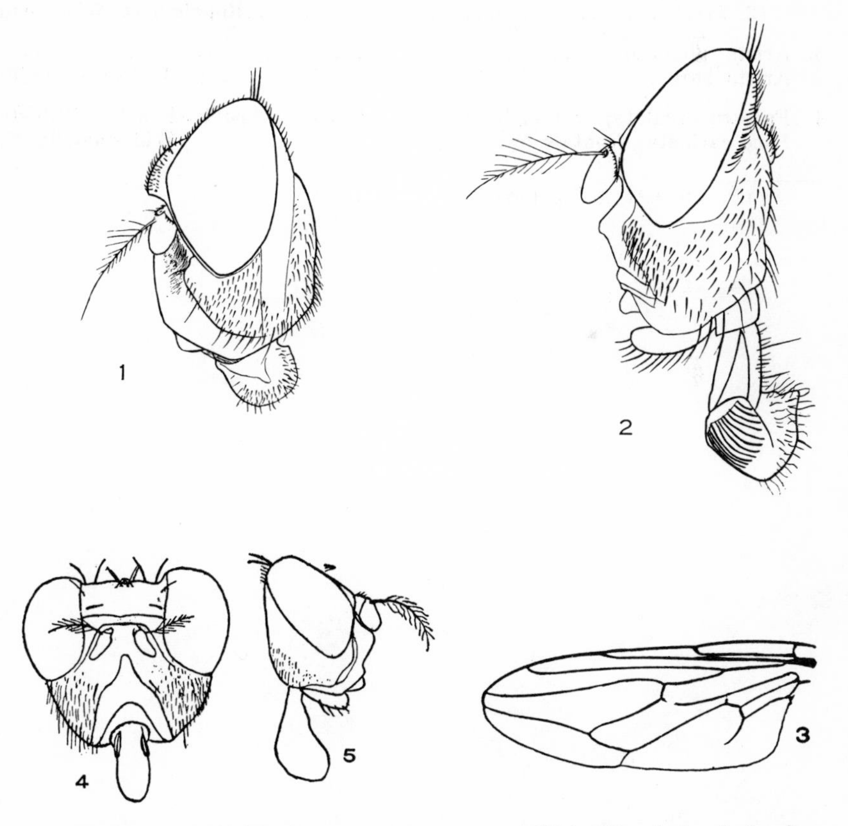

Ropalomeridæ.—1, **Willistoniella;** 2, 3, **Ropalomera;** 4, **Willistoniella;** 5, **Apophorhynchus.**

thickened; posterior tibiæ often dilated. Apical cell narrowed apically; auxiliary vein absent or present; second basal and anal cells present.

Only about a dozen species are known, all occurring in Central or South America. Evidently they are not uncommon at certain seasons of the year as Mr. Banks secured a number of specimens in Panama during July and August although I saw only two from December to March. They are evidently seashore inhabitants which extend their range up the rivers. The adults are fast in flight and are excellent hoverers. There is a recent revision of the family by Lindner.*

KEY TO GENERA

1. Auxiliary vein present 2
   Auxiliary vein absent .... **Rhinotora** Schiner

2. Scutellum oval 3
   Scutellum pyramidal, directed obliquely upward; arista plumose or bare (2, 3) .... **Ropalomera** Wiedemann

3. Arista plumose 4
   Arista bare .... **Kröberia** Lindner

4. Face tuberculate; frontal bristles absent (5).... **Apophorhynchus** Williston
   Face carinate; frontals present (1, 4)........................ **Willistoniella** Mik

* 1930. Deutsch. Ent. Zeitschr., 1930-31, pp. 122-137.

Family Tanypezidæ

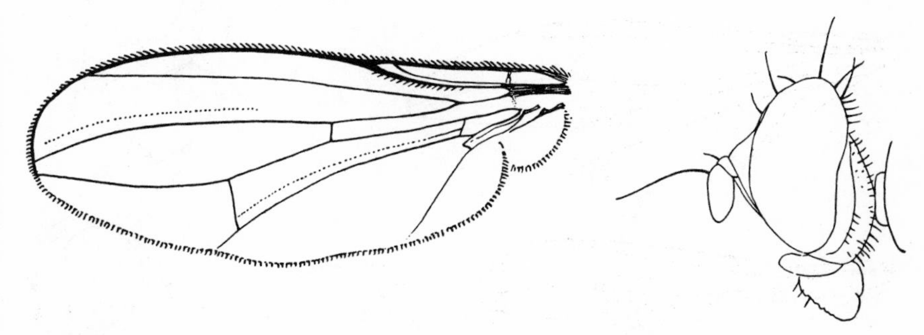

Tanypeza, head and wing.

Medium sized flies, with rather long, slender legs.

Head higher than long; face retreating below; two pairs of frontals: ocellars proclinate; antennæ pendulous, the third segment oval, moderately large; oral vibrissæ absent; palpi broadened. Thorax with only one pair of dorsocentrals; one humeral; no sternopleurals, one or two bristles on the mesopleura above, the mesopleura and pteropleura haired. Legs long, slender, without bristles. Wings with the apical cell narrowed; anal cell rounded apically, about as long as the second basal; first vein setulose above; auxiliary vein entire, touching the first vein before its end.

The adults occur in moist woods and are by no means numerous in collections. The immature stages are unknown.

Tanypeza Fallén is the only known genus unless *Tetradiscus* Bigot is distinct. However, *Tetradiscus* may not belong to this family and is too poorly described to be recognizable. There are fewer than a dozen known species belonging to the family, most of them occurring in the Neotropical region while one is known from Europe.

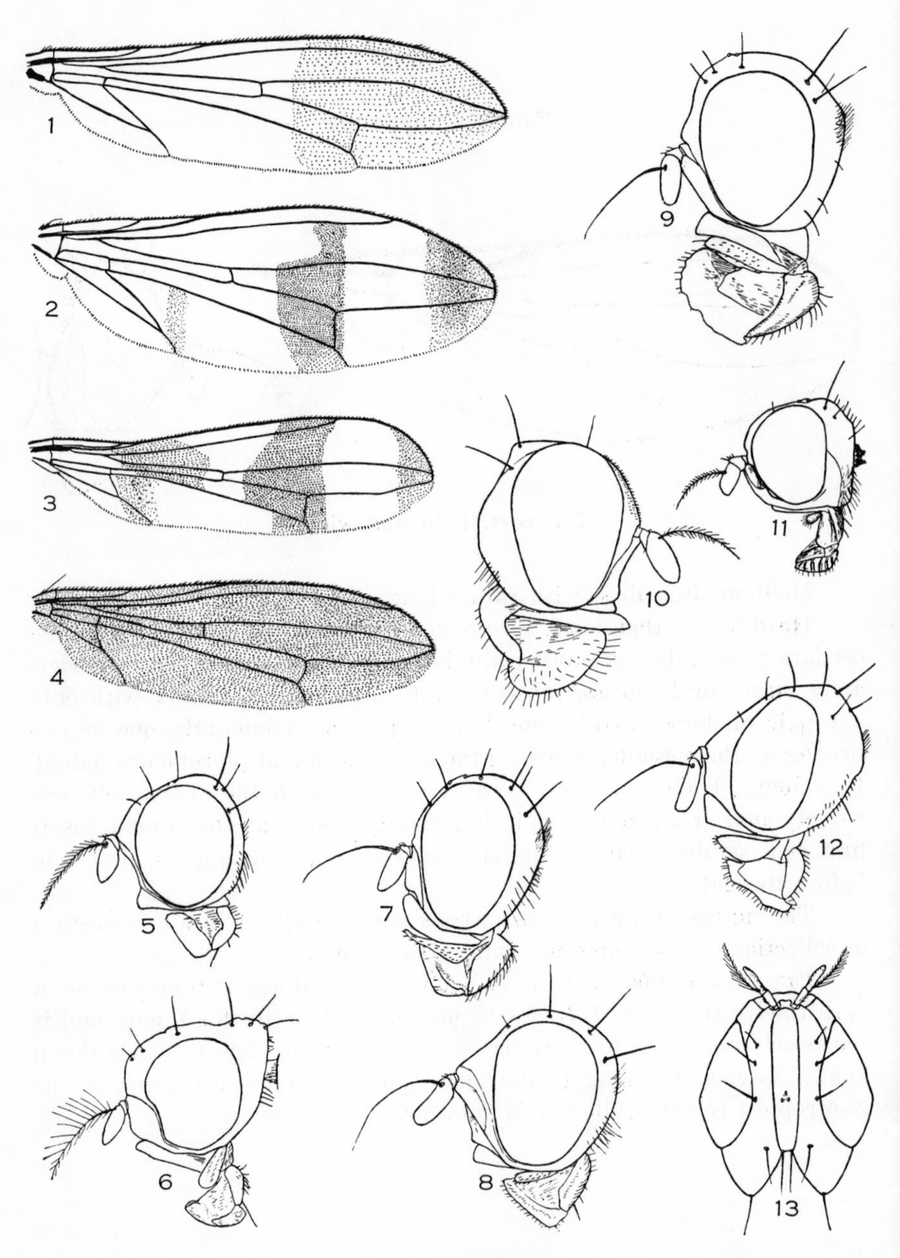

Calobatidæ I.—1, **Parasphen ruficauda**; 2, **Ptilosphen**; 3, **Rainieria**; 4, **Scipopus diversus**; 5, **Grallipeza**; 6, **Cardiacephala**; 7, **Grallomya**; 8, **Hoplocheiloma**; 9, **Scipopus**; 10, **Parasphen**; 11, **Calobata univittata**; 12, **Tæniaptera**; 13, **Cardiacephala**.

Family Calobatidæ—The Stilt-legged Flies

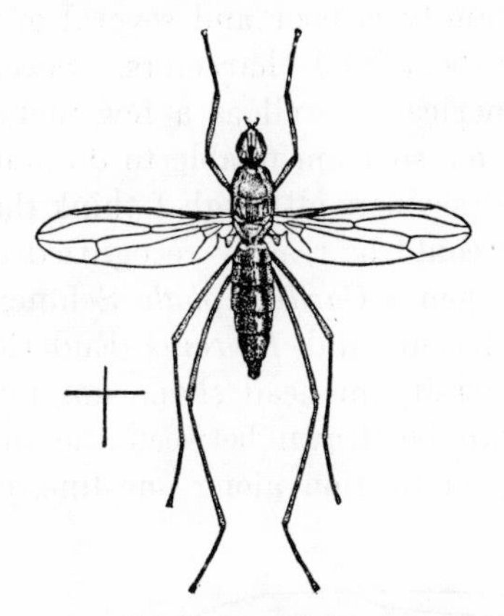

Calobata univittata.

Elongate flies with very long legs and dorsal, bare to plumose arista.

Head higher than long, rather orbicular or elongate, the front wide in both sexes and usually with bristles; face usually receding, the oral margin more or less produced, the clypeus large and polished; palpi flat and broad; antennæ of moderate length, pendulous, with dorsal, bare to plumose arista. Thorax elongate, bristled posteriorly and on the sides; sternopleura with long bristly hair behind; true sternopleural bristles absent; pteropleura bare. Legs very long, the anterior pair widely separated from the middle pair, femora rarely with small bristles, the posterior four tibiæ usually with tiny bristles. Wings long, usually marked with brown or black, the anal cell rectangular or angulate apically; apical cell usually narrowed apically; auxiliary vein lying very close to the first vein and usually partly touching it, rarely ending well before the first vein. Abdomen long and narrow, the ovipositor long.

The adults are found near moist places in the Neartic region but seem to occur everywhere in the tropics, where they are scavengers, and evidently the larvæ live in excrement. Some species have been reared from excrement and the adults are attracted to it in very large numbers. However, I have found a few of the tropical species only on foliage near streams and these may have a different habit. Enderlein* has reviewed the group and Cresson has described many species.

* 1922, Arch. für Naturg., lxxxviii, Abt. 5, pp. 140-229.

As here understood this family comprises the genera *Calobata,* and *Cardiacephala* of the old family Micropezidæ. They really have little in common with this latter group except a superficial resemblance. The classification of the family is poor and several of the genera are based upon what appear to be trivial characters. Several of the genera occurring in South America, as well as a few included in the following key, are unknown to me so I am unable to do more than use the characters cited by their describers although I think that most of the genera are well founded and could be readily recognized upon characters other than those used. The genus *Cardiacephala* Schiner, of which I consider both *Plocoscelus* Enderlein and *Rhœcius* Enderlein to be synonyms, merely displays a diversity in head shape not found in other groups, but no sharp lines can be drawn between the three proposed genera. Some insects show specialization along one line, others in other ways.

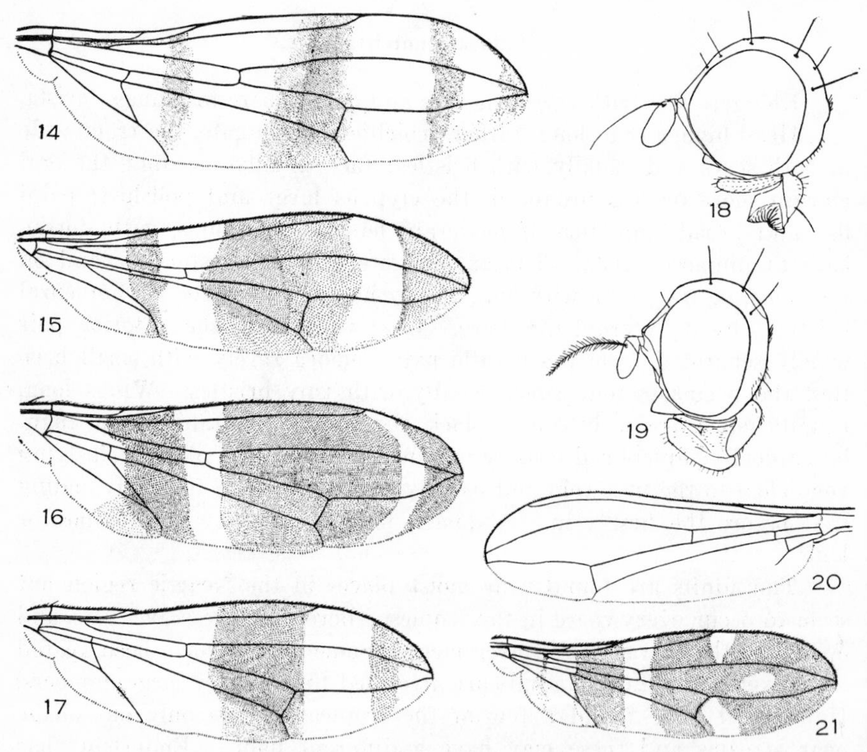

Calobatidæ II.—14, **Hoplocheiloma**; 15, **Grallomya annulata**; 16, **Tæniaptera**; 17, **Gallipeza**; 18, **Rainieria**; 19, **Ptilosphen**; 20, **Calobata univittata**; 21, **Cardiacephala.**

KEY TO GENERA

1. Anal cell extending two-thirds the distance to the wing margin, its anterior edge very oblique (16) 2
   Anal cell much shorter, the crossvein much less oblique 5

2. Distance between the tips of the second and third veins more than half as great as the length of the ultimate section of the fourth vein (16) 3
   This distance less than half the length of the ultimate section of the fourth vein (1, 10) .... **Parasphen** Enderlein

3. Arista bare 4
   Arista plumose or long pubescent (2, 19) .... **Ptilosphen** Enderlein

4. Apical cell closed and short petiolate (12, 16) ...... **Tæniaptera** Macquart
   Apical cell open (7, 15) .... **Grallomya** Rondani

5. Arista bare 6
   Arista plumose 9

6. Distance between the tips of the second and third veins equal to less than half the length of the ultimate section of the fourth vein (4, 9) .... **Scipopus** Enderlein
   This distance greater than half the length of the ultimate section of the fourth vein 7

7. Postocellar bristles absent (8, 14) .... **Hoplocheiloma** Cresson
   Postocellar bristles present, vertex with six bristles 8

8. Occiput strongly produced on either side of the vertex, concave in the middle from dorsal view .... **Mitromyia** Cresson
   Occiput at most weakly produced and very greatly concave from dorsal view (3, 18) .... ***Rainieria** Rondani

9. Posterior femora very conspicuously swollen on the apical third (6, 13, 21) .... †**Cardiacephala** Schiner
   Posterior femora regular in outline 10

10. Postocellar bristles absent 11
    Postocellar bristles long and strong (5, 17) .... **Grallipeza** Rondani

11. Stigmal cell long, the first vein ending in front of the anterior crossvein .... **Calobatina** Enderlein
    Stigmal cell short and not distinct, the first vein ending well before the anterior crossvein (11, 20) .... **Calobata** Meigen

---

* **Tanypoda** Rondani is a synonym and I do not believe that the characters cited by Cresson for his genus **Meganeria** are of sufficient value to constitute a genus.

† The dorsal view of the head shows the extreme development of the lobe-like production of the posterior orbits which may not be produced beyond the vertex. **Rhœcius** (Enderlein) has been proposed for this latter group but there is every gradation between the two extremes.

Family Micropezidæ

Slender flies of moderate size, their legs long, the second basal cell united with the discal cell.

Head orbicular or elongate and subtriangular; front without bristles; face receding, without oral vibrissæ; antennæ short, the arista dorsal. Thorax elongate, the front and middle coxæ widely separated; posterior portion of the pteropleura with long hairs; one sternopleural bristle. Legs long and slender, the tibiæ with bristles. Wings long, the second basal cell united with the discal cell; apical cell narrowed or closed and petiolate apically; auxiliary vein not distinctly separated from the first vein. Abdomen long and slender, the female ovipositor large, pendulous; male genitalia rather small, the fifth sternite usually with long pendulous lobes.

The adults are found in marshes and moist places in woods. There are three or four Nearctic, one Palæarctic and many species in the American tropics. I have seen only *Micropeza* from the United States and Canada. The immature stages are unknown. Enderlein* has reviewed the family. I give the characters of his genera although I scarcely agree that there are four genera represented. The appendiculate apical cell does not seem to me to be of generic importance and I am inclined to recognize only *Micropeza* and *Metopobrachia.*

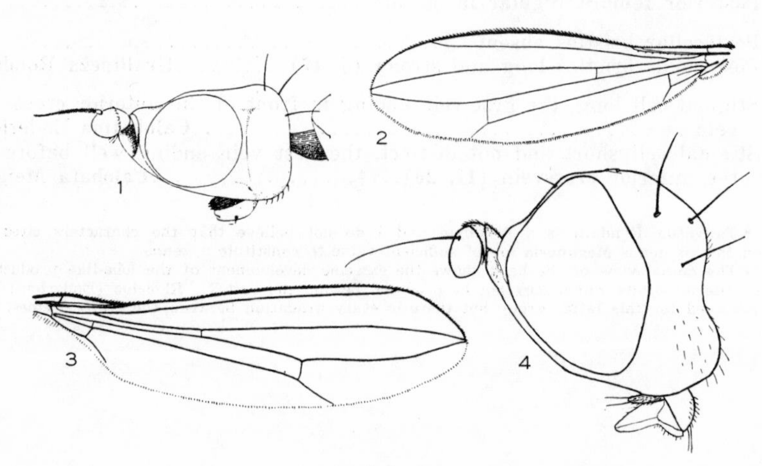

Micropezidæ.—1, 2, **Micropeza**; 3, 4, **Metopobrachia.**

KEY TO GENERA

1. Head subtriangular, much longer than high........................ 2
   Head orbicular, but little longer than high........................ 3

2. Apical cell open or closed in the wing margin (1, 2)....**Micropeza** Meigen
   Apical cell closed and petiolate.................**Neriocephalus** Enderlein

3. Apical cell open (3, 4).........................**Metopobrachia** Enderlein
   Apical cell closed and petiolate.....................**Cliopeza** Enderlein

---

* 1922, Arch. für Naturg., lxxxviii, Abt. 5, pp. 140-229.

Family Neriidæ

Slender flies of moderate size, with long legs and an apical arista.

Head longer than wide; two pairs of frontal bristles, the front wide in both sexes; face receding,* without oral vibrissæ; antennæ porrect, with a terminal bare or pubescent arista. Thorax long, the front and middle legs widely separated, the prosternum as long as the mesosternum; pteropleura bare; with or without a sternopleural bristle. Legs long and slender, the femora with short spines beneath. Wings long, the apical cell usually narrowed apically; anal and second basal cells short; auxiliary vein ending in the first vein. Abdomen long, rather flattened above; ovipositor long and pendulous, carried under the abdomen in life.

The adults are found near water or moist places. The family is strictly tropical, four of the nineteen genera occurring in North America. The immature stages are not known. Enderlein† has reviewed the group.

* In the old world Telostylinæ the oral margin is prominent while in the Neriinæ it is not conspicuous.

† 1922, Arch. für Naturg., lxxxviii, Abt. 5, pp. 140-229.

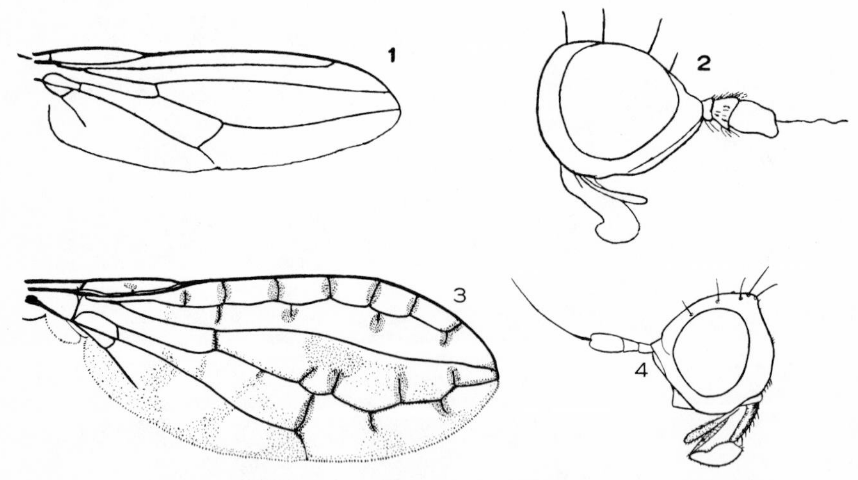

Neriidæ.—1, 2, **Nerius**; 3, 4, **Dictyonerius**.

KEY TO GENERA

1. Wings with numerous crossveins (3, 4)..........**Dictyonerius** Enderlein
   Wings with normal venation.. 2

2. Third antennal segment pointed apically; scutellum with one pair of bristles ....**Glyphidops** Enderlein
   Third antennal segment rounded or obtuse apically.................. 3

3. Ventral surface of the anterior femora with setigerous tubercles on the whole length ....**Odontoloxozus** Enderlein
   Anterior femora with bristles only apically (1, 2).......**Nerius** Fabricius

Family Piophilidæ

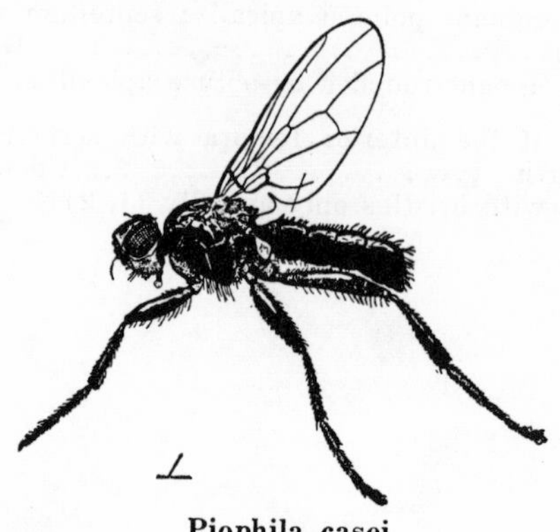

Piophila casei.

The flies included in this family rarely exceed five millimeters in length, and are usually glistening black or slightly bluish metallic in lustre.

Face not carinate, occiput more or less flattened; always two pairs of vertical bristles; postvertical bristles divergent; fronto-orbital bristles varying from two pairs to none; antennæ decumbent, the third segment elongate oval, arista bare in the American species; cheeks rarely fringed with hairs, the oral vibrissæ usually prominent, parafacials not differentiated as a linear orbital boundary; palpi well developed. Mesonotum almost always finely pubescent and polished; sternopleura never pruinose; one pair of dorsocentral bristles, four scutellar bristles. Legs of the male never toothed or deformed, the front femora usually furnished with long but delicate bristles. Abdomen more or less polished, pubescent but without bristles, broad, depressed, not constricted at the base; genitalia of the male more or less hidden asymmetrical; ovipositor extensile. Auxiliary vein terminating close to the end of the first vein, the costa broken at or near the termination, third and fourth veins parallel or more or less diverging, anal vein usually curved and evanescent apically, discal cell usually large, with the posterior crossvein usually long.

The larvæ are, in general, scavengers but some of them live in cheese and preserved meats. *Piophila casei,* the cheese-skipper, has a rather conical larva, pointed anteriorly and truncate posteriorly; body shining and smooth; antennæ two segmented; mouth hooks separated and divergent; anterior spiracles whitish, the abdominal travelling

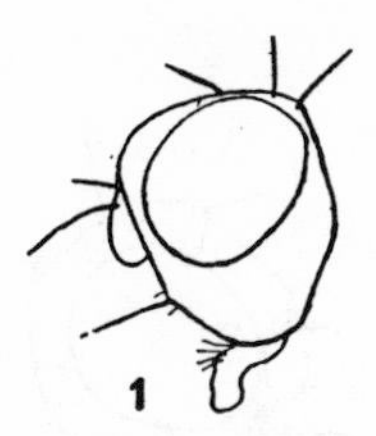

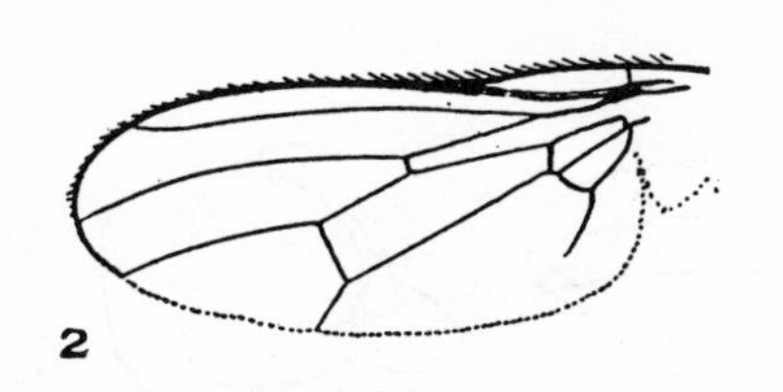

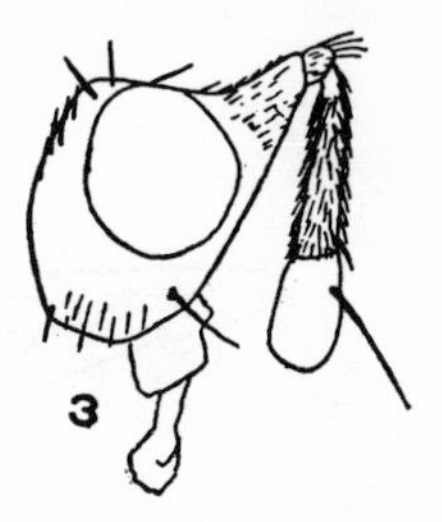

Piophilidæ.—1, 2, **Piophila**; 3, **Prochyliza.**

folds roughened, the posterior segment with four fleshy protuberances. The larva jumps by grasping the edge of the posterior truncature of the body with its mouth hooks and suddenly releasing it. The puparium is rugose and elliptic.

The members of this family have been placed in the Sepsidæ by most authors. The family differs from the Sepsidæ in several characters, particularly in having the costa broken at the end of the auxiliary vein, setulose mesonotum and the absence of a hair or fine bristle arising on the posterior edge of the posterior spiracle of the thorax. Melander* has reviewed the family.

KEY TO GENERA

1. One or two pairs of frontal bristles.............................. 2
   No frontal bristles; face strongly receding; antennæ variable in length (3) ....**Prochyliza** Walker

2. Two pairs of dorsocentral bristles.................................. 3
   One pair of dorsocentral bristles (**1, 2** and text fig.).......**Piophila** Fallén

3. One pair of frontal bristles (text fig.)............**Amphipogon** Wahlberg
   Two pairs of frontal bristles.........................**Mycetaulus** Lœw

---

* 1924, Psyche, xxxi, pp. 78-86.

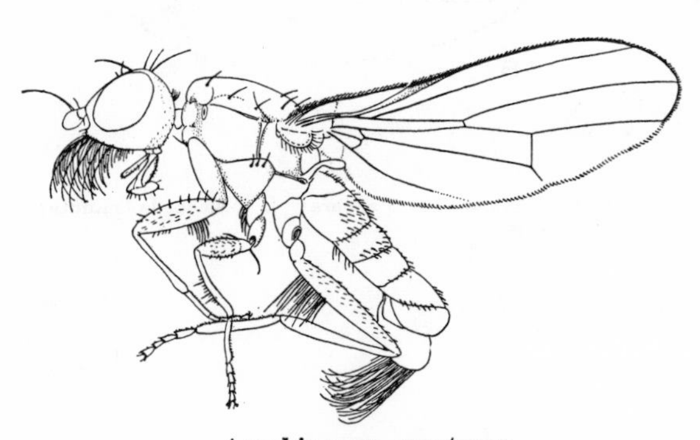

Amphipogon spectrum.

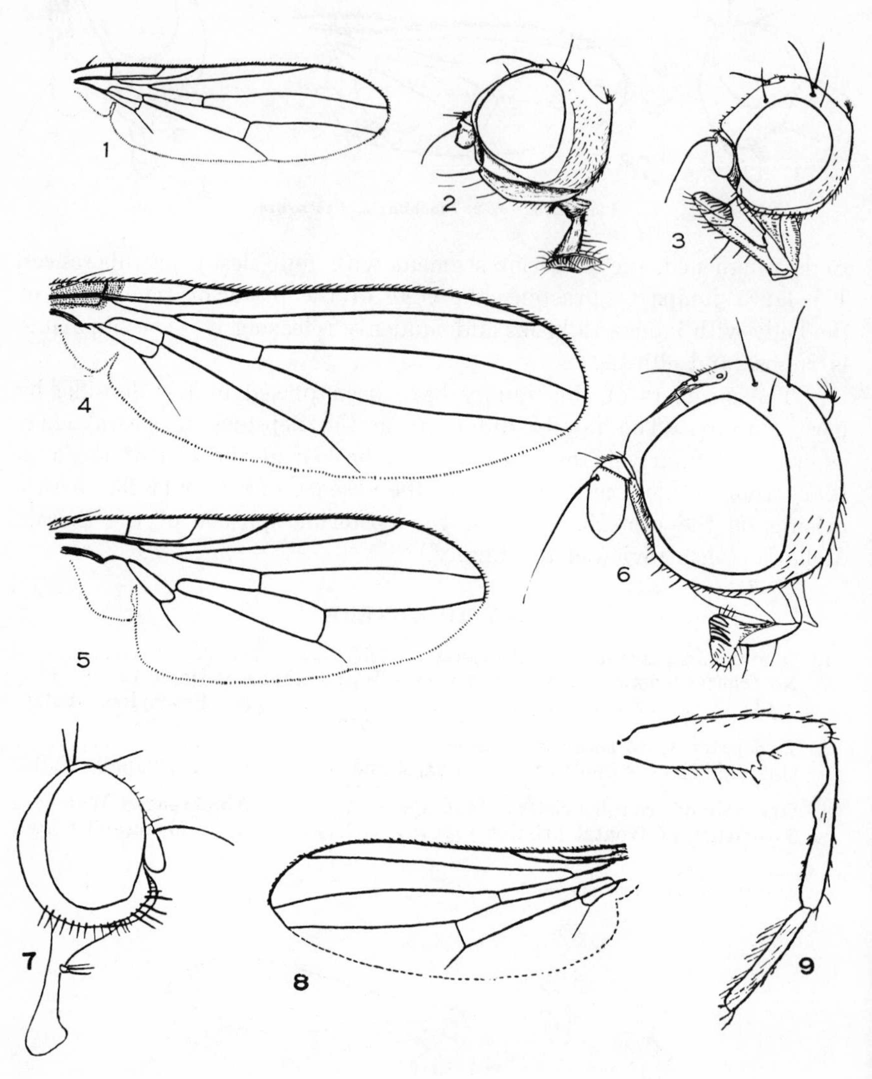

Sepsidæ.—1, 2, **Themira minor**; 3, **Pandora**; 4, **Nemopoda minuta**; 5, **Pandora**; 6, **Nemopoda minuta**; 7, 8, 9, **Sepsis.**

Family Sepsidæ

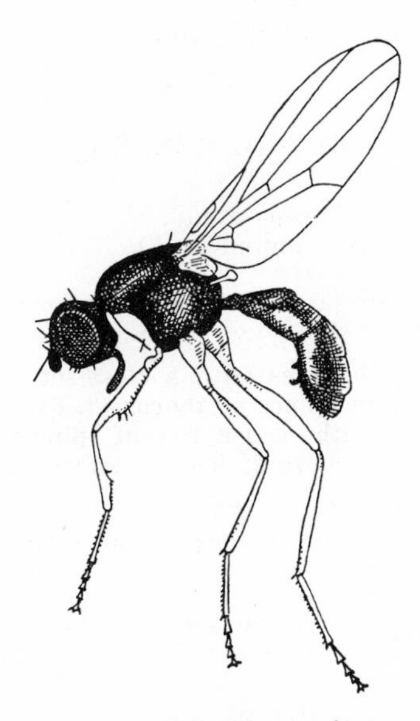

Meroplius stercorarius.

Small, shining black or reddish flies.

Head more or less spherical, the occiput usually quite convex, face carinate; one or two pairs of vertical bristles, one or no orbitals, post-vertical bristles divergent; antennæ decumbent, the third segment oval, the arista usually bare; parafacials very narrow, reduced to an orbital line; palpi vestigial. Mesonotum usually aciculate or pollinose and not pubescent, its setulæ usually in three longitudinal rows; scutellar bristles usually two, rarely four in number; either one or two pairs of dorsocentral bristles; sternopleura usually in part or entirely pruinose. Auxiliary vein curving so as to terminate obviously before the end of the first longitudinal vein, costa not broken, the third and fourth veins more or less converging; anal vein straight and abbreviated. Legs of the male usually deformed and armed with spines or thorn-like projections, usually located on the front pair. Abdomen with but sparse pubescence or fine setulæ, often constricted at the second segment and bearing a few bristles; male genitalia usually prominent, symmetrical, comprising a hypopygium with paired lateral valves, each tipped by a prong or flat blade of distinctive structure; ovipositor not extended, the female abdomen with bluntly rounded termination.

The adults are found about excrement, carrion and decaying vegetation, in which the larvæ live, and many of the species are very common. There are between forty and fifty described species from North America. Melander and Spuler* and Duda† have dealt with the species.

KEY TO GENERA

1. First and second basal cells separated.............................. 2
   First and second basal cells united (3, 5)...............**Pandora** Haliday

2. Outer verticals present.. 3
   Outer verticals absent... 5

3. Anterior femora of both sexes with a close-set row of spinules ventrally, never with stout spines or thorns (4, 6).....**Nemopoda** Desvoidy
   Anterior femora never with such a row of spinules, often with coarse spines, sparse hairs or more or less deformed.................... 4

4. No frontal bristles (7, 8, 9)...............................‡**Sepsis** Fallén
   One frontal bristle; anterior femora never tuberculate.
   Meroplius Rondani

5. Postocellar bristles long and strong; one frontal (1, 2)..**Themira** Desvoidy
   Postocellars very weak; frontals not developed.........**Enicita** Westwood

---

* 1917, Wash. Agric. Exp. Sta., Bull. No. 143.

† 1925, Ann. Naturh. Mus. Wien, xxxix, pp. 1-153, and 1926, xl, pp. 1-110.

‡ The genus **Sepsidimorpha** Frey I cannot separate from **Sepsis** and I do not consider the absence of tubercles on the anterior femora of generic importance. Those species of **Sepsis** which have a frontal bristle I would place in **Meroplius** even though the front femora are armed beneath.

Family Lauxaniidæ

Homoneura species.

Rather small flies, rarely more than 6 mm. in length, the auxiliary vein entire and ending in the costa.

Head variable, the face projecting or retreating, convex, flat or concave, without oral vibrissæ although these are rarely poorly developed. Front wide, with two pairs of frontals, the upper pair always reclinate, the lower pair sometimes decussate; ocellars present or minute. Antennæ variable, the arista plumose to bare. Thorax with bristles, at least behind the suture; scutellum usually bare except for the marginal bristles; propleural bristle present or absent; one or two sternopleurals. Tibiæ all with preapical bristle. Wing venation complete, the second basal and anal cells short; apical cell usually widely open. Abdomen oval, rarely elongate.

The adults may be found almost everywhere, but particularly in moist places where they may occur in large numbers. Many of the species are more in evidence in the evening than during the rest of the day. They are not very active and are therefore easily captured.

The larvæ of at least some of the species mine in plants and are economically important; others live upon decaying vegetation.

Sapromyzidæ has been used for this family by most American authors but *Lauxania* is older and should be used. Hendel has published extensively on the family: many changes have been made since his contribution in Genera Insectorum* and he recognizes many additional genera in his key to genera.†

---

* 1908, Fascicle No. 68.
† 1925, Encycl. Ent., B. Dipt., pp. 103-142.

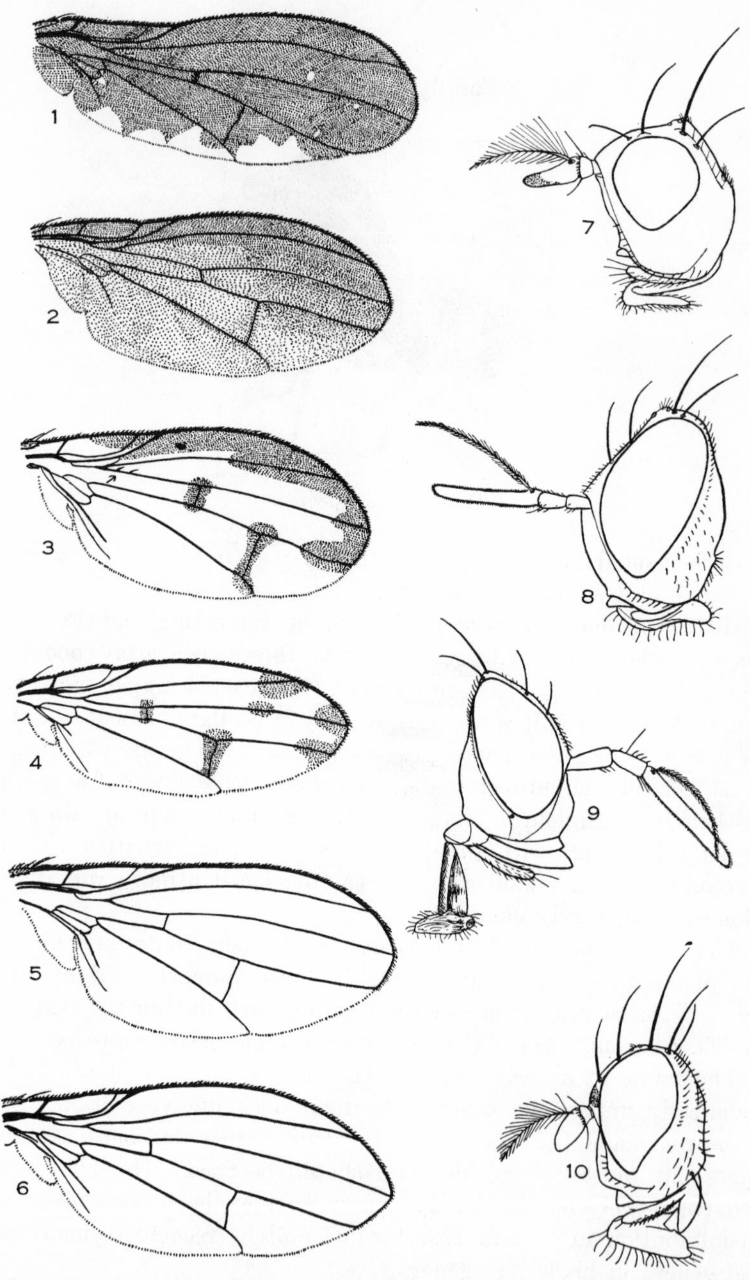

Lauxaniidæ I.—1, **Chætocœlia** sp.; 2, **Physegenua vittata**; 3, **Chætominettia latelimbata**; 4, **Homoneura philadelphica**; 5, **Pseudogriphoneura**; 6, **Neogriphoneura**; 7, **Camptoprosopella vulgaris**; 8, **Lauxaniella opaca**; 9, **Steganolauxania latipennis**; 10, **Deutominettia bimaculata**.

KEY TO GENERA

1. Antennæ long and slender, the first segment two-thirds as long as the second and with apical hairs below.............................. 2
   Antennæ not unusually elongate, the third segment usually more or less oval, rarely twice as long as wide, the first short or without bristles below 7

2. Sternopleura with a single bristle.................................. 3
   Two sternopleural bristles (**17, 18**)..................**Lauxania** Latreille

3. Propleural bristle present.. 4
   Propleural bristle absent (**23, 26**)...................**Asilostoma** Hendel

4. Anterior pair of frontals decussate; face with transverse striæ (**9, 22**). **Steganolauxania** Frey
   Anterior pair of frontals reclinate.................................. 5

5. Submarginal cell but little wider than the marginal (8)............ 6
   Submarginal cell more than twice as wide as the marginal. **Steganopsis** de Meijere

6. Face with a large, rounded convexity on either side....**Cephalella** Malloch
   Face without such swellings (**8, 21**)................**Lauxaniella** Malloch

7. Third vein setulose either above or below.......................... 8
   Third vein bare.. 10

8. First vein setulose above.........................**Dryomyzothea** Hendel
   First vein bare... 9

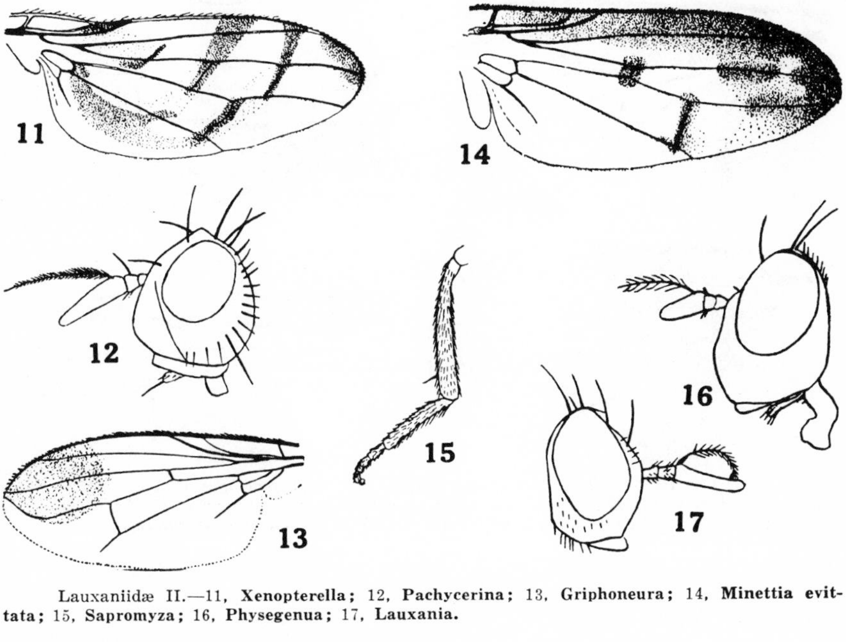

Lauxaniidæ II.—11, **Xenopterella**; 12, **Pachycerina**; 13, **Griphoneura**; 14, **Minettia evittata**; 15, **Sapromyza**; 16, **Physegenua**; 17, **Lauxania**.

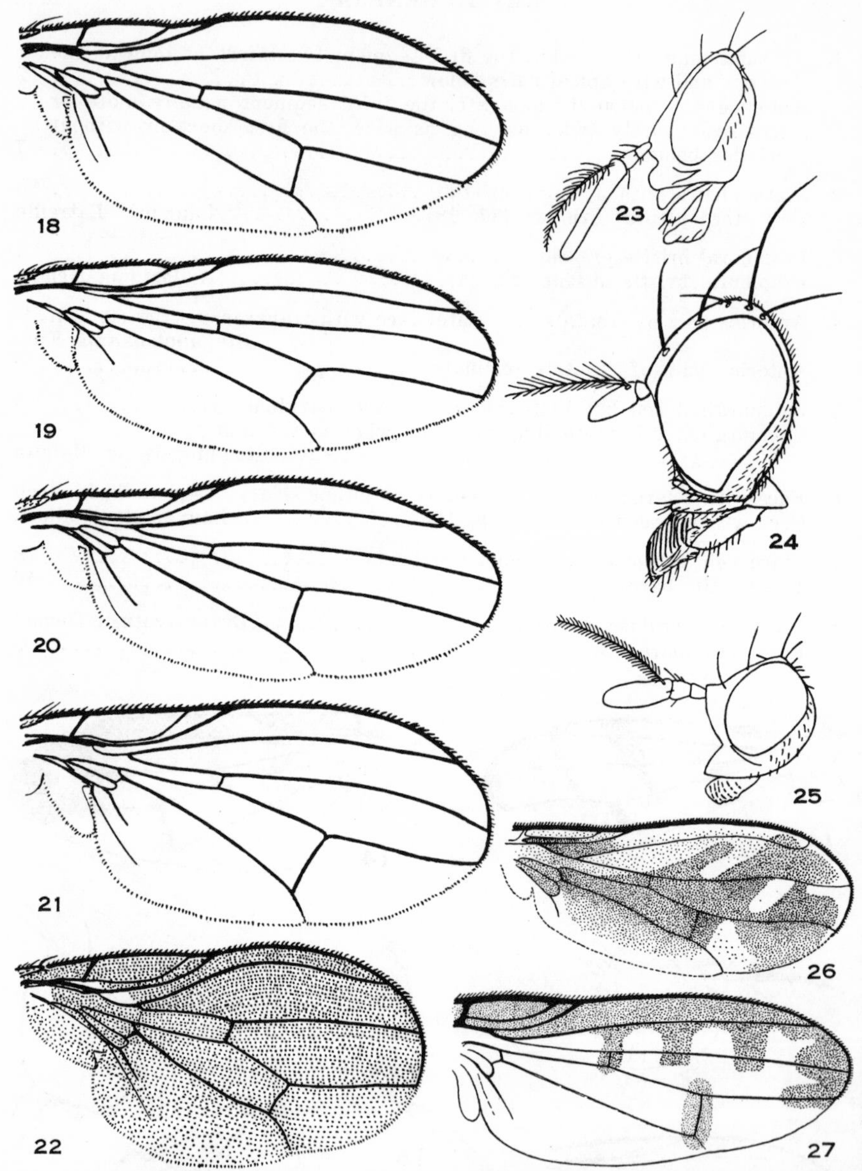

Lauxaniidæ III.—18, **Lauxania cylindricornis**; 19, **Trigonometopus vittatus**; 20, **Camptoprosopella vulgaris**; 21, **Lauxaniella opaca**; 22, **Steganolauxania latipennis**; 23, **Asilostoma**; 24, **Griphoneura**; 25, **Freyia nigrita**; 26, **Asilostoma palpalis**; 27, **Neominettia contigua.**

9. Third vein setulose below to beyond the anterior crossvein (27). **Neominettia** Hendel
   Third vein setulose above and below before the anterior crossvein (3, 31) .... **Chætominettia** Malloch

10. Second vein setulose before the origin of the third vein (30, 34). ***Xenochætina** Malloch
    Second vein bare 11

11. First vein setulose posteriorly before the humeral crossvein (28, 36). **Setulina** Malloch
    First vein bare 12

12. Wings with a crossvein dividing the apical cell beyond the posterior crossvein (11) .... **Xenopterella** Malloch
    Wings with only the usual crossveins 13

13. Anterior frontal bristle directed inward; first antennal segment as long as the second 14
    Anterior frontals reclinate; first antennal segment short 17

14. Ocellar bristles minute 15
    Ocellars long and strong 16

15. Face concave in profile .... **Freyia** Malloch
    Face convex (2, 16) .... **Physegenua** Macquart

16. Face strongly convex; anterior frontals half way between the antennæ and upper frontals (12) .... **Pachycerina** Macquart
    Face gently convex or plane; anterior frontals closer to upper frontals than to antennæ (7, 20) .... **Camptoprosopella** Hendel

17. First antennal segment as long as the second (25) .... **Freyia** Malloch
    First antennal segment short 18

18. Presutural bristle present 19
    Presutural bristle absent; face strongly retreating (19, 33). †**Trigonometopus** Macquart

19. Apical cell very strongly narrowed apically, almost closed (13, 24). **Griphoneura** Schiner
    Apical cell widely open 20

20. Sternopleura with one bristle 21
    Sternopleura with two bristles, the anterior one weaker 22

21. Front much broader than long, concave in front from dorsal view (6, 35) .... **Neogriphoneura** Malloch
    Front rarely broader than long, not concave in front (5, 38). ‡ **Pseudogriphoneura** Hendel

22. Face convex and glossy (29, 37) .... **Pseudocalliope** Malloch
    Face gently convex or flat, not polished 23

---

* Malloch, 1923, Proc. Ent. Soc. Wash., xxv, p. 49.
† Malloch, 1923, Proc. Ent. Soc. Wash., xxv, p. 48.
‡ Curran, 1934, Bull. Amer. Mus. Nat. Hist., lxvi, p. 445.

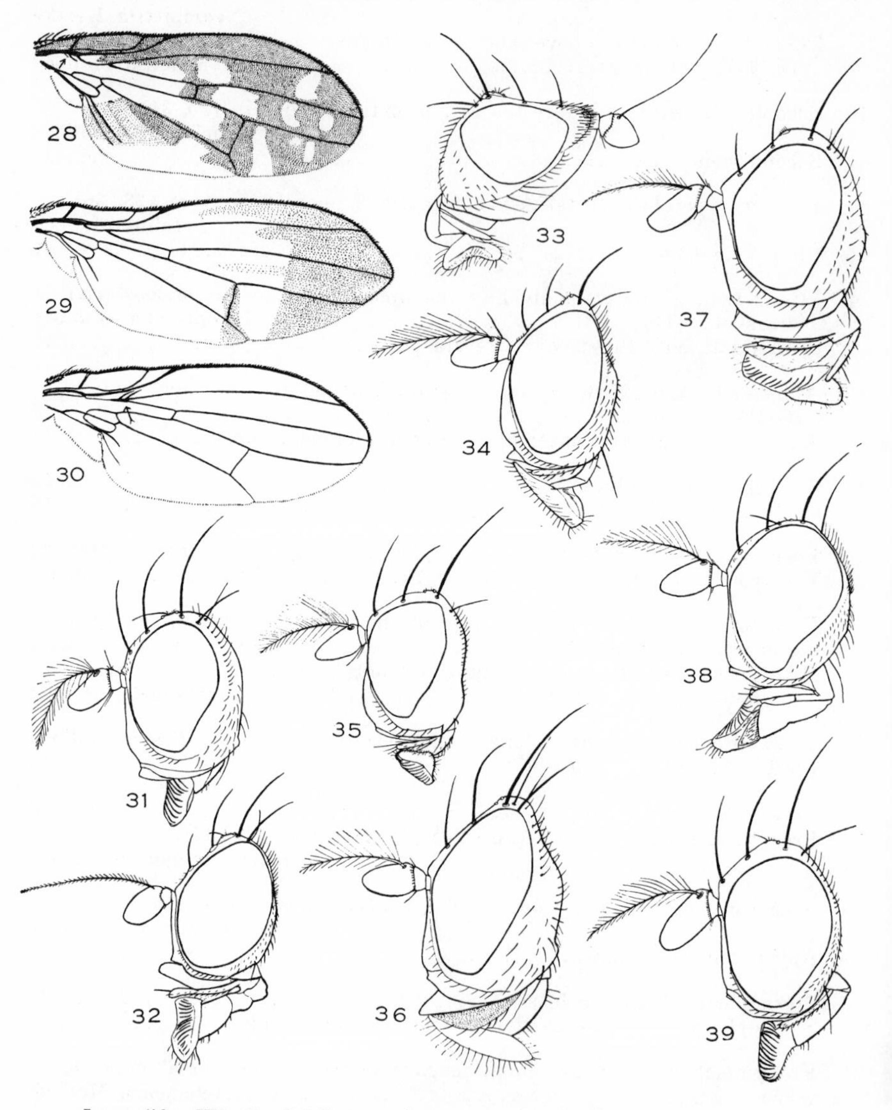

Lauxaniidæ IV.—28, **Setulina geminata**; 29, **Pseudocalliope**; 30, **Xenochætina**; 31, **Chætominettia**; 32, **Chætocœlia**; 33, **Trigonometopus**; 34, **Xenochætina**; 35, **Neogriphoneura**; 36, **Setulina**; 37, **Pseudocalliope**; 38, **Pseudogriphoneura**; 39, **Sapromyza.**

23. Intra-alar bristle present 24
Intra-alar bristle absent 26

24. Scutellum bare above 25
Scutellum setulose above (**10**) ....**Deutominettia** Hendel

25. Frontal bristles arising from tubercles (**1, 32**).....**Chætocœlia** Giglio-Tos
Frontal bristles not arising from tubercles (**14**)........**Minettia** Desvoidy

26. Second vein undulated ....**Trypetisoma** Malloch
Second vein not undulate 27

27. The tiny black costal setulæ continued to the apex of the third vein (**4**).
Homoneura Wulp
The black setulæ extend to only a little beyond the apex of the second vein, never to the third (**15, 39**) .... ****Sapromyza** Fallén

* Hendel has recognized two segregates of this genus, **Lycia** Desvoidy and **Cnemacantha** Macquart, both of which have four dorsocentral bristles. The former has the acrostical hairs two or four rowed and rather long while the latter has them six rowed and very short.

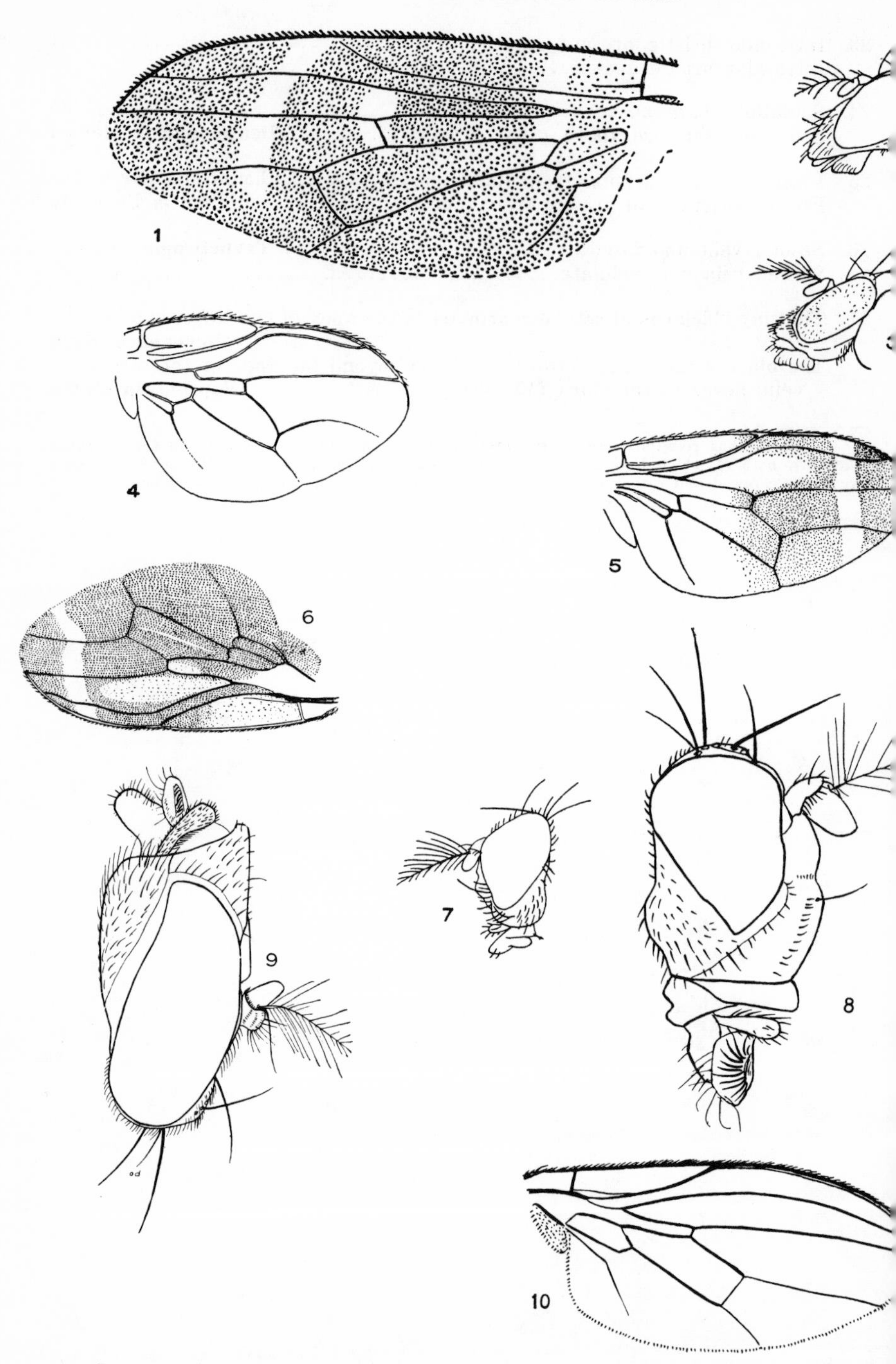

Periscelidæ.—1, **Marbenia peculiaris**; 2, **Neoscutops rotundipennis**; 3, **Scutops fascipennis**; 4, **Neoscutops rotundipennis**; 5, **Scutops fascipennis**; 6, **Panamenia chapmani**; 7, **Marbenia peculiaris**; 8, **Sphyroperiscelis** sp.; 9, **Panamenia chapmani**; 10, **Sphyroperiscelis** sp.

Family Periscelidæ

Small flies resembling the Lauxaniidæ, etc.

Face wide, more or less produced below; front with a single pair of bristles; postocellars divergent; arista plumose. Wing venation complete, the auxiliary vein short. Abdomen oval, somewhat depressed.

Members of this family are not numerous in collections and little is known about them. Malloch would retain the genera in the Sapromyzidæ and Melander included *Scutops* in his revision of the Geomyzidæ. The family contains seven genera, all occurring in America, *Periscelis* also being found in Europe.

KEY TO GENERA

1. Costa extending to the fourth vein 2
   Costa ending at the third vein 5
2. Face very strongly protruding below; auxiliary vein not curved forward apically 3
   Face somewhat protruding below; auxiliary vein with a distinct forward curve apically; oral vibrissæ absent .... **Periscelis** Lœw
3. Face evenly convex 4
   Face flattened and bare in the middle above (**3, 5**) .... **Scutops** Coquillett
4. Ocellars absent .... **Cyamops** Melander
   Ocellars long and strong (**24**) .... **Neoscutops** Malloch
5. Face most prominent below; veins strong (**6, 9**) .... **Panamenia,** n. g.
   Face not prominent below, more or less convex in the middle 6
6. Head almost or quite twice as wide as high; face very wide (**8, 10**). **Sphyroperiscelis** Sturtevant
   Head not nearly so wide; face and eyes of moderate width (**1, 7**). **Marbenia** Malloch

Panamenia, new genus

This genus is, perhaps, most closely related to *Sphyroperiscelis* Sturtevant but the shape of the head is distinctive. The face is shield-shaped, the point below, the sides sharply limited and haired. Abdomen as broad as long, tapering sharply from near the base. Scutellum flat, bearing two pairs of marginals. Wings as in figure. Genotype:—*P. chapmani,* n. sp.

Head stramineous, the upper occiput and a broad frontal triangle black; thorax deep brown or blackish, the pleura yellowish; humeri, a large rectangle on the posterior half of the mesonotum and the scutellum, except the sides, stramineous; legs reddish yellow, the tibiæ with two brown bands, the anterior femora brown basally; wings brownish, with a preapical hyaline band; abdomen blackish or dark brown. Male, Barro Colorado Island, Canal Zone, (Curran).

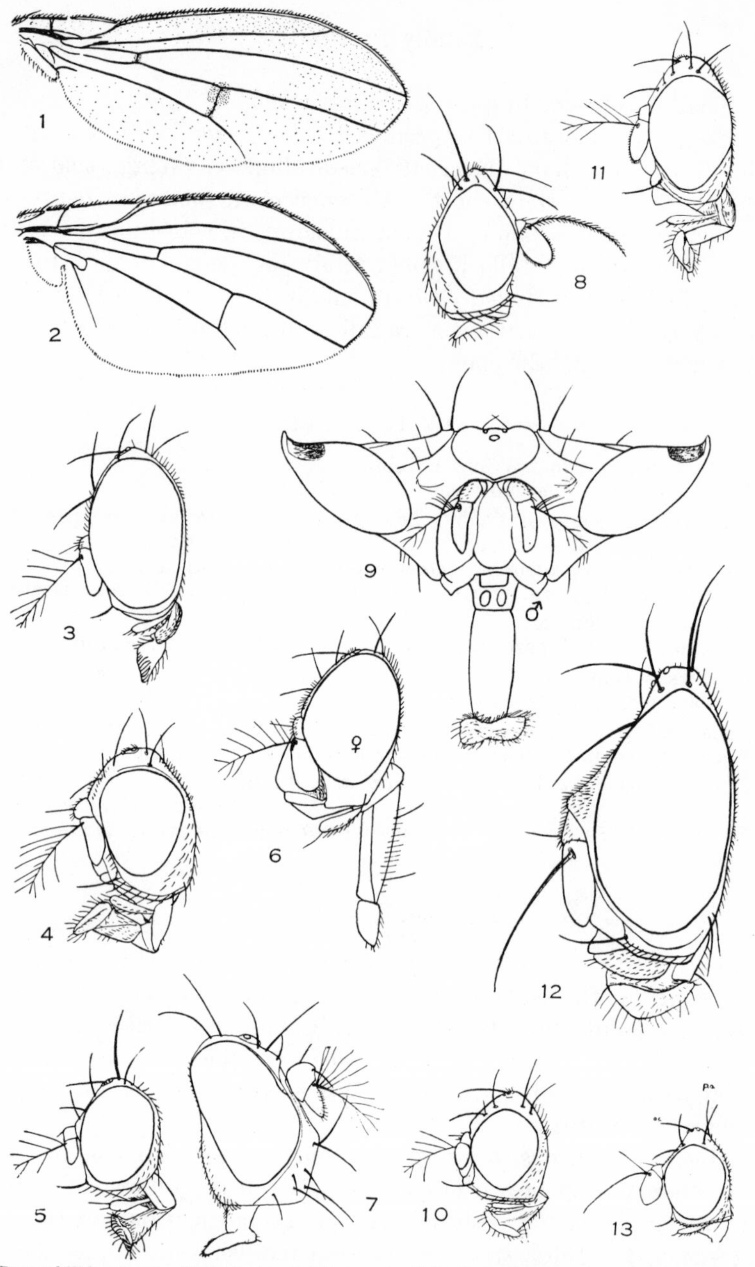

Drosophilidæ I.—1, **Cladochæta nebulosa**; 2, **Rhinoleucophenga obesa**; 3, **Leucophenga maculosa**; 4, **Drosophila funebris**; 5, **Chymomyza amœna**; 6, **Zygothrica dispar**; 7, **Planinasus ambiguus**; 8, **Diastata**; 9, **Zygothrica dispar**; 10, **Scaptomyza gramineum**; 11, **Mycodrosophila**; 12, **Rhinoleucophenga obesa**; 13, **Cladochæta nebulosa.**

Family Drosophilidæ—The Small Fruit Flies

Small flies, rarely exceeding a length of 5 mm. the head sometimes very broad, the wings often pictured.

Face nearly vertical in profile, rarely prominent, oral vibrissæ present, though sometimes weak; front with three pairs of bristles; post-ocellar bristles convergent, rarely absent. Third antennal segment oval or rounded, the basal two short; arista usually plumose, rarely pubescent or with a single long ray. Abdomen usually short, rather elongate and pendulous in *Curtonotum*. Auxiliary vein usually very short and ending in the first vein; costa broken twice; first vein short; second basal cell usually united with the discal cell; anal cell present, rarely incomplete.

The adults are found around decaying vegetation, flowing sap, fungi and ripe fruit, the larvæ being found in these substances. They are often pests to the housewife, since they apparently appear from nowhere when fruit is brought into the house and some of the fungus inhabiting species have the habit of hovering around the eyes during warm weather, causing not only irritation by their antics but pain when they get into the eye. In the tropics they sometimes occur in such numbers as to completely cover large fungi. There have been frequent complaints about them in milk bottles, the puparia becoming attached to the bottles and requiring special treatment for their removal.

One of the species, *Drosophila melanogaster* Meigen, has been used extensively for the study of inheritance, being exceedingly well suited for this purpose because of the very short life cycle and large chromosomes. The general belief has been that the larvæ live upon fruit but it has been shown that they actually live upon the yeasts developing in it.

Sturtevant* has reviewed the North American species and Duda† has dealt with the Neotropical forms. In addition there are numerous small papers scattered through the literature. In addition to the genera given in the key several others, as well as a number of subgenera, have been proposed but most of them appear to be too poorly differentiated to deserve recognition. Aldrich‡ has discussed the occurrence in North America of the genus *Leiomyza* Macquart and described two species. As I have no specimens I am unable to place the genus in the key. Sturtevant* has referred this genus to the Asteiidæ but this disposition of it does not agree with my interpretation of that family.

---

* 1921. The North American Species of Drosophila, Carnegie Inst. of Wash., pub. No. 301, 150 pp.

†1927. Die Sudamerikanischen Drosophiliden, etc., Arch für Naturgesichte, 1925, Hefts 11-12, pp. 1-229.

‡ 1919, Ent. News, xxx, p. 137.

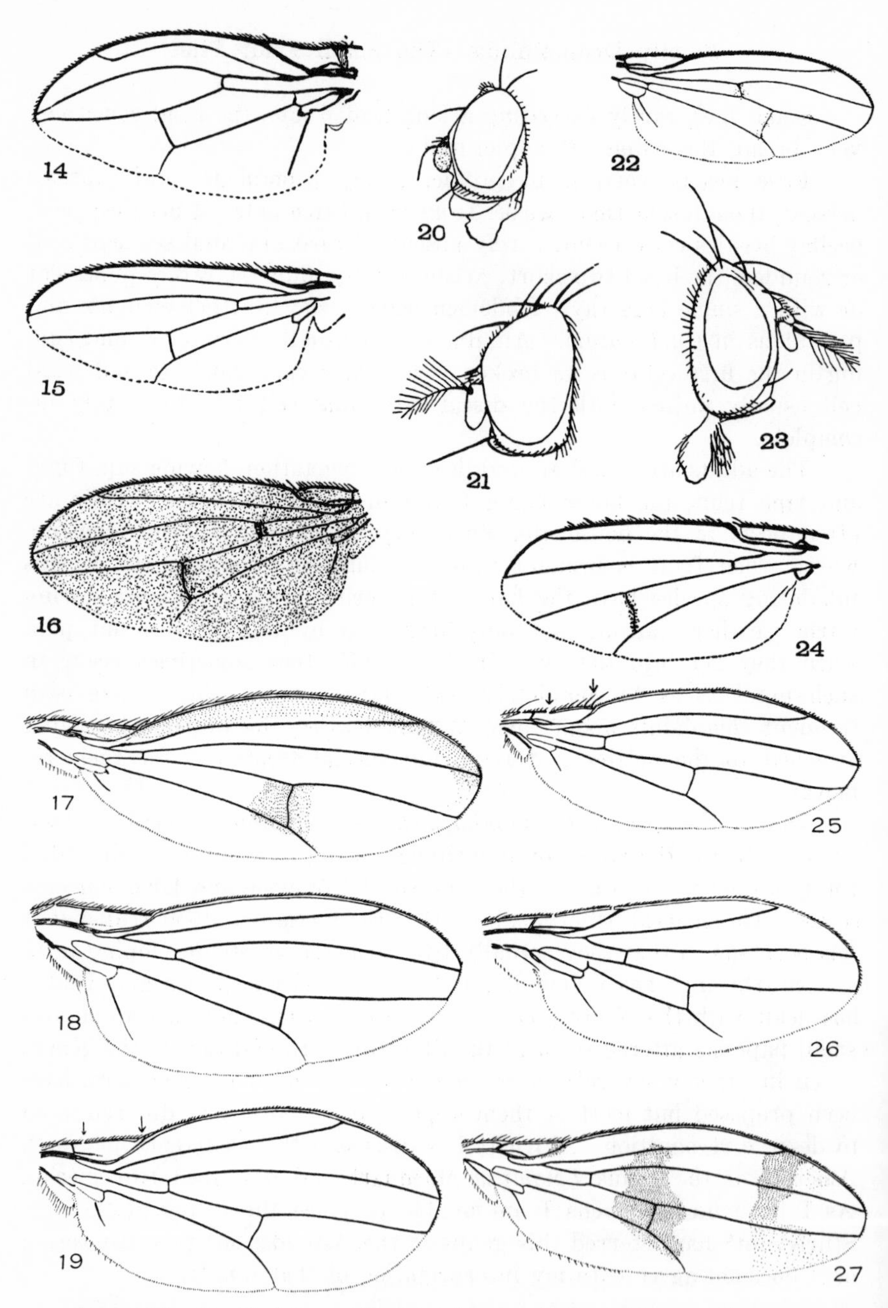

Drosophilidæ II.—14, **Stegana**; 15, **Leucophenga**; 16, **Drosophila**; 17, **Diastata vagans**; 18, **Zygothrica dispar**; 19, **Mycodrosophila dimidiata**; 20, **Sinophthalmus pictus**; 21, **Stegana**; 22, **Sinophthalmus pictus**; 23, **Curtonotum**; 24, **Curtonotum**; 25, **Scaptomyza gramineum**; 26, **Planinasus ambiguus**; 27, **Chymomyza amœna.**

KEY TO GENERA

1. Discal and second basal cells united (18)........................... 2
   Discal and second basal cells separated (17)........................... 14
2. Auxiliary vein ending in the first vein near its base................. 4
   Auxiliary vein entire or nearly so...................................... 3
3. Arista plumose; prescutellar acrosticals strong; costa pectinate (23, 24)..**Curtonotum** Macquart
   Arista pubescent; prescutellar acrosticals absent...**Aulacigaster** Macquart
4. Arista pubescent or bare with one long ray above................. 5
   Arista plumose 6
5. Arista with one long ray above (1, 13)...........**Cladochæta** Coquillett
   Arista pubescent ....**Pseudiastata** Coquillett
6. Proboscis longer than head-height; head broader than the thorax (6, 9, 18)....................................**Zygothrica** Wiedemann
   Proboscis shorter than the head; head rarely broader than the thorax. 7
7. Lower reclinate frontal bristle as far from the proclinate as from the upper reclinate 8
   Lower reclinate frontal situated nearer to the proclinate than to the upper reclinate 10
8. Prescutellar acrosticals strong; face not protuberant................. 9
   Prescutellar acrosticals weak or absent; face produced. **Pararhinoleucophenga** Duda
9. Costa ending at the third vein (3, 15)................**Leucophenga** Mik
   Costa extending to the fourth vein (2, 12)......**Rhinoleucophenga** Hendel
10. Lower reclinate frontal situated in front of the proclinate (5, 27). **Chymomyza** Czerny
    Lower reclinate situated behind the proclinate...................... 11
11. One large pair of dorsocentrals; mesonotum and scutellum usually convex; a single bristle at the second costal break (11, 19). **Mycodrosophila** Oldenberg
    Usually two pairs of dorsocentrals.................................. 12
12. Acrostical hairs moderately long and not very numerous, never in more than four rows anteriorly (10, 25)................**Scaptomyza** Hardy
    Acrostical hairs short and appressed, always in six or more rows anteriorly 13
13. Prescutellars long and strong........**Clastopteromyia** Malloch & McAtee
    Prescutellar acrosticals quite weak or absent (4, 16)....**Drosophila** Fallén
14. Arista pubescent or bare.. 17
    Arista plumose 15
15. Propleural bristle present but weak (8, 17).............**Diastata** Meigen
    Propleural bristle absent 16
16. Face flat on upper half, prominent in the middle (7, 26). **Planinasus Cresson**
    Face concave, the oral margin the most prominent (14, 21). **Stegana Meigen**
17. Antennæ extending to the oral margin, the third segment twice as long as wide ....**Tryptochæta** Rondani
    Antennæ not reaching the oral margin (20, 22)..**Sinophthalmus** Coquillett

Family Asteiidæ

Small flies, with the second vein ending only slightly beyond the first.

Head higher than long; face concave; oral vibrissæ well developed; front wide, with one or two pairs of bristles; thorax bristled posteriorly. Legs short. Wings long, with only one or two crossveins, before the basal third; auxiliary vein incomplete; costa entire, anal cell absent, the second basal sometimes open apically. Abdomen narrow.

This family comprises but few genera, three of which are recorded from America. The family may be at once recognized by the peculiar wing venation. Williston placed the two genera known to him in both the Drosophilidæ and Chloropidæ and there has been much doubt as to where they belong.

KEY TO GENERA

1. Posterior crossvein present 2
   Posterior crossvein absent, only one crossvein (3).........***Asteia** Meigen
2. Front with two bristles near the middle, half way between the ocellar triangle and antennæ........................**Crepidohamma** Enderlein
   Front with only weak bristles laterally (1, 2).........**Sigalœssa** Coquillett

---

* Aldrich, 1915, Psyche, xxii, p. 96.

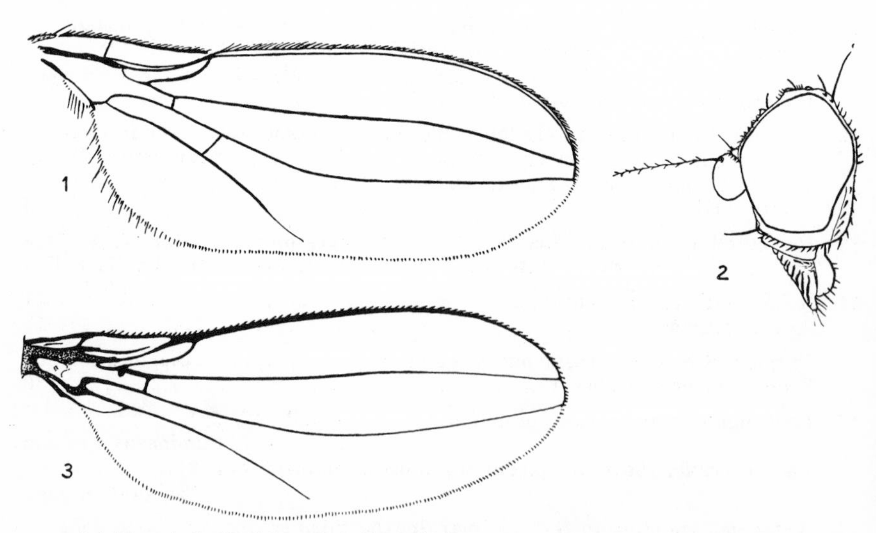

Asteiidæ.—1, 2, **Sigaloëssa rica** (**insularis** Curran, not Malloch); 3, **Asteia** sp.

Family Opomyzidæ

Small, rather elongate flies, sometimes with pictured wings.

Head not longer than high, the face long, often narrow; one or more pairs of frontal bristles; postocellars divergent, convergent, or absent; oral vibrissæ absent or differentiated, never strong; palpi small. Presutural dorsocentrals present or absent; mesopleura bare; scutellum with or without hair in addition to the bristles; preapical tibial bristles absent. Subcosta incomplete or vestigial; anal and second basal cells complete, the first vein ending before the middle of the wing. Abdomen moderately long, the segments with marginal bristles; genitalia small.

Various authors have recognized three families for this group, the Anthomyzidæ and Tethinidæ in addition to the Opomyzidæ or Geomyzidæ. Despite the differences I believe that the genera should be grouped together, as otherwise there is sufficient grounds for the creation of a family for each of the genera. At any rate we may safely unite the Anthomyzidæ and Tethinidæ since both groups possess oral vibrissæ. However the vibrissæ are weak and the characters by which these groups are separated from *Opomyza* do not appear to be important in this case.

The flies occur chiefly in moist places and along the seashore. Practically nothing is known about the life histories, but it is known that species of *Opomyza* live in grass.

KEY TO GENERA

1. Oral vibrissæ differentiated; post ocellar bristles converging, though small 2
   Oral vibrissæ absent; post ocellars diverging or absent 9

2. Presutural dorsocentrals present 3
   Presutural dorsocentrals absent 4

3. Cheeks haired only along the lateral oral margin 6
   Cheeks with hairs over much of the surface or at least toward the eyes 7

4. One pair of strong frontals (4, 7) .... **Mumetopia** Melander
   Two pairs of strong frontals 5

5. Posterior crossvein situated only about its length from the wing margin (1, 12) .... **Ischnomyia** Lœw
   Posterior crossvein situated almost twice its length from the wing margin (6, 11) .... **Anthomyza** Fallén

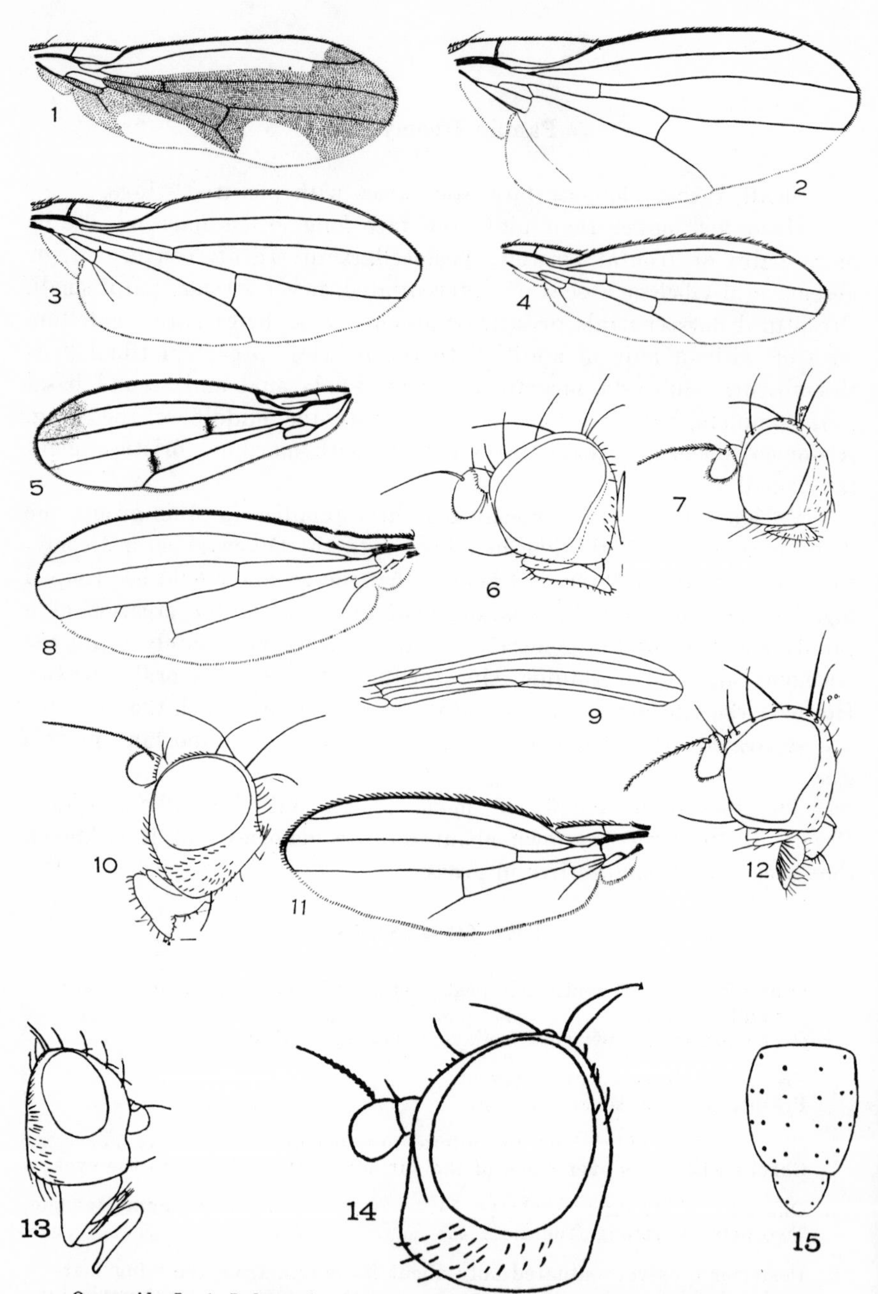

Opomyzidæ I.—1, **Ischnomyia vittata**; 2, **Tethina albula**; 3, **Pelomyia coronata**; 4, **Mumetopia nigrimana**; 5, **Geomyza**; 6, **Anthomyza**; 7, **Mumetopia occipitalis**; 8, **Opomyza**; 9, **Mutilloptera apicalis**; 10; **Opomyza**; 11, **Anthomyza**; 12, **Ischnomyia vittata**; 13, **Tethina**; 14, **Pelomyia occidentalis**; 15, **Pelomyia**, chætotaxy.

6. Frontal vitta with bristles (**2, 13**) .... ***Rhicnoëssa** Lœw
   Frontal vitta without bristles (Chyromyidæ) .... †**Neossos** Malloch

7. Acrostical hairs present 8
   Acrostical hairs absent .... ***Pelomyiella** Hendel

8. Oral margin strongly produced forward; lower edge of head straight and long .... **Neopelomyia** Hendel
   Face not strongly produced below, the lower edge convex (**3, 14, 15**). ***Pelomyia** Williston

9. Scutellum with hair; wing with anal angle (**8, 10**) .... **Opomyza** Fallén
   Scutellum with bristles only; no trace of anal angle 10

10. Hind margin of the wing strongly concave (**9**) .... **Mutiloptera** Coquillett
    Hind margin of the wing at most very weakly concave (**5**). **Geomyza** Fallén

---

* Hendel, 1934, Tijd. v. Ent., lxxvii, pp. 35-54.
† 1927, Proc. Ent. Soc. Wash.

Family Agromyzidæ—The Leaf Miners

Small flies, blackish or yellowish in color, the postocellar bristles always present.

Head usually higher than long; front with at least three pairs of bristles; ocellars and postocellars present, the latter divergent; face receding or concave in profile; antennæ decumbent, the third segment rarely much longer than wide; arista pubescent or bare; oral vibrissæ present. Eyes large, the cheeks rarely half as wide as the eye-height. Legs short, the femora with bristles. Wings of moderate size, the venation complete or with the posterior crossvein absent; auxiliary vein more or less fused with the first vein or incomplete. Abdomen more or less depressed.

The adults occur everywhere and there are few deciduous plants which are not mined by their larvæ. Owing to their small size they are easily overlooked although easily recognized.

The larvæ make characteristic mines in the leaves of plants and most of them may be identified by the mines.

KEY TO GENERA

1. Arista absent (See Ochthiphilidæ, 3 and 5).......***Cryptochætum** Rondani
   Arista present 2

2. Posterior crossvein present.. 3
   Posterior crossvein absent... 7

3. Posterior crossvein situated beyond the anterior crossvein............ 4
   Posterior crossvein situated nearer to the base of the wing than the anterior crossvein (10)..............................**Napomyza** Haliday

4. Mesopleura with one or more bristles................................ 5
   Mesopleura bare 6

5. Third antennal segment with the upper apex acutely pointed (3, 5). **Cerodontha** Rondani
   Third segment not with an acute point, though sometimes angular (6, 7). **Agromyza** Fallén

6. Front strongly produced forward, the ocelli situated on the anterior part (1, 9) ....**Traginops** Coquillett
   Front regular in outline, the ocelli situated near the vertex............ 8

7. Fourth vein ending before the wing-tip ....**Antineura** Melander
   Fourth vein ending behind the wing-tip (8, 11).........**Phytomyza** Fallén

8. Apical cell slightly narrowing apically...............**Schildomyia** Malloch
   Apical cell widening apically, the costa not extending to the fourth vein (2, 4)...**Odinia** Desvoidy

---

* I have not seen this genus and its relationship is somewhat doubtful.

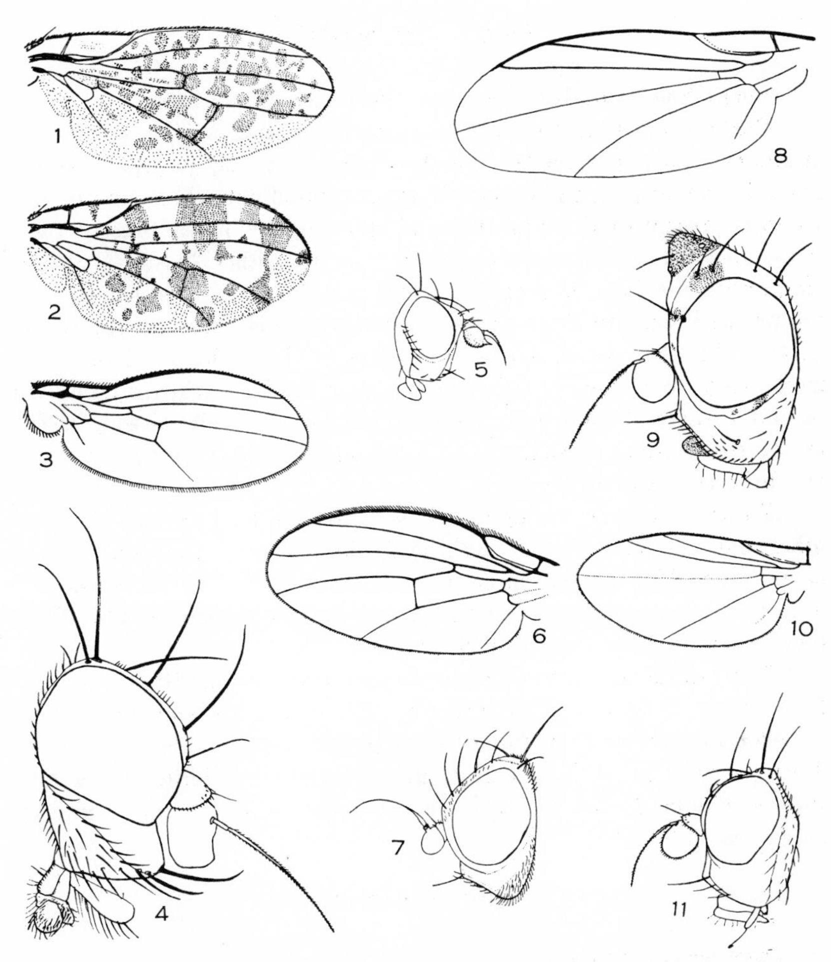

Agromyzidæ.—1, **Traginops irrorata**; 2, **Odinia williamsi**; 3, **Cerodontha dorsalis**; 4, **Odinia williamsi**; 5, **Cerodontha dorsalis**; 6, **Agromyza kincaidi**; 7, **Agromyza waltoni**; 8, **Phytomyza flavicornis**; 9, **Traginops irrorata**; 10, **Napomyza lateralis**; 11, **Phytomyza.**

Family Phyllomyzidæ

Small flies, usually black, sometimes silvery pollinose.

Costa broken at the humeral crossvein and at the apex of the auxiliary vein; postocellar bristles convergent or parallel; anterior frontals convergent, the others divergent, proclinate or reclinate; interfrontals present or there are rows of hairs; oral vibrissæ present though sometimes but poorly differentiated from the other bristles; proboscis long and geniculate, or short; antennæ not elongate, often small. Mesonotum with one to four pairs of dorsocentrals; mesopleura with or without bristles; pteropleura sometimes with distinct bristles. Legs moderately short. First vein ending near the basal third of the wing; second basal and anal cells small; posterior crossvein absent in *Paramyia;* costa usually bristly basally. Abdomen short and rather broad, the bristles weak or absent.

These flies were included by Williston in the Agromyzidæ while other authors have recognized the Milichiidæ and Carnidæ. *Phyllomyza* is an older generic name than *Milichia* and I do not consider the differences between the genera placed in the Carnidæ and Phyllomyzidæ as of more than generic value.

The adults are rather common and may frequently be found on fence posts, fences, logs, tree-trunks, etc. in the hot sun, or they may be taken by sweeping, on foliage or in grass. I have collected them only during dry weather and always in the bright sunlight. Keys to the species will be found in Melander's revision of the family,* and in a paper by Malloch†.

KEY TO GENERA

1. Posterior crossvein present 2
   Posterior crossvein absent (4, 26) .... **Paramyia** Williston

2. Costa extending to the fourth vein 5
   Costa stopping at the third vein 3

3. Proboscis very elongate and geniculate (3, 20) .... **Aldrichiella** Hendel
   Proboscis short 4

4. Mesopleura bare (2, 9, 13) .... **Euchlorops** Malloch
   Mesopleura with two or three bristles (6, 21) .... **Meoneura** Rondani

---

* 1913. Journ. N. Y. Ent. Soc., xxi, pp. 234-246.
† 1913, Proc. U. S. N. M., xlvi, pp. 127-152.

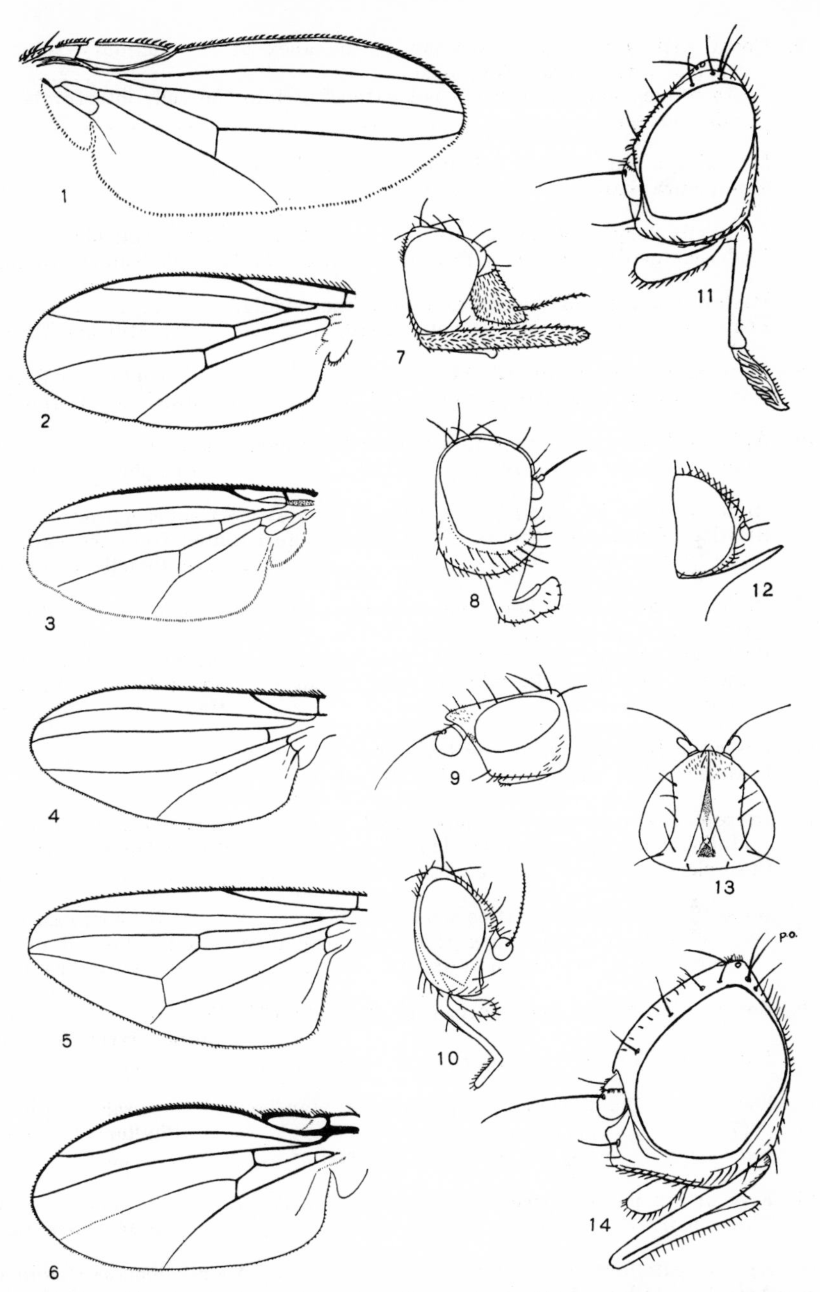

Phyllomyzidæ I.—1, **Hypaspistomyia latipes**; 2, **Euchlorops vittata**; 3, **Aldrichiella agromyzina**; 4, **Paramyia nitens**; 5, **Eusiphona mira**; 6, **Meoneura vagans**; 7, **Phyllomyza hirtipalpis**; 8, **Hemeromyia nitida**; 9, **Euchlorops vittata**; 10, **Desmometopa M-nigrum**; 11, **Hypaspistomyia latipes**; 12, **Eusiphona mira**; 13, **Euchlorops vittata**; 14, **Desmomyza confusa.**

5. Costa with a very deep excision at the apex of the auxiliary vein; cruciate interfrontals developed 6
Costa broken but the excision not extending into the cell; interfrontal hairs present 10

6. Mesopleura with strong bristles.................................. 7
Mesopleura bare 8

7. Proboscis very long, geniculate..................**Paramilichia** Malloch
Proboscis geniculate, but not unusually long (19, 23)..**Pholeomyia** Bilimek

8. Posterior margin of the eye excised at the middle.................... 9
Posterior margin of the eye not excised................**Milichia** Meigen

9. Four pairs of dorsocentrals (18, 22)................**Eccoptomma** Becker
One or two pairs of dorsocentrals (17, 22)..........**Milichiella** Giglio-Tos

10. Apical cell very widely open, at most a little narrowed apically........ 11
Apical cell only narrowly open (5, 12)..............**Eusiphona** Coquillett

11. Bristles of the head and thorax strong; eyes at most short haired..... 12
Bristles of head and thorax not strongly differentiated from the hair; eyes rather long pilose ....**Arctobiella** Coquillett

12. Proboscis geniculate, long and chitinized; vibrissal angle usually distinct 13
Proboscis shorter and more or less fleshy, the labellæ not elongate though folding back; vibrissal angles not developed; face strongly carinate (8)..............................**Hemeromyia** Coquillett

13. Posterior tibiæ flattened and broadened.................................. 14
Posterior tibiæ not unusually flat and wide.................................. 16

14. Pteropleura with one or more small bristles (**Paramadiza** Malloch; **Mallochiella** Melander) (1, 11)...............**Hypaspistomyia** Hendel
Pteropleura without bristle.................................. 15

15. Glossy black; frontal bristles weak (14, 15).............**Desmomyza,** n. g.
Dull colored; frontals stronger; two pairs of divergent frontals; interfrontals in differentiated rows (16, 10).............**Desmometopa** Lœw

16. Lower edge of the head horizontal and long (24, 25).
Platophrymyia Williston
Lower edge of the head rounded or short.................................. 17

17. Eyes hairy; palpi very large, projecting far beyond the oral margin (7) .... **Phyllomyza** Fallén
Eyes bare or nearly so; palpi not projecting.................................. 18

18. Five or six pairs of orbitals.................................. 19
Three pairs of orbitals.............................**Cacoxenus** Lœw

19. Apical scutellars converging..................**Neophyllomyza** Melander
Apical scutellars diverging........................**Stomosis** Melander

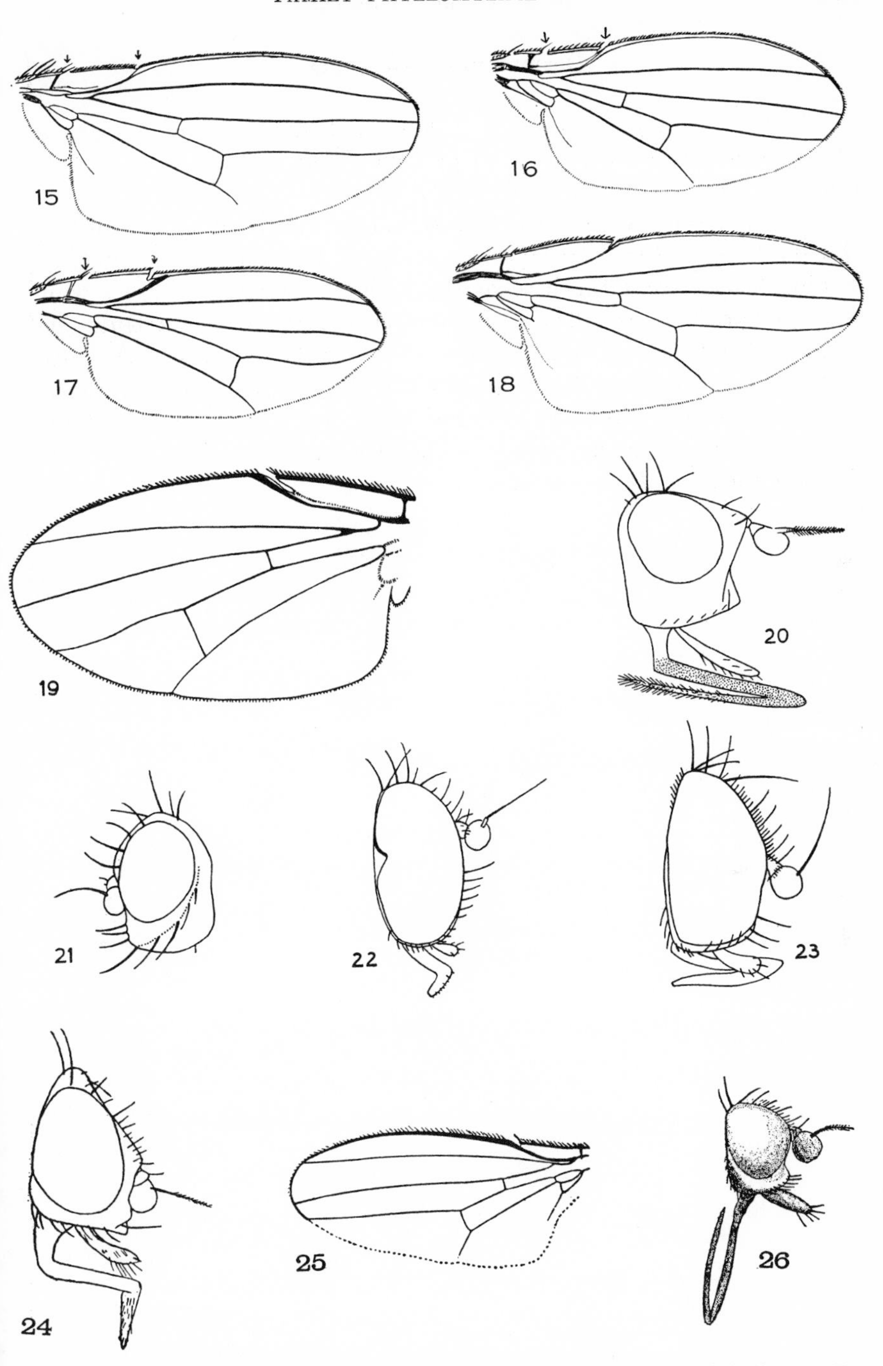

Phyllomyzidæ II.—15, **Desmomyza confusa**; 16, **Desmometopa**; 17, **Milichiella**; 18, **Eccoptomma**; 19, **Pholeomyia indecora**; 20, **Aldrichiella agromyzina**; 21, **Meoneura vagans**; 22, **Milichiella lacteipennis**; 23, **Pholeomyia indecora**; 24, 25, **Platophrymyia nigra**; 26, **Paramyia nitens.**

Desmomyza, new genus

Related to *Hypaspistomyia* Hendel but differing in having the pteropleura entirely bare instead of having some setulæ above. Genotype:—*D. confusa* n. sp. (New York).

The genotype is extremely like *H. glabra* Fallén, of which I believe *Desmometopa halteralis* Coquillett to be a synonym. It is entirely shining black except the base of the tarsi, the wings are milky white with yellowish veins. The only difference between *Desmomyza* and *Hypaspistomyia,* to which I refer *glabra,* lies in the presence in the latter of pteropleural setules. The type of *halteralis* has these, as do European specimens of *glabra* examined by me, hence my belief that Coquillett's species is the same as *glabra.* The weaker frontals will separate *Desmomyza* from *Desmometopa.*

Family Chloropidæ—The Frit Flies

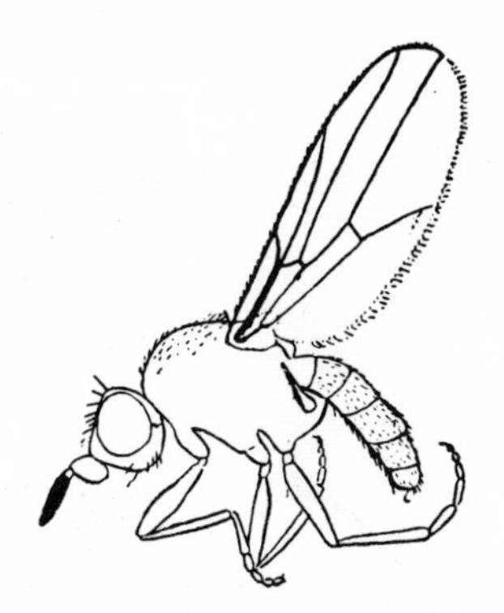

Crassiseta species.

Small to very small, bare or nearly bare flies.

Head usually rather hemispherical, sometimes more or less triangular or rectangular, the face usually nearly vertical or receding; oral vibrissæ weak or absent; front broad, sometimes with bristles, the vertical triangle very large, often extending to the anterior margin of the front. Antennæ usually short, with rounded third segment, sometimes elongate. Wings of moderate length or rather short, auxiliary vein vestigial; second basal cell united with the discal cell; anal cell absent; fifth vein almost always with a slight, characteristic irregularity near the middle of the discal cell. Legs short, the femora rarely greatly thickened.

These flies are very common and representatives of the family may be collected almost anywhere. The family will be readily recognized as the large vertical or frontal triangle is characteristic and the peculiar gentle curve of the fourth vein is typical of the group.

The larvæ live in grass and other plants and some of them are economic pests of cereals. They are thick and cylindrical, with stout mouth hooks, two segmented antennæ and fleshy abdominal protuberances for locomotion.

The generic limits in some cases are evidently weak and it is not always easy to place some species with certainty. I am not certain that the so-called horny geniculate proboscis of *Madiza* Fallén constitutes a generic character in this case since there is a gradual evolution to the normal type found in *Oscinella* Becker. The apical section of the pro-

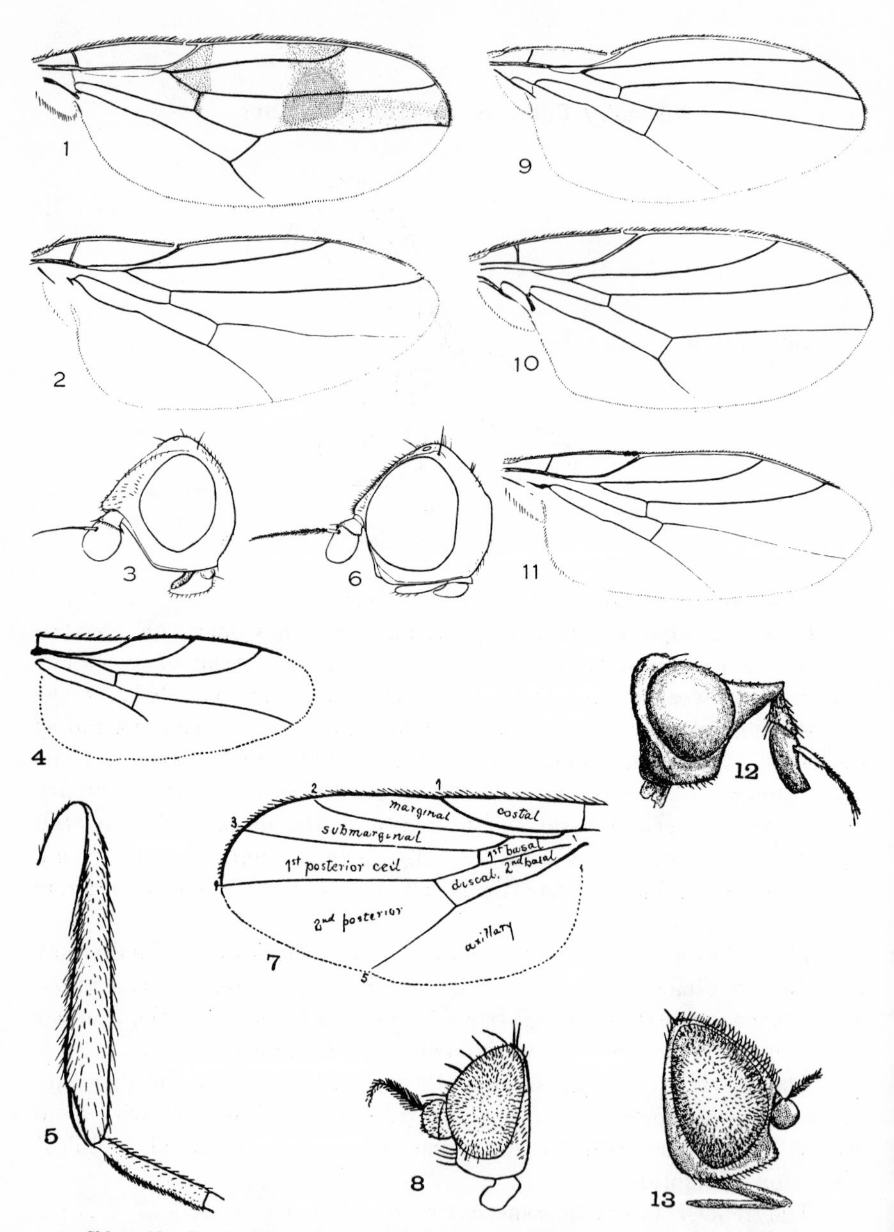

Chloropidæ I.—1, **Dactylothyrea curvinervis**; 2, **Chlorops sulphurea**; 3, **Chlorops**; 4, **Meromyza americana**; 5, **Hippelates collusor**; 6, **Cetema hypocera**; 7, **Madiza**; 8, **Pseudogaurax**; 9, **Dicræus**; 10, **Pseudogaurax**; 11, **Diplotoxa pulchripes**; 12, **Ectecephala**; 13, **Madiza**.

boscis is nothing more than the labellæ which are lengthened and narrowed and it is not always easy to decide whether the proboscis is geniculate or not. Trouble will also be experienced in connection with the pubescence of the arista and the presence of frontal bristles, both of which are characters which show gradual development in the presence of extensive collections. The only revision of the North American species of this family is by Becker.* In a recent paper on the Neotropical forms Duda† has proposed many new genera but his contribution has been so badly mangled by deletion necessitated in order to reduce its size to the absurd limits set by most publications that it is almost impossible to follow his keys.

KEY TO GENERA

1. Costa extending to the fourth vein 11
   Costa ending at the third vein or slightly beyond it 2

2. Posterior crossvein absent ....**Elliponeura** Lœw
   Posterior crossvein present 3

3. Posterior femora greatly thickened, their tibiæ strongly arcuate (4, 17) ....**Meromyza** Meigen
   Posterior femora only moderately thickened, their tibiæ but little curved 4

4. Middle tibiæ with a strong, curved apical spur; male genitalia large, carried forward under the abdomen (6, 14, 21)..........**Cetema** Hendel
   Middle tibiæ with normal terminal bristles 5

5. Posterior tibiæ with an oval, opaque "sensory organ" posterodorsally, the tibiæ somewhat broadened (18, 23, 26) ....**Chloropisca** Lœw
   Posterior tibæ without velvety sensory area........................ 6

6. The distance between the crossveins along the fourth vein is not greater than the length of the posterior crossvein (11)..**Diplotoxa** Lœw
   The distance is equal to at least twice the length of the posterior crossvein 7

7. Mesonotum entirely black, coarsely punctured.......**Ephichlorops** Becker
   Mesonotum usually vittate, not wholly black nor coarsely punctured... 8

8. Third antennal segment conspicuously longer than broad............ 9
   Third segment rather circular in outline, often broader than long, never conspicuously longer than broad (2, 3)........**Chlorops** Meigen

9. Frontal triangle shining 10
   Frontal triangle opaque (28) ....**Anthracophaga** Lœw

10. Frontal triangle very long and broad, ending in a broad, obtuse point a little before the base of the antennæ, convex in cross-section (12, 24) ....**Ectecephala** Macquart
    Frontal triangle strongly narrowing anteriorly and ending in an acute point, flat in cross-section (16, 25) ....**Parectecephala** Becker

* 1912, Ann. Mus. Nat. Hung., x, pp. 21—.

† 1930, Fol. Zool. Hydrobiol., ii. pp. 46-128.

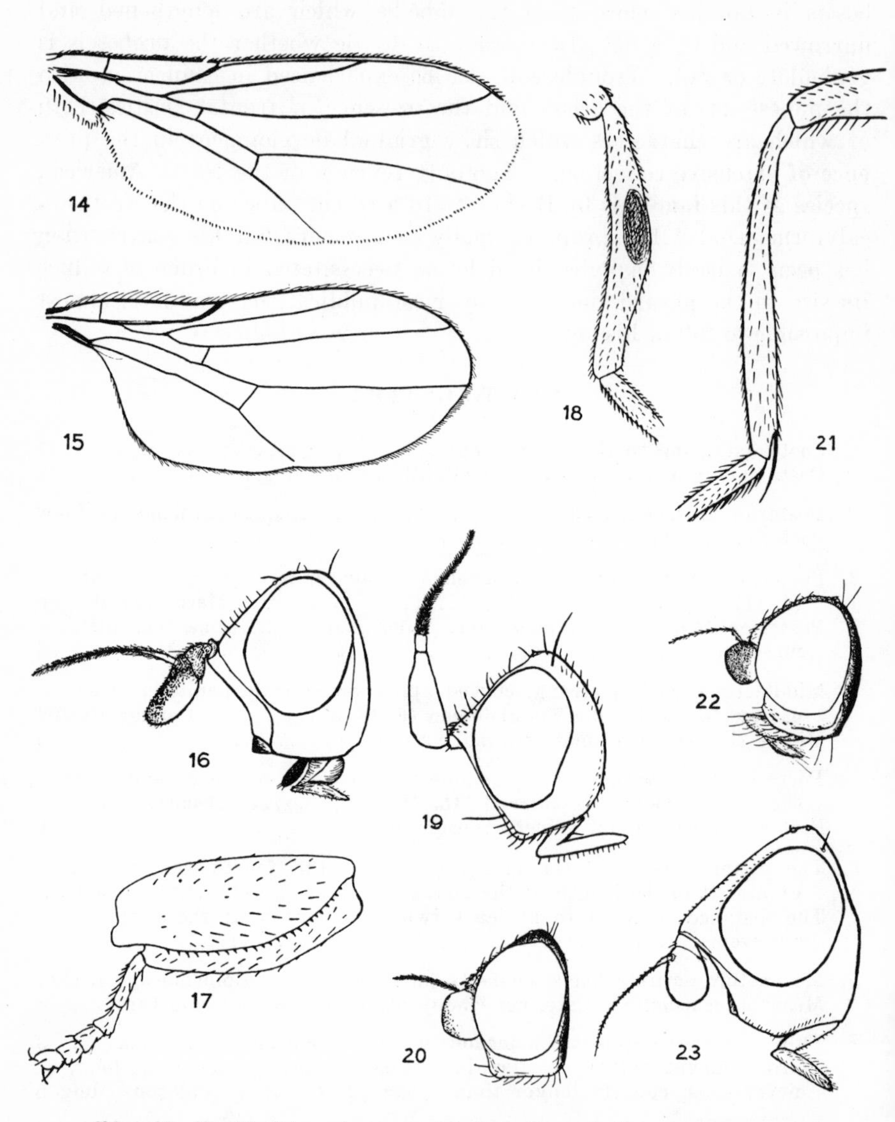

Chloropidæ II.—14, **Cetema hypocera**; 15, **Oscinella varipalpus**; 16, **Parectecephala**; 17, **Meromyza americana**, hind leg; 18, **Chloropisca variceps**, hind tibia; 19, **Ceratobarys pulophus**; 20, **Oscinella tripunctata**; 21, **Cetema**, middle tibia; 22, **Oscinella magnipalpoides**; 23, **Chloropisca.**

11. Posterior tibiæ with a strong, curved ventral spur at or before the excavated apex (5) 12
    Posterior tibiæ normal 15

12. Arista flattened and strap-like (19) .... **Ceratobarys** Coquillett
    Arista of ordinary shape, practically bare 13

13. Scutellum elongated, with flattened disc .... **Prohippelates** Malloch
    Scutellum with convex disc and of normal length 14

14. Front with distinct bristles toward the orbits. . **Pseudohippelates** Malloch
    Front without bristles (5) .... **Hippelates** Lœw

15. Distance between the tips of the second and third veins at least twice that between the first and second .... **Siphunculina** Rondani
    Distance between tips of second and third veins but little more than that between the first and second 16

16. Arista bare or quite short pubescent 20
    Arista broadened or long pubescent 17

17. Arista appearing broadened and strap-like due to the arrangement of the dense pubescence .... **Crassiseta** Von Rössner
    Arista pubescent 18

18. Scutellum with strong marginal processes (1, 27) .... **Dactylothyrea** Duda
    Scutellum without marginal processes 19

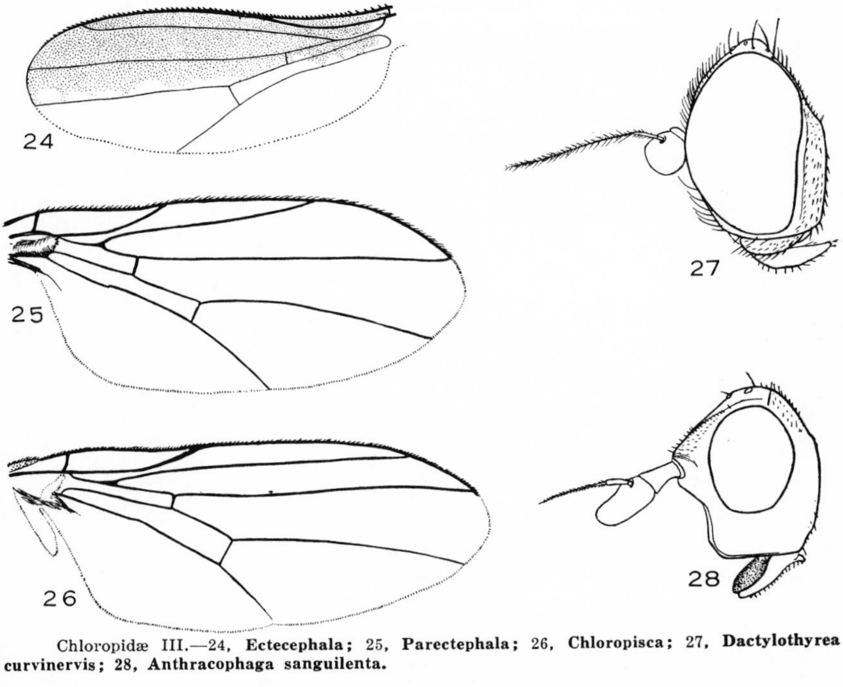

Chloropidæ III.—24, **Ectecephala**; 25, **Parectephala**; 26, **Chloropisca**; 27, **Dactylothyrea curvinervis**; 28, **Anthracophaga sanguilenta.**

19. Scutellum elongated, the disc flattened **(8, 10)**....**Pseudogaurax** Malloch
Scutellum normal, the disc gently convex ....**Gaurax** Lœw

20. Only two notopleural bristles on posterior part................... 22
At least four notopleural bristles 21

21. Notopleural bristles four in number; mesonotal setulæ in rows.
Eugaurax Malloch
Notopleural bristles very numerous; mesonotum thickly setulose.
Chætochlorops Malloch

22. Distance between the tips of the first and second veins three or four times that between the second and third **(9)** ....**Dicræus** Lœw
Distance between tips of first and second veins not more than twice that between the second and third 23

23. Proboscis elongated and geniculate, the terminal section about as long as the preceding section **(7, 13)** ....**Madiza** Fallén
Proboscis shorter, the apical section shorter and more fleshy....... 24

24. Mesonotum with three broad longitudinal punctured grooves.**Tricimba** Lioy
Mesonotum with only two narrower grooves or they are weak or absent **(15, 20, 22)** ....**Oscinella** Becker

Family Ephydridæ—The Shore Flies

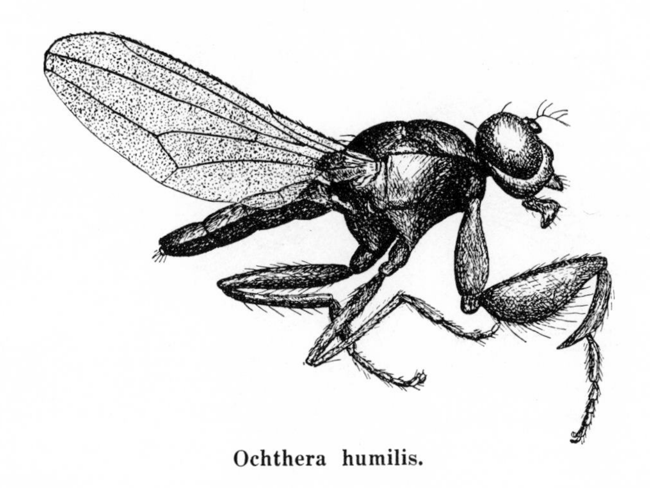

Ochthera humilis.

Small to very small flies, the anal cell absent, the second basal and discal cells united.

Face more or less, often remarkably convex, the oral cavity rounded, sometimes very large; clypeus distinct but often retracted within the oral cavity; no distinct oral vibrissæ but the sides of the face often with bristles or hairs. Antennæ short; arista bare, pubescent or pectinate, always dorsal. Thorax gently convex, bristled. Legs short; tibiæ without preapical bristle, the middle pair with apical spur. Wings rarely aborted; auxiliary vein united with the first vein except basally; costa broken before the tip of the first vein and weakened beyond the humeral crossvein; second basal and discal cells united; anal cell absent or extremely small and incomplete. Abdomen composed of six segments in the males, seven in the females, the number sometimes apparently reduced to three, variable but never elongate, often quite wide; genitalia usually retracted; body usually with but few hairs.

The adults are found in moist places, inhabiting marshes, swamps and the shores of lakes, ponds, and streams, along the edges of brooks and the sea shore. Many of the species are of local habitat but most of them are widely distributed. Some species occur in the flowers of water plants and have been found nowhere else. Water lilies are usually frequented by several species while in bloom and many occur on the

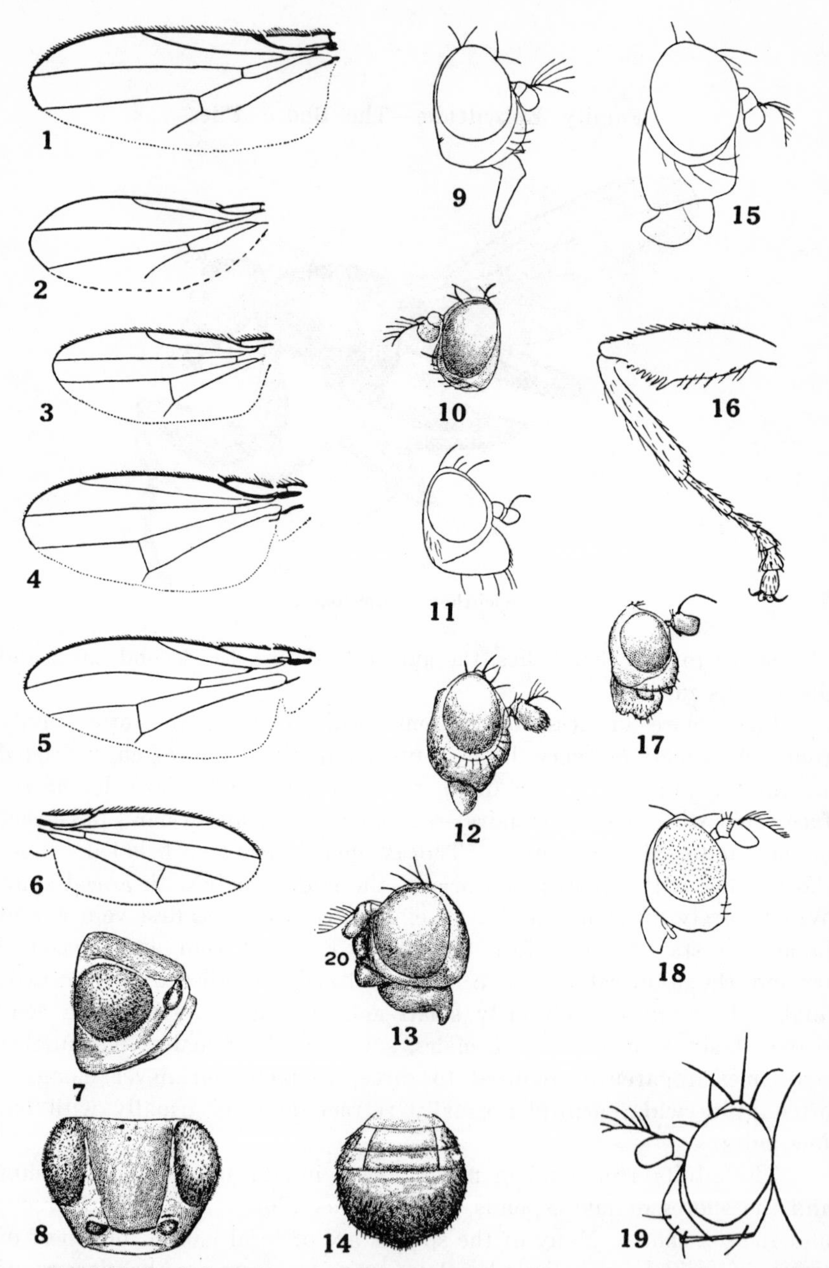

Ephydridæ I.—1, **Lytogaster**; 2, **Hydrina**; 3, **Ochtheroidea atra**; 4, **Parydra**; 5, **Brachydeutera argentata**; 6, **Notiphila**; 7, 8, **Lipochæta**; 9, **Allotrichoma**; 10, **Discocerina**; 11, **Ephydra**; 12, **Gastrops**; 13, **Brachydeutera**; 14, **Lytogaster**; 15, **Athyroglossa**; 16, **Ochtheroidea**; 17, **Lytogaster**; 18, **Hydrina**; 19, **Atissiella.**

leaves. Some of the species are able to walk on the surface of water and many of them will alight upon it if disturbed but they usually quickly return to the shore.

The larvæ live in various habitats, many are aquatic or live in mud, others in the stems of aquatic or semi-aquatic plants, a few in flowing sap. Many of them live in brackish, but may also occur in fresh, or even in alkaline water. One species, *Psilopa petrolei* Coquillett, occurs in the pools of crude petroleum found in California, breathing by projecting the posterior spiracles above the surface of the oil, but its food is unknown. Other species are found in the warm waters of geysers.

Many new genera have been described since the publication of Williston's Manual and some authors have recognized the Notiphilidæ as a separate family but there appears to be no good basis for this. Jones* reviewed the family in 1906. Since then there has been no comprehensive publication although Cresson has published several large papers containing descriptions of new species and genera and some keys.

KEY TO GENERA.

1. Scutellum normal 2
   Scutellum as large as the mesonotum and almost concealing the abdomen, from dorsal view (see text figure)........**Peltopsilopa** Hendel

2. Costa extending to the fourth vein.................................. 3
   Costa ending at the third vein 53

3. Antennæ small, inserted very far apart in cavities, the arista atrophied, very short and blunt (**7, 8, 71**) ....**Lipochæta** Coquillett
   Antennæ normal; arista always long 4

4. Middle tibiæ with dorsal bristles (**30, 57**).............†**Paralimna** Lœw
   Middle tibiæ without bristles except at the apex 5

5. Second antennal segment with a spinous bristle at the upper apical corner 6
   Second antennal segment without such bristle...................... 31

6. First and fifth abdominal segments exceptionally short, the abdomen apparently composed of three long segments, the lateral margins revolute 7
   Abdomen with five distinct segments, the lateral margins not margined. 8

7. Face with two pairs of bristles below............**Trimerinoides** Cresson
   Face with one pair of bristles below (48) ....**Trimerina** Macquart

8. Arista pectinate 9
   Arista bare (**40, 53**) ....**Mosillus** Latreille

* Tech. Bull. Calif. Exp. Sta., i. No. 2.
† Cresson, 1918, Trans-Amer. Ent. Soc., xliv, p. 45 (Costa Rica).

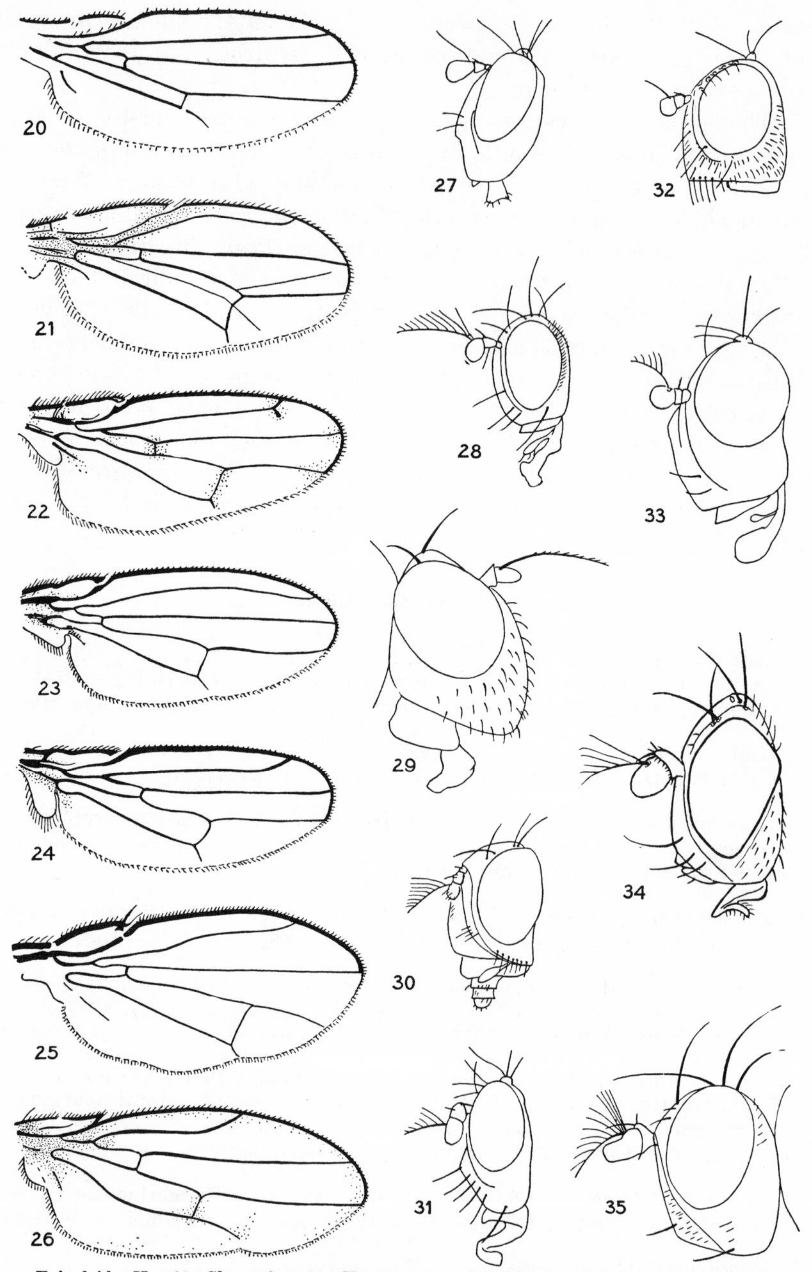

Ephydridæ II.—20, **Glenanthe**; 21, **Clanoneurum**; 22, **Parydra**; 23, **Cœnia**; 24, **Pelina**; 25, **Dichæta**; 26, **Hyadina**; 27, **Axysta**; 28, **Dichæta**; 29, **Psilephydra**; 30, **Paralimna**; 31, **Hecamedoides**; 32, **Lamproscatella**; 33, **Œdenops**; 34, **Ditrichophora valens**; 35, **Notiphila.**

9. Wings with a strong fold extending the length of the discal cell near the middle and another in the apical cell (21, 49)..**Clanoneurum** Becker
   Wings without such folds 10

10. Arista without rays below 11
    Arista with two or three rays below (38, 44).........**Ptilomyia** Coquillett

11. Face with transverse ridges, at least laterally, which may be very broad, or fine and numerous, usually limited to the lower half of the face 12
    Face without such ridges 14

12. Facial ridges very fine, extending across the face, sometimes not continuous on the lower part (58, 66)................**Leptopsilopa** Cresson
    Facial ridges very broad 13

13. Facial ridges strong, extending across the face (68).**Cerometopum** Cresson
    Facial ridges resulting from sub-lateral pits and not extending over the middle of the face (37, 52) ....**Discomyza** Meigen

14. With only one pair of dorsocentral bristles........................ 21
    With two pairs of dorsocentrals 15

15. Ocellar bristles widely separated, situated opposite the anterior ocellus. 16
    Ocellars normal, situated above the anterior ocellus.............. 19

16. Bristles on the sides of the face all convergent..................... 17
    Bristles on the sides of the face partly divergent, partly convergent.
    Polytrichophora Cresson

17. Face with two rows of bristles on either side...................... 18
    Face with one row of bristles on either side (10, 56).**Discocerina** Macquart

18. Posterior tibiæ with a strong, curved apical spine (31).
    Hecamedoides Hendel.
    Posterior tibiæ without apical spine ....**Diclasiopa** Hendel

19. Interfrontalia with two pairs of bristles (67, 72).....**Paratissa** Coquillett
    Interfrontalia without bristles, the ordinary frontals present......... 20

20. Face rather strongly carinate above, the carina ending prominently at the middle of the face (41, 63)......................*****Ilythea** Haliday
    Face very gently convex longitudinally, not carinate (**Typopsilopa** Cresson) (54)..................................**Psilopina** Becker

21. Oral opening large, the clypeus always prominent, the middle of the face usually strongly produced 22
    Oral opening smaller, the face usually convex and receding below, the face never strikingly produced in the middle..................... 24

22. Third costal section longer than the second (19)........**Atissiella** Cresson
    Third costal section shorter than the second........................ 23

23. Ocellars inserted opposite the anterior ocellus (45).......**Atissa** Haliday
    Ocellars inserted above the anterior ocellus (9)....**Allotrichoma** Becker

* Cresson, 1918, Trans. Amer. Ent. Soc., xliv, p. 50 (Costa Rica).

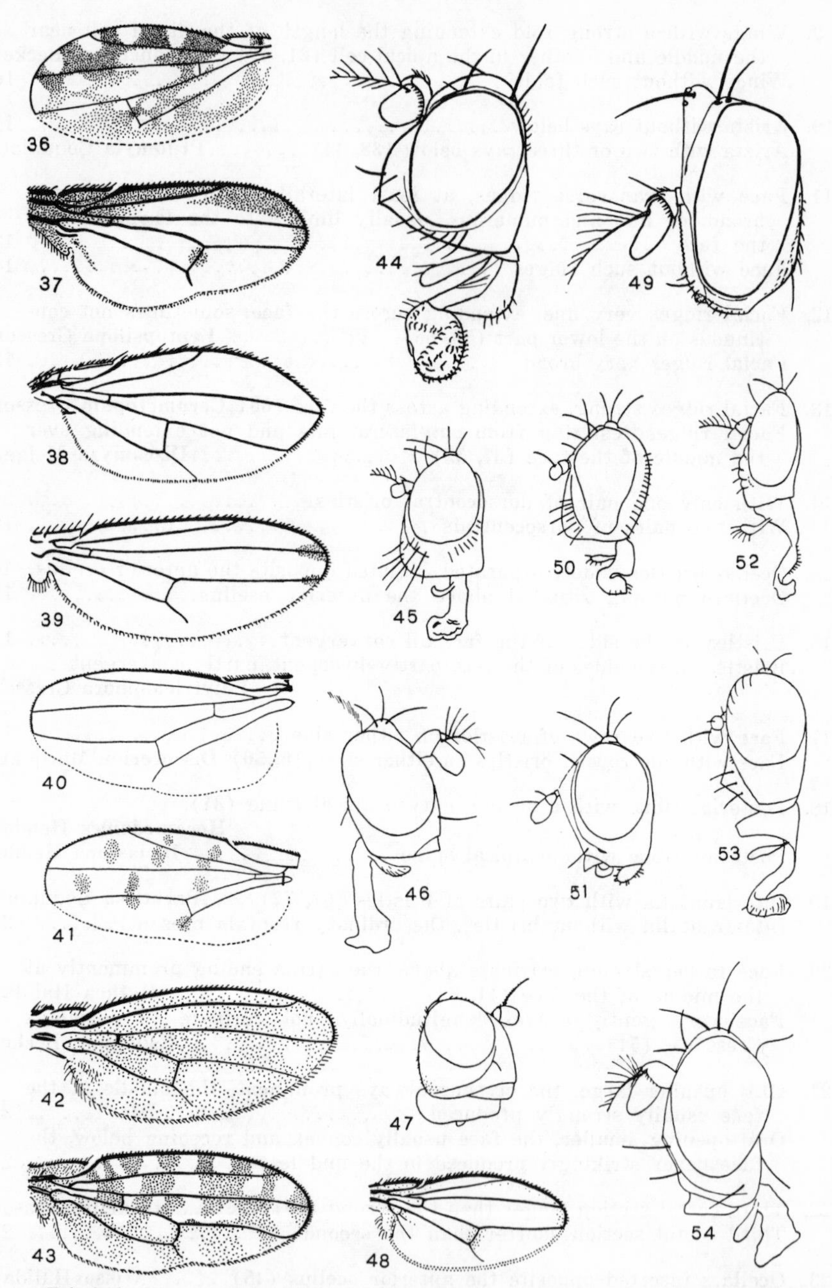

Ephydridæ III.—36, **Nostima slossonæ**; 37, **Discomyza**; 38, **Ptilomyia ænigma**; 39, **Psilopa**; 40, **Mosillus**; 41, **Ilythea**; 42, **Scatophila**; 43, **Scatella**; 44, **Ptilomyia ænigma**; 45, **Atissa**; 46, **Plagiops**; 47, **Parydra**; 48, **Trimerina**; 49, **Clanoneurum**; 50, **Glenanthe**; 51, **Pelina**; 52, **Discomyza**; 53, **Mosillus**; 54, **Psilopina**.

24. Front shining 27
    Front pollinose 25

25. Face with longitudinal ridges below (59, 73) .... **Rhysophora** Cresson
    Face without ridges below 26

26. Eyes longitudinally oval (34) .... **Ditrichophora** Cresson
    Eyes not regularly oval, widened below the middle and narrowing the face above (10, 56) .... ***Discocerina** Macquart

27. Face carinate above (15) .... **Athyroglossa** Lœw
    Face very gently convex above, without a distinct ridge 28

28. Face and front on the same plane, flat, the face slightly convex below (46) .... **Plagiops** Cresson
    Face, front or both conspicuously convex 29

29. Second and third antennal segments pendulous, the third more than twice as long as wide 30
    Antennæ not pendulous, the third segment not twice as long as wide (39, 61) .... **Psilopa** Fallén

30. Spine of second antennal segment long and strong (62). **Clasiopella** Cresson
    Spine of second antennal segment fine (77) .... **Ceropsilopa** Cresson

31. Oral opening small; eyes usually with distinct hair 32
    Oral opening large; eyes usually bare 43

32. Anterior femora greatly enlarged, their tibiæ ending in a spur 33
    Anterior femora not remarkably enlarged, their tibiæ not ending in a spur 34

33. Scutellum with four marginal bristles (see text figure). **Ochthera** Latreille
    Scutellum with two marginal bristles (64) .... **Stenochthera** Hendel

34. Arista pectinate 35
    Arista bare or pubescent 38

35. Face and front polished 36
    Face and front thickly pollinose 37

36. Sides of the face with deep punctures resulting in short, transverse ridges (3, 16, 65) .... ***Ochtheroidea** Williston
    Sides of face without pits or wrinkles .... **Ceropsilopa** Cresson

37. Acrostical hairs absent (36) .... **Nostima** Coquillett
    Acrostical hairs present .... **Hydrellia** Desvoidy

38. Mesonotum with three pairs of dorsocentrals, a strong one near the inner end of the suture, another in front; four scutellars (2, 18). **Hydrina** Desvoidy
    Mesonotum with at most one pair of strong dorsocentrals, rarely an extremely weak second pair 39

* Cresson, 1918, Trans-Amer. Ent. Soc., xliv, pp. 56, 60 (Costa Rica).

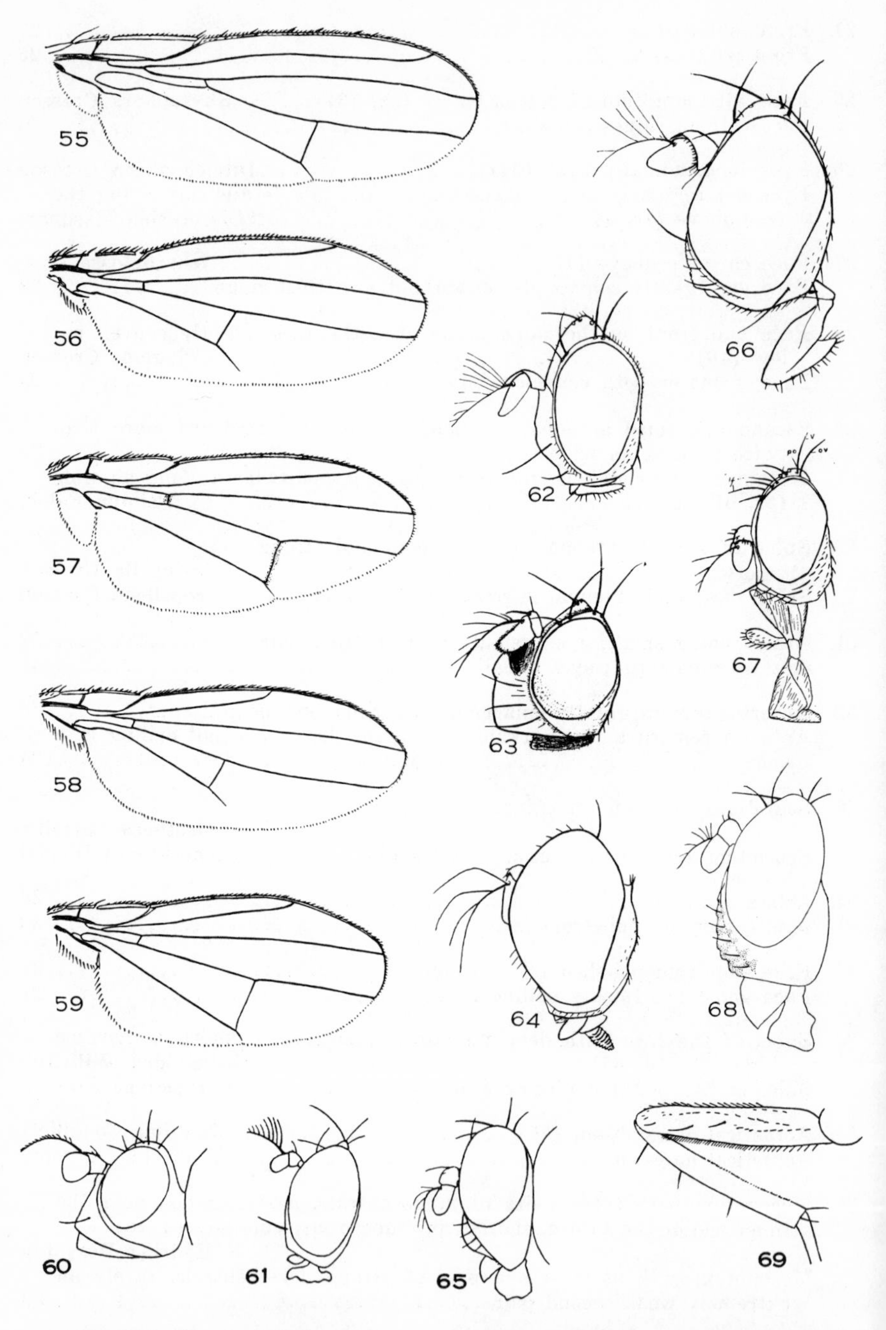

Ephydridæ IV.—55, **Ephydra milbræ**; 56, **Discocerina obscurella**; 57, **Paralimna texana**; 58, **Leptopsilopa nigra**; 59, **Rhysophora aspersa**; 60, **Parydra**; 61, **Psilopa**; 62, **Clasiopella**; 63, **Ilythea**; 64, **Stenochthera**; 65, **Ochtheroidea centralis**; 66, **Leptopsilopa nigrimana**; 67, **Paratissa pollinosa**; 68, **Cerometopum mosilloides**; 69, **Notiphila erythrocera**, middle leg.

39. Scutellar bristles arising from very strong tubercles; two pairs of frontal bristles **(12, 74)** .... **Gastrops** Williston
Scutellar bristles not arising from strong tubercles, if from weak tubercles there is but one pair of weak frontals.................. 40

40. Third antennal segment with the upper apex more or less elongate.... 41
Third antennal segment with the apex rounded 42

41. Scutellum shining **(1, 14, 17)** .... **Lytogaster** Becker
Scutellum opaque black or with an opaque black spot on either side **(26)** .... **Hyadina** Haliday

42. With one or two pairs of weak frontals **(24, 51)**........... **Pelina** Haliday
With one pair of strong and two pairs of weak frontals **(20, 50)**. **Glenanthe** Haliday

43. Clypeus prominent 44
Clypeus concealed 45

44. Arista with long rays **(33, 75)**........................ **Œdenops** Becker
Arista bare or pubescent (**Napæa** Desvoidy, preoc) **(4, 22, 47, 60)** **Parydra** Stenhammer

45. Arista with long, well separated rays 46
Arista bare or with the rays short and numerous................. 47

46. Pulvilli absent .... **Dimocœnia** Cresson
Pulvilli well developed **(23)**.......................... **Cœnia** Desvoidy

47. Mesonotum with two or more pairs of dorsocentrals; middle of face without a cluster of bristles 48
Mesonotum with only one pair of dorsocentrals; middle of face with a cluster of bristles on either side; large species (**Pogonephydra** Hendel) **(70, 76)**.................................. **Cirrula** Cresson

48. Arista minutely pubescent or pectinate on its whole length.......... 50
Arista with long, abundant rays on the basal half above........... 49

49. Third antennal segment bearing a long hair on the outer surface. **Setacera** Cresson
Third antennal segment without long hair **(11, 55)**......***Ephydra** Fallén

50. Sternopleural bristle present; face with bristles.................. 51
Sternopleural bristle absent; face without bristles **(29)**. **Psilephydra** Hendel

51. Two pairs of divergent frontals 52
A single pair of divergent frontals .... **Eustigoptera** Cresson

52. A pair of strong acrosticals nearly opposite the inner ends of the suture **(43, 78)** .... **Scatella** Desvoidy
No strong acrosticals, these all short and continuing in two rows to the scutellum **(23)**......................... **Lamproscatella** Hendel

53. Second antennal segment with an apical spine above............... 54
Second antennal segment without apical spine above............... 55

* Curran, 1933, Amer. Mus. Novit. No. 682, p. 8.

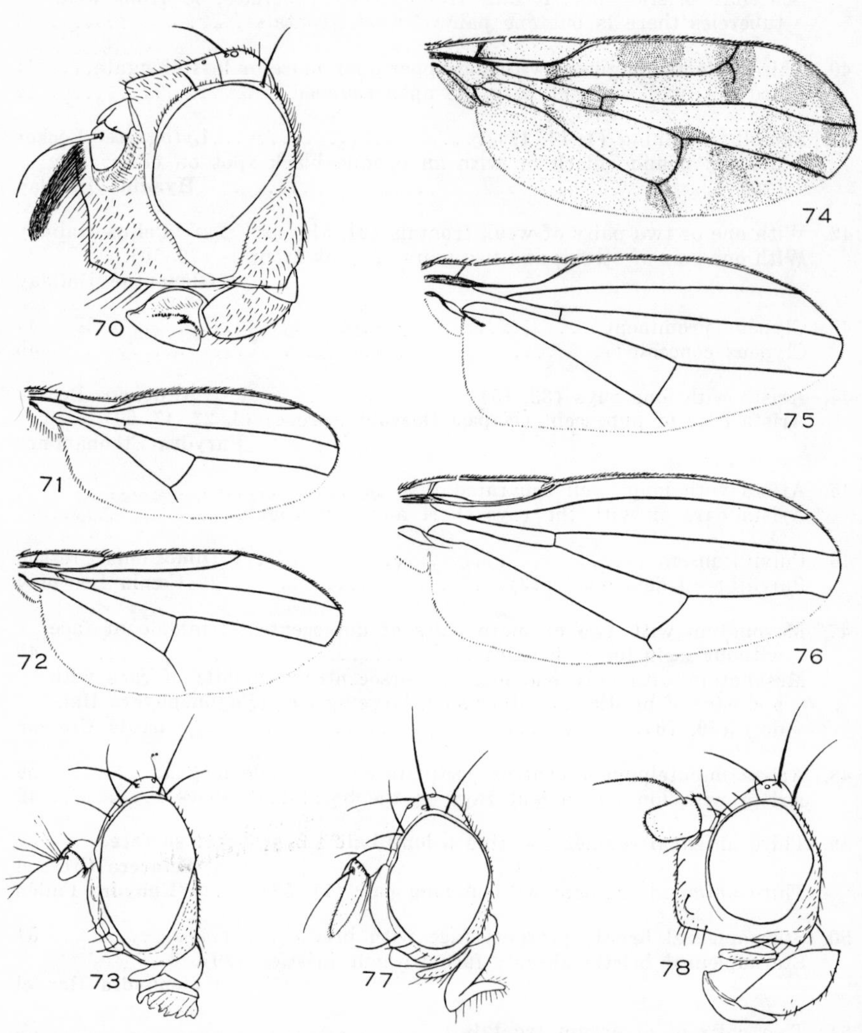

Ephydridæ V.—70, **Cirrula gigantea**; 71, **Lipochæta**; 72, **Paratissa pollinosa**; 73, **Rhysophora aspersa**; 74, **Gastrops nebulosa**; 75, **Œdenops nuda**; 76, **Cirrula gigantea**; 77, **Ceropsilopa**; 78, **Scatella.**

54. Front with a conspicuous proclinate orbital on either side; bristles of the face situated close to the facial grooves and strong (**25, 28**). ***Dichæta** Meigen

Front with hair-like orbitals in front; bristles of the face situated twice the width of the parafacial from the facial groove, rarely strong (**6, 35, 69**) .... ***Notiphila** Fallén

55. Oral opening small; face most prominent in the middle (**27**). **Axysta** Haliday

Oral opening large 56

56. Clypeus prominent (**5, 13**) .... **Brachydeutera** Lœw

Clypeus concealed (**42**) .... **Scatophila** Becker

* Cresson, 1917, Trans.-Amer. Ent. Soc., xliii, pp. 27-66.

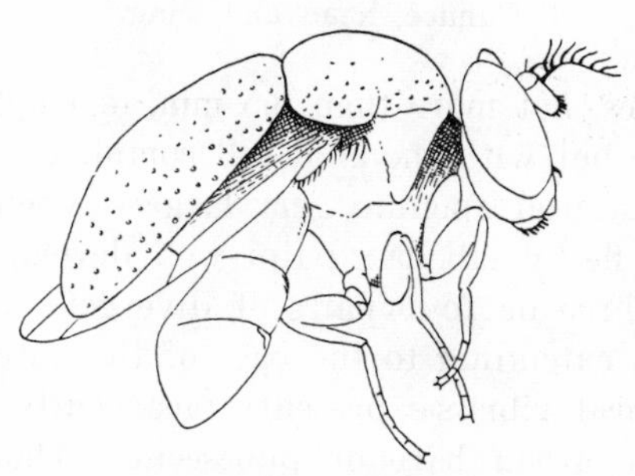

Peltopsilopa species.

Family Canaceidæ

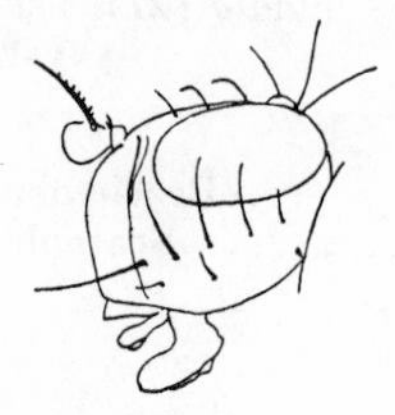
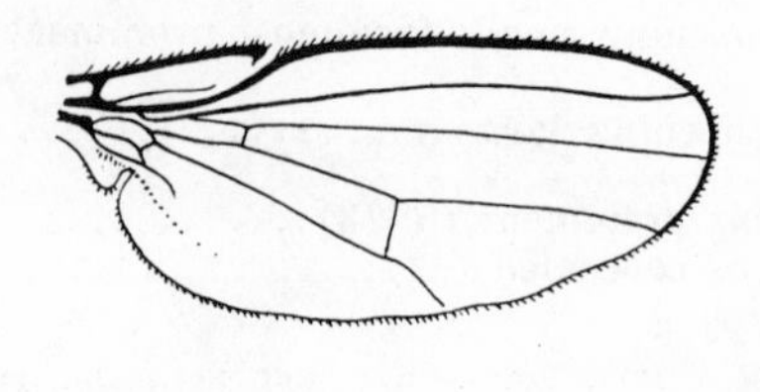

Canace, head and wing.

Very small flies, not more than 3.5 mm. in length, very similar to certain Ephydridæ but with the anal cell complete.

Head large, the oral opening very large; clypeus prominent; proboscis large, with fleshy labellæ; palpi well developed; front wide in both sexes, with three or four pairs of divergent orbitals, the ocellar triangle sometimes extending to the base of the antennæ; cheeks wide, bearing bristles; oral vibrissæ present; face gently convex in profile; antennæ short, the arista bare or pubescent. Thorax short, bearing four pairs of dorsocentrals and a pair of prescutellar acrosticals; scutellum with one or two pairs of bristles. Legs rather short. Auxiliary vein evanescent apically, the costa broken before the end of the first vein; basal and anal cells complete; anal vein short. Abdomen composed of seven segments, the first not strongly differentiated from the second which is elongate.

The members of this family occur along the seashore, the larvæ living in brackish water.

I believe that there is but one genus in the Nearctic Region. In 1924 Malloch described a species under the name *Canacea macateei,* and Johnson, in his "List of the Insects of New England" recognized the genus *Canacea.* However, I was informed by Mr. Malloch during a conversation several years ago that "*Canacea*" was a slip of the pen, that he had no intention of establishing a new name, and that he was extremely doubtful that his species differed generically from *Canace* Haliday. I have not seen representatives of *Canace* but I can find nothing in the descriptions to warrant the recognition of *Canacea.* There are three species known from the United States, one from the

Hawaiian Islands (*Procanace*) and one from Panama (*Neocanace*) and at least two from South America (*Canace* and *Neocanace*).

The following key includes the described genera of which I have records.

KEY TO GENERA

1. First vein haired above on the apical half
   Macrocanace Tonnoir and Malloch
   First vein bare above 2

2. Four pairs of dorsocentral bristles 3
   Only two pairs of dorsocentral bristles............**Xanthocanace** Hendel

3. Pleura bare.. 4
   Pleura with bristles and bristly hairs.............................. 5

4. Frontal triangle extending to about the middle of the front; antennæ reaching to the oral margin (**Dinomyia** Becker)......**Procanace** Hendel
   Frontal triangle extending to the anterior margin of the front or almost so; one pair of scutellar bristles..........**Chætocanace** Hendel

5. Face evenly convex.................................**Canace** Haliday
   Face concave below the middle, convex above (**Procanace** Curran, not Hendel) ....**Neocanace**, n. n.

Family Diopsidæ—The Stalk-eyed Flies

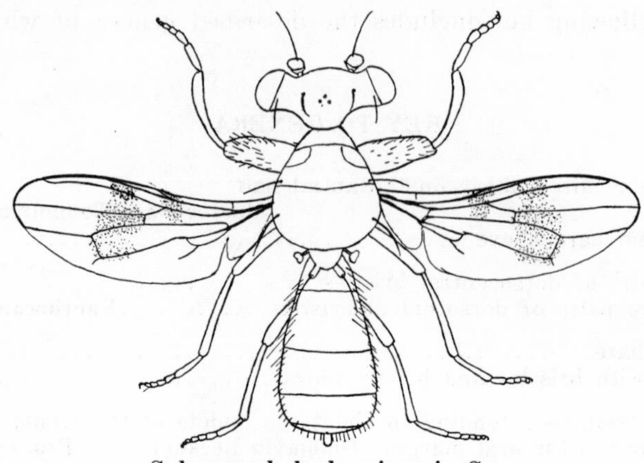

Sphyrocephala brevicornis Say.

The members of this family are mostly rather small, with the eyes situated on the ends of long stalks, a character not developed in our one genus.

Weakly haired, almost bare, the head transverse, short, conspicuously produced toward either side so that the eyes are separated by about four times their width; antennæ very widely separated, the basal segments short, the third roundish, with dorsal arista; front bare except at the vertex; oral vibrissæ absent. Legs of moderate length, the anterior femora thickened and with short spines beneath. Auxiliary vein closely approximated to the first vein for most of its length but ending far before it; second basal cell united with the discal cell; apical cell somewhat narrowed apically; anal cell long, the anal vein short.

The only American representative of this family is *Sphyracephala brevicornis* Say, a quite small and inconspicuous species. In the Nearctic region there are no flies which resemble it in the shape of its head but in the Neotropical region there are many Otitidæ and Drosophilidæ which have the eyes more or less stalked, one Otitid having much longer stalks than any true Diopsid I have seen.

Our single species is found along the edges of streams, ponds and marshy lakes and occurs from early spring to late autumn and has been taken in numbers about a privy and on skunk-cabbage. The immature stages are unknown.

This family has a particular fascination for most people owing to the peculiar structure of the head. Why the eyes are stalked we do not know and there may be no reason for it.

KEY TO GENERA OF THE WORLD

1. Mesopleura not produced to form a strong spine.................. 2
   Mesopleura produced and forming a strong spine similar to that on the hypopleura..............................**Teleopsis** Rondani
2. Mesonotum with a pair of long, black intra-alar bristles.............. 3
   Mesonotum without intra-alar bristles..................**Diopsis** Linnæus
3. Scutellum longer than deep, without bristles except on the ends of the processes 4
   Scutellum very short, as deep as long, with a pair of erect black bristles on the disc ....**Diopsina** Curran
4. Eye-stalks little longer than wide, with a strong bristle behind each antenna in addition to that behind the eye..........**Sphyracephala** Say
   Eye-stalks longer, usually very long, either with a bristle near the middle and far before the base of the antennæ or without frontal bristles, only the one behind the eye being present................ 5
5. Eye-stalks short, not over three times as long as wide, without median bristle; steropleural spine short; bend of fifth vein without appendage; anal vein continued beyond the anal cell......**Microdiopsis, n. g.**
   Eye-stalks very long, with a median bristle; pteropleural spine long and acute; bend of fifth vein with appendage; anal vein not continued beyond the anal cell............................**Diasemopsis** Rondani

Microdiopsis, new genus

Proposed for *Syhyracephala cothurnata* Bigot, from the East Indies. The genus differs from *Sphyracephala* in having longer eye-stalks, with the antennæ close to the eyes, no bristle on the middle of the stalk, no appendage at the bend of the fifth vein, etc.

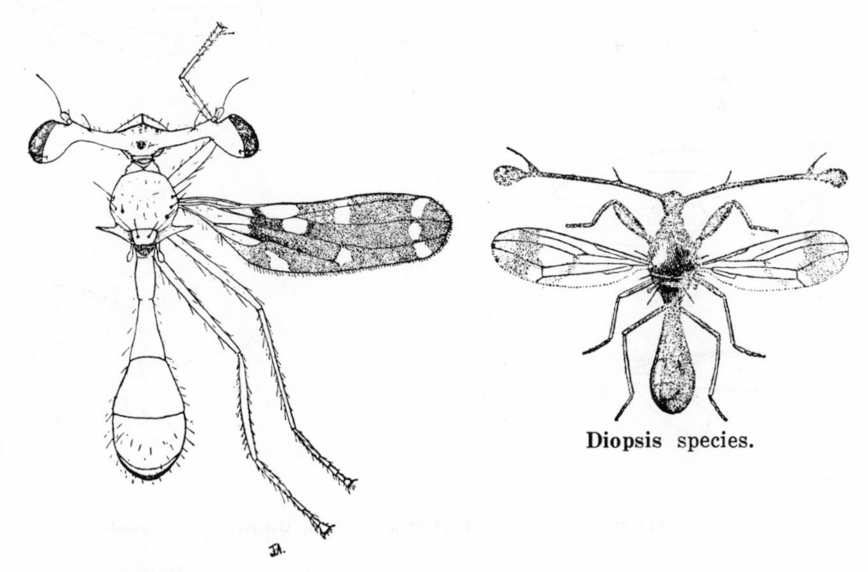

Diopsis species.

Diopsina ferruginea.

Family Borboridæ

Rather small to very small, usually black or brown flies.

Head hemispherical, the face rather perpendicular, concave or somewhat retreating; oral vibrissœ present; front broad, usually with bristles. Antennæ short, rounded or oval, with dorsal, pubescent or bare arista. Wings rarely absent; auxiliary vein incomplete or practically absent; second basal and anal cells often incomplete or absent. Legs of moderate length, the femora strong; basal segment of the posterior tarsi short and usually dilated.

The Borborids are almost always found about decomposing organic matter, in swampy places and about excrement.

The larvæ of *Borborus* live in excrement and refuse and are cylindrical, their skin roughened by minute bristles; antennæ two segmented; mouth hooks well developed; posterior segment with a conical protuberance and smaller tubercles about the spiracles. In *Limosina* the posterior spiracles are tube-like and the larvæ are found in fungi, algæ, etc.

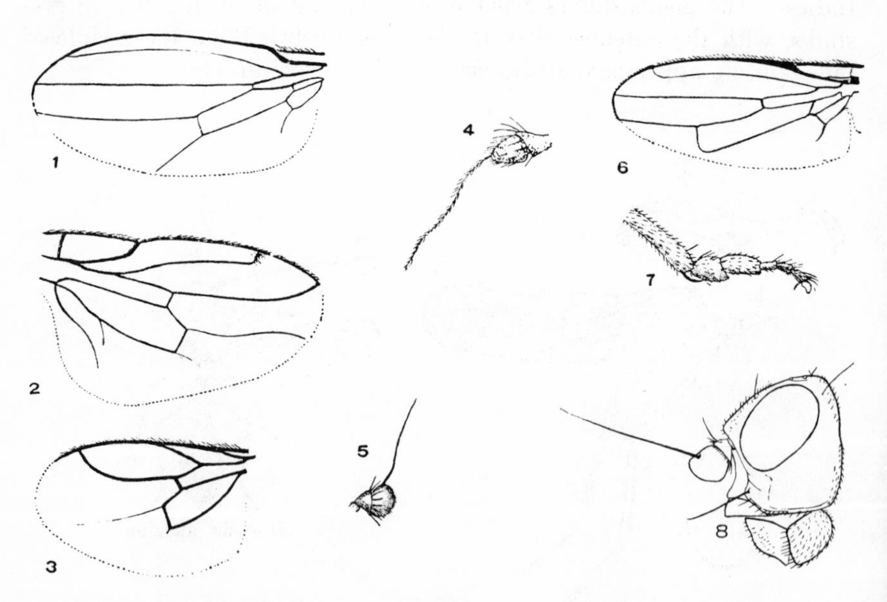

Borboridæ.—1, **Sphærocera**; 2, 3, 4, **Leptocera**; 5, 6, 7, **Borborus**; 8, **Scatophora.**

The North American species have been monographed by Spuler.* Here is one of the best examples of the short sighted policy of Entomological publications in refusing to accept long papers and Spuler's work has lost much of its value. The work appeared in seven different journals (of various sized pages) and in nine parts and the entire sequence has been lost.

KEY TO GENERA

1. Wings and halteres present 2
   Wings and halteres absent ....**Aptilotus** Mik

2. Mesonotum and scutellum with bristles.............................. 3
   Mesonotum and scutellum without bristles (1)......**Sphærocera** Latreille

3. Fourth vein reaching the margin of the wing......................... 4
   Fourth vein not nearly reaching the wing margin (2, 3, 4).
   Leptocera Olivier

4. Posterior tibiæ with an apical spur below (5, 6, 7).....**Borborus** Meigen
   Posterior tibiæ without apical spur (8)...........**Scatophora** Desvoidy

---

* 1923, Proc. Acad. Nat. Sci. Phila., lxxv, pp. 369-378; 1924 (Leptocera, part), Psyche, xxxi, pp. 121-134; 1924, (Leptocera, part) Ann. Ent. Soc. Amer., xvii, pp. 106-116; 1924, (Sphærocera and Aptilotus), Pan. Pac. Ent., i, pp. 66-71; 1925, (Leptocera, part), Can. Ent., lvii, pp. 99-104, 116-124; 1925, (Leptocera, part), Journ. N. Y. Ent. Soc., xxxiii, pp. 70-84, 147-162; 1925, (Borborus and Scatophora), Bull, Brooklyn Ent. Soc., xx, pp. 1-16.

Family Clusiidæ

Rather small flies in which the wings are almost always marked with black or brown.

Head broad, sub-hemispherical; face short, nearly vertical or gently receding below; front broad, with three or four pairs of frontals and often with a pair of cruciate interfrontals; ocellars present or absent; postverticals divergent, rarely absent. Antennæ porrect, the basal two segments short, the third rounded, with a terminal or subapical arista which may be bare, pubescent, or thickly long haired. Proboscis short, the palpi rather broad. Abdomen of moderate length, rather slender. Legs of moderate length, slender, the tibiæ with or without a preapical bristle. Wing venation complete, the second basal and anal cells very small; first vein ending near the basal fourth of the wing, the auxiliary vein narrowly separated from it.

The adults are found in moist places and about decaying wood, sometimes occurring in large numbers, although most of the species are not common.

The larvæ occur in decaying wood and under the bark of trees. They are white, slender, cylindrical and slightly thickened posteriorly. Mouth hooks small, the segments not distinctly separated but with transverse ventral swellings for locomotion. They have the power of leaping, accomplishing this by grasping the hooklets on the apical segment with their mouth hooks and suddenly letting go. The puparia are yellowish, ellipsoidal and with horns on the apical segment as in the larvæ.

Melander and Argo* have revised the American species of the family including many species from other regions. The vast majority of the species are tropical. Of the seventy known American species only a small number occur in the Nearctic region.

KEY TO GENERA

1. Eyes with microscopic pubescence; costa broken near the humeral crossvein (8, 11) .... **Acartophthalmus** Czerny
   Eyes bare; costa weakened or broken near the end of the auxiliary vein. 2

2. Anterior pair of frontal bristles convergent or proclinate 4
   All the frontal bristles reclinate 3

* Proc. U. S. N. M., 1924, Vol. xliv, Article 11, pp. 1-54.

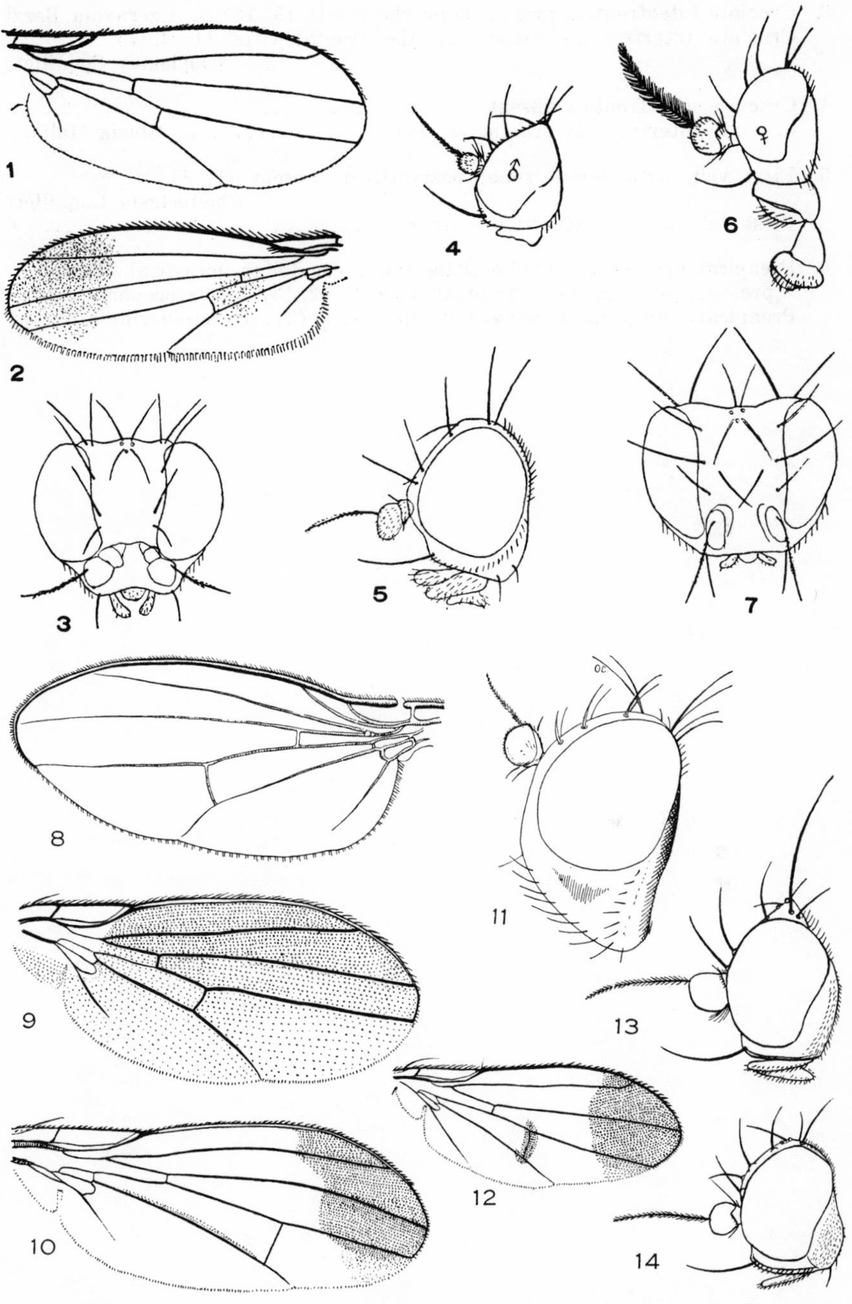

Clusiidæ.—1, **Clusioides**; 2, **Chætoclusia**; 3, **Heteromeringia**; 4, **Clusioides**; 5, **Clusia**; 6, **Chætoclusia**; 7, **Clusioides**; 8, **Acartophthalmus**; 9, **Czernyola atra**; 10, **Clusia lateralis**; 11, **Acartophthalmus**; 12, **Sobarocephala variegata**; 13, **Sobarocephala**; 14, **Czernyola.**

3. Cruciate interfrontals arising from the orbits (**9, 14**)....**Czernyola** Bezzi
   Cruciate interfrontals arising on the frontal vitta (**1, 4, 7**).
   Clusioides Coquillett

4. Cruciate interfrontals absent 5
   Cruciate interfrontals present (**5, 10**)....................**Clusia** Haliday

5. First vein with dorsal setæ; postverticals absent (**2, 6**).
   Chætoclusia Coquillett
   First vein bare; postverticals present 6

6. Preapical bristles on middle tibiæ and prescutellar acrostical bristles present; presutural dorsocentrals absent (**12, 13**)..**Sobarocephala** Czerny
   Preapicals and prescutellar acrosticals absent (**3**)..**Heteromeringia** Czerny

Family Chamæmyidæ

Small flies, usually grayish in color.

Front wide, with at most two pairs of bristles, often bare; face gently concave or strongly receding; oral vibrissæ absent; postverticals convergent or absent; proboscis short; antennæ short. Mesonotum with or without bristles; prothoracic bristle absent; one sternopleural; mesopleura usually bare, rarely setulose. Front femora with bristles; tibiæ without preapical bristle. Wings with the auxiliary vein entire, sometimes touching the first vein before its end; anal vein not reaching nearly to the wing margin, the anal and second basal cells always complete; costa not broken. Abdomen short or slightly elongate.

The larvæ of *Leucopis* are predaceous upon aphids and I have found them commonly on plant lice attacking thistle, *Oenothera*, burdock, etc. They are somewhat triangular in outline, the posterior spiracles being located at the posterior corners of the body and strongly projecting. All I have seen have been pale yellowish, with a darker median vitta. They usually conceal themselves under the aphids or in the axils of leaves. Pupation usually takes place in the axils, the head pointing upward on the stem, but the location is variable.

KEY TO GENERA

1. Front without distinct bristles 2
   Front with one or two pairs of strong bristles 4

2. Arista absent (Agromyzidæ) (3, 5) ....**Cryptochætum** Rondani
   Arista present 3

3. Shining black species ....**Paraleucopis** Malloch
   Densely cinereous pollinose species (2, 13)...........***Leucopis** Meigen

4. Face very strongly receding, the head pointed (1, 10).
   Acrometopia Schiner
   Face only a little retreating 5

5. Three or four pairs of dorsocentrals............................ 6
   Two pairs of dorsocentrals (4, 8)................†**Pseudodinia** Coquillett

6. Three pairs of dorsocentrals (**Ochthiphila** Fallén) (6, 7, 12).
   Chamæmyia Meigen
   Four pairs of dorsocentrals (9, 11)....................‡**Plunomia**, n. g.

---

* Malloch, 1921, Bull. Ill. Nat. Hist. Survey, xiii, p. 349.

† A paratype of **Pseudodinia polita** Malloch lacks the two strong frontals and I would place it in **Paraleucopis** but it lacks the setulæ on the underside of the costa.

‡ For **Chamæmyia elegans** Malloch, 1921, not Panzer.

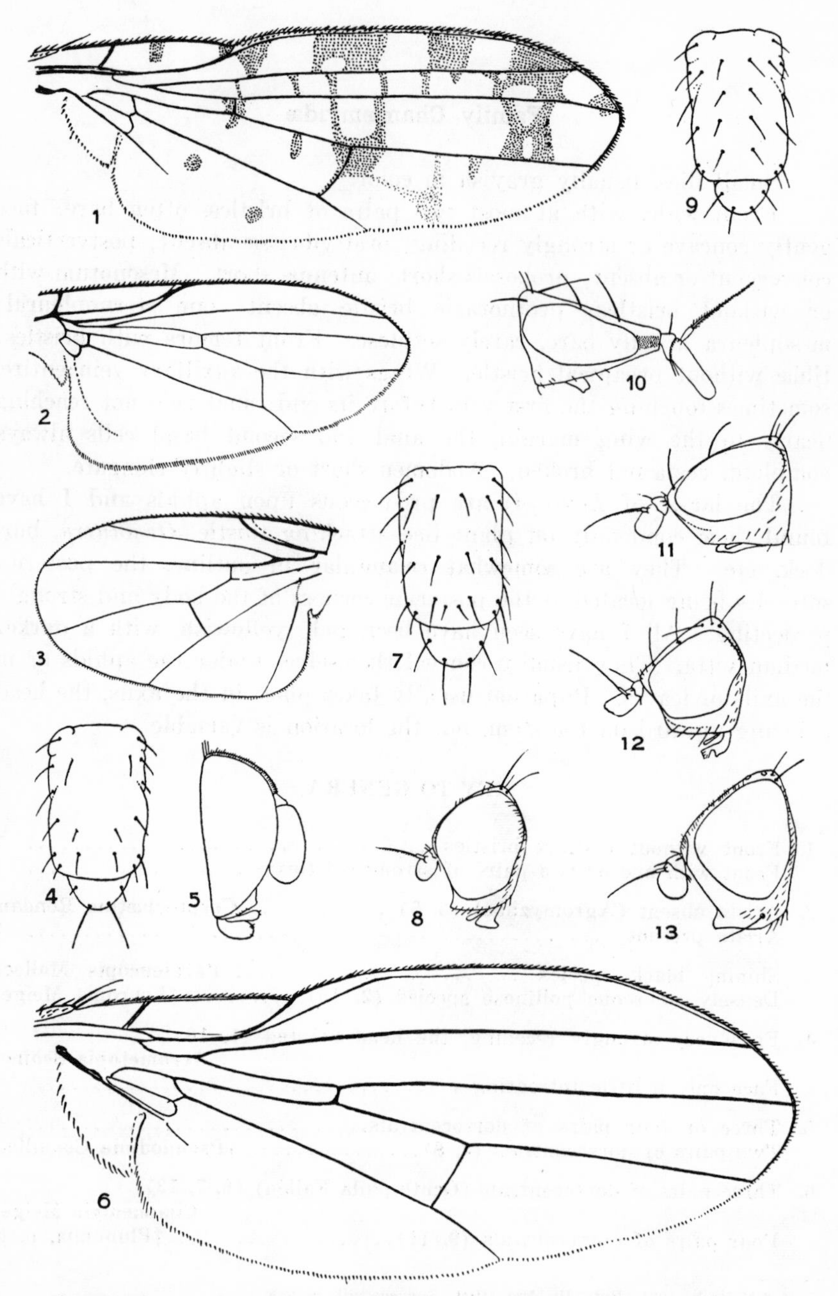

Chamæmyidæ.—1, **Acrometopia maculata**; 2, **Leucopis major**; 3, **Cryptochætum iceryæ**; 4, **Pseudodinia polita** chætotaxy; 5, **Cryptochætum iceryæ**; 6, **Ochthiphila polystigma**; 7, **Ochthiphila**, chætotaxy; 8, **Pseudodinia polita**; 9, **Plunomia elegans**, chætotaxy; 10, **Acrometopia maculata**; 11, **Plunomia elegans**; 12, **Ochthiphila polystigma**; 13, **Leucopis major.**

Family Tetanoceridæ—The Marsh Flies

Head short, as broad or broader than the thorax; face retreating, more or less perpendicular below; oral vibrissæ absent. Abdomen composed of six segments, rather long and narrow, sub-cylindrical. Wings longer than the abdomen; auxiliary vein entire, wholly separated from the first vein; posterior basal and anal cells complete, small. Legs of moderate length, the femora with bristles, the middle pair with a short bristle near the middle of the anterior surface; tibiæ with preapical bristle.

The adults are found in moist places, along the banks of streams, ponds, etc. and most of them may be recognized on sight by the shape of the head.

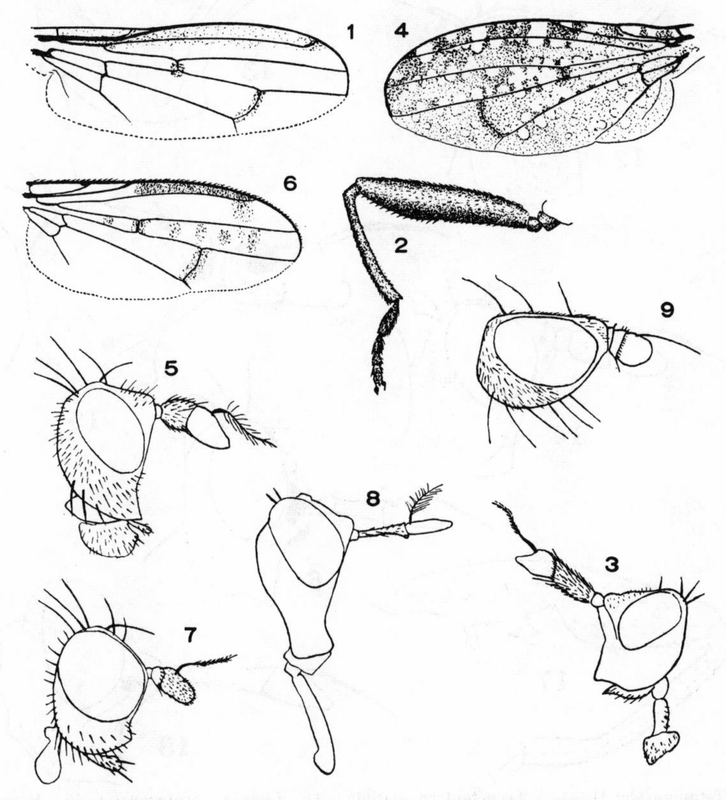

Tetanoceridæ I.—1, 2, 3, **Sepedon**, wing, hind leg and head; 4, **Dictya** sp.; 5, **Tetanocera**; 6, **Dyctia nana**; 7, **Dyctia**; 8, **Thecomyia** (S. America); 9, **Trigonometopus** (Sapromyzidæ) (Williston).

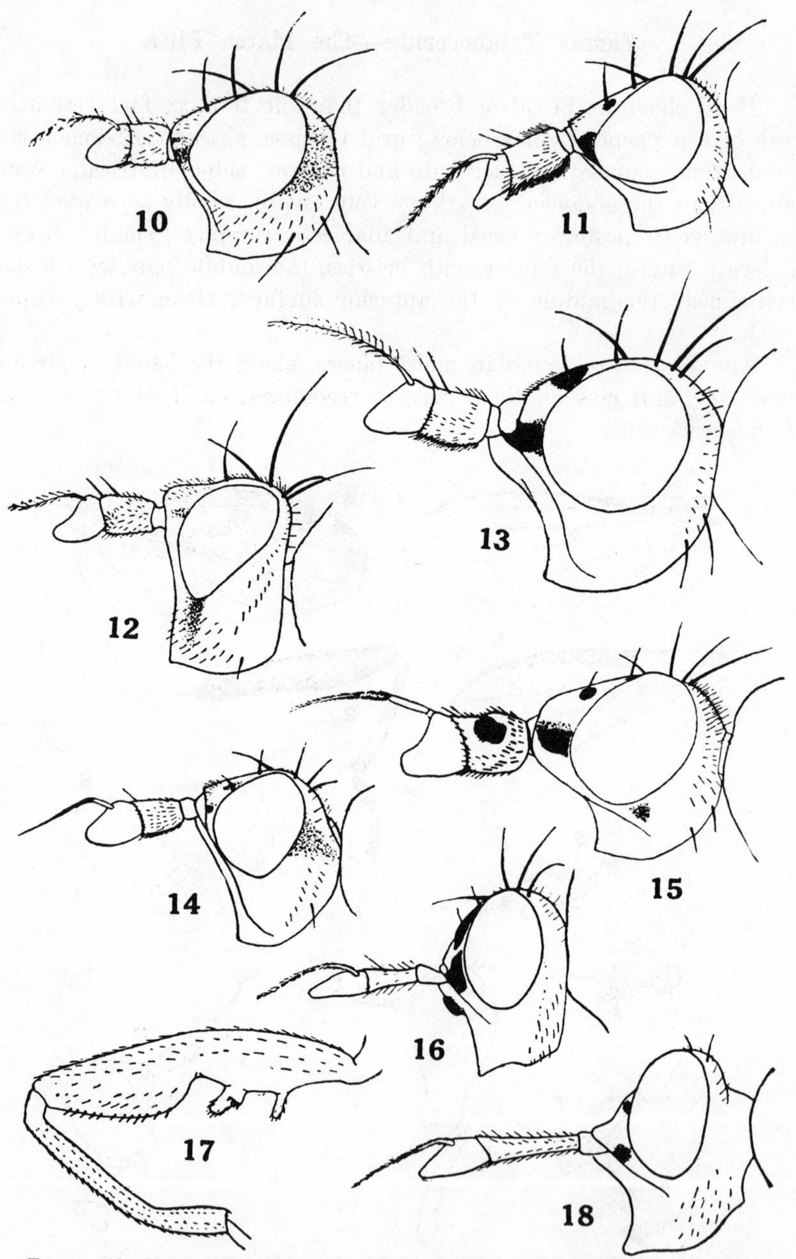

Tetanoceridæ II.—10, **Trypetoptera pallida**; 11, **Limnia saratogensis**; 12, **Hoplydyctia setosa**; 13, **Euthycera arcuata**; 14, **Hedroneura**; 15, **Limnia shannoni**; 16, **Dictyomyia ambigua**; 17, **Sepedon armipes**, posterior femur and tibia of ♂; 18, **Sepedon tenuicornis**.

The larvæ are slender, cylindrical, thin anteriorly, the terminal segment with six or eight conical, fleshy tubercles. They are aquatic.

The North American species have been reviewed by Cresson (1920, Trans. Amer. Ent. Soc., xlvi, pp. 27-89) and Melander (1920, Ann. Ent. Soc. Amer. xiii, pp. 305-332), the former under the name Sciomyzidæ.

KEY TO GENERA

1. Propleural bristle present 2
   Propleural bristle absent 5

2. Anterior tibiæ with two approximate preapical bristles dorsally....... 3
   Anterior tibiæ with one dorsal preapical bristle.......................... 4

3. Arista densely short white haired (19)...............**Oidematops** Cresson
   Arista with long, black rays (20)......................**Sciomyza** Fallén

4. Front polished black; cheeks narrow (21)..............**Pteromicra** Lioy
   Front dull; cheeks moderately broad (22)..............***Melina** Desvoidy

5. Scutellum with two pairs of bristles.. 7
   Scutellum with one pair of bristles.. 6

6. Second antennal segment longer than the third (**1, 2, 3, 17, 18**). **Sepedon** Latreille
   Second antennal segment shorter than the third...**Hemitelopteryx** Cresson

7. Third antennal segment oval, three times as long as the second; front distinctly narrowed anteriorly 8
   Third antennal segment rarely oval, usually flattened or concave above, the second segment at least half as long as the third............ 9

8. Posterior tibiæ with two preapical dorsal bristles (**2, 3**). †**Renocera** Hendel
   Posterior tibiæ with one preapical dorsal bristle......**Antichæta** Haliday

9. Mesopleura and pteropleura with one or more bristles.............. 10
   Mesopleura and pteropleura at most with short hairs.............. 11

10. One sternopleural bristle (**12**)........................**Hoplodictya** Cresson
    No sternopleural bristle (**4, 6, 7**)........................‡**Dictya** Meigen

11. Two or three pairs of dorsocentrals.. 12
    One pair of dorsocentrals (**14**) ....**Hedroneura** Hendel

12. Two pairs of dorsocentrals.. 13
    Three pairs of dorsocentrals (**25**) ....**Pœcilographa** Melander

13. Mesopleura and pteropleura bare.. 14
    Mesopleura and pteropleura with setulæ 16

14. Frontal lunule exposed; wings brown with rounded clear spots...... 15
    Frontal lunule mostly concealed; wings never with rounded, clear spots (**5, 24, 26, 27**) ....**Tetanocera** Dumeril

---

* **Dyctia** Desvoidy is an older name but its use conflicts with **Dictya** Meigen.

† Curran, 1933, Amer. Mus. Novit. No. 682, p. 9.

‡ Curran, 1932, Amer. Mus. Novit. No. 517.

15. Second antennal segment slender, much longer than the third (16).
Dictyomyia Cresson
Second antennal segment broad, slightly longer than the third (13).
Euthycera Latreille
16. Arista practically bare; infrasquamal swellings with bristles.
Elgiva Meigen
Arista with long rays or long pubescent............................17
17. Arista with long, black rays (10)..................**Trypetoptera** Hendel
Arista white pubescent (11, 15)......................**Limnia** Desvoidy

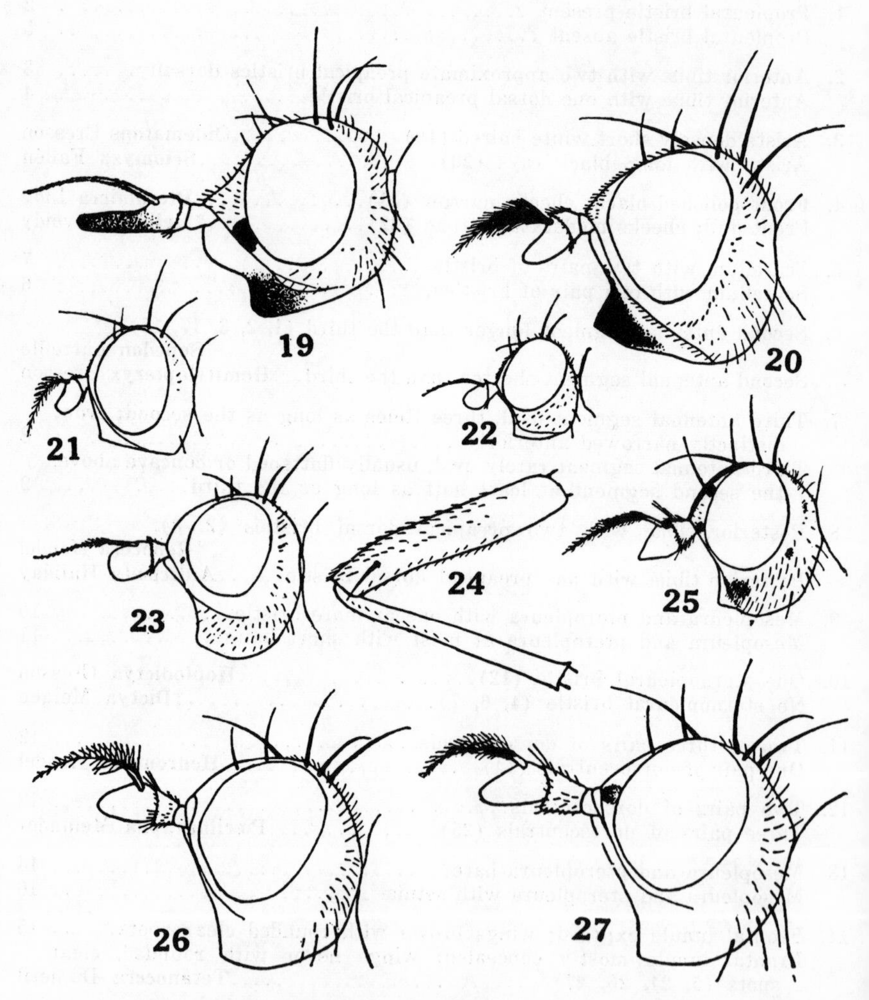

Tetanoceridæ III.—19, **Oidematops ferruginea**; 20, **Sciomyza aristalis**; 21, **Pteromicra**; 22, **Dyctia nana**; 23, **Renocera johnsoni**; 24, **Tetanocera**, middle femur and tibia; 25, **Pœcilographa decora**; 26, **Tetanocera valida**; 27, **Tetanocera plebeja** (10-27 after Cresson).

Family Chyromyidæ

Small flies, the wings sometimes pictured.

Subcosta entire, free and ending in the costa, the costa weakened before its end; postocellar bristles convergent; plates of the orbital bristles extending almost to the anterior border of the front; head higher than long, more or less receding below, the oral margin never conspicuously produced; two pairs of frontal bristles; palpi not large; proboscis short and fleshy; antennæ shorter than the face; arista pubescent. Mesonotum usually with five pairs of dorsocentrals, two pairs of scutellar bristles; mesopleura with one or more bristles; sternopleurals, two to four in a straight line along the upper edge; propleural bristle present. Tibiæ usually with preapical bristles. Anal and second basal cells complete; costa with spines. Abdomen rather narrow, bearing bristles on the apices of the segments; genitalia small.

The species of *Chyromya* differ from those of the other genera in having three pairs of frontal bristles, the anterior pair convergent, four pairs of dorsocentrals and no preapical tibial bristles. There are at least two North American species, *flava* Linnæus, and another that is either *minima* Becker or an undescribed form since it bears only a single pair of dorsocentrals. Some species placed in the genus *Aphaniosoma* Becker have five pairs of dorsocentrals or the number may be reduced to one or two distinct pairs with a row of bristly hairs in front of the suture. These two genera have been placed in a separate family, based upon the absence of preapical bristles on the tibiæ, but I do not see how the family can be maintained.

I am not well acquainted with the habits of these insects but believe that all are found on foliage near the sea coast and in moist places. The number of known species is not large and most of the American species are southern in distribution or occur along the coastal regions.

Malloch would unite this family with the Helomyzidæ but the head characters appear to indicate a very distinct difference and I fail to see any really close relationship. Melander included the genera in the Geomyzidæ* and keys to the species will be found in his work.

* 1913, Journ. N. Y. Ent. Soc., xxi, pp. 283-300.

KEY TO GENERA

1. All the tibiæ with preapical bristles 2
   Tibiæ without preapical bristles 4

2. Cheeks half as wide as the third antennal segment 3
   Cheeks not over one-third as wide as the third antennal segment.
   Spilochroa Williston

3. Cheeks not half as wide as the eye-height; bristles black 5
   Cheeks almost as wide as the eye-height; bristles wholly yellow **(3, 4)**.
   Zagonia Coquillett

4. Anterior pair of orbitals convergent **(5, 6)** .... **Chyromya** Desvoidy
   All the orbitals reclinate .... **Aphaniosoma** Becker

5. Mesopleura with hairs and a strong bristle **(1, 2)** .... **Trixoscelis** Rondani
   Mesopleura bare .... **Neossos** Malloch

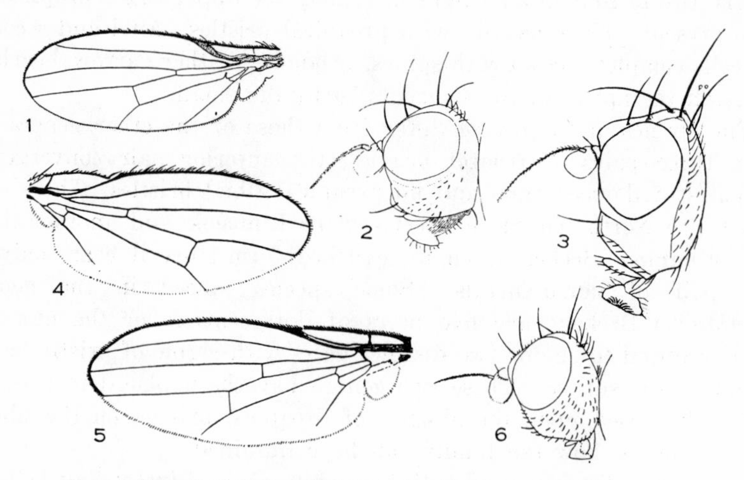

Chyromyidæ.—1, 2, **Trixoscelis**; 3, 4, **Zagonia flava**; 5, 6, **Chiromya flava.**

Family Megamerinidæ

Small, elongate, slender flies with petiolate abdomen and incrassate posterior femora.

Head nearly spherical, broader than high; front moderately broad in both sexes; frontal bristles absent, the ocellars and verticals strong; face very gently convex, without vibrissæ; antennæ of moderate length, decumbent. Thorax elongate and narrow, with bristles posteriorly; mesosternum long, the posterior two pairs of legs approximate; scutellum short and broad. Abdomen elongate and clavate, the basal segments slender and fused. Legs of moderate length, the posterior femora strongly swollen and with bristles below on the apical half. Wings narrow; auxiliary vein absent; first vein ending at basal third of the wing; first basal cell long, the anal cell as long as the second basal, more or less rounded apically.

The single genus representing this family in America occurs in the tropics. I have seen only four specimens collected on Barro Colorado Island, Canal Zone, and Cresson had the same number from Costa Rica. I found the specimens among rather thick foliage in moist places. They resemble species of *Sphegina* (Syrphidæ) although much smaller, but, of course, the resemblance is only superficial.

Syringogaster Cresson is our only genus and is represented by two described species, both of which occur in Panama.

I am not certain that this genus belongs to the Megamerinidæ as the species show striking differences from a species of *Megamerina* (so named) in the American Museum of Natural History.

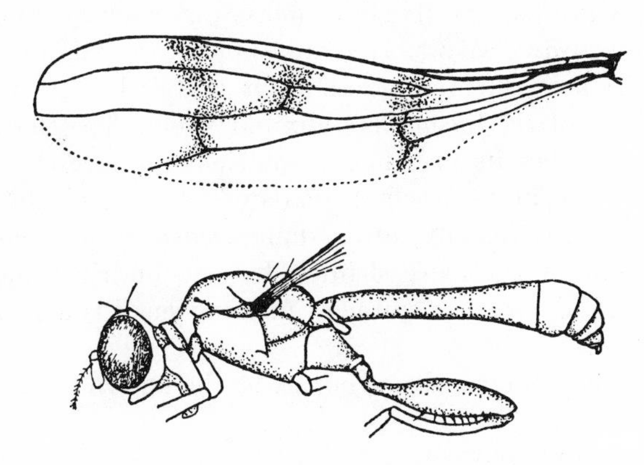

Syringogaster, wing, body.
(Cresson)

Family Psilidæ

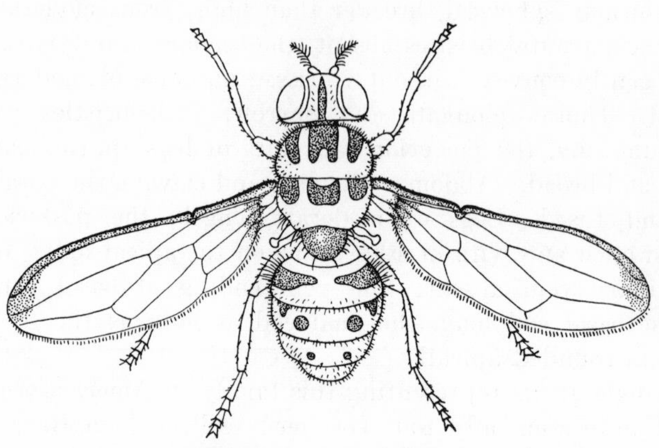

Somatia xanthomelas.

Flies of medium or small size.

Front broad, with bristles on the upper part; face perpendicular or receding in profile; oral vibrissæ absent; antennæ decumbent, rather short to very long; arista pubescent, rarely long plumose. Abdomen slender or moderately slender; genitalia not prominent, the ovipositor usually elongate. Wings moderately large, the auxiliary vein absent or incomplete; apical cell not narrowed apically; second basal and anal cells large. Legs rather elongate; tibiæ without preapical bristles.

The adults are usually found in moist places or shady woods. The Psilidæ are not always easy to recognize but all the known species have a peculiar ridge or weakening across the basal third of the wing extending from the end of the incomplete auxiliary vein. The character is not at all conspicuous but its presence is sufficient to place the insects.

The larvæ live in the roots or galls of plants and one of them is known as the carrot rust fly, often doing considerable damage to this crop. The larvæ of *Psila* are slender, bare, cylindrical and of a pale yellowish color, the posterior spiracles forming small rounded or button-like processes.

Melander* has published a synopsis of the known species.

* 1920, Psyche, xxvii, pp. 91-101.

KEY TO GENERA

1. Third antennal segment shorter than the arista.................... 2
   Third antennal segment longer than the arista (4, 5)..**Loxocera** Meigen

2. Pteropleura bare 3
   Pteropleura with hairs ....**Strongylophthalmyia** Heller

3. A pair of dorsocentrals in front of the suture (1, 6).
   Pseudopsila Johnson
   Only the prescutellar dorsocentrals present.......................... 4

4. Cheeks almost half as wide as the eye-height (3, 7).........**Psila** Meigen
   Cheeks at most one-sixth as wide as the eye-height.............. 5

5. Arista pubescent (2, 8) ....**Chyliza** Fallén
   Arista long plumose (Tropical) (Text figure) ....**Somatia** Schiner

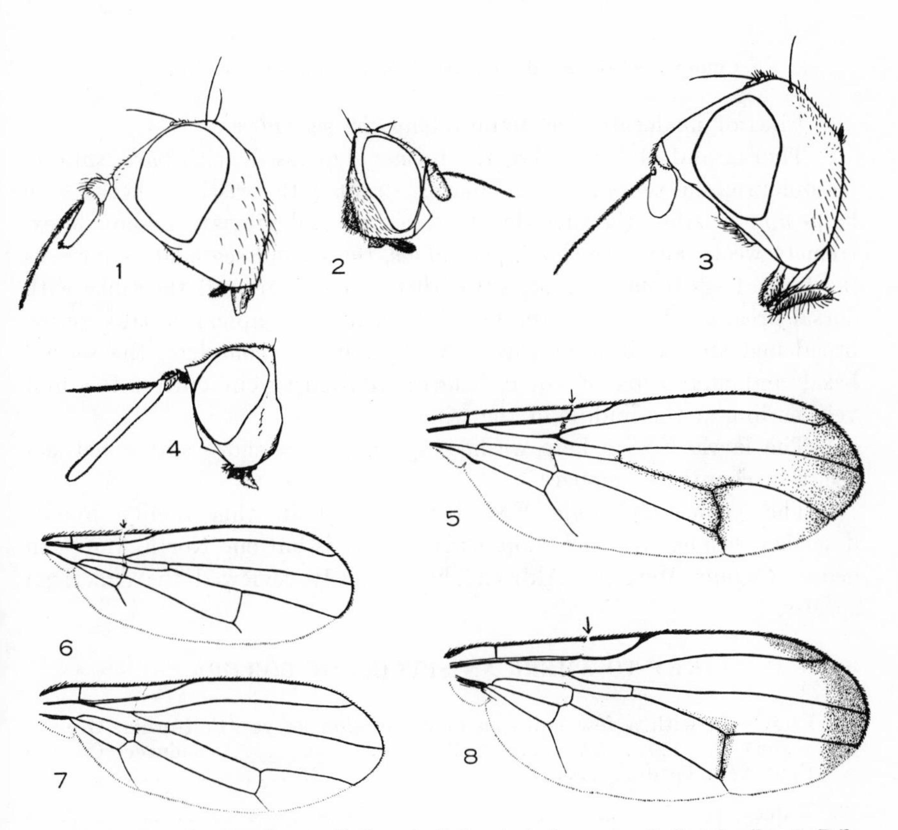

Psilidæ.—1, **Pseudopsila**; 2, **Chyliza**; 3, **Psila**; 4, 5, **Loxocera**; 6, **Pseudopsila**; 7, **Psila lævis**; 8, **Chyliza.**

Family Cœlopidæ

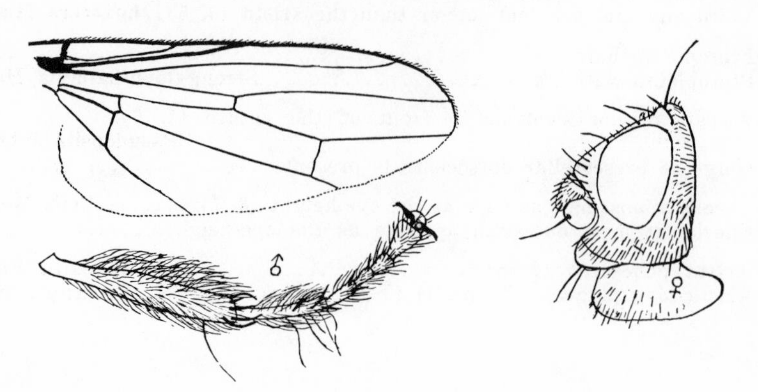

Cœlopa, wing, head and front tibia and tarusus of ♂.

Flies of moderate size, living along the sea-shore.

Thorax and abdomen flat, the former depressed, with bare, shining mesopleura, the scutellum flat above. Front with bristles; cheeks with hairs and bristles, the face deeply concave; oral vibrissæ absent or extremely weak; antennæ short, pendulous, the second segment as large as the first. Legs usually stout, with bristles and hairs, all the tibiæ with dorsal preapical bristles; basal tarsal segment long; apical tarsal segment broadened and with stout claws. Wing venation complete, the second basal and anal cells of equal length; auxiliary vein entire, the first vein ending at the middle of the wing.

The larvæ live in kelp washed up on the sea-shore and sometimes occur in countless numbers.

The genus *Omomyia* Coquillett, placed in this family by its describer, belongs to the Pallopteridæ. There is but one North American genus, *Cœlopa* Meigen. Aldrich* has recently reviewed the American species.

KEY TO AMERICAN SPECIES OF CŒLOPA.

1. First vein with a few hairs on apical section above (California, Oregon) .... **vanduzeei** Cresson
   First vein bare.. 2

2. Males 3
   Females 5

* Revision * * * Cœlopa, Proc. U. S. N. M., lxxvi, Article 11, pp. 1-6.

3. Legs with spines, bristles or bristly hairs.......................... 4
   Legs with soft hair only..........................**stejnegeri** Aldrich

4. Abdomen with bristles on the disc of the apical segments.
   nebularum Aldrich
   Abdomen with bristles only on the sides and apices of the segments
   (Atlantic Coast) ....**frigida** Fabricius

5. Legs usually blackish (western coast).......................... 6
   Legs reddish yellow...............................**frigida** Fabricius

6. Cheeks with dense, soft, rather short hair; arista pubescent under high
   power ....**stejnegeri** Aldrich
   Checks with sparse hair which is coarse above; arista quite bare.
   nebularum Aldrich

Family Helomyzidæ

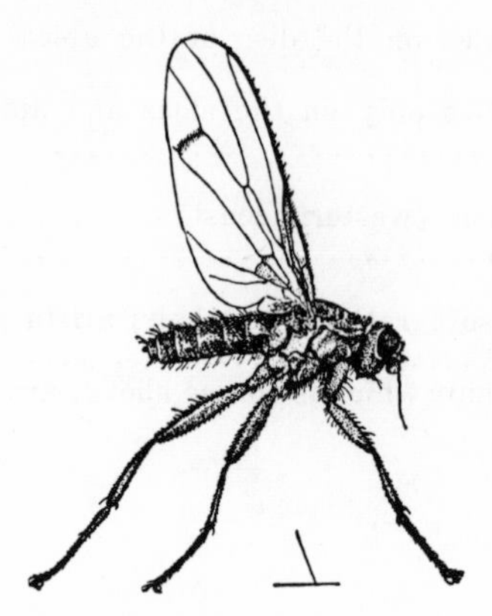

Pseudoleria pectinata Lœw.

Flies of moderate size, with oral vibrissæ.

Face vertical or retreating; front bristly on a little more than the posterior half; antennæ short, the third segment more or less rounded. Abdomen composed of six segments, the male genitalia conspicuous. Wings moderately large, the costa usually with short bristles; second basal and anal cells small; first vein bare. Tibiæ with preapical bristle.

The so-called frontal plates, characteristic of this family and poorly developed in most other families are actually a differentiated, broad, pollinose strip on either side of the front. They are slightly oblique, diverging from the eyes anteriorly and the frontal bristles are situated on them. The presence of these "plates", in conjunction with the shape of the antennæ serve as a ready means of identifying a Helomyzid.

The flies are found in various habitats, generally in shady or damp places. Adults have been collected by burying a tin can with its open end flush with the ground and examining it early in the morning.

The larvæ are scavengers and live upon decaying animal and vegetable substances, in fungi, excrement, etc. They are cylindrical, rather pointed anteriorly, obtuse behind; antennæ situated upon long conical processes; mouth hooks large; abdominal segments widened in front laterally, with bristly pseudopods ventrally.

Czerny* has monographed the family while Garrett and others have published papers dealing with the North American species since that time.

---

* 1924, Abh. zool.-bot. Gesellsch., Wien., xv. pp. 1-166; also, 1926, Konowia, v. pp. 53-56; 1927, Konowia, vi, pp. 35-49; 1928, Konowia, vii, pp. 52-55.

KEY TO GENERA

1. Propleural bristle absent; anal vein not reaching wing margin........ 2
   Propleural bristle present; anal vein reaching wing margin......... 4

2. Humeral bristle absent 3
   Humeral bristle present (12)............................**Allophyla** Lœw

3. Five pairs of dorsocentrals (15) ....**Suillia** Desvoidy
   One pair of dorsocentrals (14) ....**Porsenus** Darlington

4. Middle tibiæ with several bristles on dorsal surface 5
   Middle tibæ with only the preapical bristle dorsally.............. 6

5. Two pairs of fronto-orbitals; one pair of presutural dorsocentrals; wings usually mutilated (4, 16) ....**Criddleria** Curran
   One pair of fronto-orbitals; no presuturals; wings entire (10, 13). ****Œcothea** Haliday*

6. Pteropleura in part bristly or hairy............................. 7
   Pteropleura bare 9

7. Mesopleura hairy 8
   Mesopleura bare (8, 11)............................**Pseudoleria** Garrett

8. Prosternum with one pair of bristles ....**Scoliocentra** Lœw
   Prosternum with several bristles ....**Trichochlamys** Czerny

9. Humeral bristle present 10
   Humeral bristle absent; 3 pairs of scutellars...........**Orbellia** Desvoidy

10. Without prosternal bristles 13
    With one or more pairs of prosternals........................... 11

11. With one pair of prosternals 12
    With two or more pairs of prosternals (2) ....**Helomyza** Fallén

12. Anterior orbital bristle as long as the posterior........**Anypotacta** Czerny
    Anterior orbital bristle much shorter than the posterior (9). † **Amœbaleria** Garrett

13. Middle tibiæ with several apical bristles on ventral surface......... 15
    Middle tibiæ with only one apical bristle on ventral surface......... 14

14. First vein ending opposite or before the small crossvein (1, 6). **Tephrochlamys** Lœw
    First vein elongate, ending distinctly beyond the anterior crossvein. **Heteromyza** Fallén

15. Second vein joining the costa far beyond the tip of the first......... 16
    Second vein joining the costa only a little beyond the tip of the first. **Lutomyia** Aldrich

16. Third antennal segment more or less angulate dorsally; middle femora with several partial rows of bristles anteriorly; middle tarsi with spines at apices of segments 17
    Third antennal segment evenly rounded; otherwise different......... 18

* Czerny, 1928, Konowia, vii, p. 52.
† Czerny, 1927, Konowia, vi, p. 38.

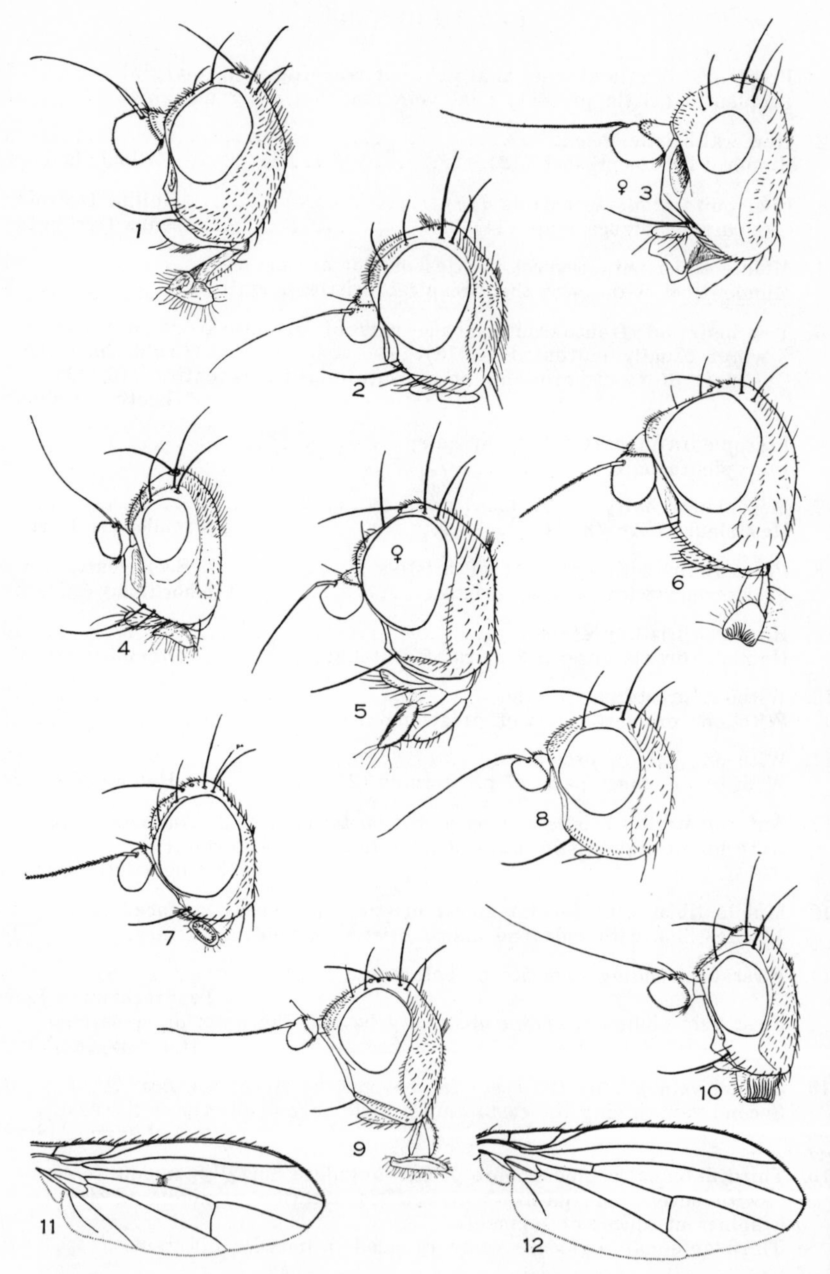

Helomyzidæ I.—1, **Tephrochlamys borealis**; 2, **Helomyza** sp.; 3, **Eccoptomera simplex**; 4, **Criddleria hemiptera**; 5, **Acantholeria** sp.; 6, **Tephrochlamys canescens**; 7, **Neoleria leucostoma**; 8, **Pseudoleria pectinata**; 9, **Amœbaleria helvola**; 10, **Œcothea fenestralis**; 11, **Pseudoleria pectinata**; 12, **Allophyla** sp.

17. One frontal bristle; eyes very small (3) ....**Eccoptomera** Lœw
    Two frontals; eyes of moderate size ....**Viatica** Garrett

18. Anterior frontal bristle much shorter than the posterior............ 19
    Anterior frontal bristle as long as the posterior (**Postleria** Garrett) (7) ....**Neoleria** Malloch

19. Mesopleura wholly bare 20
    Mesopleura with some bristles posteriorly **(17, 18)**....***Anorostoma** Lœw

20. Antennal grooves distinct ....**Schrœderella** Enderlein
    Antennal grooves not distinctly outlined 21

21. Antennæ separated from each other by about half the width of the third antennal segment ....**Morpholeria** Garrett
    Antennæ separated from each other by more than the width of the third antennal segment (5)......................**Acantholeria** Garrett

* Czerny, 1927, Konowia, vi, p. 36; Curran, 1933, Amer. Mus. Novit. No. 676, pp. 1-9.

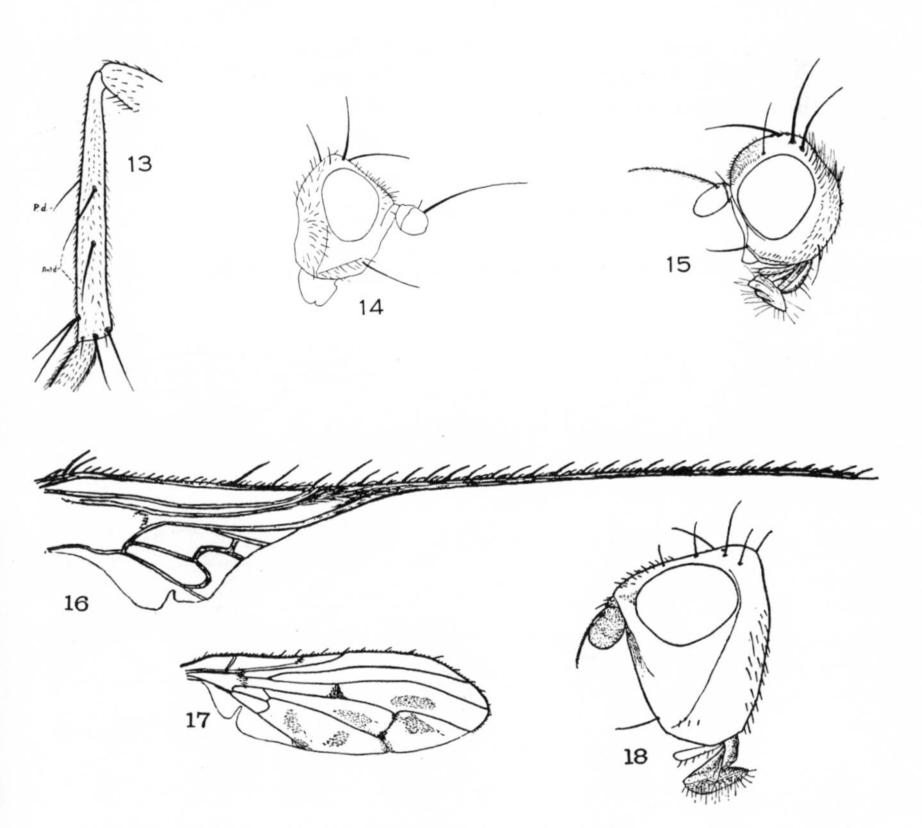

Helomyzidæ II.—13, **Œcothea fenestralis**; 14, **Porsenus johnsoni**; 15, **Suillia fuscicornis**; 16, **Criddleria hemiptera**; 17, 18, **Anorostoma cinereum**.

Family Dryomyzidæ

Flies of moderate size, the femora without bristles.

Head short, as broad or broader than the thorax, the face retreating, more or less perpendicular below, without oral vibrissæ. Abdomen composed of six segments, moderately long and narrow, more or less cylindrical. Wings longer than the abdomen, the auxiliary vein separated from the first vein; posterior basal and anal cells complete. Legs of moderate length, the tibiæ with a preapical bristle.

The adults are found in moist places, along the edges of streams, ponds, etc. Swampy woods are excellent collecting spots.

The larvæ are aquatic. They are slender, cylindrical, thin anteriorly, the terminal segment with six or eight conical, fleshy tubercles.

The flies placed in this family have been included in the Tetanoceridæ and Helomyzidæ. From the former they are separated by the absence of femoral bristles and from the latter by the absence of oral vibrissæ. The latest revision of the family is by Melander* who included the genera in the Tetanoceridæ.

* Review of the Nearctic Tetanoceridæ, 1916, Ann. Ent. Soc. Amer., xiii, pp. 305-322.

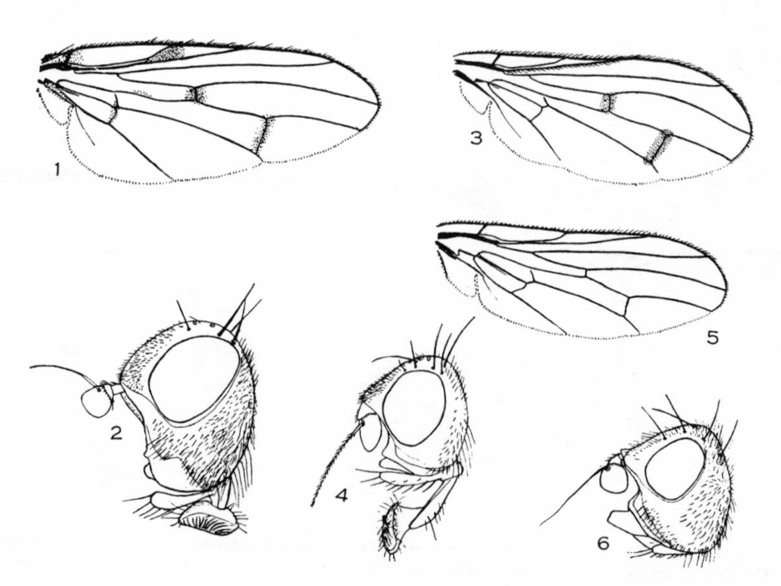

Dryomyzidæ.—1, 2, **Macromelanderia mirabilis**; 3, 4, **Neuroctena anilis**; 5, 6, **Œdoparena glauca.**

KEY TO GENERA

1. First longitudinal vein bristled (3, 4) .... **Neuroctena** Rondani
   First vein wholly bare 2

2. Only two pairs of scutellar bristles 3
   Three pairs of scutellars (**Œdoparea glauca** Coquillett) (5, 6).
   Œdoparena, n. g.

3. Costa not bristled 4
   Costa with conspicuous short bristles on the apical half (**Helcomyza mirabilis** Melander) (1, 2) .... **Macromelanderia,** n. g.

4. Two pairs of dorsocentrals; face concave .... **Dryomyza** Fallén
   At least seven pairs of dorsocentrals; face not concave in profile.
   Heterocheila Rondani

Family Muscidæ

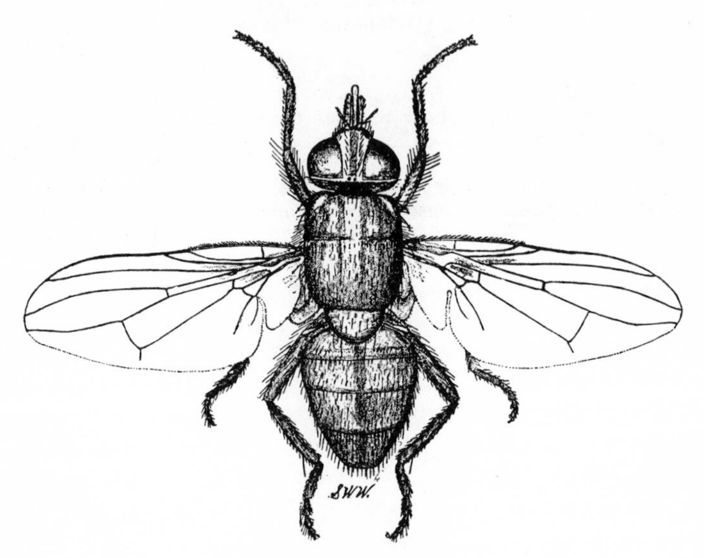

Lyperosia irritans L.

Flies of medium to small size, usually dull colored, the squamæ large or of medium size, hypopleural bristles absent, the second antennal segment grooved above.

Arista plumose, pubescent, bare or pectinate, eyes approximate or widely separated in the males, the front rarely narrowed in both sexes; frontal bristles always present, intrafrontals frequently present; orbitals developed but rarely in the males. Abdomen composed of four segments in the male, five in the female. Male genitalia usually not prominent but sometimes conspicuous; fifth sternal lobes sometimes prominent.

As here understood this family includes the Scatophagidæ, Anthomyidæ and those Muscidæ (of the Williston Manual) lacking hypopleural bristles. In some cases the hypopleura is haired but there need be no question in connection with known North American genera about intergradation with the Metopiidæ. There is no means by which the Scatophagidæ can be separated from the Anthomyidæ, unless the size of the lower lobe of the squamæ is used, in which case the genus *Anthomyia* must be associated with the Scatophagids while many of the other genera would form a different family. Wing venation is not a character to be used in separating families in this group, nor can the character of the plumosity of the arista be used.

The Muscidæ are found everywhere and many of them are serious pests. The raddish maggot, cabbage maggot, onion maggot, seed corn maggot, and many others take annual toll of our crops. So much has been written about the house fly as a carrier of disease that only a brief review need be given here. Others are pests of domestic animals and also pay attention to man. The Tse-tse flies, formerly considered as belonging to this family, and not greatly distinct at best, are carriers of trypanosomes causing sleeping sickness.

Many entomologists believe that the *House Fly* (*Musca domestica*) has been responsible for more human suffering than any other insect and the evidence in support of this is very strong. It is said that deaths due to diseases carried by flies have exceeded those caused by wounds during the wars preceding the world war (1914-1918), whereas during this latter conflict the mortality from such diseases was negligible, due to efficient sanitary practices. The House Fly breeds in manure, garbage and almost any decaying matter and its control consists of the screening and disposal of such material at frequent intervals. Manure should be kept, as much as possible, either on such a maggot trap as recommended by Hutchison*, sprayed occasionally with a mixture of one pound of powdered hellebore to twenty gallons of water at the rate of one gallon of the spray to one cubic foot of manure, or sprinkled with powdered borax at the rate of one pound to 16 cubic feet of manure. The borax treatment must not be repeated, the fresh manure being piled in such a way that it may be treated separately. All garbage should be destroyed at least twice a week.

Because the House Fly feeds on filth of all kinds and visits our foodstuffs, alighting with impunity upon the things we would eat, it is particularly loathsome. It is attracted to almost anything that is moist, such as sputum, feces, garbage, etc., and may fly directly from any of these to food used for human consumption. The diseases carried on its body (in the form of the causative organisms) are *Typhoid Fever, Dysentery, Cholera, Yaws, Anthrax* and some forms of *Conjunctivitis.* Many other bacteria, some of them undoubtedly capable of causing disease, are also carried.

In addition to destroying the breeding places of flies efforts should be made to prevent them from coming in contact with foodstuffs by screening all buildings. Sickrooms should be particularly well screened in order to prevent flies from carrying the disease to other individuals.

---

* U. S. Dept. Agric. Bull. 200, 1915.

The *Stable Fly* (*Stomoxys calcitrans*) is a biting insect and is sometimes known as the *Biting House Fly*. It is not a general visitor in houses but may be common in yards and on porches near stables, and is most active in the hot sun. It is also a pest on beaches and along streams on bright, sunny days. It breeds in manure and decaying vegetation so may be controlled by measures taken against the House Fly. Domestic animals suffer greatly from its bites and milk production may be greatly reduced when the fly is abundant. The flies enter the stable on cattle and horses and many of them remain there over night. Use of a fly spray in stables will greatly reduce their numbers. The view has been expressed that infantile paralysis is carried by this fly but the accusation has not been proved. However, under certain conditions it may transmit sleeping sickness.

The *Horn Fly* (*Lyperosia irritans*) so named because of its habit of feeding about the base of the horns of cattle, is also a biting fly. It rarely attacks man.

The classification of this family is still in an unstable condition and it is seldom that two authors use the same generic limits and very frequently different names are used for the same generic concept. Unfortunately several of the genera are not available for study and I have been forced to include about a score of them from descriptions only, while four of those recorded from North America are excluded. A half dozen genera occurring in South America and not yet recognized from our region are keyed out as it is likely that they occur in the tropics. In one or two cases the characters I have used will change the limits of genera, and I have recognized as genera groups sometimes considered to be no more than subgenera.

In order to facilitate the use of the Key I have prepared a synoptic key leading to the main subdivisions employed.

SYNOPTIC TABLE

A. With at most one sternopleural bristle.............................. 1
   With two or more sternopleurals .... B

B. Anal vein extending to the wing-margin.............................. 39
   Anal vein not extending to the wing-margin.......................... C

C. Arista plumose, pubescent or bare................................... D
   Arista pectinate, without rays below................................144

D. First vein setulose on most of its length........................... 77
   First vein bare beyond the humeral crossvein........................ E

E. Pteropleura haired 83
Pteropleura bare .... F

F. One pair of presutural dorsocentral bristles.......................... 98
More than one pair of presutural dorsocentrals.......................106

KEY TO GENERA.

1. With at most one sternopleural (c. f. **Lispoides**)................. 2
With two to four sternopleurals.. 38

2. Pteropleura bare 8
Pteropleura haired 3

3. Anterior tibiæ without abundant ventral setulæ.................. 4
Anterior tibiæ beneath with abundant black setulæ..*__Allomyella__ Malloch

4. First vein bare 5
First vein setulose apically; sixth vein not reaching wing margin.
Dasypleuron Malloch

5. Sixth vein reaching wing margin 6
Sixth vein not reaching wing margin...........**Eugenacephala** Johnson

6. With distinct sternopleural bristle 7
Without sternopleural bristle; wings with several brown spots.
Ernoneura Becker

7. Propleural bristle long and strong; arista short plumose on whole length .... †**Megaphthalma** Becker
Propleural bristle very weak or absent; arista long plumose or bare (33) ....**Scopeuma** Latreille

8. Head at least as high as long; face at most moderately retreating.... 11
Head decidedly longer than high, the face strongly retreating below.. 9

9. Stigmatal bristle absent 10
Stigmatal bristle strong ....**Paratidia** Malloch

10. Third antennal segment with a fine, long hair on the outer surface near the insertion of the arista (41)............‡**Acicephala** Coquillett
Third antennal segment without such hair.....‡**Pseudacicephala** Malloch

11. Hypopleura never with bristles 12
Hypopleura with a row of bristles; costa ending at third vein, the fourth vein incomplete; front half as wide as head (Eginiinæ). (52, 59) ....§**Lutzomyia,** n. g.

12. Frontal bristles or hair long 13
Frontal bristles extremely short, the front nearly bare (40).
Hydromyza Fallén

---

* Curran, 1927, Can. Ent., lix, p. 260.

† Curran, 1933, Amer. Mus. Novit. No. 682, p. 10.

‡ Curran, 1927, Can. Ent., lix, p. 259 (**Acicephala**).

§ Differs from **Eginiella** Malloch (China) in having the front of the male half as wide as the head and in lacking bristles on the legs, with the exception of the apical tibial bristles. **Lutzomyia americana,** n. sp. from Arizona.

13. Anterior tibiæ without a short, rectangular apical spine below....... 14
    Anterior tibiæ with a short, stout, rectangular spine at apex of ventral surface ....*Acanthocnema Becker

14. Anteroventral surface of the anterior femora and tibiæ without stout bristles, the front tibiæ rarely with a single bristle on this surface. 15
    Anteroventral surface of the anterior femora and tibiæ with stout bristles .... **Norellia** Desvoidy

15. Prothoracic bristle always, the stigmatic usually, present............ 16
    Prothoracic and stigmatic bristles absent......................... 28

16. Palpi long and slender, armed at the apex with a long, outstanding bristle 17
    Palpi more or less broadened, without an outstanding bristle........ 20

17. Third vein not sinuate.. 18
    Third vein rather strongly sinuate.................**Scoliaphleps** Becker

18. Stigmatal bristle weak or hair-like, usually absent................. 19
    Stigmatal bristle strong (**46, 60**)........................**Cordilura** Fallén

19. Eyes round ....**Neogymnomera** Malloch
    Eyes with a slight emargination on the lower posterior half......... 36

* Curran, 1929, Can. Ent., lxi, p. 132.

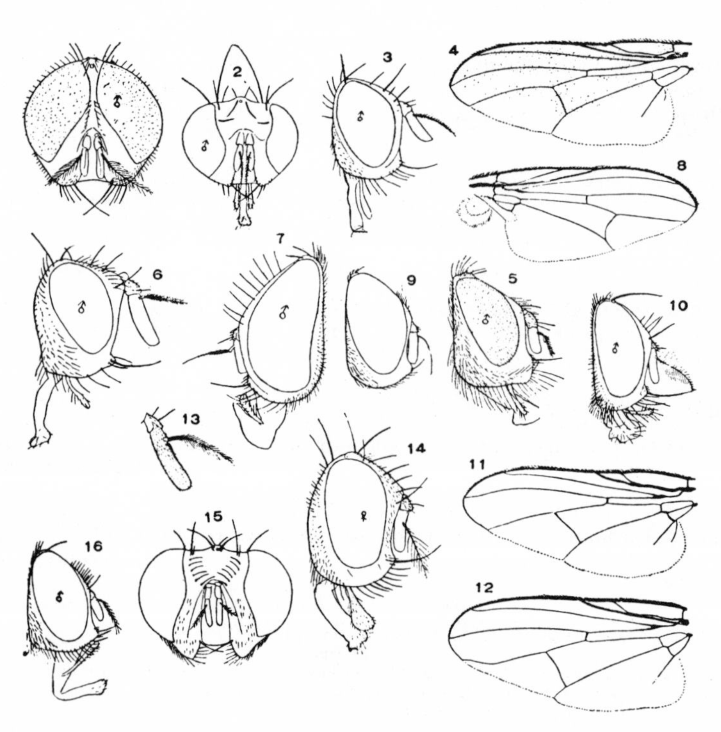

Muscidæ I.—1, **Helina lucorum**; 2, **Schœnomyza chcrysostoma**; 3, **Limosia**; 4, 5, **Lasiops spiniger**; 6, **Phyllogaster cordyluroides**; 7, 8, **Fannia**; 9, **Ophyra ænescens**; 10, **Helina**; 11, **Spilaria**; 12, **Pseudolimnophora**; 13, **Pseudolimnophora**, antenna; 14, 15, **Lispe**; 16, **Limnophora**.

20. Cheeks usually less than one-third the eye-height; face as long as the front or nearly so.... 21
Cheeks more than half as wide as the eye-height; face shorter than the front, slightly retreating below; intra-alar bristles absent; scutellum with four bristles.... **Gimnomera** Rondani

21. First vein bare.... 24
First vein setulose on apical portion.... 22

22. Scutellum with six bristles.... **Bucephalina** Malloch
Scutellum with four bristles.... 23

23. Palpi strongly widened and spatulate.... ***Cordylurella** Malloch
Palpi but little widened.... **Megaphthalma** Becker

24. Anal vein extending to the wing margin.... 26
Anal vein not reaching the wing margin.... 25

25. Third antennal segment four times as long as wide. **Micropselapha** Becker
Third antennal segment less than three times as long as wide. **Cordylurella** Malloch

26. With two or more rows of acrostical hairs.... 27
Without acrostical hairs.... **Cordilura** Fallén

27. With more than two rows of acrostical hairs (57)... **Ceratinostoma** Meade
With only two rows of acrostical hairs.... **Opsiomyia** Coquillett

28. Third antennal segment angulate at upper apex.... 29
Third antennal segment rounded apically.... 33

29. Acrostical setæ in two rows.... 30
Acrostical setæ in several rows (34).... **Spaziphora** Rondani

30. Anterior tibiæ clothed beneath with dense, black setulæ.... 31
Anterior tibiæ not clothed beneath with dense, black setulæ.... 32

31. Male wing broadly emarginate between the fourth and fifth veins. **Pleurochæta** Becker
Male wing normal in outline.... **Pogonota** Zetterstedt

32. Palpi spoon shaped, narrow basally.... **Pseudopogonota** Malloch
Palpi broad, tapering basally but the base broad.... **Trichopalpus** Rondani

33. Mesopleura with an extensive bare area above the anterior coxæ.... 34
Mesopleura haired on almost the whole surface (33).. **Scopeuma** Latreille

34. Fourth vein strongly approaching the third at the wing-tip. **Lasioscelus** Becker
Fourth vein not strongly approaching the third apically.... 35

35. Anterior tibiæ without dense, short setulæ beneath.... 36
Anterior tibiæ with dense, short setulæ beneath.... **Microprosopa** Becker

36. Anal vein almost reaching the wing margin (39)..... **Achætella** Malloch
Anal vein not nearly reaching the wing margin.... 37

37. Arista plumose or very long pubescent.... **Parallelomma** Becker
Arista pubescent .... **Americina** Malloch

* Curran, 1929, Can. Ent., lxi, p. 133.

38. Anal vein extending to the margin of the wing, at least weakly...... 39
    Anal vein never extending to the margin of the wing............... 75

39. Under surface of the scutellum with fine, soft, erect hairs........... 51
    Under surface of the scutellum bare................................ 40

40. Three sternopleurals 44
    Two sternopleurals (cf. **Fucellia**)................................ 41

41. Upper apex of third antennal segment acute or angulate; scutellum with four bristles... 42
    Third antennal segment rounded apically; scutellum with one pair of marginals 43

42. Arista thickened on basal half, its penultimate segment much longer than wide (43).............................. **Pselaphephila** Becker
    Arista thickened on basal fourth, its penultimate segment short. **Chætosa** Coquillett

43. Three pairs of postsutural dorsocentral bristles....**Hexamitocera** Becker
    Two pairs of postsutural dorsocentral bristles......**Cleigastra** Macquart

44. Scutellum with one or two pairs of marginal bristles; palpi without long outstanding apical bristle.................................. 45
    Scutellum with six marginals; palpi with strong apical bristle. **Plethochæta** Coquillett

45. First vein bare 46
    First vein setulose on apical third (38).............**Orthacheta** Becker

46. Anterior femora without strong bristles on the anterior surface...... 47
    Anterior femora with strong bristles on the anterior surface, propleura haired ....*****Amaurosoma** Becker

* Curran, 1927, Can. Ent., lix, p. 293.

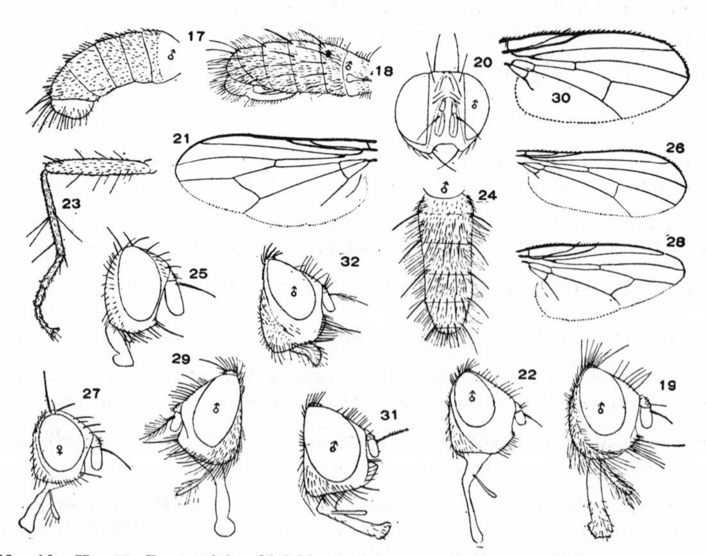

Muscidæ II.—17, **Pentacricia aldrichi**, ♂ abdomen; 18, **Eremomyia humeralis**, ♂ abdomen; 19, **Eremomyia humeralis**; 20, **Neodexiopsis**; 21, 22, **Hammomya**; 23, **Coenosia**, hind leg; 24, **Hylemya**, abdomen; 25, **Tetrachæta unica**; 26, **Hoplogaster**; 27, **Pegomya bicolor**; 28, 29, **Hydrophoria divisa**; 30, **Platycœnosia pokornyi**; 31, 32, **Hylemya**.

47. Palpi short, normal.. 48
Palpi very long; stigmatal bristle strong..........**Pselaphephila** Becker

48. Front with intrafrontal bristles in both sexes........................ 50
Front without intrafrontal bristles.. 49

49. Third antennal segment sharply angulate at upper apex; arista distinctly elbowed ....**Gonatherus** Rondani
Third antennal segment obtusely angulate or rounded; arista never elbowed ....**Mesamyia** Malloch

50. Acrosticals strong but short, paired.................****Fucellia** Desvoidy
Acrosticals fine, short and irregular..................**Myopina** Desvoidy

51. Pteropleura bare† 54
Pteropleura with hair or bristles.. 52

52. Pteropleura with a single bristle................**Emmesomyia** Malloch
Pteropleura with several hairs.. 53

53. Propleura bare..**Tæniomyia** Stein
Propleura haired on the median portion........‡**Eremomyioides** Malloch

54. Eyes bare 55
Eyes haired ....**Alliopsis** Schnabl & Dziedzicki

55. Propleura bare in the middle.. 57
Propleura haired on the median portion.................................. 56

56. Arista bare ....**Kingiella** Malloch
Arista distinctly plumose........................§**Anthomyia** Meigen

57. Arista plumose 58
Arista pubescent or bare.. 61

58. Scutellum cinerous, with an opaque black spot on either side.
Eustalomyia Kowarz
Scutellum without opaque black spot on either side................ 59

59. Lower lobe of the squamæ conspicuously longer than the upper (28, 29) ....¶**Hydrophoria** Desvoidy
Lower lobe of the squamæ not as large as the upper.............. 60

60. Proboscis elongate and slender, as long as the thorax or nearly so... 61
Proboscis short and thick, not nearly as long as the thorax......... 62

61. Arista pubescent ....**Proboscimyia** Bigot
Arista long plumose..............................**Neohylemyia** Malloch

62. Hypopleura haired in front of the posterior spiracle.
Calythea Schnabl & Dziedzicki
Hypopleura bare in front of the posterior spiracle.................. 63

63. Anterior tibiæ with an extremely long dorsal bristle at the apical fourth in the male and with two or three strong dorsal bristles at the apical fifth in the female...................**Anthomyella** Malloch
Anterior tibiæ without such bristles...................................... 64

* Aldrich, 1918, Proc.-Calif. Acad. Acad. Sci., viii, p. 160.

† The genera in couplets 51 to 74 comprise the Anthomyinæ. Keys to the Eastern species will be found in Huckett, Cornell Uni. Agr. Exp. Sta. Mem. 77.

‡ Malloch, 1920, Can. Ent. liii, p. 76.

§ Malloch, 1924, Ann. Mag. Nat. Hist., xiv, p. 267.

¶ Malloch, 1920, Can. Ent. liii, p. 103.

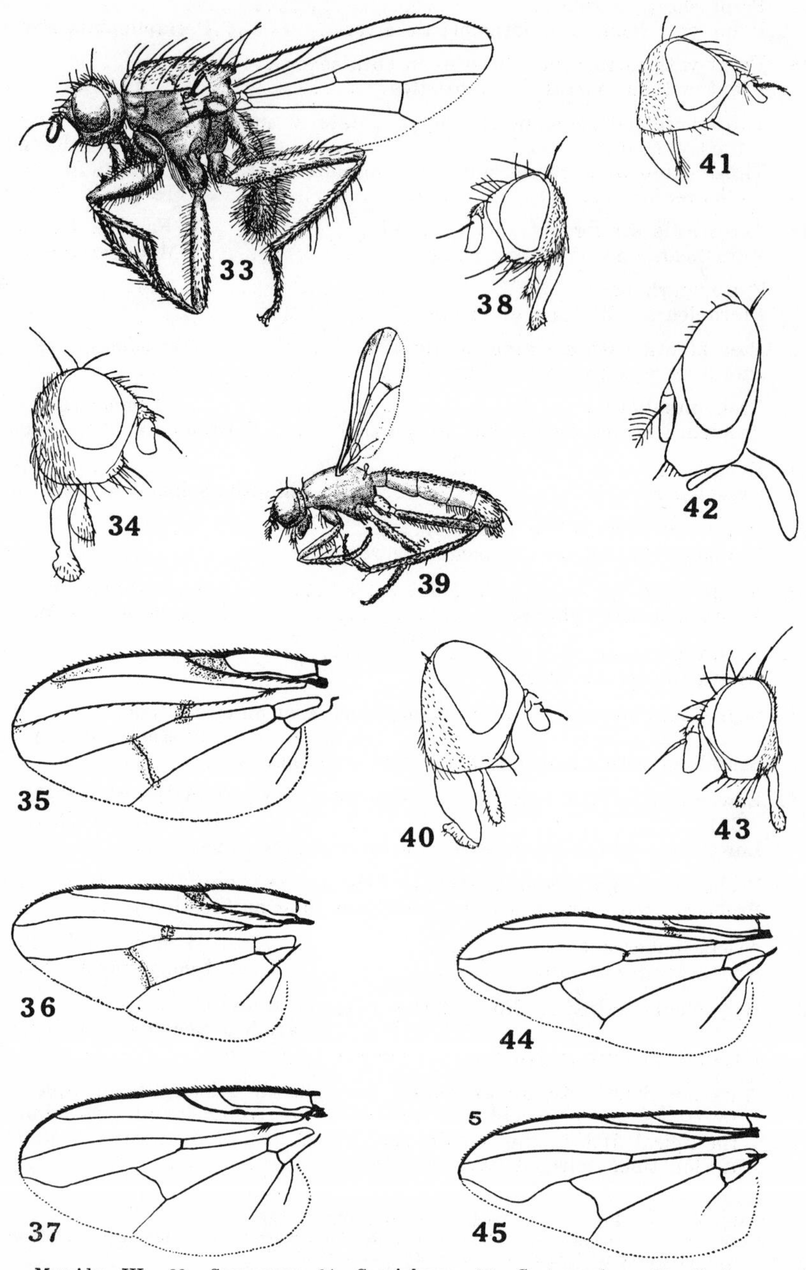

Muscidæ III.—33, **Scopeuma**; 34, **Spaziphora**; 35, **Cyrtoneurina**; 36, **Cyrtoneuropsis rescita**; 37, **Myospila meditabunda**; 38, **Orthacheta**; 39, **Achætella varipes**; 40, **Hydromyza confluens**; 41, **Acicephala polita**, hair on third antennal segment not shown; 42, **Morellia**; 43, **Pselaphelphila**; 44, **Morellia**; 45, **Graphomya maculata**.

64. Facial depression with almost parallel sides on more than the lower half or conspicuously narrower between the vibrissæ than at the middle 65
Facial depression widening below, wider at the vibrissæ than at a point above the middle 66

65. No bristly hairs on posteroventral surface of posterior tibiæ in male; ovipositor not terminating in two or more spines (27).
*Pegomya Desvoidy
A series of long hairs on posteroventral surface of hind tibiæ; ovipositor bearing two or more apical spines (21, 22).
Hammomya Rondani

66. Antennæ separated from each other by a distinct elevation which continues onto the face..........†**Egle** Desvoidy
Antennæ not conspicuously separated from each other at the base.... 67

67. Oral margin strongly produced, the hairs surrounding the vibrissæ extending well onto the sides of the face..........**Macateeia** Malloch
Oral margin not unusually produced, the hairs not extending onto the face 68

68. Middle tibiæ with anteroventral bristle near the middle.
Paregle Schnabl & Dziedzicki
Middle tibiæ without such bristle.......... 69

69. Three pairs of postsutural dorsocentrals.......... 70
Four pairs of postsutural dorsocentrals..........**Macrophorbia** Malloch

70. Proboscis unusually stout..........**Pycnoglossa** Coquillett
Proboscis not unusually robust.......... 71

71. Posterior tibiæ with two long bristles near the middle, on the upper surface, each at least half as long as the tibia...**Prosalpia** Pokorny
Posterior tibiæ without such bristles.......... 72

72. Sides of the scutellum with more than a single row of hairs below the marginals; interfrontals absent in both sexes; posthumeral and anterior sublateral bristles equally strong (18, 19)..**Eremomyia** Stein
Not with this combination of characters.......... 73

73. Eyes of males broadly separated; acrosticals hair-like and short.
Chirosia Rondani
Eyes of males approximate, very rarely separated by much more than the distance between the posterior ocelli.......... 74

74. Posterior tibiæ without posterodorsal bristles, or with two (27).
‡**Pegomya** Desvoidy
Posterior tibiæ with one posterodorsal bristle or with more than two (24, 31, 32)..........§**Hylemya** Desvoidy

75. Arista plumose, pubescent or bare.......... 76
Arista pectinate, with rays on the upper side..........144

76. First vein setose, on most of its length.......... 77
First vein bare, or with setulæ only before the humeral crossvein.... 82

---

* Malloch, 1920, Bull. Brooklyn Ent. Soc., xv, p. 121.
† Malloch, 1920, Can. Ent., liii, p. 77.
‡ Malloch, 1920, Bull. Brooklyn Ent. Soc., xv, p. 121.
§ Malloch, 1920, Ohio Journ. Sci., xx, p. 274.

77. Apex of posterior coxæ haired behind............**Chætogenia** Malloch
    Posterior coxæ bare behind.. 78

78. Prosternum setose... 80
    Prosternum bare... 79

79. Arista short plumose ....**Steinella** Malloch
    Arista long plumose (36).....................**Cyrtoneuropsis** Malloch

80. Fourth vein curved forward apically............................... 81
    Fourth vein not curved forward apically............**Smithomyia** Malloch

81. Posterior tibiæ with a strong posterodorsal bristle near the apical third ....**Pœcilophaonia** Malloch
    Posterior tibiæ without calcar (35)............**Cyrtoneurina** Giglio-Tos

82. Pteropleura haired 83
    Pteropleura bare 97

83. Propleura haired in the middle.................................... 84
    Propleura bare in the middle...................................... 85

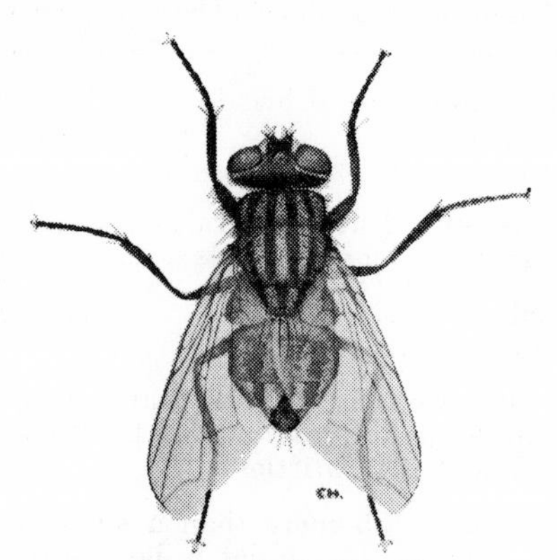

Musca domestica L.

84. Fourth vein ending well before the apex of the wing....**Musca** Linnæus
    Fourth vein ending well behind the apex of the wing.**Mallocharia** Curran

85. Proboscis tapering from the base, long, adapted for biting (as in **Stomoxys**) ....**Hæmatobosca** Bezzi
    Proboscis short and stout, the labellæ large...................... 86

86. Ridge at inner edge of lower squamal lobe bare.................... 88
    Ridge at inner edge of lower squamal lobe with hairs.............. 87

87. Fourth vein ending before the wing-tip...........**Orthellia** Desvoidy
    Fourth veing ending behind the wing-tip (51, 54)...* **Philornis** Macquart

88. Fourth vein ending distinctly behind the wing-tip................. 90
    Fourth vein ending distinctly before the wing-tip................. 89

89. Middle tibiæ with a strong anteroventral bristle beyond the middle. **Pyrellia** Desvoidy
    Middle tibiæ without anteroventral bristle beyond the middle (42, 44). †**Morellia** Desovidy

* Aldrich, 1923, Ann. Ent. Soc. Amer., xvi, p. 308.
† Malloch, 1923, Ann. Mag. Nat. Hist., xii, pp. 520, 523.

90. Prosterntum bare 93
Prosternum haired 91

91. First vein with setulæ opposite the humeral crossvein...**Clinopera** Wulp
First vein bare above on the whole length........................ 92

92. Facial depression extremely deep, with almost parallel sides; cheeks wide (**49, 53**)..................................**Charadrella** Wulp
Facial depression very shallow, widening below; cheeks narrow (**55**). **Dichætomyia** Malloch

93. Palpi spatulate, flattened, always strongly widening apically (**14, 15**). ***Lispe** Latreille
Palpi not unusually widened, not flattened apically................. 94

94. Calcar present 95
Posterior tibiæ without strong posterodorsal bristle beyond the middle.104

95. Fourth vein very strongly curved forward at the apex............. 96
Fourth vein not curved forward at the apex...**Pseudophaonia** Malloch

96. Third and fourth veins equidistant from the wing-tip. **Hypodermodes** Knab
Fourth vein ending far behind the wing-tip......**Mesembrina** Meigen

97. A single pair of presutural dorsocentral bristles.................. 98
Two pairs of presutural dorsocentrals or they are absent..........106

98. Lower lobe of the squamæ much longer than the upper............100
Lower lobe of the squamæ scarcely longer than the upper.......... 99

99. Front decidedly longer than wide (**26**)...........†**Hoplogaster** Rondani
Front wider than long, narrowing anteriorly (**2**)..†**Schœnomyza** Haliday

100. Costa extending to the fourth vein.............................101
Costa ending at the third vein or a little beyond......**Allognota** Pokorny

101. Three postsutural dorsocentrals..................................102
Two pairs of postsutural dorsocentrals............**Bithoracochæta** Stein

102. Posterior tibiæ with three long median bristles, one on the posterodorsal surface although this latter may be short................103
Posterior tibiæ without a single posterodorsal bristle at the middle, sometimes with two posterodorsals..............................104

103. Anterior tibiæ with an anterodorsal beyond the middle. **Macrocœnosia** Malloch
Anterior tibiæ without an anterodorsal bristle (**20**).‡**Neodexiopsis** Malloch

104. Posterior tibiæ with an anteroventral bristle.......................105
Posterior tibæ without an anteroventral bristle....‡**Xenocœnosia** Malloch

105. Posterior tibiæ with a long anterodorsal and long anterior bristle situated very close to each other (**23**).............§**Coenosia** Meigen
Posterior tibiæ with anterodorsal and anteroventral bristle, their bases not close together (**3**)......................¶**Limosia** Desvoidy

---

* Aldrich, 1913, Journ. N. Y. Ent. Soc., xxi, p. 131.
† Huckett, 1934, Trans. Amer. Ent. Soc., lx, pp. 87, 106.
‡ Huckett, 1934, Trans. Amer. Ent. Soc., lx, p. 74 (**Neodexiopsis**).
§ Huckett, 1934, Trans. Amer. Ent. Soc., lx, p. 83.
¶ Huckett, 1934, Trans. Amer. Ent. Soc., lx, p. 135.

106. Sternopleural bristles situated in a nearly equilateral triangle, almost always three in number....................................107
Sternopleurals not forming a nearly equilateral triangle, if only three are present the lower one is decidedly farther from the anterior...111

107. Dorsocentrals very weak, poorly differentiated......**Atherigona** Rondani
Dorsocentrals strong 108

108. Anterior tibiæ with a posterior bristle near or beyond the middle...109
Anterior tibiæ without posterior bristle except at apex.
Lispocephala Pokorny

109. Four sternopleurals, the posterior three in a straight line.
Macrorchis Rondani
Three sternopleurals 110

110. Posterior bristle on front tibiæ very long, situated before the middle.
Dialyta Meigen
Posterior bristle on front tibiæ short, situated beyond the middle.
Limnospila Schnabl

111. Sixth vein very short, the seventh curved strongly forward so that it would bisect the sixth only a little beyond the end of the latter...112
Sixth vein not unusually short, the seventh never curved so that it would bisect the sixth..114

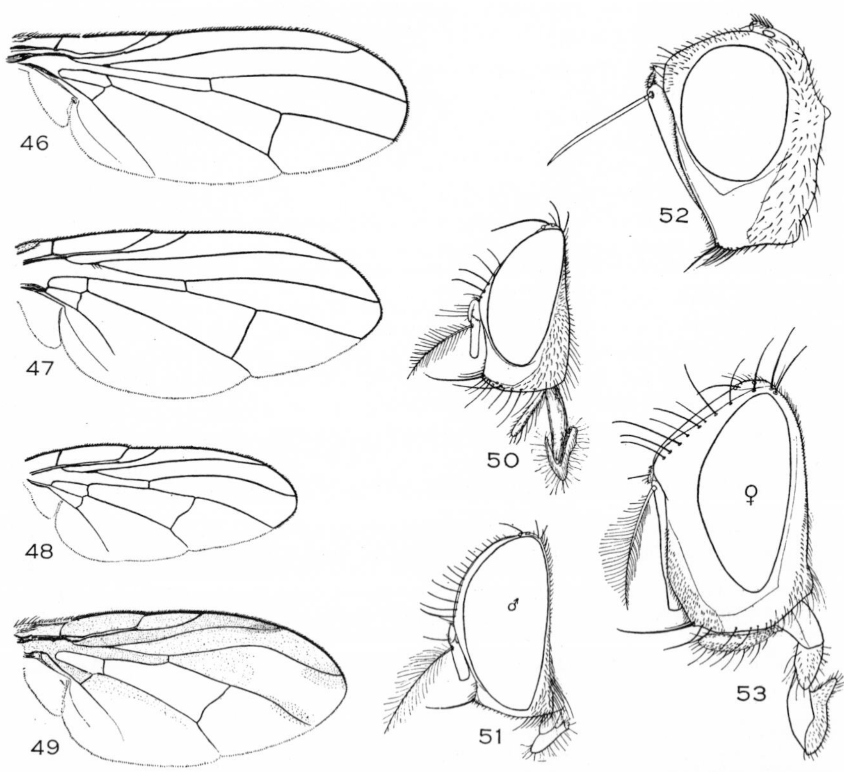

Muscidæ IV.—46, **Cordilura**; 47, **Limnophora**; 48, **Phaonia**; 49, **Charadrella macrosoma**; 50, **Phaonia**; 51, **Philornis spermophilæ**; 52, **Lutzomyia latifrons**; 53, **Charadrella macrosoma.**

112. Posterior tibiæ with dorsal bristle near or somewhat beyond the middle, or with two posterodorsal bristles..........................113
Posterior tibiæ without dorsal or posterodorsal bristles..**Azelia** Desvoidy

113. Eyes of male very broadly separated; posterior tibiæ sometimes with two posterodorsal bristles and without the dorsal....**Euryomma** Stein
Eyes of male approximate, the front at least narrowed; dorsal tibial bristle always present **(7, 8)**......................***Fannia** Desvoidy

114. Proboscis long and narrow, widened basally, adapted for blood-sucking ....**Bdellolarynx** Austen
Proboscis short and thick, the labellæ fleshy.........................115

115. Prosternum bare 119
Prosternum haired laterally 116

116. Posterior thoracal spiracle long and narrow.
Synthesiomyia Brauer & Bergenstamm
Posterior thoracal spiracle little longer than wide.................117

117. Hypopleura hairy in front of and below the spiracle...**Ariciella** Malloch
Hypopleura bare 118

118. Basal abdominal sternite bare **(16, 47)**..........†**Limnophora** Desvoidy
Basal abdominal sternite with several hairs **(12, 13)**.
†**Pseudolimnophora** Schnabl

119. Third vein with setæ basally on the upper margin or before the furcation 120
Third vein bare above 122

120. Lower lobe of the squamæ large, its inner end reaching the base of the scutellum (45)..........................**Graphomya** Desvoidy
Lower squamal lobe narrow, not produced inwardly.................121

121. Fourth vein ending in the wing tip or very close to it **(37, 56)**.
Myospila Rondani
Fourth vein ending far behind the wing tip, not conspicuously curved forward apically ....‡**Mydæa** Desvoidy

122. Posterior coxæ bare behind at apex...............................124
Posterior coxæ with hairs behind at apex..........................123

123. Eyes pilose (4, 5)...............................§**Lasiops** Meigen
Eyes bare ....**Allœostylus** Schnabl

124. Fourth vein strongly curved forward apically......................125
Fourth vein not or very slightly curved forward apically...........127

125. Fourth vein ending well behind the tip of the wing................126
Fourth vein ending before the tip of the wing.
Pararicia Brauer & Bergenstamm

126. Posterior spiracle twice as long as wide, with black hairs extending over the lower flap..............................**Muscina** Desvoidy
Posterior spiracle not nearly twice as long as wide..**Bigotomyia** Malloch

127. Posterior tibiæ, posterodorsally, bare or with two or more bristles..129
Posterior tibiæ with only the calcar, rarely with a very short posterodorsal bristle near the base...................................128

128. Cheeks below with two to five upwardly curving bristles on the anterior half ....**Dendrophaonia** Malloch
Cheeks with at most one upwardly curving bristle..................133

* Malloch, 1924, Ann. Mag. Nat. Hist., xiii, p. 416; xiv, p. 515.
† Huckett, 1932, Journ. N. Y. Ent. Soc., xl, pp. 25-76, 105-158, 279-325.
‡ Malloch, 1923, Can. Ent., lvi, p. 220.
§ Malloch, 1920, Can. Ent., liii, p. 272 (**Trichopticus**).

129. Front with an outwardly directed orbital bristle, wide in both sexes (30) .... **Platycœnosia** Strobl
Front without true orbital bristles, or they are not divergent; usually narrow in males 130

130. Parafrontals polished; frontal lunule shining white; thorax and abdomen without pollen (9) .... ***Ophyra** Desvoidy
Parafrontals pollinose on most of their length 131

131. Hypopleura haired below the spiracle (11).
†**Spilaria** Schnabl & Dziedzicki
Hypopleura bare below the spiracle 132

132. Hypopleura haired in front of the spiracle (1, 10) ...... †**Helina** Desvoidy
Hypopleura bare in front of the spiracle 136

133. Arista pubescent 134
Arista with long rays (48, 50) .... ‡**Phaonia** Desvoidy

134. Hypopleura bare in front of the spiracle 135
Hypopleura haired in front of the spiracle .... **Achætina** Malloch

135. Prealar more than half as long as the following bristle.
Neohydrotæa Malloch
Prealar less than half as long as the following bristle.
§**Hydrotæa** Desvoidy

---

* Malloch, 1923, Ann. Mag. Nat. Hist., xi, p. 664.
† Malloch, 1920, Can. Ent., liii, p. 103.
‡ Malloch, 1923, Tr. Amer. Ent. Soc., xlviii, pp. 239—.
§ Malloch, 1916, Bull. Brooklyn Ent. Soc., xi, p. 109, xiii, pp. 30-33.

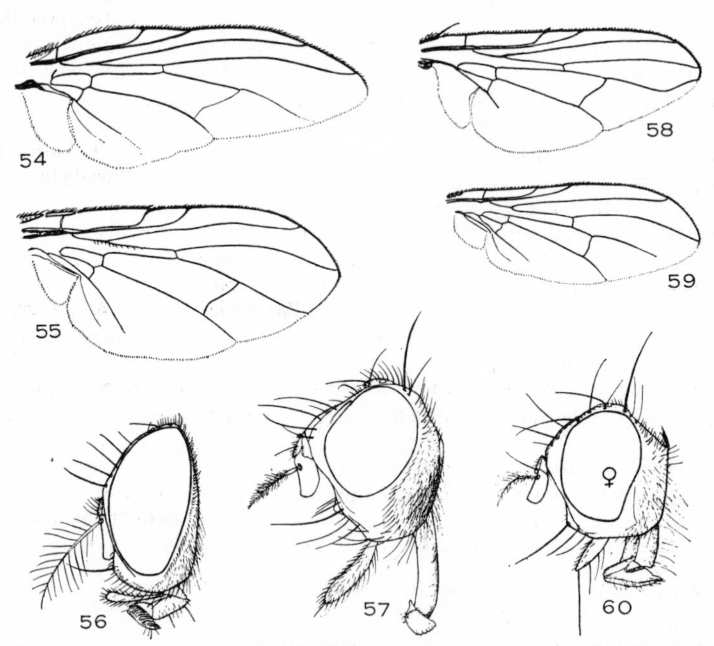

Muscidæ V.—54, **Philornis spermophilæ**; 55, **Dichætomyia**; 56, **Myospila meditabunda**; 57, **Ceratinostoma ostiorum**; 58, **Muscina stabulans**; 59, **Lutzomyia latifrons**; 60, **Cordilura.**

136. Arista plumose (short in **Dendrophaonia**)........................137
Arista pubescent 139

137. Cheeks below with two or more strong, upcurved bristles on the anterior half ....**Dendrophaonia** Malloch
Cheeks without outstanding, upcurved bristles below, though usually with upcurved hairs 138

138. Eyes of males with enlarged facets in front on the upper part and quite evidently flattened; posterior tibiæ without posterodorsal bristles, the front tibiæ bristleless; small species, the females shining ....***Hebecnema** Schiner
Eyes of males not strikingly flattened; usually larger species **(1, 10)**. †**Helina** Desvoidy

139. Cheeks half as wide as the eye-height, with bristles along the oral margin **(6)**..................................‡**Phyllogaster** Stein
Cheeks narrower, with hair on lowest three-fourths or more........140

140. Fourth vein conspicuously curved forward apically. **Neomuscina** Townsend
Fourth vein at most weakly curved forward apically...............141

141. Prealar bristle absent 143
Prealar bristle present 142

142. Lower squamal lobe produced inwardly **(51, 54)** §**Philornis** Macquart
Lower squamal lobe small and not produced inwardly. ¶**Pogonomya** Rondani

143. Two strong intra-alar bristles...................**Lispoides** Coquillett
At most one weak intra-alar.................**Pogonomyioides** Malloch

144. Proboscis elongate and horny.......................................145
Proboscis short and thick, the labellæ fleshy...........**Hemichlora** Wulp

145. Palpi short ....**Stomoxys** Geoffroy
Palpi very long and narrow........**Hæmatobia** St. Fargeau & Serville

* This genus cannot be distinguished from **Helina** with any degree of success and should no doubt be united with it.
† Malloch, 1920, Can. Ent. liii, p. 103.
‡ Malloch, 1923, Can. Ent. lvi, p. 11.
§ Aldrich, 1923, Ann. Ent. Soc. Amer., xvi, p. 308.
¶ Malloch, 1918, Tr. Amer. Ent. Soc., xliv, p. 277.

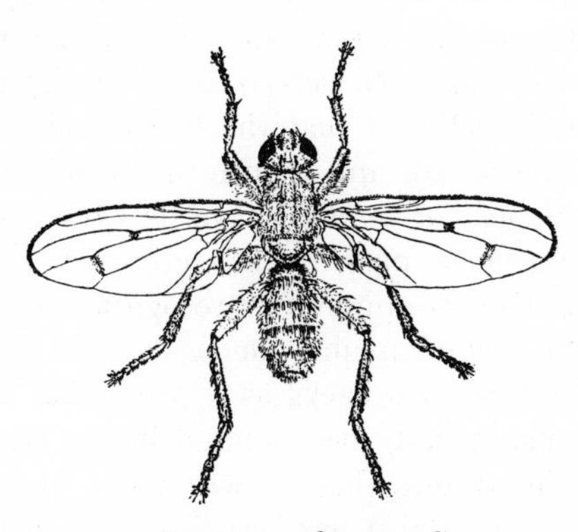

Scopeuma furcata Say.

Family Gasterophilidæ—The Horse Bot Flies

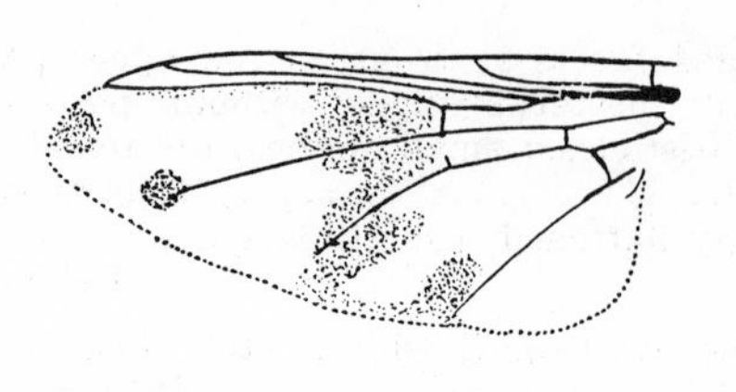
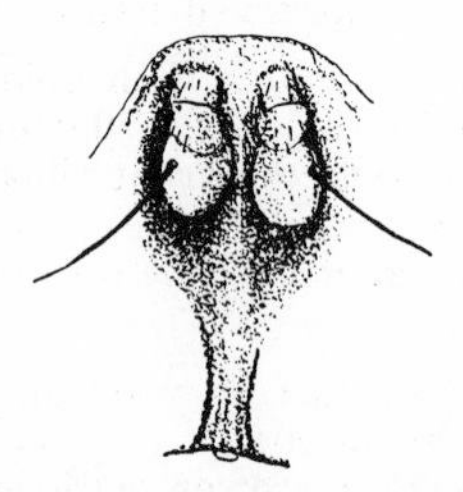

Gasterophilus intestinalis, wing and part of head showing antennæ.

Flies of moderate size, without bristles, the thorax pilose; mouth parts very small; apical crossvein absent.

Head short and deep, pilose; front broad; antennæ small, situated in deep pits separated by a carina; second segment without groove; arista bare; mouth parts very small, the palpi swollen, though short, larger than the proboscis; ocelli present. Scutellum large; postscutellum absent. Legs of moderate length. Apical crossvein absent, the vein closing the discal cell also absent and the fourth and fifth veins evanescent apically. Squamæ small. Abdomen elongate oval in the male, slightly tapering, in the female tapering apically, the ovipositor large and protuberant.

The bot flies are frequently serious pests of horses and may be collected in the neighborhood of these animals, although they are remarkably good fliers. The larvæ live in the stomach, throat and nasal passages of horses and related animals and reports of their occurrence in other animals are very rare. The eggs are laid by *G. intestinalis* on the legs or shoulders of the victim and are taken into the mouth when the animal licks these parts; *G. veterinus* lays its eggs on the underside of the head and it is believed that the larvæ make their way through the skin and into the mouth and thence to the pharynx where they attach themselves. *G. hæmorrhoidalis* lays its eggs about the lips of the horse and the young larvæ pass to the rectum where they fasten themselves to the walls. Horses apparently recognize the flies, at least those of *veterinus,* and it is not an uncommon sight to see horses with their heads resting on each other's backs as a protection against egg laying.

Gasterophilus has usually been placed in the Œstridae but Girschner long since pointed out that it was more closely related to the Muscidæ (Anthomyidæ) and it has been included in that family. Other authorities have placed it in the Acalypteræ where it would seem to belong on account of the shape of the second antennal segment. However, the species possess strong posterior calli and it is possible that the family is, despite the antennal character, more nearly related to the Muscidæ.

The family contains but one genus, *Gasterophilus* Clark, and there are three North American species.

KEY TO THE NEARCTIC SPECIES OF GASTEROPHILUS

1. Wings with dark spots.............................**intestinalis** Degeer
   Wings without dark spots.. 2

2. Discal cell closed beyond the first basal cell; apex of abdomen broadly reddish pilose ....**hæmorrhoidalis** Linnæus
   Discal cell closed almost opposite the end of the first basal cell; basal cells of equal length; abdomen with whitish pile crossed by a black median band ....**veterinus** Clark

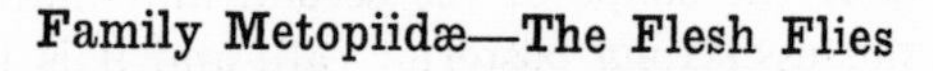

Family Metopiidæ—The Flesh Flies

Sarcophaga sarraceniæ.

Flies of medium to moderately small size, the abdomen usually dark and tessellate or metallic green or blue.

Front in both sexes broad, usually somewhat narrowed in the males, rarely very narrow; face variable; vibrissæ present; antennæ long or short, the arista plumose, pubescent or bare. Abdomen composed of four segments in the males, the fifth short in the females; abdominal bristles usually strong, at least on the apical segments. Hypopleura with a row of bristles; postscutellum developed only in *Mesembrinella.* Apical cell usually open, rarely closed and petiolate, usually ending far before the apex of the wing.

As here considered this family comprises the Sarcophagidæ, part of the Muscidæ and part of the Tachinidæ of Williston's Manual. The absence of the postscutellum distinguishes it from the Tachinidæ while the presence of hypopleural bristles separates it from the *Muscidæ* and the well developed mouth parts from the Œstridæ. A study of pupal and larval characters indicates that the association of the genera now included in the family is a natural one, although the genus *Mesembrinella* is a doubtful member.

Insofar as known the larvæ are flesh feeders, parasites or scavengers on excrement and all have the posterior spiracles situated within a deep depression.

As indicated in the introduction I consider *Myasis* in man is generally an accidental occurrence. There is evidence that it may occur under conditions where an open wound is not dressed and incidents of this kind were not rare during the World War. Indeed, the condition of maggot-infested wounds led to the discovery of the value of flies as an aid in curing serious wounds and also in the treatment of *Osteomyelitis.* It is true that some medical men express doubt about the efficacy of the maggot treatment of this disease but the evidence seems to be in its favor. The maggots feed, for the most part at any rate, only on decayed tissue and the bacteria present in the wound. Whether healing results from the consumption of bacteria or the secretion of a substance stimulating the growth of new flesh is immaterial.

The larvæ of the *Screw Worm Flies* (*Cochliomyia macellaria* and *americana*) occasionally attack man. The eggs are laid in open wounds or nasal or other discharges from the body and the larvæ quickly bore into healthy tissue. From fifty to more than two hundred eggs may be laid at a time. There have been a number of fatal cases in the United States while, in the tropics, death from the attacks of the maggots is said to be not rare. Sheep and range animals are normally attacked when wounded or when the wool becomes fetid due to filth.

The classification of the group is in chaotic condition. A great many genera have been proposed upon characters possessed by one sex or the other and upon characters which are apparently of not more than specific or group value and which, when large collections are studied, are found to be entirely unsatisfactory. There are no doubt several North American genera not included in the key but, without specimens, it is impossible to locate them. I have included all the North American genera known to me but am acquainted with several others occurring in South America which may possibly occur in the North American Tropics although there are, as yet, no records.

There are three papers which will be found most useful in the study of the insects belonging to this family, published by Aldrich*, Allen† and Shannon‡. In the former many of the specific names have been replaced by older names as the result of a study of the types of species described by older authors. For these corrections see Aldrich*.

It is unfortunate that the name of this family must be changed to Metopiidæ, but since there has been no previous grouping of the included genera into a single family the shock should not be great. The basic use of *Miltogramma* for tribal name has always been erroneous

* 1916, Sarcophaga and Allies, (Thomas Say Foundation, Vol. i). 1930, Notes on Types, etc., Proc. U. S. N. M., lxxviii, Art. 12.

† 1926, N. Amer. Miltogrammini, Proc. U. S. N. M., lxviii, Art. 9.

‡ 1926, Syn. Amer. Calliphoridæ, Proc. Ent. Soc. Wash., xxviii, pp. 115-139.

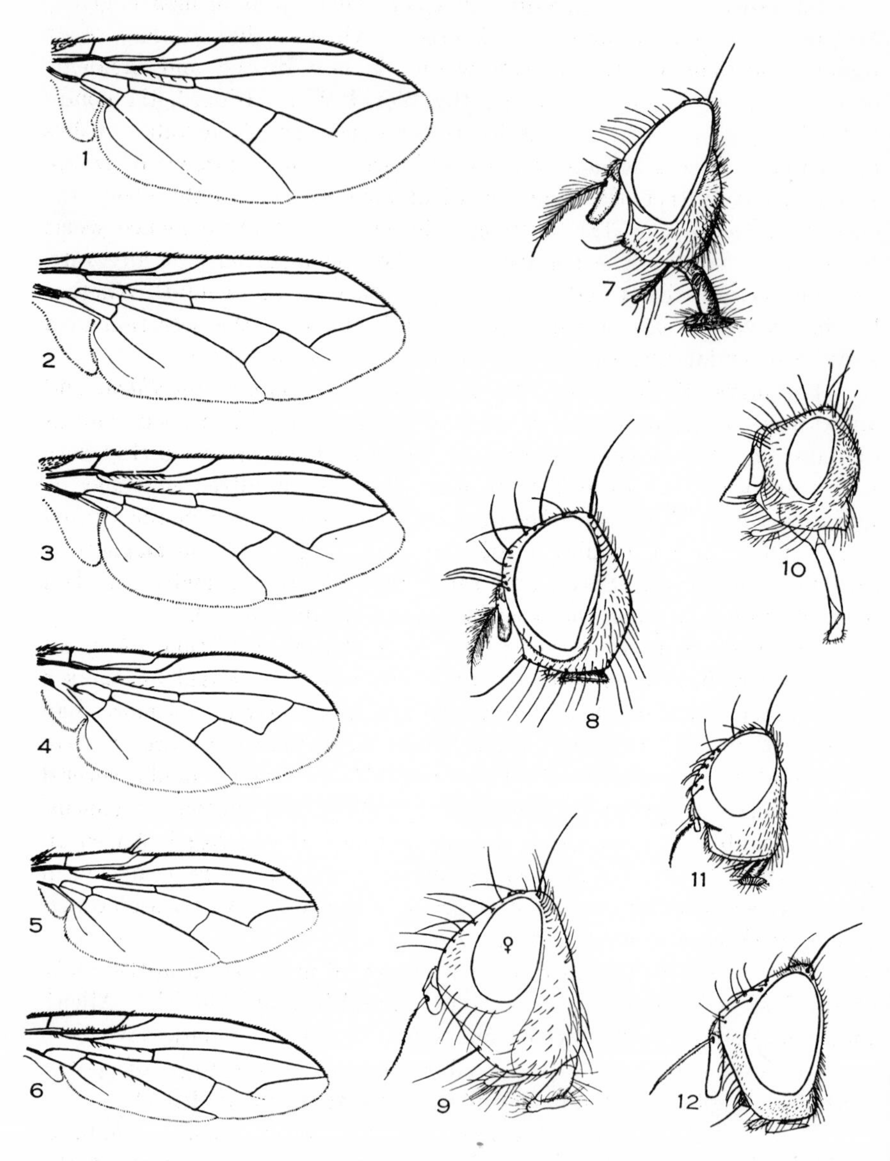

Metopiidæ I.—1, **Metopia**; 2, **Euaraba**; 3, **Helicobia**; 4, **Phytodes herculus**; 5, **Neophyto setosa**; 6, **Johnsonia**; 7, **Opsodexia**; 8, **Johnsonia**; 9, **Neophyto setosa**; 10, **Brachicoma devia**; 11, **Melanophora**, (Tachinidæ); 12, **Euaraba.**

and the same is true of *Calliphora* as *Onesia* has page priority. Since *Sarcophaga* was proposed long after *Metopia* and *Calliphora* the name could scarcely be used in any event.

KEY TO GENERA

1. Arista pubescent or bare.. 2
   Arista plumose 23

2. First vein bare 3
   First vein setose ....**Opsidiopsis** Townsend

3. Apical cell closed 4
   Apical cell open.. 6

4. Distal section of the fifth vein longer than the penultimate section (16) ....**Taxigramma** Perris
   Distal section of the fifth vein little more than half as long as the penultimate section 5

5. Apical cell ending far before the wing tip, short petiolate (19). **Hilarella** Rondani
   Third vein ending only a little before the wing tip, the apical cell long petiolate (4, 30)...................................**Phytodes** Townsend

6. Facial ridges without bristles or they are short and hairlike, the parafacials often bristly... 7
   Facial ridges with bristles on lower half or more (12)................ 6a

6a. Arista thin on apical third...................**Sphenometopa** Townsend
   Arista wholly thickened (2, 12)......................**Euaraba** Townsend

7. Parafacials with only fine hair, without bristles, or with only one below. 11
   Parafacials with a row of bristles (cf. **Camptopyga**)................. 8

8. Antennæ reaching almost to the oral margin.......................... 9
   Antennæ very short, the third segment scarcely longer than the second (5, 9)..**Neophyto** Townsend

9. Facial ridges divergent below, the depression wider than parafacial.... 10
   Facial ridges with parallel sides, the depression deep, narrow and not as wide as either parafacial (18)..................**Opsidea** Coquillett

10. Third antennal segment not more than twice as long as the second; face not strongly receding (10)......................**Brachicoma** Rondani
   Third antennal segment more than three times as long as the second; face very strongly receding (1, 20)...................**Metopia** Miegen

11. Apical cell ending in the wing tip..................**Opelousia** Townsend
   Apical cell ending far before the wing tip.......................... 12

12. Head at vibrissæ much shorter than at base of antennæ, the oral margin not produced 13
   Head at vibrissæ almost or quite as long as at base of antennæ, the oral margin usually prominent..................................... 17

13. Abdominal bristles strong.. 14
   Abdominal bristles poorly differentiated from the hair; abdomen subglobose ....**Œstrohilarella** Townsend

14. Frontals not extending below the base of the antennæ................ 15
   Frontals descending to the middle of the second antennal segment. **Phrosinella** Desvoidy

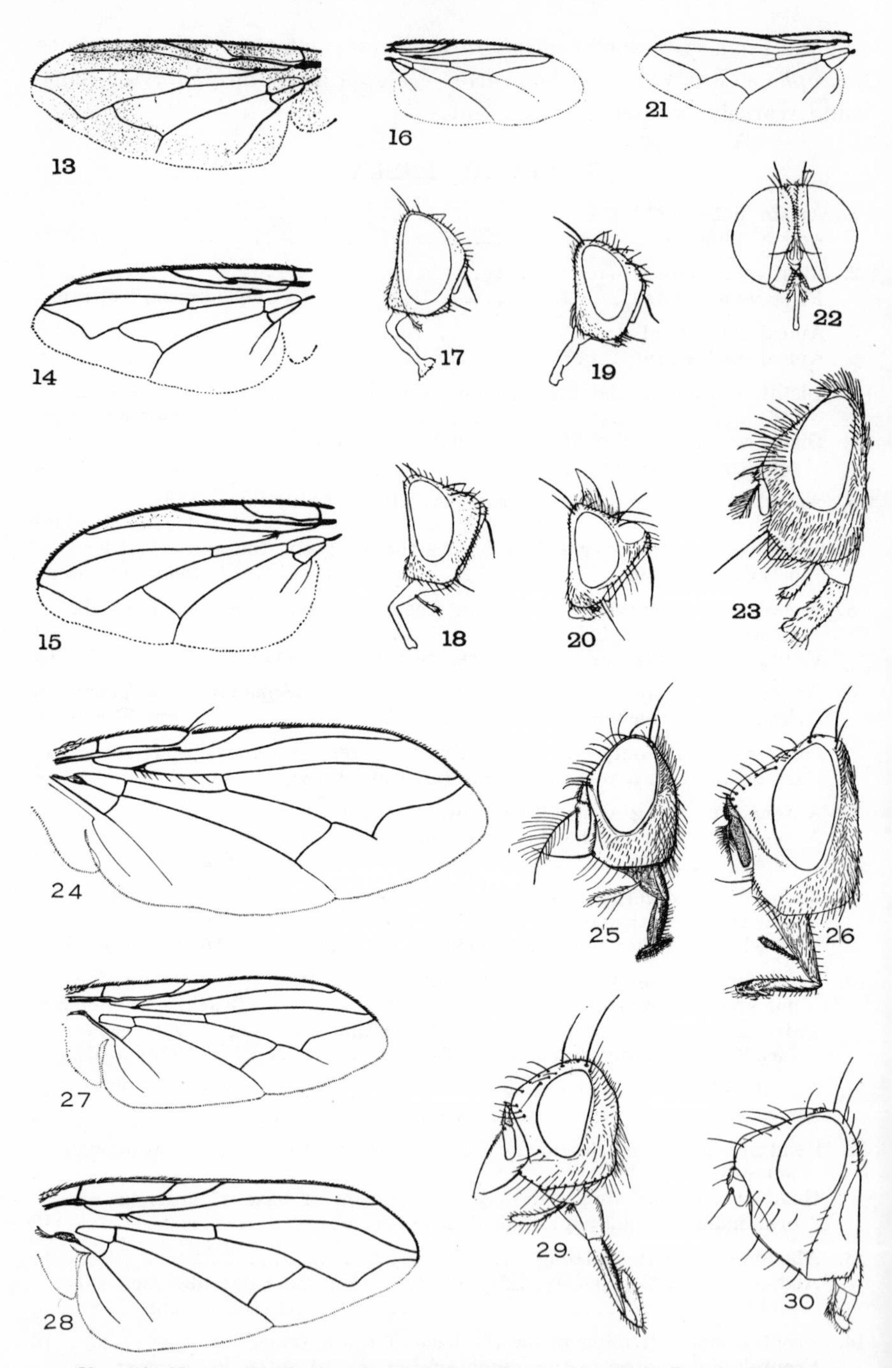

Metopiidæ II.—13, **Hemilucilia**; 14, **Pollenia rudis**; 15, **Mesembrinella**; 16, **Taxigramma**; 17, **Senotainia**; 18, **Opsidea**; 19, **Hilarella**; 20, **Metopia leucocephala**, ♂; 21, 22, **Pachyophthalmus**; 23, **Pollenia rudis**; 24, **Camptopyga**; 25, **Sarcophaga**; 26, **Raviniopsis**; 27, **Senotainia**; 28, **Opsodexia**; 29, **Camptopyga**; 30, **Phytodes herculus**.

15. Third vein usually bristled half way to the crossvein or the arista thickened on not more than the basal half.......................... 16
Third vein with only one to three small basal setulæ, the arista thickened on almost its whole length; third antennal segment five times as long as second..15a

15a. Vibrissæ situated level with the anterior oral margin.....**Ouelletia, n. g.**
Vibrissæ situated almost the length of the second antennal segment above the oral margin.........................**Eusenotainia** Townsend

16. Three pairs of almost equally strong marginal scutellars.
Gymnoprosopa Townsend
Apical pair of scutellars weak or absent.......**Eumacronychia** Townsend

17. A row of proclinate hairs on the parafrontals close to the frontals (**21, 22**).........................**Pachyophthalmus** Brauer & Bergenstamm
No such row of hairs, the parafrontals sometimes haired over most of the surface or bearing one or more pairs of orbitals................ 18

18. Costal spine very long and strong; two pairs of strong scutellars (**24, 29**) ....**Camptopyga** Aldrich
Costal spine short 19

19. Parafacial hairs conspicuous, moderately long....................... 20
Parafacial hairs inconspicuous, very short.......................... 22

20. Second abdominal segment with erect median marginals.............. 21
Second abdominal segment without median marginals.
Wohlfahrtia Brauer & Bergenstamm

21. Frontals not descending below the base of the antennæ..**Amobia** Desvoidy
Frontals descending below the base of the antennæ and divergent below (**10**) ....**Brachicoma** Rondani

22. Three pairs of almost equally strong scutellars (**17, 27**).
Senotainia Macquart
Apical scutellars very much weaker than the other two pairs.
Eumacronychia Townsend

23. Fifth vein bare 24
Fifth vein bristled (**6, 8**)..........................**Johnsonia** Coquillett

24. Lower lobe of the squamæ haired above at least on basal half........ 25
Lower lobe of the squamæ bare or pubescent above................. 29

25. Propleura pilose 26
Propleura bare ....**Adiscochæta** Enderlein

26. First vein setose posteriorly before the humeral crossvein.
***Paralucilia** Brauer & Bergenstamm
First vein not setose posteriorly................................ 27

27. Abdomen metallic blue or green................................ 28
Abdomen black in ground color, tessellate..........**Squamatoides** Curran

28. One sublateral bristle................................**Cynomya** Desvoidy
Two or three sublateral bristles...................†**Calliphora** Desvoidy

---

* **Chrysomya desvoidyi** belongs here.

† **Steringomyia** Pokorny is a synonym and **Onesia** Desvoidy is very doubtfully distinct. If the two genera are united **Onesia** will have priority.

29. First vein setose posteriorly between the humeral crossvein and base of the wing 30
First vein bare posteriorly.... 37

30. First vein setulose below as well as above.... 31
First vein bare below.... 32

31. Postsutural acrosticals absent ....**Sarconesia** Bigot
Postsutural acrosticals present....**Sarconesiopsis** Townsend

32. Face yellow, clothed with yellow hairs.... 33
Face black, the hairs black.... 35

33. Palpi short and slender ....**Cochliomyia** Townsend
Palpi long, normal.... 34

34. Vibrissæ situated the length of the second antennal segment above the oral margin (13)....**Hemilucilia** Brauer
Vibrissæ almost on a level with the oral margin......**Chloroprocta** Wulp

35. Aristal rays quite short and appressed; head almost as long as high. **Boreëllus** Aldrich & Shannon
Aristal rays long, not appressed; head decidedly higher than long..... 36

36. Upper lobe of the squamæ haired above....***Phormia** Desvoidy
Upper lobe of the squamæ haired only on the margin. **Protocalliphora** Hough

37. Antennæ very short, the third segment little longer than the second; face receding below, the vibrissæ closely approximate. **Neophyto** Townsend
Antennæ elongate 38

38. Suprasquamal ridge with erect black hairs.... 39
Suprasquamal ridge bare or pubescent.... 40

39. Subcostal sclerite setulose....**Lucilia** Desvoidy
Subcostal sclerite bare....**Phenicia** Desvoidy

40. Thorax with abundant yellow tomentose hairs among the black hairs (14, 23) ....**Pollenia** Desvoidy
Thorax without tomentose hairs.... 41

41. Postscutellum strongly developed; propleura bare; prosternum setulose laterally; bend of fourth vein broadly rounded (15). **Mesembrinella** Giglio-Tos
Postscutellum not developed.... 42

42. Three or more sternopleurals.... 50
Two sternopleurals 43

43. Fourth vein ending almost in the tip of the wing.... 44
Fourth vein ending well before the tip of the wing.... 45

44. Arista long plumose (7, 28)....†**Oposodexia** Townsend
Arista short plumose....**Opelousia** Townsend

---

* **Protophormia** Townsend is separated by the absence of strong acrostical bristles but the character is of not more than specific value in this instance, some specimens possessing distinct acrosticals.

† Reinhard, 1929, Pr. U. S. N. M., lxxvi, Art. 20, p. 6.

45. Abdomen largely pollinose.. 46
    Abdomen shining black........................**Phrissopodia** Macquart

46. Hairs on sides of the scutellum extending to the lower edge.......... 47
    Scutellum without hairs outside the marginals..........**Camptops** Aldrich

47. Middle of propleura bare.. 49
    Middle of propleura haired... 48

48. Frontal bristles not extending below the base of the antennæ.
    Harpagopyga Aldrich
    Frontal bristles extending below the base of the antennæ and diverging below ....**Notochæta** Aldrich

49. Parafacial hairs inconspicuous; large species.........**Sthenopyga** Aldrich
    Parafacial hairs evident; small species.............................. 58

50. First vein not setose... 51
    First vein setose (3)............................***Helicobia** Coquillett

51. Propleura haired on median portion.................................. 52
    Propleura bare 53

52. Third antennal segment but little longer than the second; arista short plumose; both sexes with orbitals..................**Harbeckia** Aldrich
    Third antennal segment usually twice as long as the second; males without orbitals (**Bœttcheria** Parker) (**25**)........†**Sarcophaga** Meigen

53. Sternopleurals arranged in a nearly equilateral triangle............. 54
    Sternopleurals not arranged in a nearly equilateral triangle.......... 55

54. Costal spine long and strong...................... **Hypopelta** Aldrich
    No costal spine ....**Agria** Desvoidy

55. Third antennal segment more than twice as long as the second; cheeks less than half as wide as eye-height; parafacials rarely with more than two rows of hairs.. 56
    Third antennal segment less than twice as long as the second; cheeks more than half as wide as eye-height; parafacials with several irregular rows of hairs............................**Emblamasoma** Aldrich

56. Arista with several rows of hairs dorsally and a single row of shorter hairs ventrally; vibrissæ situated far above the oral margin (**26**).
    Raviniopsis Townsend
    Arista normally plumose 57

57. Front of male with one or two orbitals; at most a single hair on the notopleura in addition to the two bristles; fourth vein ending rather near the apex of the wing.. 58
    Front of male without orbitals; always more than a single hair on the notopleura in addition to the two bristles or the sternopleurals are all strong and the fourth vein ends far before the apex of the wing (**25**) ....**Sarcophaga** Meigen

58. Parafacials with two or three rows of hairs; metacephalon swollen.
    Sarothromyia Brauer & Bergenstamm
    Parafacials with a single row of hairs; metacephalon not conspicuously swollen ....**Sarcophagula** Wulp

* If there are orbitals in the male see **Sarcophagula.**
† In some species the males have the propleura haired while the females do not.

Ouelletia, new genus

Rather similar to *Senotainia* but the facial ridges are haired on almost the lower half, the arista is wholly thickened and the face retreating. Differs from *Eusenotainia* in having the vibrissæ more widely separated and situated level with the anterior oral margin. Differs from *Euaraba* in the haired facial ridges and much narrower frontal vitta. Front three-fourths as wide as either eye, slightly more than one-third as wide as the head, the parafrontals wider than the vitta, frontals ending at base of antennæ; two pairs of orbitals in the male and a reclinate frontal in the orbital row, ocellars long; outer verticals weak. Cheeks one-fifth as wide as the eye-height. Parafacials wide, setulose on upper half. Palpi of moderate length. Facial depression very deep. Antennæ elongate, the third segment very long and broad; arista wholly thickened, the penultimate segment short. Acrosticals 1-1, weak, dorsocentrals 2-3, the front ones fine; three pairs of marginal scutellars; sternopleurals 1-1. Bend of fourth vein with a slight fold; base of third vein with a single bristle. Squamæ produced inwardly. Abdomen oval, without discals, the apical two segments with weak marginals. Black, with whitish pollen; frontal pollen mostly brownish yellow, the mesonotal pollen with brownish yellow tinge. Abdomen with a broad median dark vitta and large black triangles on the second and third segments. Genotype, *O. aristalis*, new species, from Lauzon, Quebec, June.

Phrissopodia præceps Wiedemann.

Family Cuterebridæ—The Robust Bot Flies

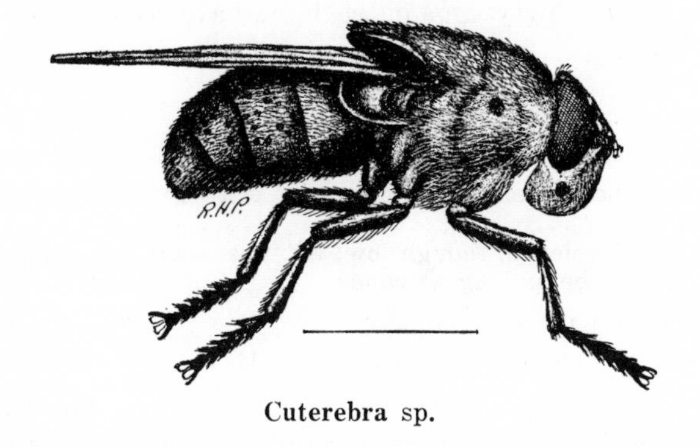

Cuterebra sp.

Flies of large size, the hair very short, sparse except on the thorax; squamæ large; metascutellum not at all developed.

This family differs from the Œstridæ in having the scutellum elongate, the postscutellum entirely undeveloped, the arista is usually plumose or pectinate, the form is generally more robust and the body less evidently hairy. In addition the oral opening is larger, subtriangular (produced in front toward the vibrissal angles) and the palpi are always small.

The remarks concerning the Œstridæ apply fairly well to this family. These flies are, in North America at least, mostly parasitic upon rodents and they have been reared from rabbits, rats, mice and squirrels. The larvæ have been found along rabbit runs, but the adults are only infrequently encountered.

It seems probable that this family is an offshoot of the Metopiidæ type rather than of the Tachinid stock as is evidenced by the absence of the postscutellum and the usually feathered arista. There does not seem to be a close relationship between these insects and the Œstridæ despite the similar habits and reduced mouth parts while the Gasterophilidæ are still further removed, coming, as they do, close to the Muscidæ. The Tachinidæ having reduced mouth parts have more or less distinct abdominal bristles.

Probably the most unusual habit in the insect world is that of *Dermatobia hominis* (*cyaniventris*), the human bot fly. The fly lays its eggs on other insects, usually mosquitoes, and they are carried by the latter to the host. The eggs contain mature first stage larvæ and these emerge from the eggs when the carrier begins feeding and penetrate the skin. The maggots remain in the host for from forty-five to fifty-five days and cause rather severe muscular pains as well as inducing drowsiness. It is said that the adult flies lurk in the vicinity of mosquito infested pools and capture the mosquitoes as they emerge, laying from ten to thirty eggs on each. I have seen mosquitoes heavily laden with the eggs. Ticks and species of Muscidæ are also carriers.

KEY TO GENERA

1. No facial carina; antennæ elongate, the third segment three times as long as wide 2
   Facial carina developed, though low; antennæ short, the second segment rarely over twice as long as wide.................................. 3

2. Arista rather thickly long plumose................**Pseudogametes** Bischof
   Arista with rays on upper side only (**1, 2, 4**)...........**Dermatobia** Brauer

3. Arista bare (South America)........................**Rogenhofera** Brauer
   Arista pectinate above and usually with one or more rays below on the apical part (**3, 5, 6**)..............................*Cuterebra Clark

* I can find no character by which to separate **Bogeria** Austen, described from a damaged specimen lacking the aristal rays and based upon the bare arista. Townsend (Ins. Ins. Mens., v, p. 23) attempts to separate the two genera on the shape of the facial depression but I cannot follow him in this.

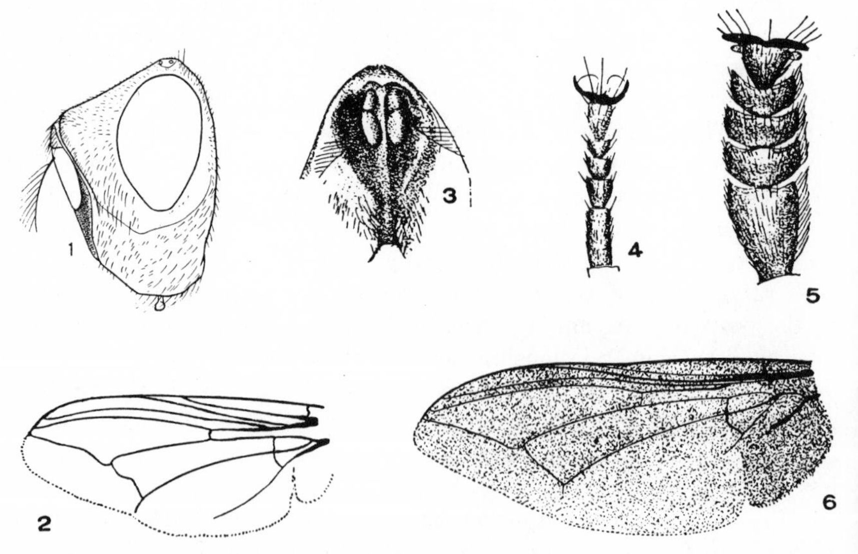

Cuterebridæ.—1, **Dermatobia cyaniventris**; 2, **Dermatobia**; 3, **Cuterebra**, antennæ; 4, **Dermatobia**, tarsus; 5, **Cuterebra**, tarsus; 6, **Cuterebra**.

Family Œstridæ—The Bot Flies

Flies of moderate to large size, thick set and for the most part more or less pilose, the squamæ large.

Head large, the lower part more or less swollen; mouth opening small, the mouth parts reduced in size, very small. Front broad in both sexes, widening anteriorly in the male; ocelli present. Antennæ short, composed of three segments, decumbent and partly sunken in the facial depression or antennal grooves; arista bare. Eyes bare, rather small. Thorax robust, with transverse suture; hypopleura bearing dense, long hair. Abdomen short, conical or but little elongate; genitalia hidden. Squamæ large. Wing venation as in the Tachinidæ, the first vein ending beyond the middle of the wing, the auxiliary vein long and ending in the costa; fourth vein ending before the apex of the wing, close to the third; both basal cells present, the second basal and anal cell short.

The Œstrids are not common in collections and good series of all but a very few species are unusual. The adults are remarkably good fliers, are excellent hoverers and extremely difficult to catch as well as being rarely encountered. Some collectors have had success in locating larvæ and pupæ in pastures, and rearing the adults. Otherwise one usually runs across them only by accident.

In some cases the eggs are laid on the hind legs, the larvæ working their way under the skin and through the muscles until they reach the back, where they make an opening through which to breath. The larvæ of some species live in the nasal sinuses and, in sheep, are responsible for ''staggers''. The exact means by which some of the species reach their feeding places is not known, and, in fact, relatively little is known about most species which have been described.

In America the larvæ of *Œstrus ovis* have been formed in the eye of man. Normally the living larvæ are deposited in the nostrils or eyes of sheep, the fly dashing in and depositing a maggot. The larvæ work their way to the nasal sinuses and mature the following spring when they either drop out or are ejecting during sneezing. In man they have been found only in the eye, larviposition probably having taken place as described for sheep. However, there are no records of the victim having been aware of the attack so it is possible that the larva was deposited while the victim was sleeping.

The literature dealing with the family is scattered and a thorough revision of the American species is badly needed. The genitalia of both sexes furnish good taxonomic characters.

It is not an easy matter to decide the relationship of this family but it seems probable that it originated from Tachinid stock, since the postscutellum is strongly developed, and the scutellum usually short and broad. The Tachinidæ with reduced mouth opening and mouth parts are more or less bristled and are consequently easily distinguished. However, as these are inhabitants of the Old World tropics we need not discuss them here. More is said about the affinities of the old family *Œstridæ* under the *Cuterebridæ.*

KEY TO GENERA

1. Apical cell closed and petiolate........................**Œstrus** Linnæus
   Apical cell open.. 2
2. Facial grooves only narrowly separated below (2)....**Cephalemya** Latreille
   Facial grooves very broadly separated........................ 3
3. Palpi absent; scutellum bare on apical third (3)........**Hypoderma** Clark
   Palpi small, globular; scutellum pilose apically (1)...**Œdamagena** Latreille

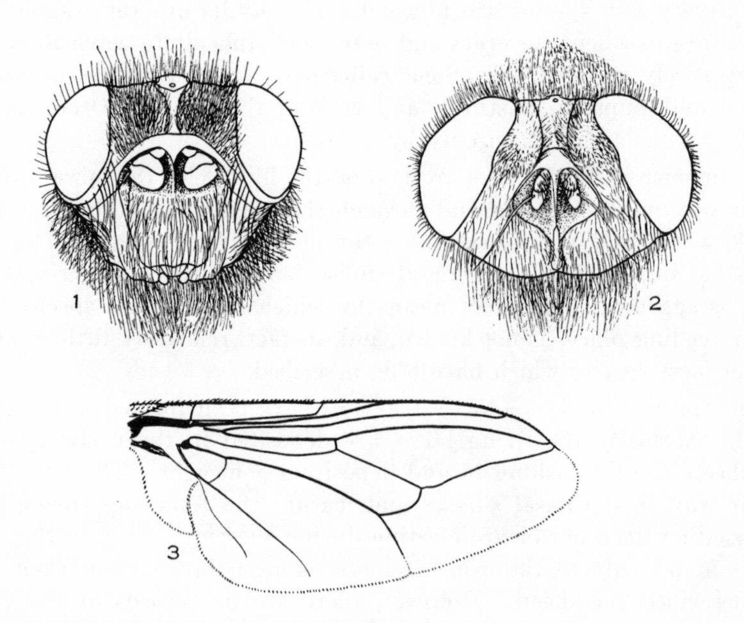

Œstridæ.—1, Œdemagena tarandi; 2, Cephalemya abdominalis; 3, Hypoderma lineatum.

Family Tachinidæ—The Tachinids

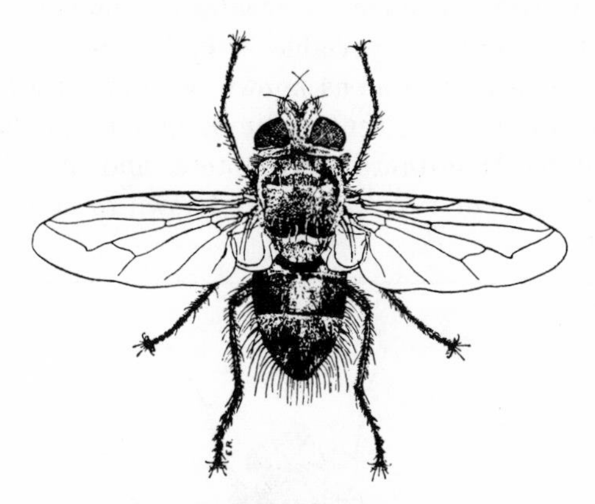

Zenillia species.

Small to rather large flies, the thorax with bristles, the head and abdomen generally with bristles.

Head variable in size, sometimes narrower than the thorax, at other times conspicuously wider; both sexes dichoptic although the eyes of the males are sometimes closely approximated, rarely so in the females; front often wide in both sexes, usually wider in the female than in the male of the same species; frontal bristles almost always present, orbital bristles usually present in the females and often in the males; ocellars present or absent; outer verticals present or not distinguishable from the postocular cilia; cheeks variable in width; oral margin variable, sometimes strongly produced, at other times receding; oral vibrissæ usually present; proboscis variable in length and thickness, sometimes very elongate, on the other extreme very small; palpi present or absent; antennæ variable, consisting of three segments, the second with a longitudinal seam above on the outer side and usually bearing stout hairs and one or more bristles; arista composed of two or three obvious segments, plumose, pubescent or bare. Thorax with bristles; hypopleural bristles present, rarely weak, postscutellum well developed. Legs variable, bearing bristles; pulvilli always present on at least the posterior four legs, often elongate. Wings variable in shape, sometimes pictured; all the veins simple; apical crossvein usually present, formed by the curvature of the fourth longitudinal vein, this vein rarely straight or almost so, sometimes obsolete apically; posterior crossvein rarely absent; first, third and fifth veins sometimes bristled; basal and anal cells complete. Squamæ almost invariably large. Abdomen variable in shape, usually bearing conspicuous bristles on the sides, apex and disc, but these variable; genitalia variable in both sexes.

The Tachinids are, insofar as known, all parasitic on other insects, particularly Lepidopterous, Tenthredinid, and beetle larvæ and adult beetles, as well as Hemiptera, Orthoptera and possibly some other orders of insects. One or two species are known to be parasitic on other

Paradejeania species.

flies (Syrphidæ). The species parasitic on Hemiptera usually have a bristleless, or near bristleless abdomen while many of those parasitizing beetles have a long, piercing ovipositor, but this character is not limited to such species. The eggs are variable, some being very small (microtype), while others are large (macrotype). A small number of species deposit living larvæ or eggs just ready to hatch. The study of the immature stages of the Tachinids should prove to be a most fascinating one as is indicated by such work as has already been done. The species of *Gonia,* which lay microtype eggs, scatter hundreds of them (as many as a thousand) over vegetation and the ground; they are eaten by feeding caterpillars and ultimately destroy their host. This may seem a haphazard way of doing things but the flies are efficient parasites as evidenced by their numbers. In at least one species the larvæ, resembling little coiled cones, remain for long periods on leaves, until they are brushed by the hair of a caterpillar, when they suddenly become active, make their way up the hair and enter the body. Most species, however, apparently oviposit in or on the host and in the case of many caterpillars the egg shells remain attached to the larva for long periods, and may be found on them as long as the larval skin exists. This is commonly the case with silk worm caterpillars parasitized by species of *Achaetoneura,* but the characteristic is not restricted to this genus. The literature on this subject is more extensive than one might imagine although I must confess that I am not familiar with it in its entirety.

The study of the immature stages has been greatly stimulated because of the economic importance of these insects. A goodly number of species have been imported to America in connection with the natural control of foreign pests which have become established here and the study of the group has resulted. The best known of the imported Tachinids is *Compsilura concinnata* Bouché, which is now well established in the northeastern states and parts of eastern Canada, and is spreading rapidly. This species is one of the chief parasites of the Gypsy Moth but it apparently attacks almost any kind of caterpillar. *Microphthalma michiganensis* Townsend, has been established in New Zealand from shipments made by the Canadian government. Some of the species imported have occurred in this country for many years and are perhaps indigenous but it is not by any means certain that the native flies will attack the alien hosts. This point is mentioned merely to illustrate the fact that the same species may have different habits in different regions. It also demonstrates our lack of knowledge concerning these insects. Parasites are searched for in all parts of the world, but most of those we have introduced are from Europe and Asia. Just how many of these introductions have resulted in the definite establishment of species in this country we do not know, but there are some failures as well as notable successes. Immediate results in control must not be expected, but it seems likely that in due time a natural control of the pests will occur. To expect the Tachinids, or other parasites, to control the pests they are brought to fight within a few years is just as absurd as to have expected the Pilgrim Fathers to have completely settled this country in ten years.

Tachinids occur everywhere and many species are common. Clearings or lanes in woods are excellent for some species; most of them visit flowers at some time or other, and many are found in grass. A few species are nocturnal, others fly at dusk or on dark days and a number of them are attracted to light. "Honey dew" is very attractive to many of the species. The adults are frequently very busy creatures and many females seem to fly incessantly in search of a suitable host for their offspring.

It is extremely unfortunate that this important family is in such a hopeless state taxonomically. The forms I include were at one time placed in two distinct families, the Tachinidæ and Dexiidæ, and some authors have recognized a number of families for the group. The Dexiids were separated because of the plumose or haired arista but the character is not of value. During my studies of this family I have searched in vain for reliable characters by which to differentiate groups. Many characters are good up to a certain point but beyond that they cease to be of real value. In many genera the propleura is haired but in some this character is not reliable. The same is true in regard to the hairiness of the lower squamal lobe, a character occurring in but a few genera in the world. The chætotaxy is variable and there is every gradation between extremes.

Complex antennæ found in Tachinidæ.

The question of generic limits in this family is a most perplexing one. No two people have the same conception of generic limits and it will be found that I disagree in many respects with Townsend, Villeneuve, Aldrich and others, although agreeing rather well with Dr. Aldrich. I have been unable to correlate all of Townsend's genera with my conception of genera but I have indicated, in the index, a great many which I think should be placed in the synonymy. It might be, of course, that I have gone too far in reducing the number of described genera and that some of those relegated to the synonymy should be recognized as distinct. I feel, however, that the number of genera recognized is still too large and that we may safely reduce it to the benefit of the taxonomy of the family. It is true that in the present work I have added a number of new names and my excuse for doing so is to be found in the fact that I am unable to place the species in any described genus known to me. No one can correct the classification of this family without a very large collection from all parts of the world and a very extensive study will be necessary before any satisfactory generic limitation can be fixed. Indeed, the classification can never be settled because we are continually discovering new connecting links between genera and species. Some genera are well established and fairly well limited but the number is small.

It is unfortunate that Dr. C. H. T. Townsend has been unable (up to the present time) to find a publisher for his volumes on the classification of this family. No one has ever equalled Townsend in knowledge of the Tachinidæ and his keys would prove to be of inestimable value and would throw light on the position of the hundreds of genera described in various places. At the present time one is absolutely lost unless specimens are available, and it is only by chance that an occasional specimen can be determined.

The student will find a number of changes in nomenclature incorporated in this work and I fear that this will cause some confusion. However, due to the work of Townsend and others we have now discovered older names for many of our species and genera and many misconceptions in identification have been corrected. It is suggested that, if a name occurs in literature and cannot be found in the key, it be looked for in the index. In this way most of the names will be found. Nevertheless, there will be confusion because most of the older authors had little conception of the position of the species described and many very different forms have been placed in the same genus. Things are not quite as hopeless as they may seem, but the beginner will find himself badly handicapped, at least until a catalogue is published.

A preliminary key has been prepared in order to obviate the necessity of going through the entire key and turning many pages before arriving at suitable couplet. Any figures on the right of the page of the abbreviated key refer to a couplet in the key proper and the search for the genus should be taken up from that point.

SYNOPTIC TABLE OF KEY GROUPS

A. Lower lobe of squamæ bare above .... B
   Lower lobe of squamæ pilose above.............................. 2

B. Middle of propleura bare C
   Middle of propleura with pile or hair.............................. 4

C. Infrasquamal setulæ absent; abdomen with bristles................ E
   Infrasquamal setulæ present or the abdomen without dorsal bristles.. D

D. Eyes haired 55
   Eyes bare or almost so.. 84

E. Eyes bare or with inconspicuous short hair........................ G
Eyes pilose .... F

F. Parafacials with hairs or bristles extending to the lower half......161
Parafacials bare at least on the lower half..........................181

G. Parafacials with hairs or bristles..................................236
Parafacials bare on at least the lower half........................ H

H. Thorax without plumose hairs I
Thorax with plumose hairs..............................**Teleothyria**

I. Facial ridges bristled on less than the lower half.................. J
Facial ridges with strong bristles on lower half or more.............293

J. Apical crossvein present .... K
Apical crossvein absent 342

K. Palpi present and well developed L
Palpi absent or very greatly reduced................................348

L. Apical cell at most with an extremely short petiole................ M
Apical cell long petiolate..355

M. Ultimate section of fifth vein less than half as long as the preceding section .... N
Ultimate section of fifth vein three-fourths as long as the preceding section ....**Catalinovoria**

N. Penultimate aristal segment not over twice as long as wide........ O
Penultimate aristal segment three times as long as wide............361

O. No appendage or strong fold at bend of fourth vein..............385
A strong appendage or fold at bend of fourth vein..................372

KEY TO GENERA

1. Lower lobe of squamæ bare or pubescent above..................... 3
Lower lobe of squamæ with long, fine hairs above................. 2

2. Parafacials haired to below the middle (**113**)....**Bombyliopsis** Townsend
Parafacials with but a few hairs below the frontals (**91**).
Hystricia Macquart

3. Middle of propleura bare.. 53
Middle of propleura with pile or hair............................. 4

4. Eyes thickly hairy, the head almost as long below as at base of antennæ 5
Eyes bare, or, if pilose, the face retreating and the facial ridges usually bristled on the lower half.................................. 8

5. Parafacials bare 6
Parafacials haired on lower half.................................. 7

6. Facial ridges bristled on lowest three-fourths; first vein setulose.
Hypochæta Brauer & Bergenstamm
Facial ridges and first vein bare (**100**).
Pseudohystricia Brauer & Bergenstamm

7. Palpi well developed...............**Arthrochæta** Brauer & Bergenstamm
Palpi absent or extremely small; large, robust species.
Tachinomima Brauer & Bergenstamm

8. Thorax without plumose hair.................................. 9
Thorax, at least on the pleura, clothed with plumose hairs (Genotype: **Ptilomyia bequærti** Curran).......................**Ptilomyioides,** n. g.

9. Palpi present, strongly developed, at least as long as the second antennal segment 19
Palpi absent or very small.. 10

10. Arista plumose 11
Arista bare or pubescent.. 13

11. Posterior tibiæ rather closely ciliate.............**Opsotheresia** Townsend
Posterior tibiæ not ciliate.. 12

12. Palpi absent ....***Atelogossa** Coquillett
Palpi slender and short...........................**Phasiops** Coquillett

13. Parafacials with hairs or bristles................................ 14
Parafacials bare; ocellars strong (54)............†**Cylindromyia** Meigen

14. Ocellars strong 15
Ocellars weak or absent; parafacials without bristles................ 18

15. Parafacials with strong bristles below; apical cell petiolate.
Antillicolla Curran
Parafacials with hair... 16

16. Apical cell ending very close to wing-tip; head short.
Phosocephala Townsend
Apical cell ending far before the wing-tip; head long................ 17

17. Abdomen with ordinary bristles below, rounded apically.
Gymnomma Brauer & Bergenstamm
Abdomen with spines ventrally, emarginate apically.**Juriniopsis** Townsend

18. With ordinary bristles on the abdomen...............**Epalpus** Rondani
With blunt spinose bristles on the dorsum of the abdomen.
Rhachoëpalpus Townsend

19. Parafacials hairy or bristly to well below the middle................ 20
Parafacials with at most a few hairs below the lowest frontals....... 33

20. Parafacials with ordinary hairs..................................... 22
Parafacials with bristles 21

21. Apical cell open (73, 74)........................**Goniochæta** Townsend
Apical cell petiolate...........................**Eutrichogena** Townsend

22. Ocellar bristles strongly developed................................. 27
Ocellar bristles extremely weak or absent........................... 23

23. Palpi but little longer than the length of the oral opening, enlarged apically 25
Palpi very much longer than the length of the oral opening, with parallel sides or somewhat narrowed apically......................... 24

---

* Curran, 1930, Bull. Amer. Mus. Nat. Hist., lxi, p. 92.
† Aldrich, 1926, Pr. U. S. N. M., lxviii, Art. 23, pp. 1-27.

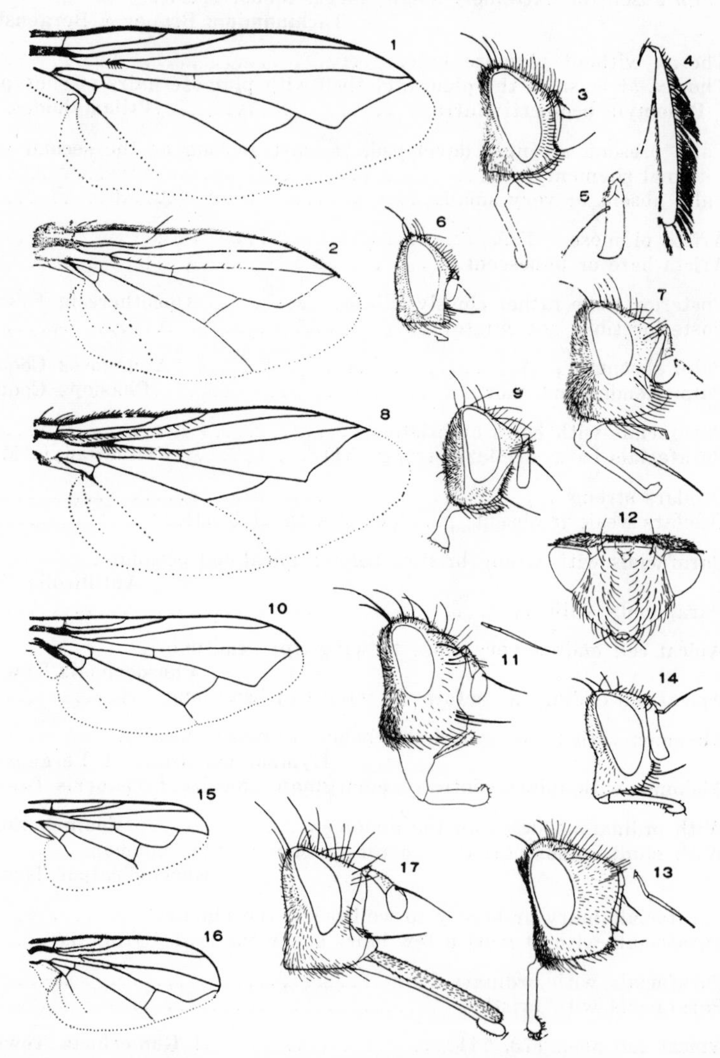

Tachinidæ I.—1, **Lydella**; 2, **Aphria occidentalis**; 3, **Spallanzania hebes**; 4, **Leschenaultia adusta**; 5, **Acemya dentata**, antenna; 6, **Atacta**; 7, **Peleteria**; 8, **Voria ruralis**; 9, **Tachinomyia robusta**; 10, **Cistogaster**; 11, **Archytas**; 12, 13, **Gonia**, head, dorsal and lateral views; 14, **Epigrimyia?**; 15, **Alophora**; 16, **Plectops**; 17, **Dejeania vexatrix**.

24. Acrostical bristles absent........................**Eudejeania** Townsend
Acrostical bristles present (**17**)........**Dejeania** Brauer & Bergenstamm

25. Abdomen convex, the apex rounded............................... 26
Abdomen very large, unusually flat above, sub-rectangular, the apex strongly emarginate (**60**).......**Paradejeania** Brauer & Bergenstamm

26. Second abdominal segment with at most four median marginals, if with discals they are arranged in pairs (**11, 102**)...***Archytas** Jænnicke
Second abdominal segment with many marginals, numerous discals or the pile very long and bristly (**95**)..................**Jurinia** Desvoidy

27. Ultimate section of fifth vein two-thirds as long as preceding section. **Metaplagia** Coquillett
Ultimate section of fifth vein not one-third as long as preceding section 28

28. Abdomen without discals, or they are fine and hair-like............. 29
Second and third abdominal segments with strong discals. **Protodejeania** Townsend

29. Face not carinate on lower half of depression..................... 31
Face carinate on whole length of depression....................... 30

30. Hair of parafacials inconspicuous....**Myiomima** Brauer & Bergenstamm
Hair of parafacials strong........................**Ursophyto** Aldrich

31. Arista plumose ....**Phalacrodexia** Townsend
Arista bare or pubescent.. 32

32. Posterior sublateral bristle present. †**Cnephaliodes** Brauer & Bergenstamm
Posterior sublateral bristle absent; proboscis long, the labellæ small. **Phytopsis** Townsend

33. Frontal bristles not or scarcely extending below the base of the antennæ; arista strongly pubescent or plumose.................... 38
Frontal bristles usually extending to the base of the third antennal segment; arista not conspicuously pubescent................... 34

34. Ocellars present 35
Ocellars absent ....‡**Belvosia** Desvoidy

35. Facial ridges with strong bristles on at least the lower half......... 37
Facial ridges with only a few hairs above the vibrissæ............. 36

36. Eyes pilose (**Zenillia submissa** A. & W.)................**Collatia,** n. g.
Eyes bare ....**Parademoticus** Townsend

37. Infrasquamal setulæ present.................**Hypochætopsis** Townsend
Infrasquamal setulæ absent..................**Chætophlepsis** Townsend

38. Arista with long rays.. 39
Arista with long rays........................§**Arctophyto** Townsend

39. Infrasquamal setulæ absent 40
Infrasquamal setulæ present (Metopiidæ)..........**Opsodexia** Townsend

---

* Curran, 1928, Can. Ent., lx, p. 202.
† Rowe, 1931, Ann. Ent. Soc. Amer., xxiv, p. 647 (**Fabriciella**).
‡ Aldrich, 1928, Pr. U. S. N. M., lxxiii, Art. 8, pp. 1-45.
§ Curran, 1924, Can. Ent., lvi, p. 302.

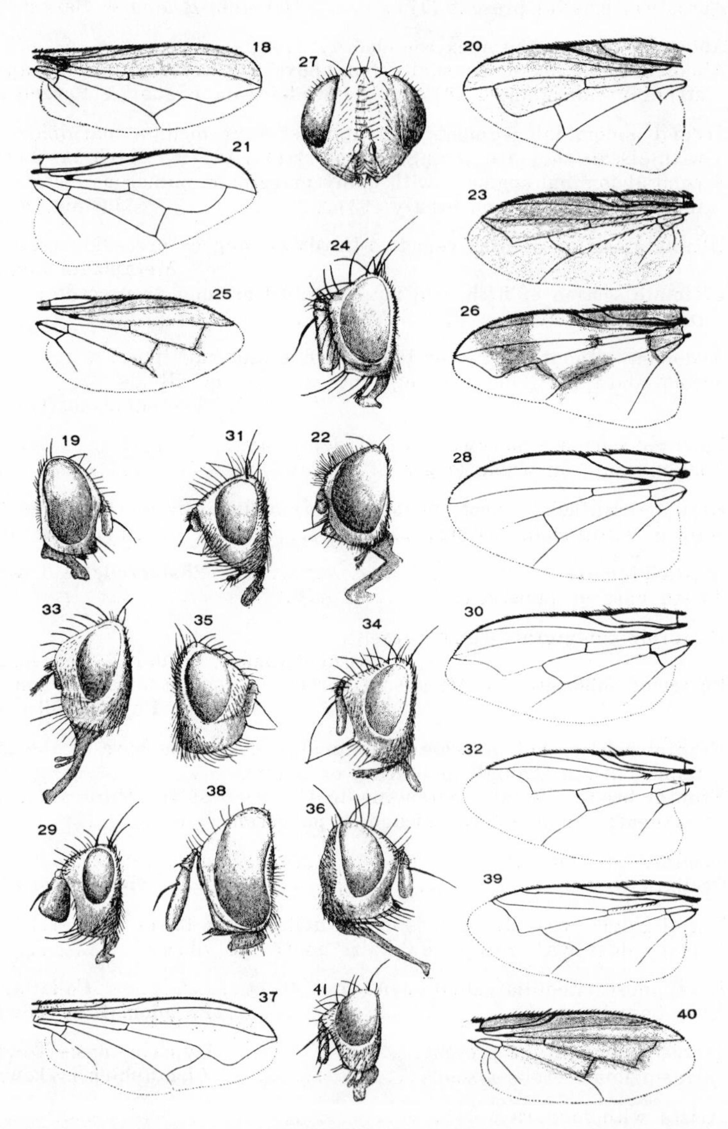

Tachinidæ II.—18, 19, **Acaulona costata**; 20, **Alophora fumosa**; 21, 22, **Alophora**; 23, 24, **Ceratomyiella**; 25, **Euscopolia dakotensis**; 26, 27, **Œstrophasia calva**; 28, 29, **Euryceromyia robertsoni**, bristles omitted from third vein of wing; 30, 31, **Neophyto setosa** (Metopiidæ); 32, 33, **Rhinophora mexicana**; 34, **Cryptomeigenia**; 35, **Myiophasia**; 36, **Binghamimyia**; 37, 38, **Hemyda aurata**; 39, **Cuphocera**; 40, 41, **Wagneria**, bristles omitted from veins.

40. Second abdominal segment with dorsal bristles.................... 46
Second abdominal segment without dorsal bristles.................. 41

41. Sides of face diverging below; cheeks wider than length of third antennal segment 42
Sides of face slightly converging below; cheeks about as wide as width of third antennal segment...................**Xanthodexia** Wulp

42. Face strongly carinate... 44
Face at most weakly carinate...................................... 43

43. Proboscis decidedly longer than the head-height...**Prosenoides** Townsend
Proboscis shorter than the head-height **(118, 122)**.......**Billæa** Desvoidy

44. Antennæ not nearly reaching the vibrissæ.......................... 45
Antennæ reaching almost to the vibrissæ........**Theresiopsis** Townsend

45. Facial carina not convex in profile............................... 48
Facial carina convex in profile..................**Opsotheresia** Townsend

46. Facial carina strong and prominent................................ 51
Facial carina weak, obsolete or nearly so......................... 47

47. Apical cell ending in or near the wing-tip.
Stomatodexia Brauer & Bergenstamm
Apical cell ending far before the wing-tip........................ 48

48. Antennæ reaching about half way to the oral margin.
Phalacrophyto Townsend
Antennæ reaching more than half way to the oral margin............ 49

49. Abdomen broadly oval; larger, more or less castaneous species.
Theresia Desvoidy
Abdomen narrower; smaller, non-castaneous......................... 50

50. Second abdominal segment without strong marginals.
Paratheresia Townsend
Second abdominal segment with a pair of strong marginals.
***Eutheresia** Townsend

51. Second abdominal segment with only one pair of marginals, or they are not spine-like 52
Second abdominal segment with three or more pairs of marginal spines; large, robust species.......**Chætogyne** Brauer & Bergenstamm

52. Claws short and thick basally, bent at almost a right angle at their middle; parafacials with inconspicuous hairs.
Myiomima Brauer & Bergenstamm
Claws normal, moderately curved apically **(118, 122)**...**Billæa** Desvoidy

53. Infrasquamal setulæ absent, abdomen always with bristles, at least on the apical segments...159
Infrasquamal setulæ present or the abdomen without well-developed bristles 54

54. Eyes thickly haired 55
Eyes bare or with inconspicuous, short, sparse hair............... 84

55. Parafacials with hairs or bristles on at least the upper half......... 56
Parafacials bare or with only a few hairs below the frontals......... 65

---

* Curran, 1929, Can. Ent., lxi, p. 33.

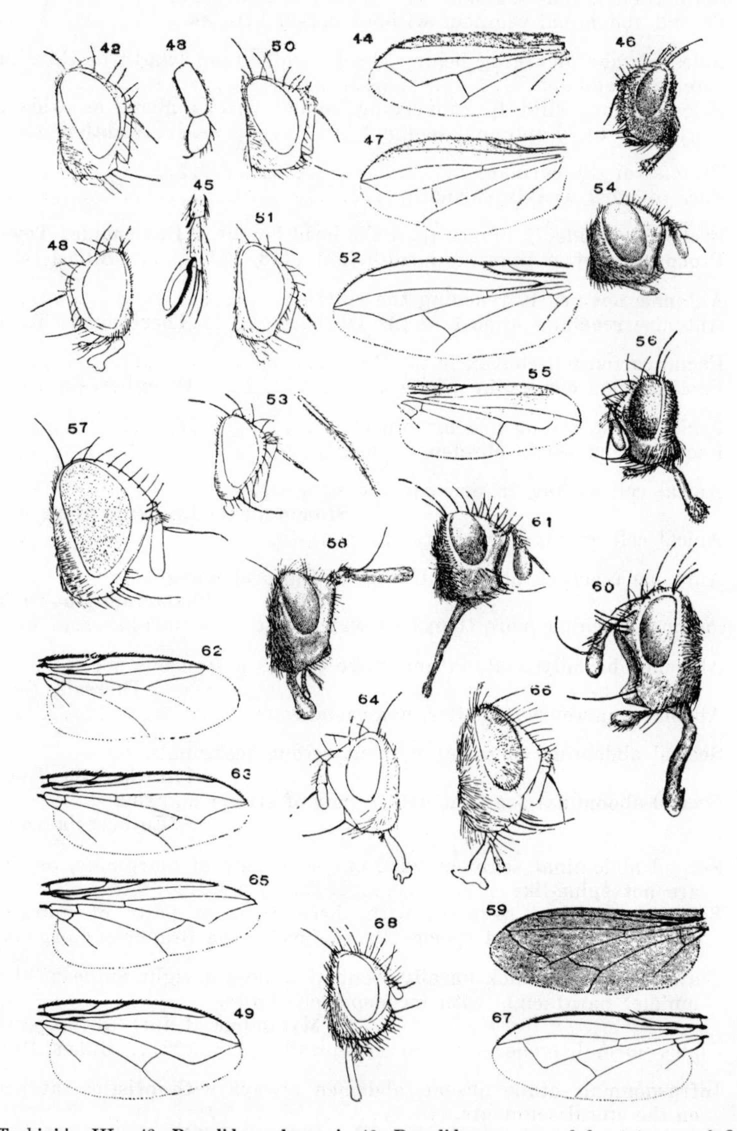

Tachinidæ III.—42, **Paradidyma braueri**; 43, **Paradidyma**, apex of front tarsus of ♀; 44, **Vanderwulpia townsendi**; 45, **Paradidyma braueri**, front tarsus of male; 46, **Spallanzania**; 47, **Beskia cornuta**; 48, 49, **Spathidexia dunningi**; 50, 51, Genera incert.; 52, **Paradidyma braueri**; 53, **Vanderwulpia townsendi**; 54, **Cylindromyia**; 55, **Catharosia nebulosa**; 56, **Gymnochæta**; 57, **Zenillia** 58, 59, **Penthosia satanica**; 60, **Paradejeania**; 61, **Cuphocera**; 62, **Taxigramma** (Metopiidæ); 63, 64, **Icelia triquetra**; 65, 66, **Uramya halesidotæ**; 67, 68, **Leucostoma.**

56. Ultimate section of fifth vein not over one-third as long as the preceding section, or the parafacials without bristles.................. 58
Ultimate section of fifth vein at least half as long as the preceding section; parafacials with one or more proclinate bristles.......... 57

57. Inner end of posterior crossvein lying immediately behind the anterior crossvein ....**Plagia** Meigen
Discal crossvein lying well beyond the anterior crossvein.
Cyrtophlœba Rondani

58. Fourth vein angulate or with sharp curve; abdomen with strong bristles 59
Fourth vein approaching the third in a gentle curve; abdomen with only weak bristles apically......**Gymnophania** Brauer & Bergenstamm

59. Parafacials without bristles along their inner edges, sometimes with bristly hairs along their middle................................ 61
Parafacials with a row of bristles along their inner edges........... 60

60. Basal two aristal segments short; antennæ simple in both sexes......60a
Basal aristal segments very elongate; third antennal segment of male composed of two or three arms **(103, 104)**........**Dichocera** Williston

60a. Third antennal segment but little longer than the second.
Muscopteryx Townsend
Third antennal segment several times as long as the second **(42, 43, 45, 52, 96)**......................**Paradidyma** Brauer & Bergenstamm

61. Parafacials without strikingly long hair, or it is irregularly spaced.... 62
Parafacials with the hairs arranged in a median series and increasingly long and strong below..................*__Eulasiona__ Townsend

62. Bend of fourth vein with at most a distinct fold.................... 63
Bend of fourth vein with a long appendage.
Metopomuscopteryx Townsend

63. Three pairs of presutural acrostical bristles or three presutural dorsocentrals ....**Lydina** Desvoidy
At most two pairs of presutural acrostical bristles................. 64

64. Two pairs of presutural acrosticals and dorsocentrals **(35, 139)**.
Myiophasia Brauer & Bergenstamm
A single pair of presutural acrosticals and two pairs of dorsocentrals. **Townsendina,** n. g.

65. Facial ridges without strong bristles............................. 69
Facial ridges with strong bristles on lower half or more........... 66

66. Parafacials not wider than antennæ............................... 67
Parafacials much wider than antennæ; oral margin scarcely produced.
Myiopharus Brauer & Bergenstamm

67. Arista long plumose................................**Comyops** Wulp
Arista at most very short plumose.................................. 68

68. Ocellars strong; face not strongly retreating below; female piercer as long as the abdomen.....................**Spathimyia** Townsend
Ocellars absent or hairlike; face strongly retreating.
Paralispe Brauer & Bergenstamm

---

* Curran, 1927, Bull. Brooklyn Ent. Soc., xxii, p. 149.

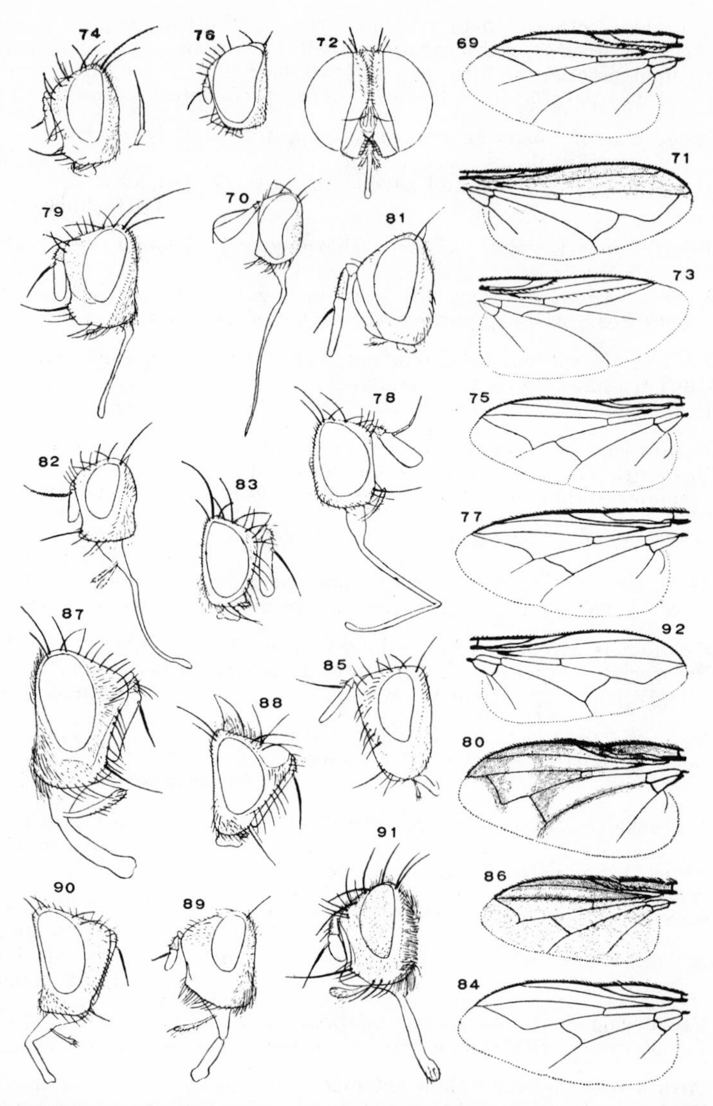

Tachinidæ IV.—69, **Plagiomima anomala**; 70, **Beskia cornuta**; 71, **Xanthomelana arcuata**; 72, **Pachyophthalmus floridensis** (Metopiidæ); 73, 74, **Goniochæta plagioides**; 75, **Pachyophthalmus floridensis** (Metopiidæ); 76, **Xanthomelana arcuata**; 77, **Linnæmya**; 78, **Siphona**; 79, **Plagiomima anomala**; 80, 81, **Euthera tentatrix**; 82, **Epigrimyia**; 83, **Chætoplagia**; 84, 85, **Euthyprosopa petiolata**; 86, **Chætoplagia**; 87, **Chætogædia analis**; 88, **Metopia** (Metopiidæ); 89, **Melanophrys insolita**; 90, **Opsidia gonioides** (Metopiidæ); 91, **Hystricia**; 92, **Chryseria flava**.

69. Not metallic green or blue.. 70
Metallic green or blue...........**Chrysotachina** Brauer & Bergenstamm

70. Parafrontals pollinose, at most bare at the vertex................ 71
Parafrontals shining black ....**Polidaria** n. g.

71. Oral margin not strongly oblique in front nor carried strongly upward toward the base of the antennæ; antennæ situated at or above the middle of the eyes; oral margin produced or not............ 72
Oral margin and antennal base unusually approximated, the oral margin strongly oblique in front; antennæ situated below the middle of the eyes; parafacials always with many hairs below the frontals.
Lydina Desvoidy

72. Ocellar bristles strong.. 75
Ocellars absent or very weak....................................... 73

73. Antennæ inserted at upper fourth of eyes; bend of fourth vein with stump (**141, 167**)...........................**Xanthophyto** Townsend
Antennæ inserted at middle of eyes; bend of fourth vein without stump 74

74. Arista plumose (**188, 195**)..............................**Zonalia,** n. g.
Arista short pubescent or bare (**146, 161, 166, 187**)......**Corozalia, n. g.**

75. Head almost as long below as at the antennæ, the oral margin produced; vibrissæ usually situated above oral margin............. 77
Face retreating below; vibrissæ level with oral margin............ 76

76. Fifth vein bristled............................**Minthoplagia** Townsend
Fifth vein bare.. 78

77. Palpi of normal length, more or less swollen apically.............. 78
Palpi not more than half the usual length, never widened apically; fourth vein with long appendage at bend (**77**)....**Linnæmya** Desvoidy

78. Pteropleural bristle extending to the apex of the squamæ........... 81
Pteropleural bristle normal.. 79

79. Face about as long below as at the antennæ....................... 80
Face strongly receding.........................**Thelairodoria** Townsend

80. Abdomen long and slender...............................**Oxydexia** Bigot
Abdomen short, robust................................**Mericia** Desvoidy

81. Posterior pair of presutural acrosticals situated very close to the suture 82
Posterior pair of presutural acrosticals situated far before the suture; female ocellars reclinate; male with outer verticals.
Trafoia Brauer & Bergenstamm

82. Pleura with fine, pale pile below; third antennal segment rounded apically ....**Neoerigone** Townsend
Pleura wholly black haired... 83

83. Front tarsi of female broadened; third antennal segment rectangular at upper apex (**142**) (**Exoristoides** Coquillett, **Exoristopsis** Townsend) ....*__Eversmannia__ Desvoidy
Third antennal segment rounded at upper apex.........**Mericina** Curran

---

* The genera **Neoerigone, Eversmannia** and **Mericina** are so poorly distinguished that I think they should be united. For key to species see Aldrich, Proc. U. S. N. M., lxxxi, Art. 9, p. 24 (**Exoristoides**).

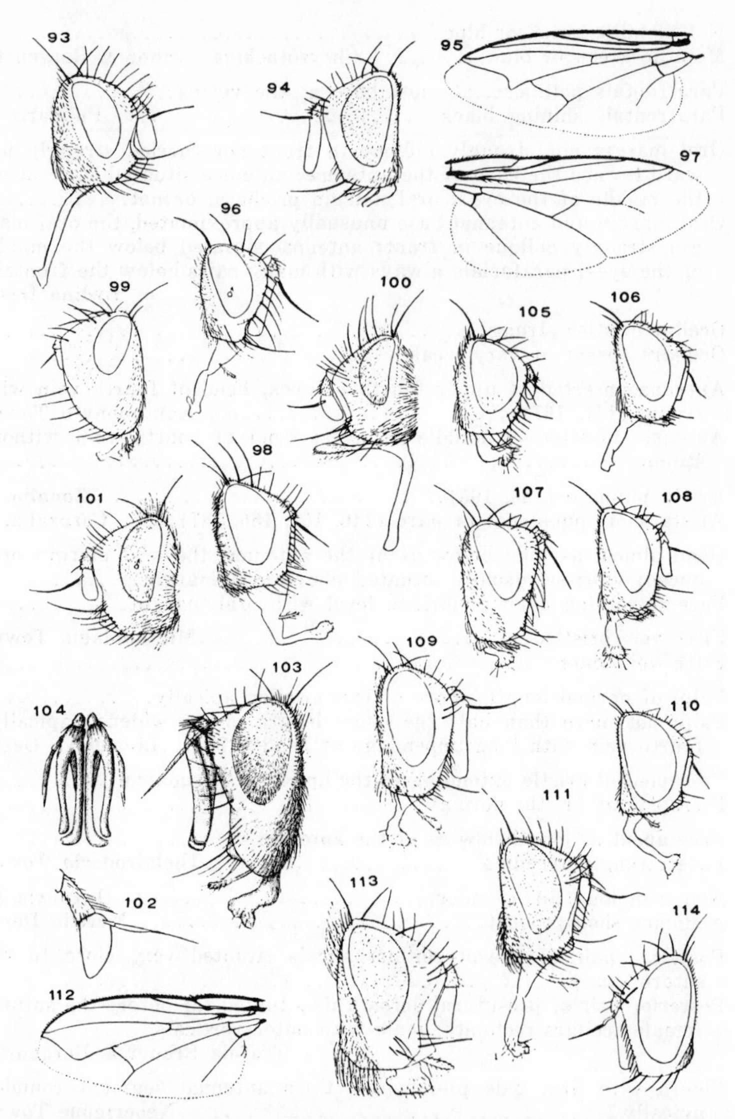

Tachinidæ V.—93, **Fischeria flava**; 94, **Zenillia**; 95, **Jurinia**; 96, **Paradidyma singularis**; 97, 98, **Stomatomya parvipalpis**; 99, **Microphthalma disjuncta**; 100, **Pseudohystricia**; 101, **Microtrichoma?**; 102, **Archytas californica**; 103, **Dichocera lyrata**; 104, **Dichocera lyrata**, antenna; 105, **Muscopteryx**; 106, **Hilarella** (Metopiidæ); 107, **Neotractocera**; 108, **Viviania**; 109, **Achætoneura**; 110, **Senotainia** (Metopiidæ); 111, **Gædiopsis**; 112, **Genea analis**; 113, **Bombyliopsis**; 114, **Chætoglossa**, proboscis omitted.

84. Arista pubescent or bare....................................100
Arista at least short plumose on basal half........................ 85

85. Oral margin distinctly produced.................................. 96
Oral margin scarcely prominent, the face almost vertical............ 86

86. Width of clypeus much greater than width of third antennal segment. 87
Width of clypeus not greater than width of third antennal segment.
Macrometopa Brauer & Bergenstamm

87. Parafacials with hair.. 92
Parafacials bare 88

88. Ocellars long and strong... 91
Ocellars hairlike 89

89. First vein bare 90
First vein bristled............................**Gymnopalpus** Townsend

90. Arista short plumose on whole length; no discals on intermediate segments; first segment without marginals.....**Pseudochætona** Townsend
Arista short plumose on basal half only; abdomen with discals, the first segment with marginals **(186, 190)**...........**Chætonalia,** n. g.

91. Aristal rays as long as the width of the third antennal segment.
Ebenia Macquart
Aristal rays about half as long as the width of the third antennal segment **(169, 191)**................................**Canalia,** n. g.

92. Antennæ reaching more than half way to the oral margin.......... 93
Antennæ reaching only half way to oral margin; prosternum with a pair of bristles..............................**Myoceropsis** Townsend

93. Hair of parafacials coarse....................................... 94
Hair of parafacials very fine; first vein bare **(121, 134)**.**Cholomyia** Bigot

94. Apical cell ending near the wing-tip............................. 95
Apical cell ending far before the wing-tip...........**Microchætina** Wulp

95. First vein setose **(154, 180)**........................**Schwarzalia,** n. g.
First vein bare...................................**Parazelia** Townsend

96. Proboscis, measured from base of apical section, at most slightly longer than length of oral opening............................. 97
Proboscis twice as long as length of oral opening.
Mochlosoma Brauer & Bergenstamm

97. Apical cell closed and short petiolate........................... 98
Apical cell broadly open (**Clinoneura,** B.B.; **Paramyocera** Towns.) **(119, 124, 125, 133)**..........................***Rhynchiodexia** Bigot

98. Third vein setose less than half way to the anterior crossvein........ 99
Third vein setose to the anterior crossvein............**Megerlea** Desvoidy

99. Bend of fourth vein with long appendage.........**Hypenomyia** Townsend
Bend of fourth vein with at most a very short appendage.
Dinera Desvoidy

100. Face without a very prominent carina appearing above the antennæ in profile 101

* Curran, 1930, Bull. Amer. Mus. Nat. Hist., lxi, p. 93.

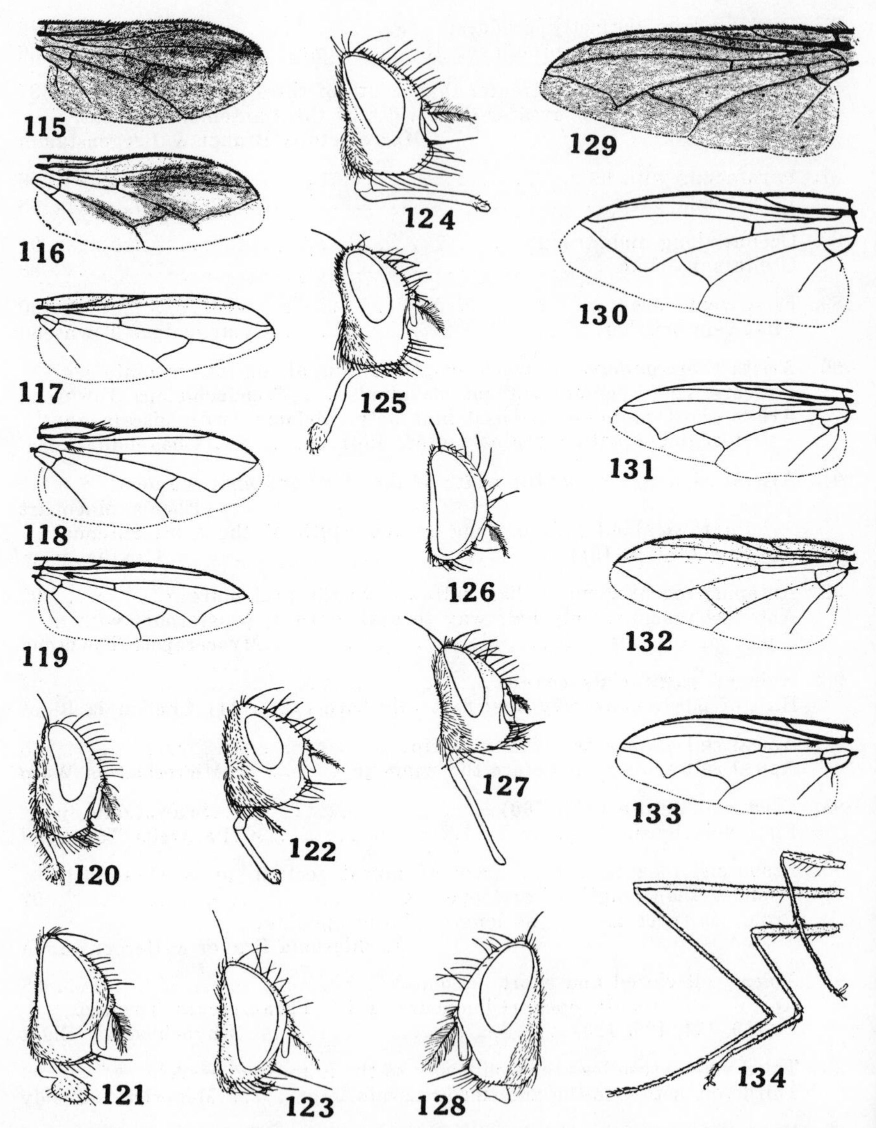

Tachinidæ VI.—115, **Melanophora**; 116, **Sophia**; 117, **Calodexia**; 118, **Billæa**; 119, **Rhynchiodexia**; 120, **Scotiptera**; 121, **Cholomyia**; 122, **Billæa**; 123, **Thelaira**; 124, 125, **Rhynchiodexia**; 126, **Calodexia**; 127, **Hystrichodexia**; 128, **Zelia**; 129, **Scotiptera melaleuca**; 130, **Hystrichodexia**; 131, **Zelia**; 132, **Chætona**; 133, **Rhynchiodexia**; 134, **Cholomyia**, legs.

Face short, with a strong facial carina, the antennal grooves deep; proboscis one-half longer than the head-height; abdomen without bristles, the apical segments with longish hairs; female genitalia with stout spines on the sides.................. **Imitomyia** Townsend

101. Second abdominal segment with at least well developed median marginals 123
Second abdominal segment without dorsal bristles................102

102. Posterior tibiæ without flattened bristles........................103
Posterior tibiæ ciliate dorsally with scale-like bristles **(163, 164)**.
Trichiopoda Latreille

103. Facial depression shallow or somewhat carinate, if deep not sub-oval in outline; arista, if wholly thickened, reddish in color...........104
Facial depression very deep and sub-oval; arista black, wholly thickened; shining black flies **(89)** ....**Melanophrys** Williston

104. Arista not wholly thickened; parafacials without transverse furrows..105
Arista wholly thickened; parafacials shining black, with many transverse furrows **(25)**.........................**Euscopolia** Townsend

105. Fourth vein strongly curved beyond the crossvein.................106
Fourth vein gently curved, the apical cell open in the wing-tip.
Gymnophania Brauer & Bergenstamm

106. Face not or but little retreating, the vibrissæ situated well above the oral margin 109
Face strongly retreating, oral vibrissæ strongly differentiated and on a level with the oral margin, or absent.........................107

107. Apical cell petiolate...108
Apical cell open near the wing-tip.............**Pseudapinops** Coquillett

108. Apical cell ending well before the wing-tip....*__Hesperophasia__ Townsend
Apical cell ending in the wing-tip **(55)**.............**Catharosia** Rondani

109. Oral vibrissæ, if strongly differentiated, situated almost level with the oral margin; abdomen short, oval, spherical or flattened, rarely elongate 110
Oral vibrissæ strongly developed, sometimes duplicated, situated well above the oral margin and without hairs above or below; abdomen long and narrow **(71, 76)**.....................**Xanthomelana** Wulp

110. Abdomen short, or if elongate not flattened........................111
Abdomen elongate and flattened; oral margin produced; apical cell petiolate; wing veins broadly bordered with black.
Bibiomima Brauer & Bergenstamm

111. Sternites broad, the female genitalia not remarkably large; oral vibrissæ usually strongly differentiated, their angle high above the oral margin; abdomen short, rather spherical in outline, strongly convex or flattened..113
Sternites linear, thread-like; second sternite large, produced downward and with very short, stout setulæ on the lower part; female genitalia very large; vibrissæ distinct, situated but little above the oral margin; palpi minute.....................................112

* Curran, 1927, Can. Ent., lix, p. 300.

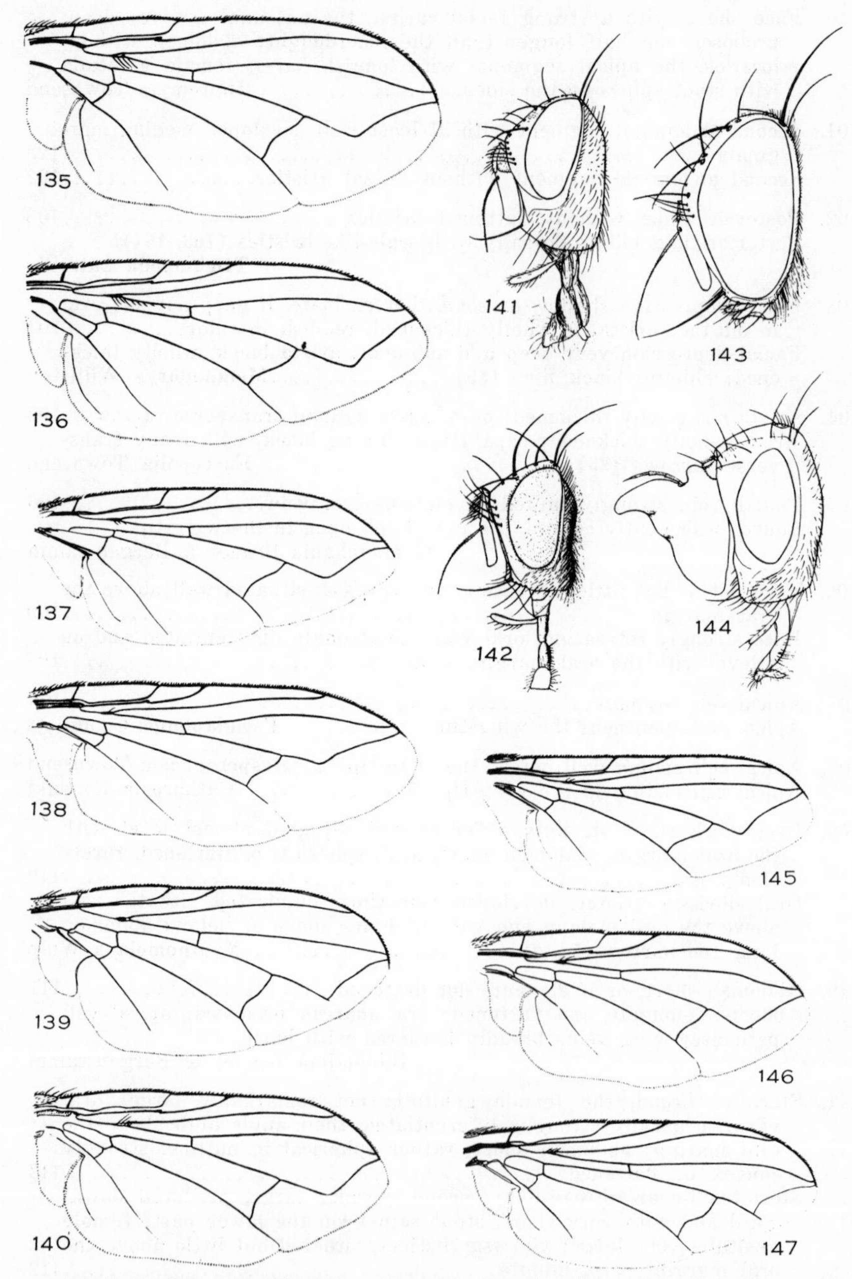

Tachinidæ VII.—135, Blondelia; 136, 137, Doryphorophaga; 138, Pelecotheca; 139, Myiophasia; 140, Compsilura; 141, Xanthophyto; 142, Eversmannia; 143, Aridalia; 144, Euryceromyia; 145, Winthemia; 146, Corozalia rufiventris; 147, Zuanalia.

112\. Apical cell long petiolate or the apical crossvein absent. **Besseria** Desvoidy
Apical cell open near the wing-tip.................. **Apinops** Coquillett

113\. Oral vibrissæ situated high above the oral margin or not strongly differentiated; if the abdomen bears bristles the apical cell is open.117
Oral vibrissæ strongly developed, level with the strongly produced oral margin 114

114\. Apical cell long petiolate (55)..................... **Catharosia** Rondani
Apical cell open or closed in or near the wing-tip..................115

115\. Parafacials bare on lower half.................................116
Parafacials with bristly hairs................... **Chiricahuia** Townsend

116\. Abdomen with bristles........................ **Erythromelana** Townsend
Abdomen with weak, bristly hairs apically; apical crossvein absent. **Bezzimyia** Townsend

117\. Anterior femora with only the usual fine or bristly hairs beneath..118
Anterior femora on the apical half of the ventral edges with row of short stout, bristly setulæ.................. **Gymnosoma** Meigen

118\. Abdomen flattened or twice as long as wide.......................119
Abdomen strongly convex, hemispherical (10)..... **Cistogaster** Latreille

119\. Apical cell broadly open or closed in the costa near the wing-tip.....120
Apical cell long petiolate...122

120\. Abdomen without bristles..121
Abdomen with well developed bristles on the apical segments. **Trichoclytia** Townsend

121\. A row of dorsocentrals, one situated in front of the suture (92). **Chryseria** Desvoidy
At most two pairs of conspicuous dorsocentrals......... **Phasia** Latreille

122\. Pleura with very dense pale hairs above (15, 20, 21, 22). **Alophora** Desvoidy
Pleura with ordinary black hairs and bristles....... **Hyalomya** Desvoidy

123\. Parafacials with one or more downwardly directed bristles below the frontal row or with hairs extending to or below the middle.......124
Parafacials with at most a few hairs below the lowest frontals......138

124\. With one or more downwardly directed parafacial bristles..........125
Without strong parafacial bristles, the hairs sometimes stout but always weaker than the lower frontals..........................129

125\. Apical cell open; apical section of fifth vein over half as long as the preceding section 126
Apical cell long petiolate....................*__Hesperophasia__ Townsend

126\. Parafacials with several downwardly directed bristles..............127
Parafacials with a single downwardly directed bristle (8). **Voria** Desvoidy

---
* Curran, 1927, Can. Ent., p. 300.

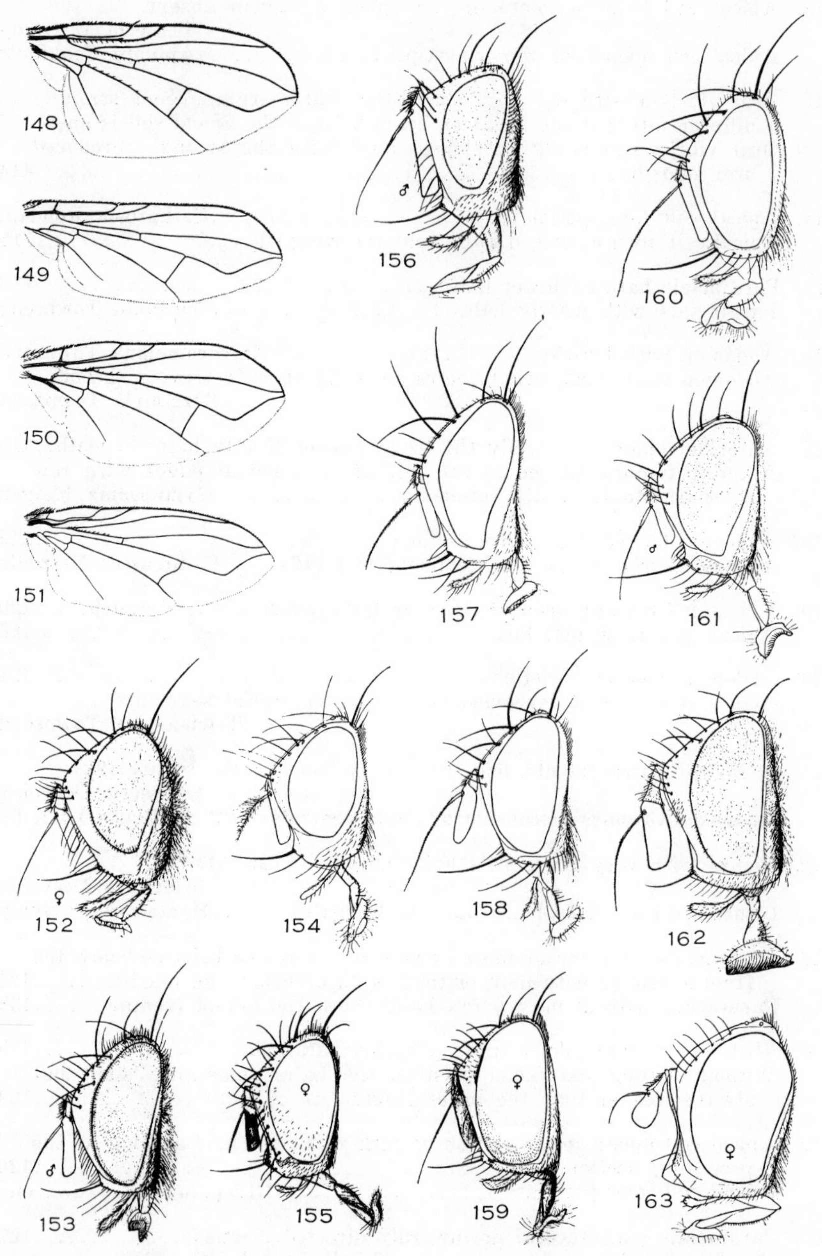

Tachinidæ VIII.—148, **Actia**; 149, **Elodia**; 150, **Epigrimyia**; 151, **Thelairalia**; 152, **Pelecotheca**; 153, **Doryphorophaga**; 154, **Schwarzalia**; 155, **Ricosia**; 156, **Compsilura**; 157, **Thelairalia**; 158, **Patillalia**; 159, **Anacamptomyia americana**; 160, **Agrarialia**; 161, **Corozalia**; 162, **Winthemia**; 163, **Trichiopoda**.

127. Pteropleural bristle normal....................................128
Pteropleural bristle reaching to the apex of the squamæ.
Meleterus Aldrich

128. Face retreating below..............................**Pædarium** Aldrich
Face as long below as at the antennæ............**Chætovoria** Villeneuve

129. Oral vibrissæ situated level with the oral margin; posterior crossvein situated near the middle of the wing............................130
Oral vibrissæ either situated well above the oral margin or the posterior crossvein near the apical third of the wing................133

130. Cheeks very much narrower than the eye-height..................131
Cheeks almost or quite as wide as the eye-height....***Uclesia** Girschner

131. Facial depression broad and shallow, the edges rather flattened......132
Facial depression deep and narrow, the edges prominent.
Menetus Aldrich

132. Parafacials rather narrow, with small hairs over a considerable part of the surface ....**Metavoria** Townsend
Parafacials wide ....**Metaplagia** Coquillett

133. Apical cell at most extremely short petiolate.......................134
Apical cell long petiolate...137

134. Face strongly receding below; third antennal segment about three times as long as the second; three pairs of strong scutellars, the apical pair widely spaced and divergent........... 136
Face usually but little receding; third antennal segment less than twice as long as the second..135

135. Costal spine short; facial depression rather narrow (**35, 139**).
Myiophasia Townsend
Costal spine long and strong; facial depression wide.....**Lasionalia, n. g.**

136. First vein setulose on apical half................**Meigeniella** Coquillett
First vein bare (34)..........†**Cryptomeigenia** Brauer & Bergenstamm

137. Third vein ending near the wing-tip (32, 33).......**Rhinophora** Desvoidy
Third vein ending far before the wing-tip........**Steveniopsis** Townsend

138. Frontal vitta opaque...139
Frontal vitta shining black (**37, 38**)..................**Hemyda** Desvoidy

139. Posterior tibiæ without scale-like bristles..........................140
Posterior tibiæ ciliate above with scale-like bristles (**102, 139**).
Trichiopoda Latreille

140. Anterior femora with a row of long bristles on at least the apical half of the posteroventral surface, appearing as widely spaced cilia.141
Anterior femora with at most two or three posteroventral bristles apically; the hairs on the posterior surface wholly appressed (**18, 19**) ....**Acaulona** Wulp

141. Apical cell open, or if closed in the wing margin there are hairs about the base of the vibrissæ..143
Apical cell closed and petiolate...................................142

---

* Curran, 1927, Can. Ent., p. 299.
† Curran, 1926, Tr. Roy. Soc. Canada, Sec. v, p. 156.

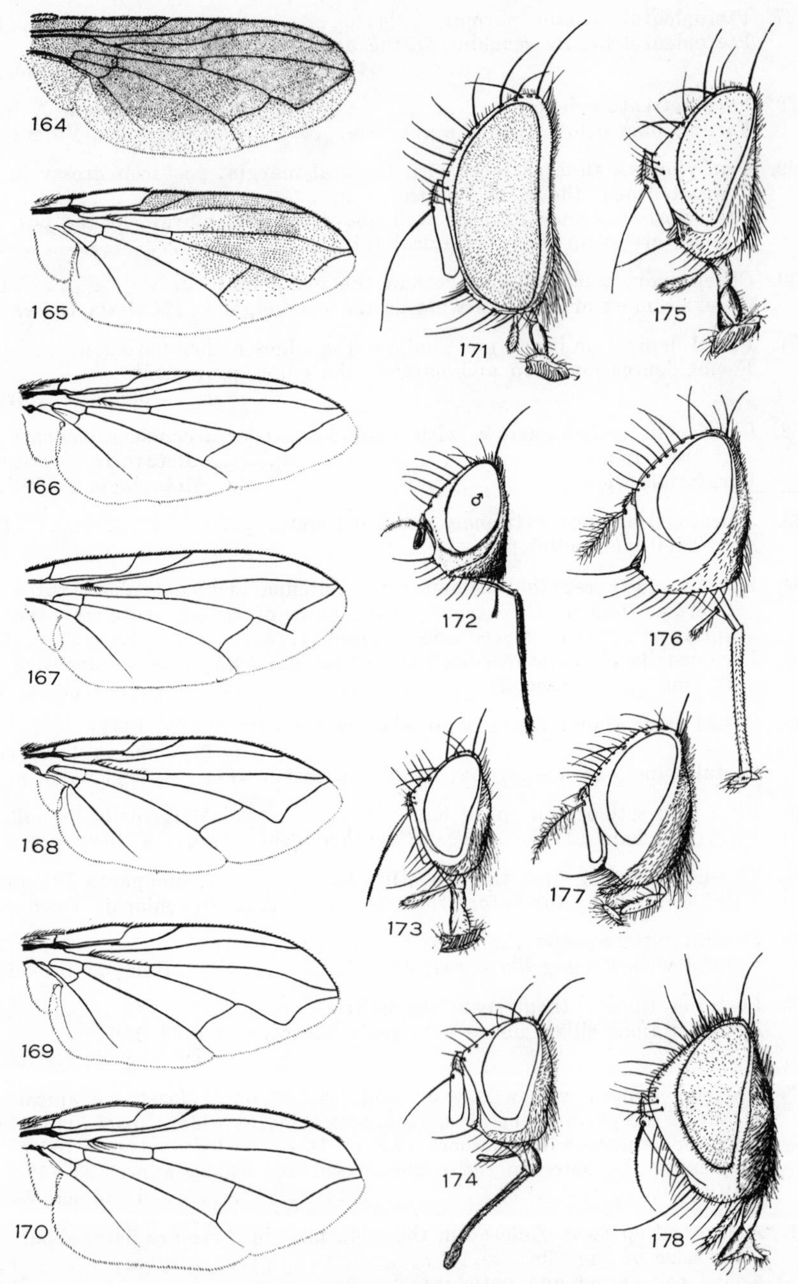

Tachinidæ IX.—164, **Trichiopoda**; 165, **Patillalia**; 166, **Corozalia panamensis**; 167, **Xanthophyto**; 168, **Aridalia**; 169, **Canalia**; 170, **Oxynopsalia**; 171, **Anadiscalia**; 172, **Prorhynchops? errans**; 173, **Elodia**; 174, **Epigrimyia**; 175, **Doryphorophaga**; 176, **Shermanalia**; 177, **Zuanalia**; 178, **Pseudeuantha.**

142. No hairs surrounding the oral vibrissæ which are situated high above the oral margin; abdomen long and slender (**71, 76**). **Xanthomelana** Wulp
Vibrissæ situated level with the oral margin, or if somewhat above with a few hairs near their base; abdomen, from dorsal view, spherical in outline............................*Clistomorpha Townsend

143. Oral vibrissæ differentiated; oral margin not rounded anteriorly in profile 144
Oral vibrissæ not differentiated, or only very weakly so; head convex below in profile; clypeal region narrow and at least two-thirds as long as upper part of face.......................**Eutrixa** Coquillett

144. Costal spine not greatly developed, never longer than the width of the costal cell and not conspicuous................................145
Costal spine as long as width of costal and subcostal cells combined; vibrissæ level with oral margin; parafacials gently convex in profile. **Phrynofrontina** Townsend

145. Face strongly retreating, vibrissæ level with oral margin or situated moderately above; three or four pairs of marginal scutellars and sometimes a weak apical pair which may be cruciate; arista rarely thickened to beyond the middle, the penultimate segment never elongate 153
Face almost as long below as at base of antennæ; arista often thickened to the apical fourth and with the penultimate segment elongate 146

146. Arista not thickened on its whole length; facial depression not oval and deeply sunken 147
Arista thickened on its whole length; facial depression oval and very deep (**89**)................................**Melanophrys** Williston

147. Parafacials more or less yellowish in ground color; abdomen usually largely yellow and extensively pollinose..........................148
Parafacials silvery pollinose on a black ground; abdomen shining black, the sides sometimes broadly red; vibrissæ level with oral margin ....**Dionæa** Desvoidy

148. Cheeks more than one-tenth as wide as the eye-height; female abdomen not truncate at apex from lateral view...................149
Cheeks at most one-fifteenth as wide as the eye-height; arista short plumose; ocellars absent or very weak (**117**).........†**Calodexia** Wulp

149. Vibrissal angles not approximated, or if so the vibrissæ situated level with the oral margin...150
Vibrissal angles conspicuously approximated, the vibrissæ situated above the oral margin (**92**).......................**Chryseria** Desvoidy

150. Anterior crossvein situated half way between the tip of the auxiliary and first veins; posterior crossvein but little oblique.............151
Anterior crossvein situated behind the tip of the first vein; posterior crossvein very oblique......................**Catalinovoria** Townsend

151. Vibrissæ situated distinctly above the oral margin; oral margin not prominent (**108**)..............................**Viviania** Rondani
Vibrissæ level with oral margin..152

* Curran, 1927, Can. Ent., lix, p. 297.
† Curran, 1934, Amer. Mus. Novit. No. 685.

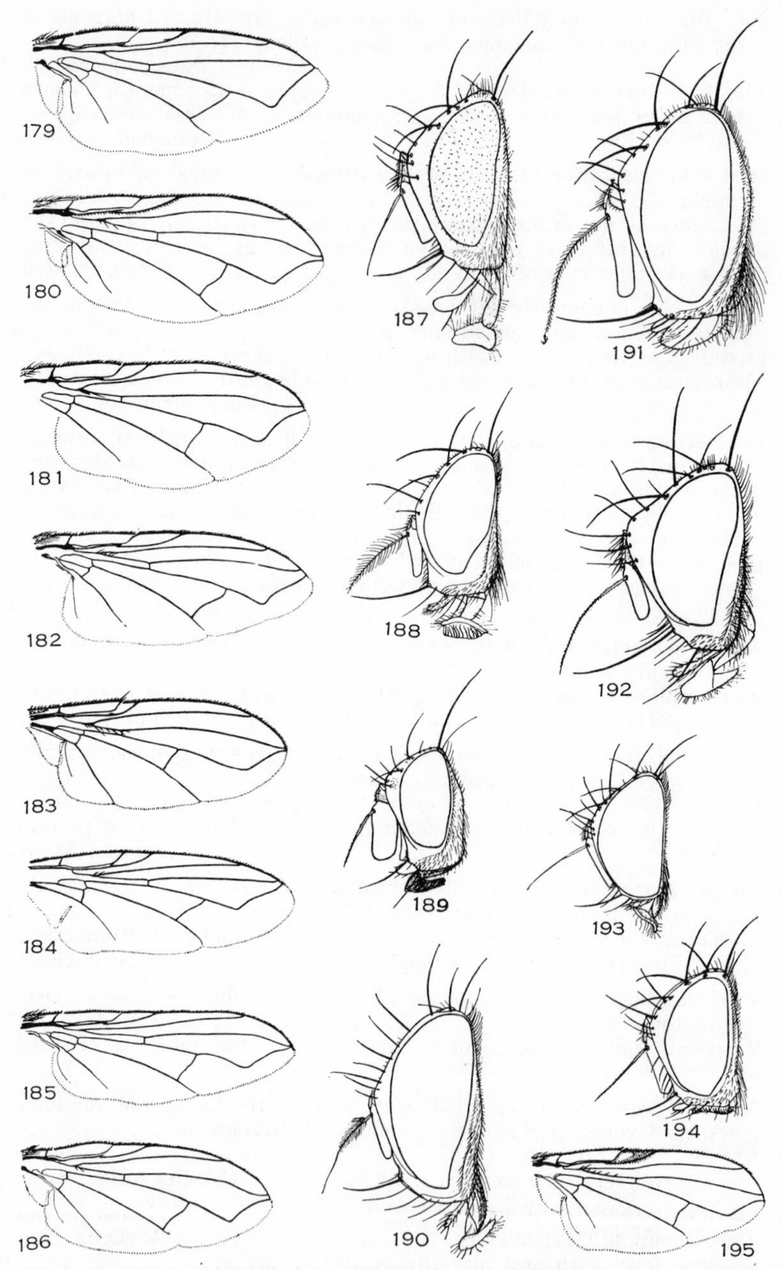

Tachinidæ X.—179, **Agrarialia**; 180, **Schwarzalia**; 181, **Microtownsendia**; 182, **Anadiscalia**; 183, **Siphona**; 184, **Pseudeuantha**; 185, **Shermanalia**; 186, **Chætonalia**; 187, **Corozalia**; 188, **Zonalia**; 189, **Actia**; 190, **Chætonalia**; 191, **Canalia**; 192, **Blondelia**; 193, **Microtownsendia**; 194, **Oxynopsalia**; 195, **Zonalia**.

152. Proboscis very long and slender; ovipositor normal. **Ginglimyia** Townsend
Proboscis short, the labellæ fleshy; ovipositor as long as abdomen. **Xiphomyia** Townsend

153. Ocellars distinct 155
Ocellars absent; three sternopleurals 154

154. Abdomen broad, oval as in **Sturmia** .... **Proroglula** Townsend
Abdomen rather narrow, tapering .... **Lixinia** Curran

155. Vibrissæ situated above the oral margin, the oral margin not prominent (**108**) .... **Viviania** Rondani
Vibrissæ practically level with the oral margin, the oral margin slightly produced 156

156. Two or three pairs of presutural acrosticals, the middle pair always strong 157
One or two pairs of weak presutural acrosticals. **Ochromeigenia** Townsend

157. First vein bare 158
First vein setulose .... **Thelairochætona** Townsend

158. Anterior tibiæ with a single posterior bristle .... **Erycioides** Curran
Anterior tibiæ with two posterior bristles (**Lydella** auct.) (**135, 192**). *__Blondelia__ Desvoidy

159. Eyes with long or dense hair 160
Eyes bare or with inconspicuous, short sparse hair 235

160. Parafacials with hairs or bristles extending to the lower half 161
Parafacials with at most a few hairs below the frontals 181

161. Palpi normal in length, usually thickened apically 162
Palpi greatly reduced, slender, never much more than twice the length of the thickness of proboscis at point of attachment; bend of fourth vein with long appendage (**77**) .... **Linnæmya** Desvoidy

162. Frontal bristles not extending below the upper third of the face, normally only one situated below the base of the third antennal segment, the parafacials with other hairs or bristles at least above 163
Frontals extending to the middle of the third antennal segment; pteropleural reaching to the apex of the squamæ .... **Lypha** Desvoidy

163. Facial ridges not bristled on more than the lowest fourth or the ocellars proclinate 165
Facial ridges bristled on at least the lower half; ocellars absent or reclinate 164

164. Ocellars absent .... **Tritaxys** Macquart
Ocellars reclinate .... **Distichona** Wulp

165. Penultimate aristal segment rarely twice as long as wide, the preceding segment always short 166
Basal two aristal segments greatly elongate .... **Digonichæta** Rondani

166. Abdomen with strong discals 173
Abdomen without strong discals 167

167. Apical cell long petiolate 168
Apical cell open 169

* Curran, 1927, Can. Ent. lix, p. 12 (**Lydella**).

168. Penultimate aristal segment elongate........... **Paradmontia** Coquillett
Penultimate aristal segment very short, the arista strongly thickened at the base.. **Websteriana** Walton

169. Posterior tibiæ evenly and closely ciliate with bristles; hair of parafacials fine 170
Posterior tibiæ not ciliate or the parafacial hair coarse..............171

170. Facial ridges bristled on almost the lower half.... **Sturmiopsis** Townsend
Facial ridges bristled on not more than the lowest third **(145, 162)**.
* **Winthemia** Desvoidy

171. Parafacials with bristly hair or a row of bristles..................172
Parafacials with two bristles below............. **Chromatocera** Townsend

172. Ocellars proclinate **(42, 43, 45, 52, 96)**.
Paradidyma Brauer & Bergenstamm
Ocellars reclinate **(155)**.............................. **Ricosia** Curran

173. Third antennal segment not more than twice as long as the second...178
Third antennal segment more than twice as long as the second.......174

174. Apical cell long petiolate...175
Apical cell not long petiolate......................................176

175. First vein setulose on basal half................ **Paradmontia** Coquillett
First vein bare.................................... **Mauromyia** Townsend

176. Penultimate aristal segment short.................................177
Penultimate aristal segment elongate; parafacials with two bristles below .... **Chromatocera** Townsend

177. Two presutural acrosticals..................... **Ictericophyto** Townsend
Three presutural acrosticals **(111)**..... **Gædiopsis** Brauer & Bergenstamm

178. Second antennal segment, if elongate, clothed with sparse, fine bristly hairs on the upper surface.......................................179
Second antennal segment as long as the third, very densely bristled above; cheeks one-third as wide as the eye-height **(105)**.
Muscopteryx Townsend

179. Vibrissæ situated on a level with the oral margin..................180
Vibrissæ situated well above the oral margin; parafacials almost as wide as the third antennal segment................ **Meriana** Desvoidy

180. Ocellars absent; prosternum bare.. **Bombyliomyia** Brauer & Bergenstamm
Ocellars long, though weak, prosternum pilose......... **Tachinalia, n. g.**

181. Palpi of normal length and shape, if apparently short, broadened apically 182
Palpi short and narrow, seldom twice as long as thickness of proboscis at point of attachment; bend of fourth vein with appendage **(77)**.
Linnæmya Desvoidy

182. Facial ridges with strong bristles on lower half or more...........183
Facial ridges with bristly hairs decreasing in length upwardly, rarely extending almost half way..204

183. Ocellars long, readily distinguished...................................190
Ocellars absent or hair-like..184

---

* Reinhard, 1931, Pr. U. S. N. M., lxxix, Art. 20, pp. 1-54.

184. Three sternopleurals; face strongly receding, gently convex in profile; abdomen with discals....186
Sternopleurals 1-1; face receding, not convex....185

185. Front slightly longer than the face, the antennæ arising near the middle of the eyes in profile **(138, 152)**....**Pelecotheca** Townsend
Front much shorter than the face, the antennæ arising near the upper fourth of the eyes in profile **(140, 156)**....**Compsilura** Bouché

186. Face strongly receding; basicosta black....187
Face gently receding; basicosta yellow **(159)**....**Anacamptomyia** Bischoff

187. With only two pairs of orbitals in both sexes or the frontal vitta half as wide as either parafrontal....188
With a row of orbitals in both sexes; frontal vitta narrow. **Metopiops** Townsend

188. Fourth abdominal segment with discals....189
Fourth abdominal segment without discals....**Phænopsis** Townsend

189. Frontal vitta two-thirds as wide as either parafrontal. **Paralispe** Brauer & Bergenstamm
Frontal vitta not half as wide as either parafrontal. ***Argyrophylax** Brauer & Bergenstamm

190. Pteropleural bristle not nearly reaching the apex of the lower squamal lobe....191
Pteropleural bristle extending to the apex of the lower squamal lobe; posterior sublateral bristle absent....**Lypha** Desvoidy

191. Penultimate segment of arista not over twice as long as wide....193
Penultimate segment of arista at least three times as long as wide...192

192. Front with a row of bristles outside of the frontals. **Madremyia** Townsend
Front without a row of bristles outside the frontals. **Murdockiana** Townsend

193. Third antennal segment never with more than three branches....194
Third antennal segment with a large number of branches on either side....**Cryptocladocera** Bezzi

194. Head decidedly more than half as long as high; parafacials wide or the face much wider than either eye, always wider than the front..195
Head half as long as high; parafacials less than half as wide as the elongate third antennal segment; face but little wider than the front, scarcely retreating, its sides parallel on the lower three-fourths **(159)**....**Anacamptomyia** Bischoff

195. Frontal bristles not extending below the base of the arista....196
Frontal bristles extending to the middle of the third antennal segment....**Thrycolyga** Rondani

196. Two or more bristles below the base of the antennæ....197
A single bristle below the base of the antennæ....**Cyzenis** Desvoidy

197. Abdomen of ordinary form, decidedly wider than deep, the genitalia usually exposed, at least not enclosed in a slit-like opening......198

* Curran, 1929, Suppl. to Gowdey's Catalogue Dipt. Jamaica, p. 28.

Abdomen in both sexes wide and deep, the terminal segment large, normally concealing the genitalia within a slit-like opening. *Pateloa Townsend

198. Middle coxæ of female with normal bristles; males without orbitals..199
Middle coxæ of female with closely placed, curved apical spines; males with two pairs of orbitals (**136, 137, 153, 175**). **Doryphorophaga** Townsend

199. Posterior sublateral bristle present..............................200
Posterior sublateral absent ....†**Phorocera** Desvoidy

200. Abdomen with discals...201
Abdomen without discals..........................**Euthelaira** Townsend

201. Ocellars long and strong...202
Ocellars weak; posterior presutural acrostical absent. **Eupelecotheca** Townsend

202. Ocellars proclinate 203
Ocellars reclinate ....**Coloradalia,** n. g.

203. Anterior tibiæ with two posterior bristles; apical cell ending far before the wing-tip (**Amphichæta** B. B.)...........†**Phorocera** Desvoidy

Anterior tibiæ with a single posterior bristle; apical cell ending close to the wing-tip (**170, 194**)........................**Oxynopsalia,** n. g.

204. Not metallic green or blue.......................................206
Metallic green or blue...205

205. Oral margin strongly produced................**Chlorotachina** Townsend
Oral margin scarcely produced (**56**).............**Gymnochæta** Desvoidy

206. Pteropleural bristle of normal length or weak, if long the parafrontals are shining black or the frontal bristles do not extend below the base of the arista 209
Pteropleural very long and strong, extending to the apex of the squamæ; frontals usually extending to the middle of the third antennal segment; parafrontals pollinose...........................207

207. Male without orbitals; parafacials almost or fully half as wide as third antennal segment..208
Male with orbitals; parafacials below not over one-fourth as wide as the elongate third antennal segment; front wide in both sexes. **Homalactia** Townsend

208. Frontal bristles extending to the middle of the parafacials. **Lypha** Desvoidy
Frontals not extending below the base of the arista.**Hineomyia** Townsend

209. Parafrontals pollinose 210
Parafrontals bare; pteropleural long; apical cell terminating near the wing-tip; abdomen shining black.....................**Polidaria** n. g.

210. Fifth longitudinal vein bare.....................................212
Fifth longitudinal vein setose....................................211

---

* Aldrich and Webber, 1924, Pr. U. S. N. M., lxiii, Art. 17, pp. 45, 51 (**Phorocera**).
† Aldrich and Webber, 1924, Pr. U. S. N. M., lxiii, Art. 17, pp. 45, 51.

211. Penultimate aristal segment nearly three times as long as wide.
Acronaristopsis Townsend
Penultimate aristal segment less than twice as long as wide.
Minthoplagia Townsend

212. Posterior sublateral bristle present....................................225
Posterior sublateral bristle absent....................................213

213. Penultimate aristal segment not over twice as long as wide..........214
Penultimate aristal segment and the preceding one more than twice as long as wide............................**Ostracophyto** Townsend

214. Oral margin strongly produced; face never carinate................215
Oral margin not or but little produced; face sometimes carinate......217

215. Abdomen broad and thick; robust species, usually with four postsutural dorsocentrals; three or more sternopleurals...............216
Abdomen elongate and narrow; three sternopleural and three pairs of postsutural dorsocentrals.........................**Eriothrix** Meigen

216. Normally only three postsutural dorsocentrals; parafacials almost as wide as the length of the third antennal segment.
Metaphyto Coquillett
Four postsutural dorsocentrals; parafacials narrower than width of third antennal segment..........................**Ernestia** Desvoidy

217. Posthumeral bristle present; bend of fourth vein sub-angulate......218
Posthumeral bristle absent....................................222

218. Two sternopleurals, rarely a very weak third.......................221
Three sternopleurals; male abdomen strongly produced apically.....219

219. Apical cell ending very close to the wing-tip..........**Cleonice** Desvoidy
Apical cell ending far before the wing-tip..........................220

220. Prosternum with bristly hairs....................................224
Prosternum bare **(65, 66)**........................*__Uramya__ Desvoidy

221. Prosternum bare **(178, 184)**..................†**Pseudeuantha** Townsend
Prosternum haired; lower squamal lobe haired above toward the outer edge; large, robust, tropical species.............**Tropidopsis** Townsend

222. Third abdominal segment with two or three arched rows of long discals ....**Grisdalemyia** Curran
Third abdominal segment with one or two pairs of discals; prosternum bare 223

223. Three sternopleurals..224
Two sternopleurals................‡**Hyalurgus** Brauer & Bergenstamm

224. Discals present on second to fourth abdominal segments.
Xanthocera Townsend
Discals absent ....**Euthelairopsis** Townsend

225. Second antennal segment usually less than half as long as the third..227
Second antennal segment almost as long as the third.............226

---

* Aldrich, 1921, Ins. Ins. Mens., ix, p. 85.
† Aldrich, 1921, Ins. Ins. Mens., ix, p. 87.
‡ Pseudeuantha may trace here but has white haired pleura.

226. Head as long below as at the antennæ; antennæ arising below the middle of the eyes............................**Tricogena** Rondani
Head shorter below than at antennæ; abdomen flattened.
*__Nemorilla__ Desvoidy

227. Vibrissæ situated at most slightly above the oral margin............229
Vibrissæ situated more than half the length of the second antennal segment above the oral margin...228

228. Abdomen with strong discals...†**Macromeigenia** Brauer & Bergenstamm
Abdomen without discals on the intermediate segments.
Bolomyia Brauer & Bergenstamm

229. Apical abdominal segment closing slit-like, deeper than wide........230
Apical abdominal segment not closing slit-like, wider than deep at the base 231

230. Several coarse setulæ below the frontals; facial depression very deep; parafacials as wide as the facial depression...**Organomyia** Townsend
No hairs below the frontals; parafacials not over half as wide as the shallower facial depression...............**Leptostylum** Macquart

231. Anterior tibiæ with at least two posterior bristles.................232
Anterior tibiæ with a single posterior bristle.......................233

232. Third antennal segment more than twice as long as wide **(57, 94)**.
‡**Zenillia** Desvoidy
Third antennal segment subtriangular, almost as wide as long.
Obolocera Townsend

233. Discals absent; abdomen broad; cheeks linear **(171, 182)**.
Anadiscalia, n. g.
Discals present; cheeks at least one-fifth the eye-height...........234

234. Frontal vitta of male very narrow; female with stout spines on the apex of the middle coxæ; abdomen broad **(136, 137, 153, 175)**.
Doryphorophaga Townsend
Frontal vitta not unusually narrow; female without spines on middle coxæ ....**Ptilodegeeria** Brauer & Bergenstamm

235. Parafacials with hair or bristles on the lower half.................236
Parafacials bare on the lower half...................................291

236. Ocellar bristles present, directed obliquely forward or divergent......248
Ocellar bristles directed obliquely backward, absent or hair-like......237

237. Ocellars directed obliquely backward.................................238
Ocellars hair-like or absent..240

238. Facial ridges with strong bristles on the lower half, or the penultimate aristal segment not over twice as long as wide; head not strongly inflated in appearance.......................................239
Facial ridges bristled on less than the lowest fourth, the head inflated in appearance; penultimate aristal segment always more than three times as long as wide **(12, 13)**......................**Gonia** Meigen

---

* Aldrich & Webber, 1924, Pr. U. S. N. M., lxiii, Art. 17, p. 5.
† Reinhard, 1930, Ent. News, xli, p. 262.
‡ Aldrich & Webber, 1924, Pr. U. S. N. M., lxiii, Art. 17, p. 11.

239. Apical cell open or closed in the wing margin **(3, 46)**. **Spallanzania** Desvoidy
Apical cell rather long petiolate....................**Aravaipa** Townsend

240. Arista plumose or strongly pubescent, the clypeal region as long as the distance from the upper pair of vibrissæ to the antennal base...249
Arista bare or weakly pubescent; oral margin produced and not narrowed 241

241. Apical cell petiolate....................242
Apical cell open....................243

242. Prosternum bare....................**Neometachæta** Townsend
Prosternum with hair and a long bristle on the sides..**Epidexia** Townsend

243. Palip absent or very slender on their whole length....................244
Palpi normal, enlarged apically....................247

244. Palpi extremely short or absent, never more than twice the length of the thickness of the proboscis at point of attachment....................245
Palpi elongate and slender, very rarely short; parafacials always with two or more bristles below **(7)**....................***Peleteria** Desvoidy

245. Parafacials with one or more bristles below **(39, 61)**.**Cuphocera** Macquart
Parafacials without bristles below....................246

246. Abdomen without discal bristles....................**Euepalpus** Townsend
Abdomen with discal bristles on intermediate segments. **Xanthozona** Townsend

247. Parafacials with one or more bristles in addition to the hair. **Chætoprosopa** Townsend
Parafacials with fine hair only......**Chætoprocta** Brauer & Bergenstamm

248. Clypeal region not long and narrow, short and not conspicuous, cheeks rarely more than half as wide as the eye-height....................251
Clypeal region long and narrow; cheeks two-thirds as wide as the eye-height 249

249. Posterior sublateral bristle absent....................250
Posterior sublateral bristle present; sternites with at most weak bristles **(99)**....................**†Microphthalma** Macquart

250. Sternites with long, very strong bristles........**Megaprosopus** Macquart
Sternites without strong bristles....................**Megaparia** Wulp

251. Palpi normal in shape and length.................... 254
Palpi absent or reduced to about half the normal length, wholly slender and bearing only one or two apical bristles....................252

252. Apical cell open....................253
Apical cell long petiolate **(115)**....................**Melanophora** Meigen

253. Palpi absent or extremely small; large, robust, **Archytas**-like species, the apical cell ending far before the wing-tip..**Vibrossomyia** Townsend
Palpi about half the normal length; apical cell ending close to the wing-tip ....**Atrophopalpus** Townsend

* Curran, 1925, Trans. Roy. Soc. Canada, Section V, p. 226.
† Aldrich, 1926, Pr. U. S. N. M., lxix, Art. 13, p. 2.

254. Ultimate section of fifth vein less than half as long as the preceding section 261
Ultimate section of fifth vein or its fold more than half as long as the preceding section...255

255. Parafacials with one or more downwardly directed bristles.........256
Parafacials with only short hairs...................................260

256. Pteropleural bristle extending to the apex of the squamæ...........257
Pteropleural bristle of normal length..............................258

257. Posterior crossvein lying wholly beyond the anterior crossvein. **Blepharigena** Rondani
Posterior crossvein situated partly before the anterior crossvein (**73, 74**) ....**Goniochæta** Townsend

258. Arista short plumose ....**Microchætina** Wulp
Arista bare 259

259. Parafacials more than two-thirds as wide as the facial depression. **Cockerelliana** Townsend
Parafacials narrow (type **Voria neotropica** Curran)......**Vorialia**, n. g.

260. Proboscis long and slender; first vein setulose (**69, 79**). **Plagiomima** Brauer & Bergenstamm
Proboscis short and stout; first vein bare.........**Metaplagia** Coquillett

261. Face strongly carinate, the arista plumose........................262
Facial carina weak or absent; arista bare to plumose..............263

262. Apical cell closed and petiolate...............**Hesperodinera** Townsend
Apical cell open (**119, 124, 125, 133**)..............*__Rhynchiodexia__ Bigot

263. Facial ridges never strongly bristled on the lower half, if almost so the bristles becoming weak above...............................271
Facial ridges strongly bristled on lower half or more...............264

264. Third antennal segment usually less than three times the length of the second; face only moderately retreating below; usually over 9 mm. in length; posthumeral bristle always strong..............268
Third antennal segment more than four times as long as the second, or if not the posthumeral bristle weak or absent; face very strongly receding 265

265. Apical cell long petiolate.........................**Eleodiphaga** Walton
Apical cell open or very short petiolate...........................266

266. Parafacials much narrower than the facial depression. †**Admontia** Brauer & Bergenstamm
Parafacials as wide as the facial depression.......................267

267. Fifth vein setulose ....**Actinochæta** Brauer & Bergenstamm
Fifth vein bare..............................**Baumhaueria** Meigen

268. Penultimate aristal segment less than twice as long as wide........269
Penultimate aristal segment at least three times as long as wide (**87**). **Chætogædia** Brauer & Bergenstamm

* Curran, 1930, Bull. Amer. Mus. Nat. Hist., lxi, p. 93.
† Curran, 1927, Can. Ent., lix, p. 294.

269. Base of wings deep brown; abdomen piceous or largely castaneous (4) .... **Leschenaultia** Desvoidy
Base of wings never brown; abdomen largely gray pollinose, more or less reddish laterally or apically 270

270. Apical cell ending far before the wing-tip; large species.. **Gædia** Meigen
Apical cell ending near the wing-tip; small species.
*__Admontia__ Brauer & Bergenstamm

271. Apical cell closed and rather long petiolate 286
Apical cell open, closed in the margin or extremely short petiolate... 272

272. Penultimate aristal segment not over twice as long as wide 273
Basal two aristal segments each at least three times as long as wide.
Digonichæta Rondani

273. Posterior sublateral bristle very strong 284
Posterior sublateral bristle absent; face strongly retreating 274

274. Third abdominal segment with at most two pairs of discals 275
Third abdominal segment with a row of discals..... **Gibsonomyia** Curran

275. At least the third abdominal segment with discals 276
Intermediate segments without discals, the marginals rarely simulating discals 279

276. Both the second and third abdominal segments with discals or the marginals not situated far forward 277
Second segment without discals but the marginals situated far forward .... **Paralispidea** Townsend

277. Second antennal segment almost or quite half as long as the third... 278
Second antennal segment not nearly half as long as the third.
Phyllomya Desvoidy

278. Cheeks about half as wide as the eye-height.... **Eubrachymera** Townsend
Cheeks not one-third as wide as the eye-height........ **Peteina** Meigen

279. Apical cell petiolate 280
Apical cell open 281

280. Arista almost wholly thickened............. **Hypertrophocera** Townsend
Arista thin on apical fourth or more **(23, 24)**... **Ceratomyiella** Townsend

281. Presutural acrosticals present 282
Presutural acrosticals absent.......................... **Peteina** Meigen

282. Arista more or less distinctly plumose 283
Arista bare or practically so, thickened on almost its whole length.
Hypertrophocera Townsend

283. First and fifth veins setose......... **Actinochæta** Brauer & Bergenstamm
First and fifth veins bare....................... **Phasiophyto** Townsend

284. Parafacials with fine hairs only 285
Parafacials with three or more downwardly directed bristles **(83, 86)**.
Chætoplagia Coquillett

285. Intermediate abdominal segments with discals; no orbitals in male.
†**Spathimeigenia** Townsend

---

* Curran, 1927, Can. Ent., lix, p. 294.
† Aldrich, 1931, Pr. U. S. N. M., lxxx, Art. 11, p. 3.

Intermediate abdominal segments without discals; a row of orbitals in male (**Eupogona** auct.) .... **Eipogona** Rondani

286. Parafacials at least half as wide as median depression, with scattered bristly hairs; abdomen largely pollinose 288
Parafacials less than one-third the width of the median depression, with a row of bristles; abdomen shining 287

287. Third antennal segment at least twice as long as the second; front of both sexes at least two-thirds as wide as either eye (**40, 41**). *__Wagneria__ Desvoidy
Third antennal segment but little longer than the second; front strongly narrowed in both sexes............ †**Hesperophasia** Townsend

288. Two or three presutural acrosticals and dorsocentrals.............. 289
No presutural acrosticals and only two pairs of weak presutural dorsocentrals (**58, 59**) .... **Penthosia** Wulp

289. Proboscis not longer than length of head; parafacials about two-thirds as wide as median depression.......................... 290
Proboscis much longer than the head-height; parafacials as wide as the median depression........................ **Trochilodes** Coquillett

290. Face receding, longer than the front (**84, 85**).... **Euthyprosopa** Townsend
Oral margin prominent, the face shorter than the front. **Steveniopsis** Townsend

291. Thorax without plumose hairs.............................. 292
Thorax in part with plumose yellowish hairs.......... **Teleothyria** Wulp

292. Facial ridges bristled on less than the lower half, the bristles almost always decreasing in length above; oral vibrissæ always strongly developed 341
Facial ridges with strong bristles on the lower half or more or the vibrissæ very weak or absent.............................. 293

293. Oral vibrissæ strongly differentiated and long.................. 297
Oral vibrissæ not differentiated.............................. 294

294. Facial ridges with two or three rows of hairs on the lower half, the parafacials "rolled" over the ridges above.................... 295
Facial ridges with a single row of bristles on the lower half, the ridges continuous to the base of the antennæ, not hidden on the upper half by the parafacials; presutural acrosticals present..... 296

295. Arista pectinate.............................. **Trixodes** Coquillett
Arista pubescent .... **Trixa** Meigen

296. Apical cell long petiolate; arista about half as long as the third antennal segment .... **Paraphasmophaga** Townsend
Apical cell short petiolate; arista much longer than antenna (**26, 27**). **Œstrophasia** Brauer & Bergenstamm

297. Ocellars well developed, directed obliquely forward, rarely almost divergent 304
Ocellars reclinate, absent or scarcely differentiated................ 298

298. Ocellars absent or extremely weak.............................. 300
Ocellars reclinate.............................. 299

---

* Curran, 1928, Can. Ent., lx, p. 48.
† Curran, 1927, Can. Ent., lix, p. 300.

299. Penultimate aristal segment elongate..................**Distichona** Wulp
Penultimate aristal segment not over twice as long as wide.
Vibrissovoria Townsend

300. Cheeks not wider than the third antennal segment..................302
Cheeks much wider than the third antennal segment..................301

301. Posterior tibiæ evenly, closely ciliate; parafacials narrow; smaller species ....**Sturmia** Desvoidy
Posterior tibiæ not closely ciliate; parafacials wide; large species.
***Belvosia** Desvoidy

302. Both sexes with reclinate orbital bristles..................303
Neither sex with reclinate orbitals..................**Prosopæa** Rondani

303. Ocellars entirely absent..................**Pseudochæta** Townsend
Ocellars very small but distinct and cruciate; male with two reclinate and one proclinate orbital..................**Argyrochætona** Townsend

304. Apical crossvein present..................306
Apical crossvein absent..................305

305. Parafacials much wider than antennæ..................**Rœseliopsis** Townsend
Parafacials very narrow below..................**Schizotachina** Walker

306. Posterior tibiæ not ciliate, or if so the bristles are rather widely separated with two or more of them longer or the parafacials are not hairy below the frontal bristles..................308
Posterior tibiæ evenly closely ciliate, at most one of the bristles conspicuously longer than the rest; parafacials usually haired on the upper half 307

307. Cilia on posterior tibiæ long, very dense and contiguous; parafacials usually with hairs below the frontals (**Thysanopsis** Tns., **Blepharipeza** Macq.) (4)..................**Leschenaultia** Desvoidy
Cilia less numerous, not quite contiguous; parafacials bare (109).
†**Achætoneura** Brauer & Bergenstamm

308. Frontal bristles extending but little below the base of the third antennal segment, usually a single bristle below the base; fourth vein without a fold or the facial ridges bristled on more than the lower half 309
Frontals extending to the middle of the third antennal segment, at least two bristles below the base of the arista; eyes sparsely short haired; bend of fourth vein with a long fold; facial ridges usually bristled on the lowest third..................**Exorista** Meigen

309. Middle coxæ without stout apical spines..................310
Middle coxæ with short, stout curved spines on the apex (♀) (136, 137, 153, 175)..................**Doryphorophaga** Townsend

310. First vein with at most two or three weak bristles..................311
First vein bristled on at least the apical half....**Chætophleps** Coquillett

311. Appendage or fold of fifth vein less than one-third as long as the preceding section 313
Appendage or fold of fifth vein more than half as long as the preceding section 312

* Aldrich, 1928, Proc. U. S. N. M., lxxiii, Article 8, pp. 1-45.
† Webber, 1930, Proc. U. S. N. M., lxxviii, Art. 10, pp. 1-37.

312. Eyes quite bare; ultimate section of fifth vein only about half as long as the preceding section....................315
Eyes with short, sparse hair; apical section of fifth vein two-thirds as long as preceding section (**97, 98**)..........**Stomatomya** Rondani

313. Apical cell open or closed in the wing margin....................317
Apical cell closed and petiolate....................314

314. Arista almost wholly thickened....................315
Arista slender on apical fourth or more.
Anachætopsis Brauer & Bergenstamm

315. Arista slender on apical half or more..........**Phœniceomyia** Townsend
Arista almost wholly thickened....................316

316. Penultimate aristal segment four times as long as wide (**114**).
Chætoglossa Townsend
Penultimate aristal segment not twice as long as wide.
Archiclops Bischoff

317. Proboscis shorter than the head-height....................318
Proboscis twice as long as the head-height; aristal segments of almost equal length....................**Eucoronomyia** Townsend

318. Males 319
Females 332

319. Orbital bristles present although sometimes situated almost in the frontal row 320
Orbitals absent 325

320. Abdomen with discals, not unusually deep....................321
Abdomen without discals, elongate and deep; antennæ arising below the middle of the eyes; two pairs of presutural acrosticals and dorsocentrals ....**Chætonodexodes** Townsend

321. Anterior tibiæ with two or three strong posterior bristles..........323
Anterior tibiæ with a single posterior bristle....................322

322. Third antennal segment divided into two lobes.....**Schizotachina** Walker
Third antennal segment entire, not unusually wide...**Celatoria** Coquillett

323. Frontal vitta wider anteriorly than the least width of either parafrontal 324
Frontal vitta nowhere wider than the least width of either parafrontal, not widening anteriorly.....**Paralispe** Brauer & Bergenstamm

324. Front almost or quite as wide as either eye........**Racodineura** Rondani
Front less than two-thirds as wide as either eye (**Arrhinomyia** B. B.) (**149, 173**).................... ....*__Elodia__ Desvoidy

325. Second antennal segment not unusually bristly above but with some longer bristles apically....................326
Second antennal segment densely bristled above; facial ridges with bristles on more than the lower half (**9**).....†**Tachinomyia** Townsend

* Villeneuve and Aldrich (1929, 1933) recognize **Arrhinomyia** as distinct from **Elodia** but I see no reason for this.
† Curran, 1926, Tr. Roy. Soc. Canada, Sec. V, p. 168.

326. Anterior tibiæ with at least two posterior bristles; species over 5 mm. in length 328
Anterior tibiæ with a single posterior bristle; species about 4 mm. in length 327

327. Apical cell ending very close to the wing-tip.........**Oxynops** Townsend
Apical cell ending far before the wing-tip...............**Bessa** Desvoidy

328. Abdomen tapering or not, often with discals; posterior forceps split on apical portion, never laterally compressed.................... 329
Abdomen elongate, tapering, rarely with discals; posterior forceps of male united into a long, compressed organ (9).***Tachinomyia** Townsend

329. Apical scutellars cruciate.. 330
Apical scutellars absent or divergent................................ 331

330. Antennæ reaching slightly beyond the oral margin, the third segment at least six times the length of the second (Europe)..**Frontina** Meigen
Antennæ not reaching the oral opening; third segment not over four times the length of the second................**Allophorocera** Hendel

331. Parafacials wide, the cheeks two-thirds as wide as the eye-height, the parafacials setulose on the upper half..........**Centeter** Aldrich
Parafacials narrower, the cheeks less than one-third the eye-height. **Degeeria** Meigen

332. Genital opening not slit-like; abdomen broader than deep............ 334
Genital opening slit-like; abdomen broad and deep.................. 333

333. Orbitals scarcely divergent; abdomen rarely with discals (9). ***Tachinomyia** Townsend
Orbitals conspicuously divergent; abdomen always with discals. **Allophorocera** Hendel

334. Third vein with a single strong basal bristle.......................... 339
Third vein with two or more basal bristles............................ 335

335. Arista pubescent or bare; third vein with not more than five bristles basally 336
Arista short plumose; third vein bristled almost to the small crossvein. **Paralispe** Brauer & Bergenstamm

336. Parafacials almost as wide as the median depression, setulose on almost the upper half............................**Centeter** Aldrich
Parafacials narrower, bare below the lowest frontals................ 337

337. Penultimate aristal segment very elongate. **Trichopareia** Brauer & Bergenstamm
Penultimate aristal segment short; abdomen with or without short discals; two sternopleurals.. 338

338. Middle tibiæ with two strong anterodorsal bristles.**Frontiniella** Townsend
Middle tibiæ with only one strong anterodorsal bristle.**Oxynops** Townsend

339. Lower margins of the second tergite strongly produced downward and with numerous spinose setulæ; ovipositor long and slender, often hidden ....**Celatoria Coquillett**

* Curran, 1926, Tr. Roy. Soc. Canada, Sec. V, p. 168.

Tergites not produced downward, the edges rarely setulose; ovipositor not elongate 340

340. Face narrower than either eye; penultimate aristal segment short (149, 173).................... **Elodia** Desvoidy
Face wider than either eye; penultimate aristal segment elongate. **Schizotachina** Walker

341. Apical crossvein present....................347
Apical crossvein absent....................342

342. Posterior crossvein present....................343
Posterior crossvein absent.................... **Phytomyptera** Rondani

343. Antennæ reaching the lowest fifth of the face....................344
Antennæ not reaching below the lowest third of the face. **Hemithrixion** Brauer & Bergenstamm

344. A single bristle at the base of the third vein....................345
Three or more bristles on the third vein....................346

345. Parafacials narrower than the third antennal segment. **Schizotachina Walker**
Parafacials twice as wide as the third antennal segment. **Rœseliopsis** Townsend

346. Antennæ arising near upper edge of eyes, enormous in size; head almost rectangular; bristles of thorax not unusually depressed (**28, 29, 144**) .... **Euryceromyia** Townsend
Antennæ arising lower down; head not nearly rectangular; bristles of thorax depressed (**148, 189**).................... **Actia** Desvoidy

347. Palpi present and well developed....................354
Palpi absent or but little longer than the width of the proboscis at point of attachment 348

348. Arista bare or pubescent....................349
Arista plumose; face strongly carinate.................... **Prosena** Serville

349. Third antennal segment usually less than three times the length of the second, if long the abdomen pedunculate....................350
Third antennal segment five times the length of the second, broadened apically, concave above (**47, 70**).................... **Beskia** Wulp

350. Apical cell open 351
Apical cell closed and petiolate (**54**)....................***Cylindromyia** Latreille

351. Face not conspicuously receding, concave in profile, the oral margin produced; vibrissæ situated well above the oral margin....................352
Face receding; oral margin not produced; vibrissæ level with oral margin (**63, 64**).................... **Icelia** Desvoidy

352. Second abdominal segment strongly narrowed..... **Polistiopsis** Townsend
Second abdominal segment not narrowed, much broader than deep....353

353. Palpi entirely absent.................... **Paraphasiopsis** Townsend
Palpi narrow, four times as long as wide, or longer.. **Phasiopsis** Townsend

* Aldrich, 1926, Pr. U. S. N. M., lxviii, Art 23, pp. 1-27.

354. Apical cell at most with an extremely short petiole................359
Apical cell with a petiole almost one-third the length of the apical crossvein 355

355. Antennæ shorter than the face, the middle of the face depressed; vibrissæ situated on a level with or above the anterior oral margin.356
Antennæ longer than the face; middle of face longitudinally convex, not depressed; vibrissæ situated below the anterior oral margin; wings pictured (**80, 81**)................................**Euthera** Loew

356. Ocellar bristles proclinate..357
Ocellar bristles directed more or less backward (**67, 68**). **Leucostoma** Meigen

357. Third vein ending in the wing-tip; oral margin produced............358
Third vein ending well before the wing-tip (**44, 53**). **Vanderwulpia** Townsend

358. Front of female wide; four pairs of marginal scutellars. **Psalidopteryx** Townsend
Front of both sexes strongly narrowed; three pairs of marginal scutellars ....*__Clistomorpha__ Townsend

359. Ultimate section of the fifth vein less than half as long as the preceding section 360
Ultimate section of the fifth vein three-fourths as long as the preceding section ....**Catalinovoria** Townsend

360. Penultimate aristal segment not over twice as long as wide.........371
Penultimate aristal segment three times as long as wide, or if somewhat shorter, widened apically and the proboscis geniculate.......361

361. Proboscis not geniculate..362
Proboscis long and geniculate, the labellæ turned back, narrow and more or less fused (**78, 183**)......................†**Siphona** Meigen

362. Proboscis, beyond the basal articulation, not as long as the head-height 364
Apical section of the proboscis longer than the head-height..........363

363. Antennæ reaching almost or quite to the oral margin; face not receding; parafacials at most one-third as wide as the third antennal segment (**14, 82, 150, 174**)....................**Epigrimyia** Townsend
Antennæ not reaching to the moderately produced oral margin; parafacials more than half as wide as third antennal segment; face receding above (**2**)...............................**Aphria** Desvoidy

364. Third antennal segment of the male not furcate......................365
Third antennal segment of the male furcate......**Acronarista** Townsend

365. Third vein with not more than three bristles basally................368
Third vein bristled more than half way to the small crossvein.......366

366. Bristles of the thorax erect..367
Bristles of the thorax rather appressed (**148, 189**).......‡**Actia** Desvoidy

---

* Curran, 1927, Can. Ent., lix, p. 297.
† Curran, 1932, Amer. Mus. Novit. No. 534, p. 13 (**Bucentes**).
‡ Curran, 1933, Amer. Mus. Novit. No. 614, pp. 1-7.

367. Head about as long as high........**Masistylum** Brauer & Bergenstamm
Head much higher than long..................**Phantasiomyia** Townsend

368. Cheeks less than half the eye-height in width........................369
Cheeks nearly as wide as the eye-height (**28, 29, 144**).
Euryceromyia Townsend

369. Palpi normal 370
Palpi very greatly swollen, unusually large..........**Lispidea** Coquillett

370. Third antennal segment more than twice as long as wide.
Clausicella Rondani
Third antennal segment less than twice as long as wide (**16**).
Plectops Coquillett

371. No appendage or fold at bend of fourth vein, if an adventitious appendage is present it is not continued in the same line as the fourth vein 385
An appendage or distinct fold at the bend of the fourth vein, the appendage continued in almost the same line as the preceding section of the vein..372

372. Posterior pair of presutural acrostical bristles situated very close to the suture and much behind the posterior pair of presutural dorsocentrals 373
Posterior pair of presutural acrosticals almost in a line with the posterior presutural dorsocentrals or in front of them.............374

373. Frontal bristles extending almost to the middle of the third antennal segment; genital opening not slit-like................**Exorista** Meigen
Frontals descending but little below the base of the third antennal segment; genital opening rather slit-like (**9**)..***Tachinomyia** Townsend

374. Arista with long rays..378
Arista pubescent or bare...375

375. Intermediate abdominal segments without discals..................376
Intermediate abdominal segments with paired discals; fourth vein with very short appendage, or none; face never carinate.
†**Dexodes** Brauer & Bergenstamm

376. Cheeks not over one-third as wide as the eye-height................377
Cheeks about half as wide as the eye-height........**Ochrocera** Townsend

377. Abdomen long and narrow; ultimate section of proboscis elongate.
Catenophrys Townsend
Abdomen oval; proboscis short and robust.......‡**Neophryxe** Townsend

378. Face not strongly carinate, more or less carinate in the middle above.381
Facial carina strongly developed and reaching to the clypeal region..379

379. Prosternum bare 380
Prosternum with two pairs of bristles..........**Trichoduropsis** Townsend

---

* Curran, 1926, Tr. Roy. Soc. Canada, Sec. V, p. 168.
† Curran, 1927, Can. Ent., lix, p. 20.
‡ This genus was described from specimens reared in Massachusetts from material originating in Japan.

380. Pteropleural bristle extending to beyond the apex of the squamæ; apical abdominal segment of the male very strongly produced.
Trichodura Brauer & Bergenstamm
Pteropleural bristle short as usual; abdomen not cylindrically produced in male..**Dexia** Meigen

381. Abdomen slender basally, spatulate................................384
Abdomen not spatulate, even though cylindrical....................382

382. Abdomen very slender and not tapering from near the base; costa with an extremely strong bristle near the base on the inner side **(116)** ....**Sophia** Desvoidy
Abdomen broader and more tapering; costal bristles short and fine...383

383. Abdomen metallic blue **(147, 177)**......................**Zuanalia,** n. g.
Abdomen black in ground color **(128, 131)**................**Zelia** Desvoidy

384. Lower squamal lobe very small..............**Eucordyligaster** Townsend
Lower squamal lobe large as usual.............***Cordyligaster** Macquart

385. Vibrissal angles not unusually prominent, if situated high above the oral margin the facial depression is not deeply sunken below; head not twice as high as long, or if so the face strongly retreating....386
Vibrissal angles high, the facial depression carried far below them at a much lower level; head twice as high as long; prosternum swollen ....**Ormia** Desvoidy

386. Posterior pair of presutural acrostical bristles situated very close to the suture and much behind the posterior pair of presutural dorsocentrals; always three pairs of presutural dorsocentrals...........387
Posterior pair of presutural acrosticals situated but little behind the posterior presutural dorsocentrals, or there are but two pairs of the latter; presutural acrosticals sometimes absent..................422

387. Vibrissæ at most half the length of the second antennal segment above the anterior oral margin..392
Vibrissæ situated high above the oral margin.....................388

388. Antennæ reaching at least to the lowest third of the face, the second segment not nearly as long as the third; vibrissæ only moderately above the oral margin..389
Antennæ unusually small, the second segment almost as long as the third; vibrissæ situated very high above the oral margin **(6)**.
†**Atacta** Schiner

389. Abdomen without discals...390
Abdomen with discals.............................**Meigenia** Desvoidy

390. Parafrontals with numerous hairs on the anterior half..............391
Parafrontals with but few hairs on the anterior half.
Masiphya Brauer & Bergenstamm

391. Oral margin carried rather strongly forward below the vibrissæ.
‡**Siphosturmiopsis** Townsend
Oral margin not conspicuously produced..............**Sturmia** Desvoidy

* Aldrich, 1927, Journ. Wash. Acad. Sci., xvii, p. 85.
† Aldrich, 1925, Pr. U. S. N. M., lxvi, Art. 18, p. 29.
‡ Reinhard, 1931, Pr. U. S. N. M., lxix, Art. 11, p. 9.

392. Posterior tibiæ evenly and closely ciliate above with fairly long bristles, only one of which may be longer and stronger............420
Posterior tibiæ not evenly ciliate....................................393

393. Arista bare or pubescent...395
Arista plumose 394

394. Cheeks half as wide as eye-height (128, 131)............**Zelia** Desvoidy
Cheeks much narrower..........................**Minthozelia** Townsend

395. Apical cell ending far before the wing-tip...........................409
Apical cell ending at or near the wing-tip............................396

396. Costal spine not strongly developed, never as long as the width of the costal cell and not outstanding, if somewhat long the parafacials are decidedly narrower than the width of the third antennal segment 398
Costal spine longer than the width of the costal cell................397

397. Facial ridges convex in profile; discals present.
Phrynofrontina Townsend
Facials ridges concave below; discals absent (48, 49).
Spathidexia Townsend

398. Female abdomen not strongly keeled...................................399
Female abdomen strongly keeled, the edges of the tergites spined.
Jicaltepecia Townsend

399. First vein bare..400
First vein with strong bristles on the apical half; antennæ arising above the middle of the eyes...................**Clausicellana** Curran

400. Lower margin of head not strongly oblique on anterior half; posterior sublateral present 401
Lower margin of the head strongly oblique on the anterior half; posterior sublateral absent; three pairs of scutellars.
Pelatachina Meade

401. Apical abdominal segment horizontal, the genital opening visible from posterior view 402
Apical abdominal segment vertical, the genital opening wholly ventral.
Panacemyia Townsend

402. Male with orbitals (rarely with a single one in the frontal row); outer verticals of ♀ two-thirds as long as the verticals............406
Male without orbitals; outer verticals of ♀ little more than half as long as verticals 403

403. Third antennal segment at least three times as long as wide, or not unusually large 404
Third antennal segment very large, long and almost half as wide as its length ....*****Elephantocera** Townsend

404. Palpi not unusually swollen; third vein with two or three basal setulæ 405
Palpi greatly swollen; third vein setulose to small crossvein.........406

* Curran, 1930, Bull. Amer. Mus. Nat. Hist., lxi, p. 96.

405. Tergites of female produced downward and finely spined.
Schizocerophaga Townsend
Tergites of female normal......................*__Lixophaga__ Townsend

406. Third vein bristled to the small crossvein; facial ridges convex in profile ....**Hypertrophomma** Townsend
Third vein with only two or three basal bristles; sublateral bristle present 407

407. Facial depression deep, the parafacials prominent in profile.........408
Facial depression shallow, the parafacials very low in profile, the ridges flat; head short **(158, 165)**..................**Patillalia, n. g.**

408. Frontal vitta linear..........................**Argyrochætona** Townsend
Frontal vitta not remarkably narrow.......**Microceromacia** Villeneuve

409. Head receding below 413
Head as long below as at the oral margin..........................410

410. Abdomen with strong marginals on the intermediate segments......411
Abdomen without strong marginals on the intermediate segments; vibrissæ situated far above the oral margin.
Masiphya Brauer & Bergenstamm

411. First vein setulose except apically................**Microsillus** Aldrich
First vein bare 412

412. Ocellars present ....**Myothyriopsis** Townsend
Ocellars absent ....**Laximasicera** Curran

413. First vein bare 414
First vein setulose.............................**Houghia** Coquillett

414. Front scarcely longer than the face, more or less convex, not prominent anteriorly 415
Front longer than the face, not convex in profile, produced anteriorly; abdomen with discals; apical scutellars erect ......**Meigenia** Desvoidy

415. Ocellars absent or very weak.....................................419
Ocellars present; discals present or absent.......................416

416. Face unusually flat, the head short; parafacials very narrow below **(158)** 417
Face not unusually flat, the head more elongate **(1)**....†**Lydella** Desvoidy

417. Third vein bristled to small crossvein.............................418
Third vein with two or three very strong basal bristles **(158, 165)**.
Patillalia, n. g.

418. Ocellars very strong **(160, 179)**.....................**Agrarialia,** n. g.
Ocellars short and rather weak **(143, 168)**..............**Aridalia,** n. g.

419. Abdomen with discals..........................**Parathelaira** Townsend
Abdomen without discals...420

420. Parafrontals each much less than four times as wide as the frontal vitta; front not convex; ocellars present.........................421

* Aldrich, 1925, Pr. Ent. Soc. Wash., xxvii, p. 133.
† Curran, 1932, Amer. Mus. Novit. No. 526, p. 11 (**Erycia**).

Parafrontals wide, the median vitta less than one-fourth as wide as the parafrontals at the middle; ocellars absent; front gently convex. **Argyrophylax** Brauer & Bergenstamm

421\. Oral margin rather strongly produced........... **Siphosturmia** Coquillett
Oral margin but slightly produced.................. **Sturmia** Desvoidy

422\. Face at least moderately retreating.................................449
Face but little retreating, almost or quite as long below as at base of antennæ 423

423\. Apical section of the proboscis much shorter than the head-height or the apical cell ending far before the wing-tip..................427
Apical section of the proboscis at least as long as the head-height; apical cell ending close to the wing-tip..........................424

424\. First vein bare above..425
First vein setulose above.......... **Leskiomima** Brauer & Bergenstamm

425\. Arista bare or pubescent..426
Arista with very long rays (**176, 185**)............... **Shermanalia,** n. g.

426\. Head decidedly higher than long (**14, 82, 150, 174**). **Epigrimyia** Townsend
Head as long below as its height................... **Weberia** Desvoidy

427\. Parafacial decidedly less than half as wide as the facial depression; face not strongly carinate.....................................432
Parafacial at the narrowest part almost or quite half as wide as the facial depression, or the face strongly carinate..................428

428\. Arista long plumose..429
Arista pubescent or bare......................... **Apachemyia** Townsend

429\. Facial carina weak (**128, 131**)...................... **Zelia** Desvoidy
Facial carina strong 430

430\. Antennæ reaching little more than half way to the oral margin......431
Antennæ reaching three-fourths of the way to the oral margin (**120, 129**) .... **Scotiptera** Macquart

431\. Third antennal segment three times as long as the second. **Eudexia** Brauer & Bergenstamm
Third antennal segment not three times longer than wide, in the male only slightly longer than the second (**127, 130**).. **Hystrichodexia** Röder

432\. Apical cell ending in or near the wing-tip........................435
Apical cell ending well before the wing-tip........................433

433\. Third vein with only a few basal bristles..........................434
First and fifth veins bristled above (**123**)............ **Thelaira** Desvoidy

434\. Frontal vitta not wider than either parafrontal..... **Demoticus** Macquart
Frontal vitta twice as wide as either parafrontal; a row of orbitals. **Euhalidaya** Walton

435\. Third antennal segment near the base not wider than the second, or if so, the abdomen elongate and narrow.........................437
Third antennal segment conspicuously wider than the second; abdomen short, oval 436

436\. Presutural acrosticals scarcely developed.... **Chætostigmoptera** Townsend
Presutural acrosticals well developed (**148, 189**)...... * **Actia** Desvoidy

* Curran, 1933, Amer. Mus. Novit. No. 614, pp. 1-7.

437. Apical abdominal segment horizontal, the genital opening evident from posterior view........438
Apical abdominal segment vertical at apex, the genital opening ventral (**117, 126**)........*__Calodexia__ Wulp

438. Costal spine not strongly developed; oral margin prominent; wings not brown with pale spots........439
Costal spine long; oral margin and vibrissal angles scarcely raised; wings brown with hyaline spots........**Jamacaria** Curran

439. Largely yellowish species........441
Wholly black species; wings partly brown........440

440. First vein bare; third with a single basal bristle (**Plectops?**). **Nephopteropsis** Townsend
First vein setulose........**Slossonæmyia** Townsend

441. Third antennal segment narrower than the second or the fifth vein bare........442
Third antennal segment wider than the second, the fifth vein setulose. **Trichotopteryx** Townsend

442. Head at most one and one-half times as high as long........443
Head almost twice as high as long........**Xanthodexia** Wulp

443. Palpi variable, sometimes shortened, usually curved, never broad and flattened........444
Palpi long, broad and flattened on the apical half or more, never curved (**112**)........**Genea** Rondani

444. At most two presutural acrostical or dorsocentral bristles........446
Three presutural acrostical and dorsocentral bristles........445

445. Abdomen with discals (**36**)........**Binghamimyia** Townsend
Abdomen without discals........**Pyrrhosia** Rondani

446. Abdomen cylindrical or wider than deep apically........447
Abdomen laterally compressed on the apical half; small, slender species........**Xanthomelanopsis** Townsend

447. First abdominal segment with marginals........448
First abdominal segment without marginals (**93**)........**Fischeria** Desvoidy

448. Three sternopleurals........**Solieria** Desvoidy
Two sternopleurals........**Opsoleskia** Townsend

449. Arista bare or pubescent........456
Arista plumose, very long pubescent or short pectinate........450

450. Arista plumose or pectinate........451
Arista long pubescent; antennæ arising at the lowest third of the eyes; clypeal region long........**Eumegaparea** Townsend

451. Abdomen without discals........452
Abdomen with discals (**132**)........**Chætona** Wulp

452. No strong presutural acrosticals........**Phyllophilopsis** Townsend
At least one pair of strong presutural acrosticals........453

453. Ocellars weak or absent........454
Ocellars well developed........**Pseudodexia** Brauer & Bergenstamm

* Curran, 1934, Amer. Mus. Novit. No. 685, pp. 1-21.

454. Fifth vein bristled............................**Polygastropsis** Townsend
Fifth vein bare..455

455. Apical abdominal segment of the male very strongly produced posteriorly; ocellars small.......................**Urophillophila** Townsend
Apical abdominal segment not produced; ocellars absent.
Opsoleskia Townsend

456. Third antennal segment never with the apical corner acutely produced 458
Apex of the third antennal segment produced as a short, sharp spur (5) 457

457. Prosternum bare ....**Acemya** Desvoidy
Prosternum haired (**Myothyria** Wulp)..................**Ceracia** Rondani

458. Apical cell ending at or near the wing-tip.........................458
Apical cell ending far before the wing-tip; cheeks usually twice as wide as third antennal segment; abdomen with discals; two presutural acrosticals and three dorsocentrals.
*__Dexodes__ Brauer & Bergenstamm

459. Third antennal segment rarely unusually wide and long, if so the palpi yellow or the facial depression not unusually deep..........460
Third antennal segment more than six times as long as the second, unusually wide; facial depression very deep; palpi white.
Œdematocera Townsend

460. Over 9 mm. in length; apical cell narrowly opened or closed in the costa; discal crossvein joining the fourth vein three-fourths the distance beyond the small crossvein; abdomen with discals.
Pelatachina Meade
Usually less than 8 mm. in length; not possessing the above combination of characters..461

461. Cheeks not over one-third as wide as the eye-height................462
Cheeks two-thirds as wide as the eye-height..............**Clista Meigen**

462. Second abdominal segment with dorsal bristles.....................463
Second abdominal segment without dorsal bristles.**Calpodomyia** Townsend

463. Bristles of the thorax suberect; first and fifth veins never bristled....464
Bristles of the thorax subappressed; first and fifth veins often bristled (**148, 189**) (cf.**Spathidexia**)...................†**Actia** Desvoidy

464. Ventral margin of at least the second tergite in the female with stout, spinose setulæ; knob of halteres brown in male............465
Tergites without such setulæ in female; halteres yellow............466

465. Second antennal segment of male large, half as wide as long.
Elephantocera Townsend
Second antennal segment of male not large, three times as long as wide ....**Celatoria** Coquillett

466. Arista bare, short pubescent or extremely short plumose...........468
Arista very conspicuously short plumose; genital opening apical.....467

467. Three pairs of strong presutural acrosticals (**151, 157**).
Thelairalia, n. g.

* Curran, 1927, Can. Ent., lix, p. 23.
† Curran, 1933, Amer. Mus. Novit. No. 614, pp. 1-7.

At most two pairs of strong presutural acrosticals, the posterior pair not situated very close to the suture (132)............**Chætona** Wulp

468. Arista wholly thick, tapering apically........**Phantasiomyia** Townsend
Arista slender apically 469

469. Genital opening ventral, not visible from behind...**Panacemyia** Townsend
Genital opening apical, visible from behind........................470

470. Frontal vitta linear (very narrow in ♀ ?).....**Argyrochætona** Townsend
Frontal vitta wide..471

471. Anterior tibiæ with a single posterior bristle........................473
Anterior tibiæ with two posterior bristles..........................472

472. Small slender species, under 5 mm. (149, 173).........**Elodia** Desvoidy
Larger, robust species, over 6 mm..............**Calothelaira** Townsend

473. Frontal vitta twice as wide as the parafrontals, not at all narrowed medianly; anterior tibiæ without a conspicuous posterodorsal bristle (181, 193)..........................**Microtownsendia, n. g.**
Frontal vitta narrower than either parafrontal; anterior tibiæ with a single conspicuous posterodorsal bristle situated near the middle. **Tachinophyto** Townsend

Scotiptera melaleuca.

Collatia, new genus

This genus is proposed for the reception of *Zenillia submissa* Aldrich and Webber. It possesses the characters of *Zenillia* but has the propleura haired on the middle portion.

Townsendina, new genus

Differs from *Myiophasia* Brauer and Bergenstamm in having only one pair of presutural acrosticals and long, bristly hairs on the parafacials. Front narrow above, widening anteriorly; cheeks half as wide as the eye-height; antennæ reaching four-fifths the distance to the oral margin, the second segment only one-third shorter than the third; arista thickened on basal fourth; proboscis short; eyes short pilose. Dorsocentrals 3-3; acrosticals 1-2; propleura bare; infrasquamal setulæ present. Apical cell ending moderately before the wing tip; third vein with two bristles basally. Abdomen with discals and marginals. Thorax cinereous pollinose, weakly vittate; abdomen with broad, basal cinereous fasciæ on segments two to four. Genotype:—*T. fasciata*, n. sp., (Colorado).

Polidaria, new genus

Proposed for *Tachina areos* Walker, a species placed in the genus *Polidea* by most authors. As it does not belong to *Polidea*, a new genus is proposed for its reception.

Zonalia, new genus

Female.—Head short, almost twice as high as long; two pairs of proclinate frontals; ocellars short; outer verticals absent; cheeks narrow; face slightly retreating below; facial ridges with weak bristles on the lower half; antennæ reaching to the oral margin; arista long plumose. Acrosticals 1-0; dorsocentrals 2-3; one sublateral; posthumeral absent; propleura bare; infrasquamal setulæ present; two sternopleurals; prosternum bare; three pairs of marginal scutellars. Anterior tibiæ with one posterior bristle. Apical cell ending close to the wing-tip; third vein bristled more than half way to the anterior crossvein. Abdomen without discals; first segment without marginals; ovipositor normal. Front, thorax and sides of abdomen with whitish pollen, although the whole insect appears shining black from most views. Length, 5 mm. Genotype:—*Z. nitens*, n. sp. (Panama).

Corozalia, new genus

Male.—Eyes haired; front moderately narrow, without orbitals or ocellars; outer verticals absent; cheeks narrow; face moderately retreating, the oral margin produced; facial ridges bare; antennæ reaching lowest fifth of face, the second segment somewhat less than half as long as the third; arista practically bare; proboscis short; palpi clavate. Acrosticals and dorsocentrals 3-3, the posterior acrosticals close to the suture; posterior sublateral present; posthumeral absent; sternopleurals 2-1; infrasquamal setulæ present. Anterior tibiæ with one long posterior bristle. Apical cell ending moderately before the wing-tip; third vein with two basal bristles. Abdomen elongate, tapering, with paired discals; first segment with marginals. Black, with cinereous pollen, the mesonotal pollen sometimes with yellowish tinge, with narrow, distinct vittæ; apical half of abdominal segments bare. Length, 8 to 10 mm. Genotype:—*C. longula,* n. sp. (Panama).

Chætonalia, new genus

Male.—Head almost twice as high as long; cheeks very narrow; face and front narrow; no orbitals; ocellars very small and hair-like; outer verticals not developed; face slightly receding below, the ridges bare; antennæ long, the second segment short; arista short plumose on basal half; proboscis short; palpi slightly clavate. Acrosticals 1-1; dorsocentrals 2-3; posterior sublateral and posthumeral absent; two sternopleurals; infrasquamal setulæ present. Apical cell ending a little before the apex of the wing; third vein with two basal bristles. Abdomen with paired discals; first segment with pair of marginals. Pollen cinereous yellow, yellow on the front; mesonotum strongly quadrivittate; abdominal segments with about the apical half bare. Length, 5.5 mm. Genotype:—*C. lateralis,* n. sp. (Panama).

Canalia, new genus

Female.—Front rather narrow; two pairs of orbitals; ocellars long; outer verticals strong; cheeks very narrow; face gently receding, the oral margin slightly produced; ridges bare; proboscis short; palpi very slightly clavate; antennæ reaching almost to the vibrissæ, the second segment short; arista short plumose. Acrosticals 2-1; dorsocentrals 2-3; posterior sublateral and posthumeral bristle absent; two sternopleurals; infrasquamal setulæ present; prosternum haired. Wings tinged with brown, especially toward the apex; apical cell ending a little in front of the wing-tip; third vein bristled to the anterior crossvein. Abdomen elongate oval, without discals, the first segment without marginals.

Black, the antennæ, coxæ and base of the abdomen on the broad sides, yellow; apex of abdomen red; pollen of the head white, of the mesonotum cinereous yellow, a broad brown fascia immediately behind the suture; abdominal segments narrowly white pollinose basally. Length, 7 mm. Genotype:—*C. fasciata*, n. sp. (Panama).

Schwarzalia, new genus

Female.—Arista long plumose; parafacials with short, fine hair; front of moderate width, with two pairs of orbitals; ocellars long; outer verticals weak; cheeks wide; face retreating, the oral margin produced; ridges bare; proboscis short; palpi scarcely clavate; antennæ practically reaching the oral margin. Acrosticals weak, 3-1; dorsocentrals 2-3; posterior sublateral and posthumeral bristle absent; two sternopleurals; prosternum bare; infrasquamal setulæ present. Apical cell ending a little before the wing-tip; third vein bristled half way to the anterior crossvein; first vein bristled on whole length. Abdomen elongate oval, without discals, the first segment without marginals. Black, the palpi, coxæ, femora mostly, humeri and basal half, or less, of the abdomen yellowish-red; head and the broad bases of the abdominal segments white pollinose; thorax cinereous pollinose, mesonotum with a broad black band behind the suture. Length, 7.5 mm. Genotype:—*S. luteipennis*, n. sp. (Panama).

Tachinalia, new genus

Female.—Robust, the abdomen broader than the thorax and not much longer than wide. Eyes with long hair; parafacials haired; front rather narrow, with two pairs of orbitals; ocellars long, outer verticals absent; cheeks wide; face retreating, the oral margin produced; ridges bare; proboscis short; palpi slightly clavate; antennæ reaching the lowest fifth of the face; arista bare. Acrosticals 2-3; dorsocentrals 3-3; posterior sublateral absent; posthumeral present; sternopleurals 2-1; prosternum bare; scutellum with many spinose bristles. Apical cell ending moderately before the wing-tip; third vein bristled basally. Abdomen almost wholly covered with spinose bristles. Head with cinereous pollen, thorax thinly pollinose; scutellum reddish, abdomen castaneous. Length, 10 to 11 mm. Genotype:—*T. hispida*, n. sp. (California).

Coloradalia, new genus

Male.—Front wide, the frontals not strong; ocellars long, reclinate; cheeks one-third as wide as eye-height; face strongly retreating, the ridges bristled on almost their whole length; middle of face deeply sunken, the oral margin not produced; antennæ almost as long as the face, the second segment short; proboscis short, palpi clavate; eyes with short hair. Acrosticals and dorsocentrals 3-3, the acrosticals not strong; posterior sublateral weak, the posthumeral hair-like; two sternopleurals; prosternum concealed. Apical cell ending a little before the wing-tip; third vein with two basal bristles, one of them long; first vein bristled on its whole length. Abdomen elongate oval, very deep, the genitalia large, but normally mostly concealed; discals and marginals on segments two to four. Black, cinereous pollinose; the mesonotum and front with yellowish tinge; apices of segments less thickly pollinose. Length, 5 mm. Genotype:—*C. ocellaris,* n. sp. (Colorado).

Lasionalia, new genus

Male.—Related to *Townsendina,* n. g., but the apical cell is closed, the posterior sublateral present, etc. Eyes bare; front narrow, widening anteriorly; ocellars long; outer verticals not developed; cheeks almost half as wide as the eye-height; parafacials with a complete row of bristly hairs and a second partial row on the upper half; ridges bare; face strongly retreating, the oral margin scarcely produced; proboscis short, the palpi slightly clavate; antennæ not reaching to the vibrissæ, the second segment somewhat shorter than the third; arista bare. Acrosticals and dorsocentrals 2-3; posterior sublateral present, the posthumeral absent; two sternopleurals; prosternum bare. Apical cell ending a little before the wing-tip, very short petiolate; third vein with one or two basal bristles. Abdomen elongate-oval, each segment with discals and marginals. Black, yellowish cinereous pollinose; palpi yellow; tibiæ rather reddish. Length, 5.5 mm. Genotype:—*L. cinerea,* n. sp. (Minnesota).

Oxynopsalia, new genus

Female.—Front of moderate width; two pairs of orbitals; ocellars long; outer verticals well developed; cheeks narrow; face strongly receding, the oral margin not produced; ridges bristled on more than the lower half; proboscis short; palpi clavate; antennæ reaching to the oral margin, the second segment somewhat elongate; arista bare. Eyes short pilose. Acrosticals and dorsocentrals 3-3, the posterior presutural acrosticals situated close to the suture; posterior sublateral and posthumeral bristle present; two sternopleurals; prosternum bare, narrow. Apical cell ending close to the wing-tip; third vein with three bristles basally. Abdomen elongate oval, each segment with marginals, the second and third with discals; ovipositor simple. Black, the head and thorax cinereous pollinose, the mesonotum mostly brownish; bases of abdominal segments very narrowly white pollinose. Length, 4.5 mm. Genotype:—*O. nitida,* n. sp. (Panama).

Anadiscalia, new genus

Male and female.—Head twice as high as long; front narrow, female with two pairs of orbitals; ocellars long; outer verticals weak; cheeks and parafacials extremely narrow; face retreating but slightly; oral margin not prominent, the ridges bare; proboscis short, the palpi clavate; antennæ reaching almost to the oral margin, the second segment short; arista bare; eyes short haired. Acrosticals and dorsocentrals 3-3; posthumeral and posterior sublateral present; two sternopleurals; prosternum haired. Apical cell ending moderately before the wing-tip; third vein with two bristles basally. Abdomen oval, not deep. Black, cinereous pollinose; palpi, humeri and abdomen reddish yellow, the abdomen with a more or less distinct median vitta, the apices of the segments more or less, and the fourth segment almost entirely black. All segments with marginals but without discals. Length, 6 to 7 mm. Genotype:—*A. basalis,* n. sp. (Panama).

Zuanalia, new genus

Female.—Arista long plumose; front wide, with two pairs of orbitals; ocellars long; outer verticals moderately strong; cheeks almost half as wide as eye-height; parafacials bare; face strongly retreating on upper part, the oral margin slightly produced; proboscis short; palpi clavate, antennæ reaching almost to the oral margin. Acrosticals 3-1, the presuturals very weak; dorsocentrals 3-4; posterior sublateral absent; posthumeral present; sternopleurals 2-1; prosternum bare. Apical cell ending a little before the wing-tip; bend of fourth vein with appendage; base of third vein with about four bristles. Abdomen short oval, rather deep. Head, thorax and legs reddish in ground color; head yellow pollinose; mesonotum metallic blue, cinereous pollinose, trivittate; abdomen wholly metallic blue, the bases of the segments cinereous pollinose. Length, 10 mm. Genotype:—*Z. azurea,* n. sp. (Panama).

Patillalia, new genus

Female.—Front of moderate width; two pairs of orbitals; ocellars long; outer verticals strong; cheeks narrow; face receding, the oral margin not produced; proboscis short; palpi clavate; antennæ reaching almost to the vibrissæ; arista very short pubescent. Dorsocentrals and acrosticals 3-3; posthumeral and posterior sublateral present; two sternopleurals; prosternum haired. Apical cell ending a little before the wing-tip; third vein with two strong basal bristles. Abdomen oval; all segments with marginals, the fourth with discals. Black; head white pollinose; the front yellowish above; thorax with white pollen on the sides, yellowish above, distinctly vittate; abdomen with very broad cinereous bands on the bases of the segments. Length, 7 mm. Genotype:—*P. fasciata,* n. sp. (Panama).

Agrarialia, new genus

Male.—Front wide, only a little narrower than the face; two pairs of strong orbitals; ocellars long; outer verticals strong; cheeks very narrow; face retreating, the oral margin scarcely produced; ridges bare; proboscis short; palpi clavate, hairy; antennæ reaching practically to the oral margin, the second segment short, arista very short pubescent. Acrosticals 3-3, dorsocentrals 3-4; posthumeral and posterior sublateral present; sternopleurals 2-1; prosternum haired. Apical cell ending well before the wing-tip; third vein bristled almost to the anterior crossvein. Abdomen elongate oval, somewhat tapering; each segment with marginals, but no discals; third segment with large sexual patch below. Black, cinereous pollinose, the head largely silvery; mesonotum with yellowish tinge, strongly vittate; apical third of abdominal segments shining black. Length, 7.5 mm. Genotype:—*A. sexualis,* n. sp. (Panama).

Aridalia, new genus

Female.—Front about as wide as the face; two pairs of orbitals; ocellars rather short and weak; outer verticals well developed; cheeks very narrow; face receding, the ridges bare, the oral margin not produced; proboscis short; palpi weakly clavate; antennæ reaching to the oral margin; arista short pubescent. Acrosticals 3-3; dorsocentrals 3-4; posthumeral and posterior sublateral present; sternopleurals 2-1. Apical cell ending well before the wing-tip; third vein bristled to the anterior crossvein. Abdomen elongate oval, tapering apically; each segment with marginals but without discals. Black with cinereous pollen; palpi yellow; sides of the abdomen broadly reddish on the basal half, the apex also reddish; pollen of front rather golden, of mesonotum more or less ochreous and strongly vittate; apices of abdominal segments broadly bare. Length 8 mm. Genotype:—*A. lateralis,* n. sp. (Panama).

Shermanalia, new genus

Male.—Arista long plumose; front moderately narrow; ocellars long; outer verticals absent; cheeks one-third as wide as eye-height; face scarcely retreating, the oral margin prominent, the ridges bare; apical section of the proboscis as long as the head-height; palpi somewhat clavate; antennæ not reaching to the oral margin, the second segment short. Acrosticals 1-1, the anterior pair weak; dorsocentrals 2-3; posthumeral and posterior sublateral absent; sternopleurals 2-1; prosternum bare. Apical cell almost closed a little before the wing-tip; third vein with two weak bristles basally. Abdomen elongate, more than twice as long as wide, rather cylindrical, all the segments with marginals but without discals. Black, clothed with thick yellowish pollen; mesonotum with three black vittæ, the median one wide; first abdominal segment with an hourglass-shaped black spot, the base black, the following segments broadly black apically, the black expanding triangularly just below the sides. Length, 6 mm. Genotype:—*S. pretiosa,* n. sp. (Panama).

Prorhynchops errans Curran (fig. 172) traces to this genus but the aristal rays arise from only the upper and lower surfaces. It is probably not a *Prorhynchops* as it lacks discal bristles.

Thelairalia, new genus

Male.—Front rather wide, with a single pair of strong orbitals; ocellars short and hair-like; outer verticals distinct; cheeks narrow; face receding, the oral margin not produced; proboscis short; palpi weakly clavate; antennæ not reaching to the oral margin; arista very short plumose. Acrosticals 3-3; dorsocentrals 2-3; posterior sublateral poorly developed, the posthumeral absent; sternopleurals 1-1; prosternum haired. Apical cell ending moderately before the wing-tip; third vein bristled more than half way to the anterior crossvein. Abdomen tapering, each segment with marginals, only the fourth with discals. Black, yellow pollinose; mesonotum with four vittæ which unite to form a broad postsutural fascia; first abdominal segment wholly, the others on the apical half, shining. Length, 8 mm. Genotype:—*T. fasciata*, n. sp. (Panama).

Microtownsendia, new genus

Female.—Front as wide as the face; two pairs of orbitals; ocellars moderately strong; outer verticals strong; cheeks extremely narrow; face receding, the ridges bare; oral margin not produced; proboscis short; palpi clavate; antennæ reaching the oral margin, the second segment short; arista bare. Acrosticals and dorsocentrals 2-3; posthumeral and posterior sublateral present; two sternopleurals; prosternum haired. Apical cell ending a little before the wing-tip; third vein with two basal bristles. Abdomen oval, the fourth segment elongate; discals absent, each segment with marginals. Black, with cinereous white pollen; mesonotum thinly pollinose and weakly vittate; bases of abdominal segments narrowly pollinose; palpi yellow. Length, 3.75 mm. Genotype:—*M. nitens*, n. sp. (Panama).

Family Braulidæ—The Honey-bee Parasite

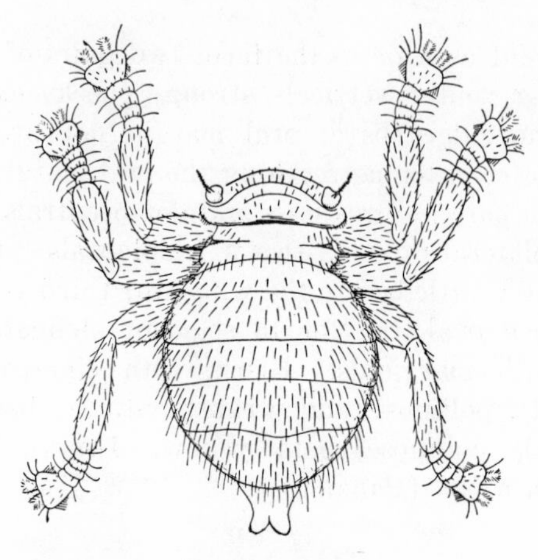

Braula cœca.

This family is comprised of a single species of *Braula,* parasitic upon honey bees.

Scutellum absent, the mesonotum not differentiated from the abdominal segments, the abdomen sessile; eyes minute; ocelli absent; antennæ set in lateral grooves; vertex without bristles. Fifth tarsal segment broad and bearing an inflexed comb of many miscroscopic teeth. Wings entirely absent.

The Braulidæ are not larviparous, but lay eggs.

Braula cœca Nitzsch is a small convex insect found only in the hives of honey bees. It is said to be cosmopolitan in distribution but is rare in this country, at least in collections.

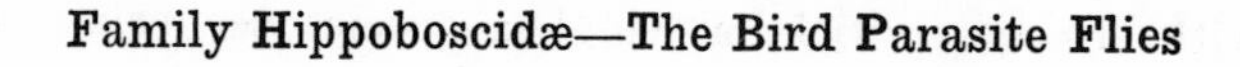

Family Hippoboscidæ—The Bird Parasite Flies

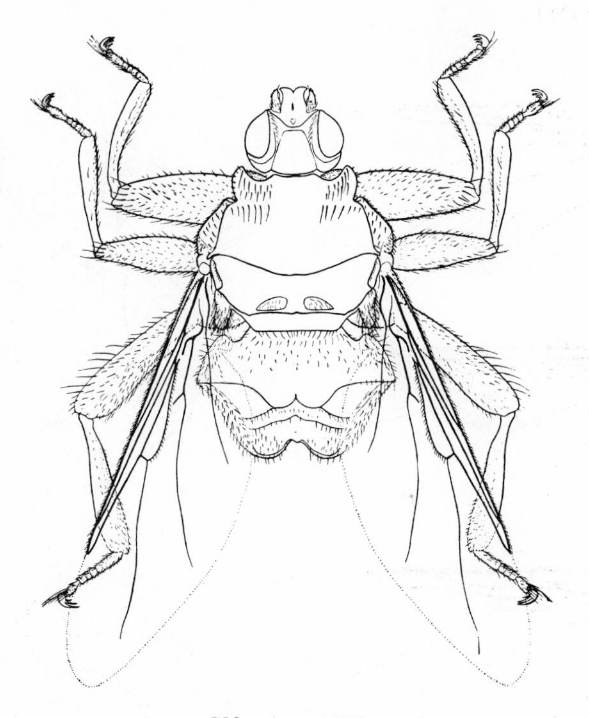

Olfersia sordida.

Small, flat flies of leathery consistency, usually with wings, the posterior veins weaker.

Head flattened, usually attached to an emargination of the thorax. Face short; palpi forming a sheath for the proboscis, projecting in front of the head; antennæ inserted in pits or depressions near the border of the mouth, apparently with a single segment, with or without a terminal bristle or hairs. Eyes round or oval; ocelli present or absent. Thorax flattened; scutellum short and broad. Halteres present or rudimentary, rarely absent. Abdomen sac-like, the sutures indistinct, the basal segments usually fully chitinized. Legs short and strong, broadly separated by the sternum; tarsi short; claws strong and often with one or two teeth. Wings present or absent, the veins approximated to the anterior border, with weak ones running obliquely across the posterior two-thirds of the wing. Larviparous.

The adults occur on birds and mammals. They are most frequently found on birds, seldom flying. In the old world species of *Hippobosca* are found on horses, camels, etc. and often occur in large numbers, as is the case with the sheep tick, a wingless species occurring wherever sheep are raised.

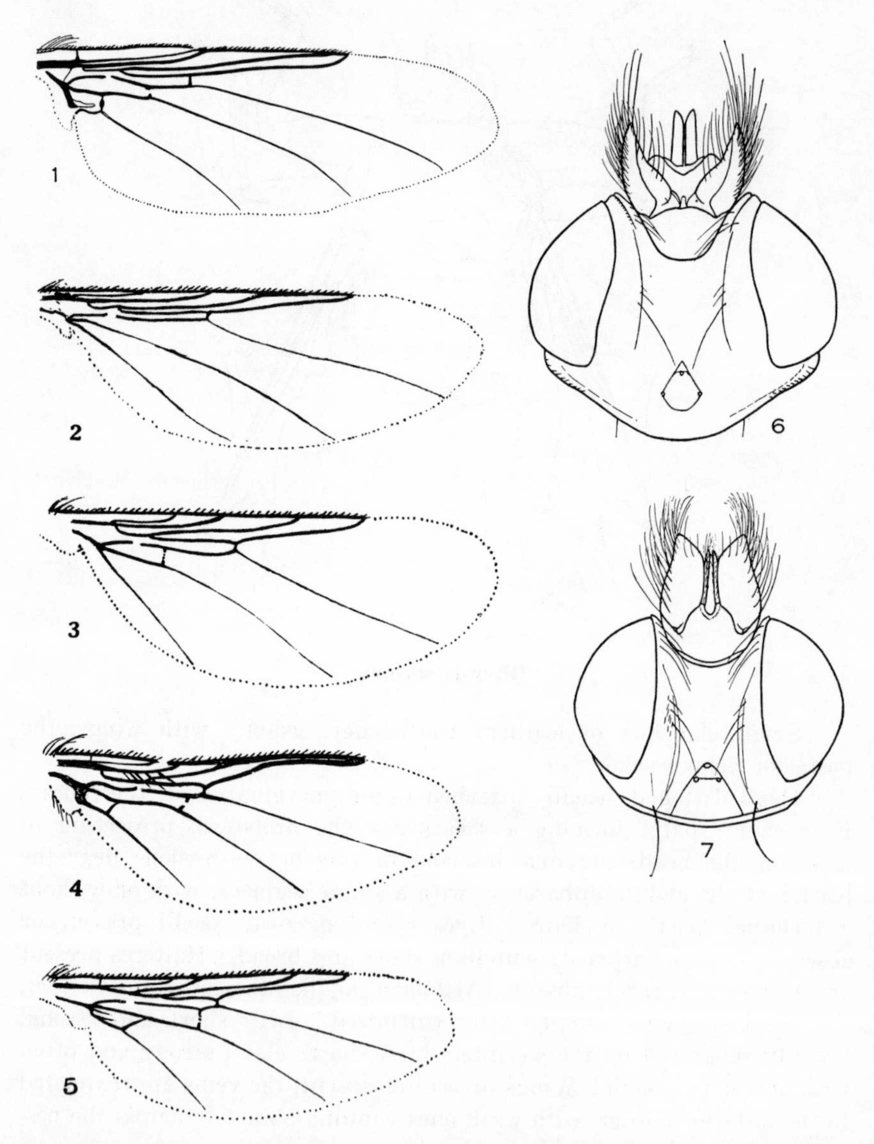

Hippoboscidæ.—1, **Stilbometopa impressa**; 2, **Pseudolynchia maura**; 3, **Lynchia americana**; 4, **Ornithoica**; 5, 6, **Ornithomyia**; 7, **Ornithoctona erythrocephala.**

Aldrich* has published a key to the genera but the species are very difficult to determine, there are no keys to the American species, and although most of them have been figured, the illustrations and descriptions are scattered.

KEY TO GENERA†

1. With functional wings, longer than abdomen........................ 2
   Wings rudimentary, broken off or absent........................ 12
2. Wing with five or six distinct veins behind the costa................ 3
   Wing with only three distinct veins behind the costa, the first, third and fifth ....**Lipoptena** Nitzsch
3. Anal cell closed by a crossvein (4)................................ 4
   Anal cell open apically (2).. 9
4. Ocelli present 6
   Ocelli absent 5
5. Claws bidentate; head rounded behind and free from thorax (not naturalized in America)..........................**Hippobosca** Linnæus
   Claws tridentate; head truncate behind, in a deep emargination of the thorax (1)..................................**Stilbometopa** Coquillett
6. Third vein joining the tip of the costal vein at a distinct angle; claws tridentate 7
   Third vein confluent with the costal vein on the apical third; claws bidentate (4).....................................**Ornithoica** Rondani
7. Antennal processes two-thirds as long as the head, straight and parallel with each other, broadly rounded at tip..........**Ornithopertha** Speiser
   Antennal processes much shorter, more or less pointed.............. 8
8. Antennal processes broad, concave above, with projecting outer rim, curved inwardly so as to almost or quite touch each other (7).
   Ornithoctona Speiser
   Antennal processes narrow, without outer rim, divergent and curving downward (5, 6) ....**Ornithomyia** Latreille
9. Crossvein closing the second basal cell entirely absent (2)............ 11
   Crossvein closing the second basal cell at least half present (3)...... 10
10. Lateral lobe of the metanotum swollen and bearing a mammiform process; fourth vein setulose (see text figure).....**Olfersia** Wiedemann
    Lateral lobe of metanotum less swollen and without processes; fourth vein bare (3)..................................**Lynchia** Weyenbergh
11. Ocelli entirely absent; scutellum angulate laterally (2).
    Pseudolynchia Bequaert
    Ocelli occasionally present but minute; scutellum convex posteriorly.
    Microlynchia Lutz, Neiva and Costa Lima
12. Halteres present 13
    Halteres absent; wings aborted, reduced to short knobs.
    Melophagus Latreille
13. Ocelli present, claws bidentate; with basal stumps of broken wings.
    Lipoptena Nitsch
    Ocelli absent, claws tridentate; wings present, much shorter than the abdomen. (**Brachypteromyia** Williston)...........**Myophthiria** Rondani

* 1923. Ins. Ins. Menstr., xi, pp. 75-79.
† Checked by Dr. J. Bequaert.

Family Nycteribiidæ

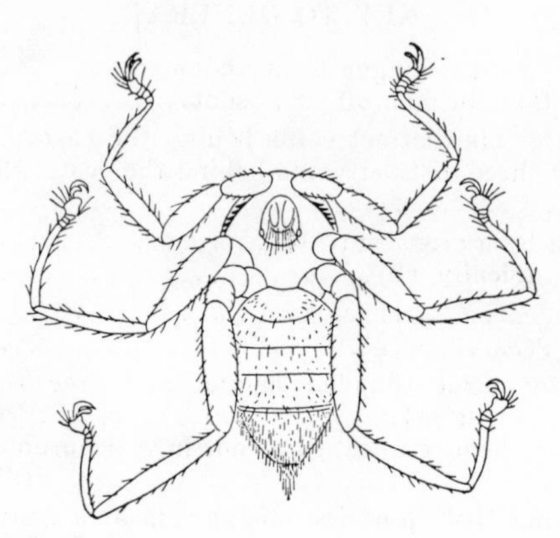

Basilia species.

Small, spider-like, wingless flies.

Head oval, folding back when at rest in a groove on the dorsum of the thorax. Antennæ short, two segmented, the oval terminal segment with bristles, inserted in cavity; eyes and ocelli vestigial. Thorax depressed, laterally and anteriorly with comb-like bristles. Abdomen oval, with more or less distinct segmentation. Legs long, the knees at rest prominent above the thorax; femora broad; tibiæ clubbed or shovel-shaped; basal tarsal segment very long. Halteres pendunculate or sessile, often indistinct. Larviparous.

The members of this family are all parasitic upon bats and occur throughout the tropics and subtropics but are most numerous in the Old World.

Ferris* considers that we have but one genus in North America and perhaps two genera in the western hemisphere. *Nycteribia* possibly occurs in Brazil but there are no positive records from other parts of the continent. The two genera are separable as follows:

1. Eyes absent .... **Nycteribia** Latreille
   Eyes present, two-facetted .... **Basilia** Ribeiro

* 1924. Ent. News, xxxv, pp. 191-199.

Family Streblidæ—The Bat Flies

Pterellipsis aranea.

Head of moderate size, with a freely movable neck. Eyes, when present, small, without or with very few facets; ocelli absent. Antennæ inserted in a pit, two segmented, the second segment with a bristle. Proboscis short, not protrusible, thickened basally; palpi broader than long, projecting leaf-like in front of the head, not forming a sheath for the proboscis. Abdomen with a distinct basal segment, the other segments rarely distinguishable, the basal segment with special bristles for the protection of the wings when at rest. Posterior coxæ always enlarged; fifth segment of the tarsi usually elongate and enlarged; pulvilli present, the claws never toothed. Wings sometimes vestigial or wanting, when present the veins stout and covered with hairs. Halteres present.

All but one species are parasitic upon bats but they are restricted to the tropics and the subtropico-temperate zones. Kessel* has reviewed the family.

KEY TO GENERA †

1. With a ctenidium of black bristles on the ventral surface of the head.. 2
   Without a ctenidium on under surface of head...................... 4

2. Eyes present; wings well-developed, with six veins (1)............. 3
   Eyes absent; wings reduced to oval pads, much shorter than the thorax.
   Metelasmus Coquillett

* 1925. Journ. N. Y. Ent. Soc., xxxiii, pp. 11-34, 4 plates.
† Checked by Dr. J. Bequaert.

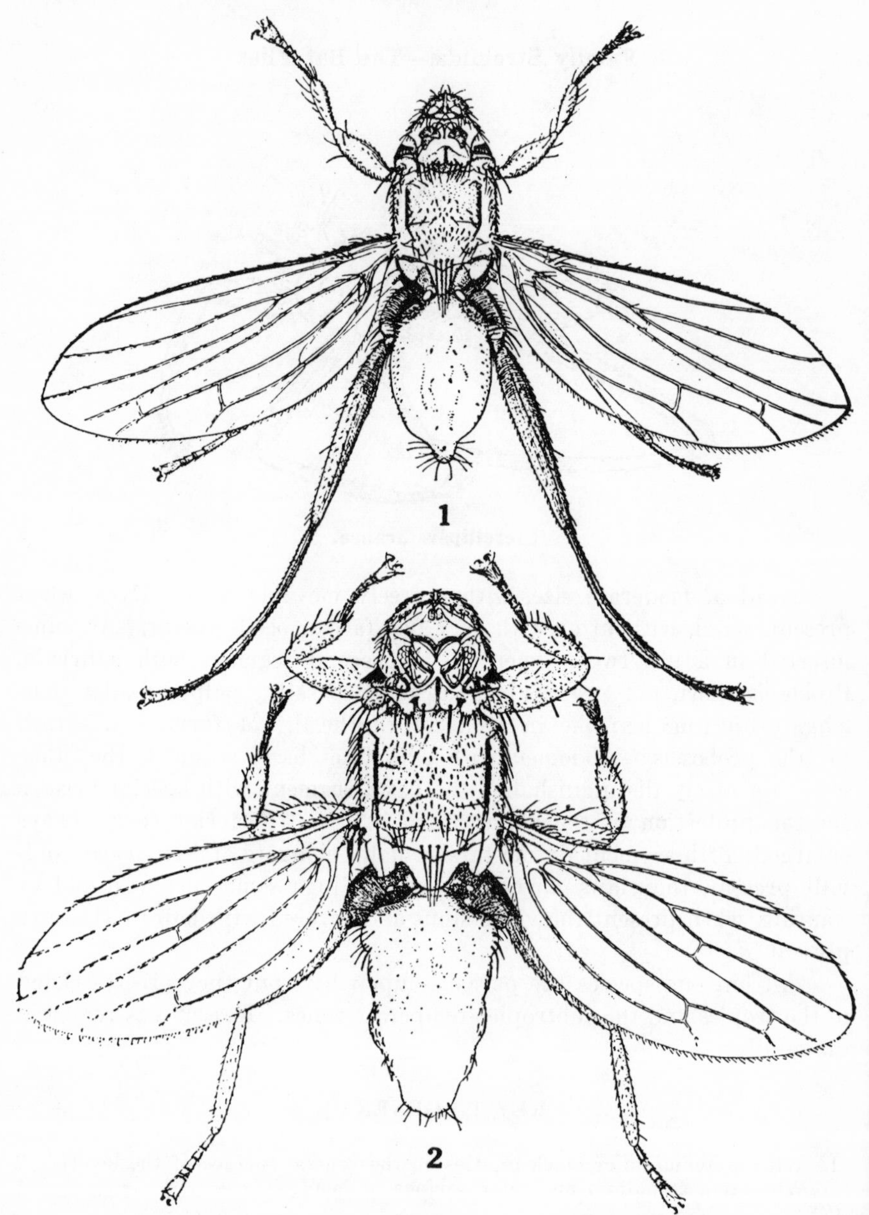

Streblidæ I.—1, **Strebla vespertilionis**; 2, **Euctenodes mirabilis.**

3. Ctenidium extending to the sides of the head and visible laterally from dorsal view 3a
Ctenidium ending far before the sides of the head (E. breviceps, Panama) ....**Eldunnia,** n. g.

3a. Posterior femora about twice as long as the anterior ones; anterior cross-vein before the middle of the wing (1)......**Strebla** Wiedemann
Posterior femora decidedly less than twice as long as the anterior ones; anterior crossvein beyond the middle of the wing (2).
Euctenodes Waterhouse

4. Wings entirely lacking 5
Wings present, though small 6

5. Posterior legs about twice as long as the anterior ones.
Megistopoda Macquart
Posterior legs not twice as long as the anterior ones.
Paradyschiria Speiser

6. Wings of normal size.. 8
Wings small, narrow or short.. 7

7. Wings erect and narrow; posterior legs about twice as long as anterior ones (5, also text figure)......................**Pterellipsis** Coquillett
Wings lying flat, short; posterior legs not twice as long as anterior ones (4) ....**Aspidoptera** Coquillett

8. Wings with a single crossvein and three longitudinal veins; thorax compressed (3) ....**Nycterophilia** Ferris
Wings with at least two crossveins and six longitudinal veins; thorax depressed 9

9. Posterior legs at least twice as long as the anterior pair............. 10
Posterior legs obviously less than twice as long as the anterior pair (6) ....**Trichobius** Gervais

10. Posterior legs three times as long as the body..**Paratrichobius** Costa Lima
Posterior legs about twice as long as the front pair......**Speiseria** Kessel

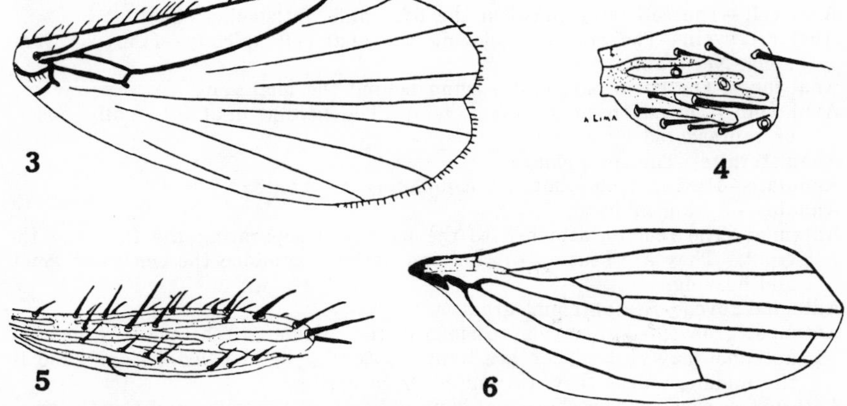

Streblidæ II.—3, **Nycterophilia coxata;** 4, **Aspidoptera minuta;** 5, **Pterellipsis aranea;** 6, **Trichobius sparsus.**

GLOSSARY OF TERMS USED IN DIPTEROLOGY

Abdomen—The hindermost of the three main body divisions.

Acalypteratæ—The Acalypterate Muscoidea—those with very small or linear squamæ.

Acrostical bristles—The rows of mesonotal bristles between the dorsocentrals—the two median rows of bristles of the thorax.

Acrostical hairs—Hairs lying between the dorsocentral bristles.

Acrostical setulæ—Very short hairs between the dorsocentral bristles.

Adventitious veins—Veins occurring in abnormal positions, sometimes rather regularly placed, and sometimes normally present.

Ædeagus—Part of the male negitalia: the penis and its sheath.

Alate—Having wings.

Alula—A lobe at the base of the wing posteriorly.

Ceria. Ceriomydas. Conops.

Examples of mimetic resemblances in flies.

Anal cell—The cell lying between the fifth and sixth veins (Cu).

Anal crossvein—The crossvein closing the anal cell apically—(Cu_2) of Comstock-Needham.

Anal lobe—The basal part of the wing behind the anal vein.

Anal vein—The sixth longitudinal vein. The second anal is usually absent or represented by a fold.

Anepisternite—The mesopleura.

Annulate—Having rings, but not completely segmented.

Annulus—A ring or band.

Antennæ—The feelers, attached to the head and separating the face and the front. They are sensory organs and perhaps combine the senses of smell and hearing.

Antennal fovea—See antennal grooves.

Antennal grooves—Definite depressions in the middle of the face in which the antennæ may rest. They are limited laterally by the facial ridges and in the middle, unless they are united, by a carina.

Anterior crossvein—The short crossvein connecting the third and fourth longitudinal veins on the basal half of the wing—(r-m).

Apicad—Toward the apex.

Apical cell—The first posterior cell—the space between the third and fourth longitudinal vein beyond the anterior crossvein (R_5).

Apical scutellars—The apical pair of marginal bristles on the scutellum. The term is loosely applied and often means the sub-apical scutellars, in cases where the true apicals are absent.

Apical spurs (of tibia)—Short, rather stout bristles often present on the under or ventral surface of the tibiæ. The number varies, and may differ on different pairs of legs.

Appendage (vein)—The presence of a short vein at the angle of a bend.

Apterous—Wingless.

Arcuate—Arched like a bow.

Arista—A bristle-like portion of the third antennal segment which may be apical or dorsal and sub-basal. It is composed normally of three segments; the first is usually minute and the second short, although all three may be elongate.

Auxiliary vein—The subcostal vein; that vein lying between the costa and first vein, often absent. (Subcostal; mediastinal.)

Axillary cell—The area behind the anal vein.

Axillary lobe—The area behind the anal vein. See axillary cell.

Axillary vein—The second anal vein when this is present (2nd A).

Basad—Toward the base.

Basicosta—The second distinct "scale" at the base of the wing in Muscoids. It is bare. The basal "scale" is the epaulet and is haired.

Basitarsus (si)—A term applied to the basal segment of the tarsi.

Bend of fourth vein—The curve of the fourth vein beyond the posterior crossvein (Muscoids).

Bilobed—Divided or split into two parts.

Calcar—A single posterodorsal bristle usually strong, situated on the posterior tibiæ at or beyond the middle (Muscidæ).

Calypter (Calypters, Calypteræ)—See squamæ.

Calypteræ—See Calypteratæ.

Calypteratæ—The Calypterate Muscoidæ—Tachinidæ, Metopiidæ, Muscidæ, Œstridæ and Cuterebridæ.

Capitate—Enlarged at the apex.

Carinate—Ridged or bearing a raised line or keel.

Caudad—Toward the posterior end of the abdomen or hind margin of the wing.

Caudal—Pertaining to the apex of the abdomen.

Cephalad—Toward the front of the head.

Cell—A space in the wing bounded by veins.

Cheeks—The space below the eyes. Sometimes termed the peristoma.

Chitinized—Hardened or horn-like: not membranous. There has been a great deal of discussion as to the proper use of the term chitin. As generally, and I think properly, used it refers to the leather-like, or hard part of insects; now commonly written sclerotized.

Clavate—Clubbed or enlarged at the apex.

Claws—Tarsal claws, borne on the fifth (or apical) tarsal segment.

Clypeus—A distinct sclerite at the base of the proboscis adjacent to the anterior oral opening. Some authors have contended that the clypeus is absent and that the middle of the face is the true clypeus. This seems very doubtful and I do not accept the contention. The term has been applied recently to the middle of the face, but epistoma is a much better term for that part.

Coarctate—Narrowed between the base and apex at some point.

Comb—A row of closely set, short bristles. (Often occurring on the femora or tarsi: Drosophilidæ, etc.)

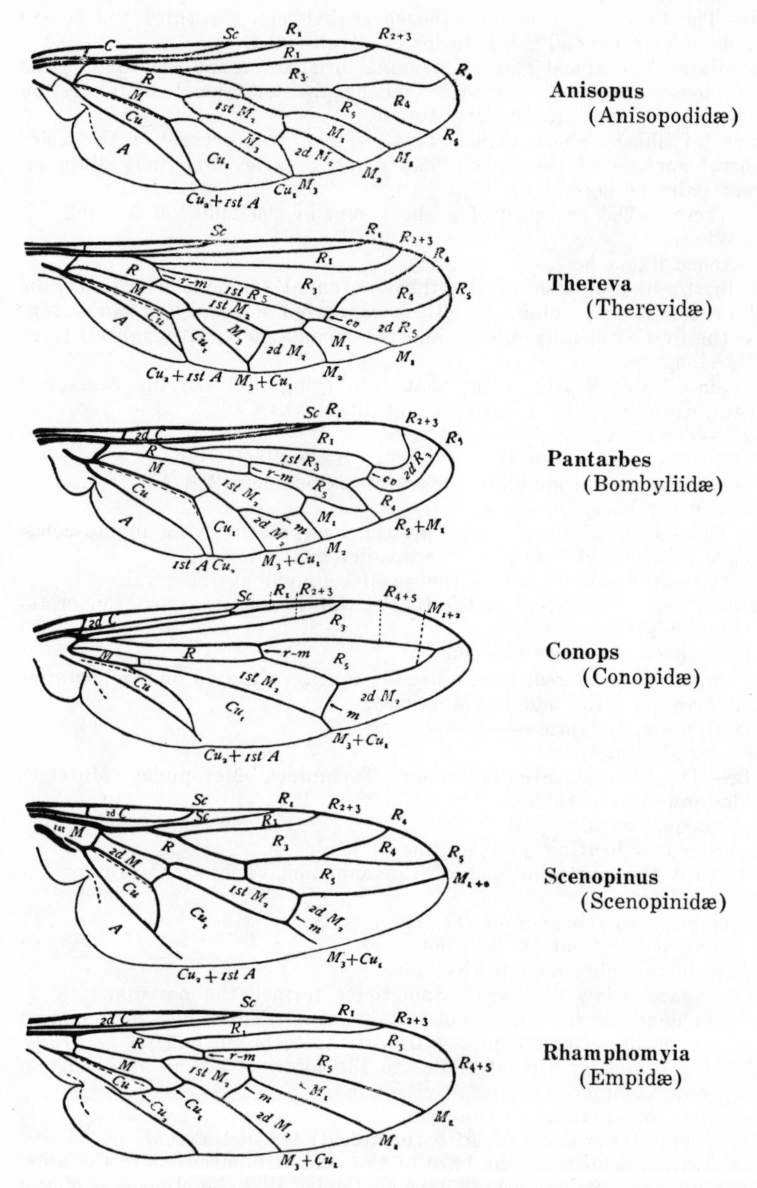

THE VEINS AND CELLS, COMSTOCK-NEEDHAM SYSTEM

COMSTOCK-NEEDHAM SYSTEM OF WING VENATION.

The comparison of the system here used is with that of Comstock-Needham, not as revised by Tillyard and others.

Anal cell—Cu.
Anal crossvein—Cu_2.
Crossveins—h;r-m; m; M_3; Cu_2; Sc_2.
Discal cell—1st M_2.
Discoidal crossvein—M_3.
Fifth longitudinal—$Cu_{1,2}$.
First basal cell—R.
First vein—R plus R_1. (the main stem of the vein, basad of Rs, is R,—beyond Rs, R_1).
Large crossvein—m and outer section of M_3.
Marginal cell—R_1.
Posterior cells—R_5 to Cu_1.
Posterior crossvein—m, and sometimes also outer section of M_3.
Præfurca—Rs.
Second vein—Rs, and its anterior branch, R_{2+3}.
Small crossvein—r-m.
Subcostal crossvein—Sc_2.
Submarginal cells—R_3, R_4.
Third long. vein—Posterior branch of Rs,—R_{4+5}.

Compressed—Flattened from side to side—laterally compressed.
Connate—Fused and immovable.
Constricted—Narrowed.
Corneous—Horn-like in texture or appearing so.
Costa—See costal vein.
Costal cell—The cell between the costa and subcostal or auxiliary vein.
Costal vein—The vein extending along the front margin of the wing.
Crossveins—There are five typical crossveins in the wings: humeral, anterior, posterior, discoidal and anal (The equivalents of these in the Comstock-Needham system are, in order,—h; r-m; m; M_3 and Cu_2). In addition to these there is the subcostal crossvein (Sc_2), and there may be one or more veins simulating crossveins. The apical crossvein is merely the anteriorly curved fourth longitudinal vein (Muscoids). The base of the third vein, base of posterior branch of the fourth vein and the base of the branches of the fifth vein may simulate crossveins. In some families there may be additional crossveins (see Nemestrinidæ, Bombyliidæ, etc.).
Cruciate—Crossing each other.
Ctenidium—A comb-like row of bristles.
Cubitus—Fifth longitudinal vein.
Decumbent—Depressed; hanging down.
Decussate—Crossing or cruciate.
Depressed—Flattened dorsoventrally, contrasting with compressed.
Dichoptic—Eyes separated by the front.
Digitate—Bearing a finger-like process.
Discal cell—A (usually) closed cell (on the disc of the wing, lying between the fourth and fifth veins). It may be absent, open apically, or united with one of the basal cells, usually the second basal, abnormally with the first basal (1st M_2).
Discal crossvein—The vein separating the discal and second basal cells. (See discoidal crossvein.) (M_3 of Comstock-Needham system).
Discal scutellars—Bristles on the disc of the scutellum.
Discoidal crossvein—The vein separating the discal and second basal cells. (See discal crossvein.) (M_3 of Comstock-Needham system).
Dorsad—Toward the upper surface.

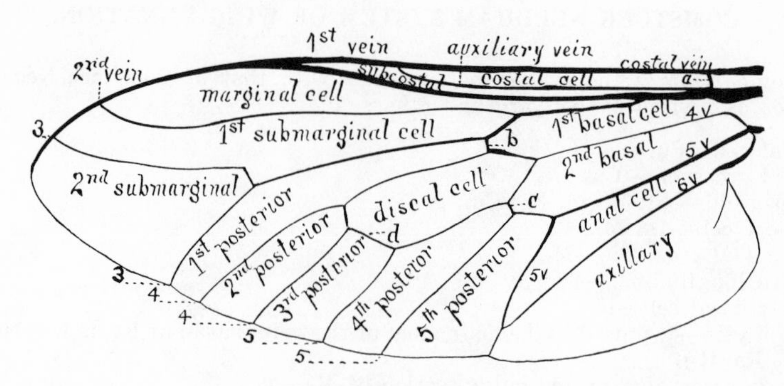

WING OF TABANUS

The terminology of the veins and parts shown on this figure is that used in the present work, except in the Tipuloidea.

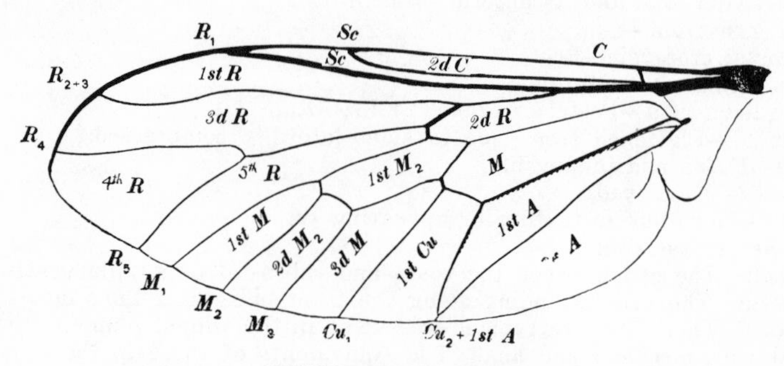

WING OF SILVIUS

Comstock-Needham system. **Veins.** C—costa, Sc—subcosta, R—radius. M—media, Cu—cubitus, A—anal. **Cells.** C—costal, Sc—subcostal, R—radial, M—medial, Cu—cubital, A—anal.

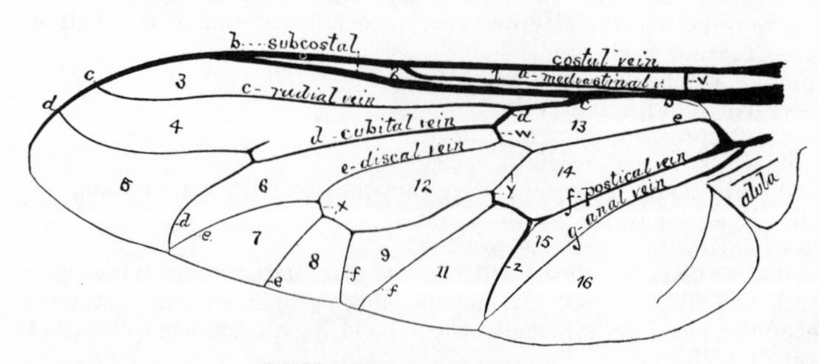

WING OF PANGONIA

Schiner's system. Cells. 1, costal; 2, mediastinal; 3, subcostal; 4, 5, cubital; 6, 7, 8, 9, 11, first to fifth posterior cells; 12, discoidal cell; 13, 14, 15, first to third basal cells; 16, axillary cell.

Dorsal—Pertaining to the upper surface of the body.
Dorsocentrals—Dorsocentral bristles of the thorax.
Dorsopleural suture—See notopleural suture.
Dorsum—Upper surface. Refers to thorax and abdomen.
Epaulet—The first "scale" at the base of the costa. It is haired and is followed by a bare "scale", the basicosta.
Empodium (ia)—A bristle, hair or pad borne on the apical tarsal segment between the pulvilli.
Epiphysis—A lappet-like process or lobe.
Epistoma—Correctly, the anterior oral margin. Frequently used to denote the facial depression or middle of the face from the oral margin to the antennæ.
Eyes—The compound eyes, composed of, usually, many facets.
Face—The front of the head between the mouth and the antennæ.
Facets—The divisions comprising the compound eyes.
Facial depression—The middle of the face. Facial plate.
Facial plate—The central part of the face.
Femur (femora)—The long part of the leg nearest the thorax, but separated from the thorax by the coxa and trochanter. The thigh.
Fifth longitudinal vein—The vein running along the posterior side of the second basal cell, and of the discal cell, usually two-branched, the second branch separating the fourth and fifth posterior cells. ($Cu_{1,2}$; postical.)
First basal cell—A cell lying between the first, second and third and the fourth longitudinal veins on the basal half of the wing.
First vein—The vein lying immediately behind the auxiliary vein, or when that is absent, immediately behind the costa. (R and R_1.)
Flagellum—In flies having six or more antennal segments the portion beyond the scape.
Fourth longitudinal vein—The vein, usually arising near the base of the wing, separating the two basal cells and bordering the discal cell anteriorly, often branched, the posterior branch often partly closing the discal cell. (Medial, $M_{1,2,3}$; discoidal.)
Front—The space between the eyes lying above the antennæ and limited by the vertex or top of the head.
Frontalia—The central stripe of the front. Frontal vitta.
Frontal lunule—The space between the bases of the antennæ and the ptilinal or frontal suture, actually occurring only in Cyclorrhaphous flies, but the term, or "lunula", is loosely applied to some other flies.
Frontal orbits—The space contiguous to the eyes on the front.
Frontals or frontal bristles—Bristles situated along the inner edge of the parafrontals.
Frontal triangle—The triangle in holoptic flies bounded above by the eyes and below by the antennæ.
Frontal vitta—The softer area between the rows of frontal bristles or hairs extending from the antennæ to the ocelli. This allows the head to expand laterally in Cyclorrhaphous Diptera when the ptilinum is expanded.
Fronto-orbital bristles—The orbitals or orbital bristles. The term is variously used and is often applied to the frontals in the Acalypteratæ.
Gena (næ)—The cheek. Often refers to the parafacials. The term is best avoided.
Geniculate—Abruptly bent or elbowed.
Genitalia—The external sexual organs together with the adjacent parts.
Gibbous—Puffed out; hunch-backed.
Glabrous—Without hairs; smooth.
Halteres—Appendages arising on the posterior of the pleura, with a long stem and apical knob. These occur in practically all Diptera, rarely being

reduced to slight swellings in some apterous forms. They are supposed to be the rudiments of the second pair of wings but I doubt this. The removal of the halteres renders the insects unable to fly.

Holoptic—Eyes contiguous, dividing the front into an upper and lower part.

Humeral crossvein—A crossvein situated near the base of the wing and extending from the costa to the auxiliary or subcostal vein and continuing to the first vein.

Humeri—The anterior corners of the mesonotum usually more or less well marked.

Hyaline—Transparent.

Hypopleura—The space below the posterior spiracle and above the posterior coxæ.

Hypopleural bristles—Bristles on the hypopleura, usually in a vertical row.

Hypopygium—The male genitalia together with the adjacent parts. It is composed of several of the apical abdominal segments and is variously modified.

Infra-squamal setulæ—Fine hairs below the point of attachment of the squamæ.

Intercalary vein—A term sometimes applied to the posterior branch of the fourth vein in cases where its base partly closes the discal cell (M_2).

Interfrontal (bristles or hairs)—Hairs or bristles on the frontal vitta.

Interfrontalia—The frontal vitta.

Intra-alar bristles—Bristles situated behind the suture and between the supra-alar and dorsocentral bristles.

Jowls—The cheeks, behind the depressed anterior part. Sometimes termed the peristoma.

Labellæ—The lips of the proboscis. Supposed to be the modified labial palpi. Sometimes broadly expanded, at other times much reduced or apparently lacking.

Lamella (e)—A leaf-like plate.

Lamellate—Broadened and flat: leaf-like; bearing lamellæ.

Large crossvein—The crossvein closing the discal cell; posterior crossvein (m and M_3).

Lateral—At, toward, or pertaining to the sides of the body.

Lunula—A term applied to the more or less crescentric area above the antennæ in some flies, notably in the Syrphidæ. Also a lunulate marking.

Lunule—See lunula.

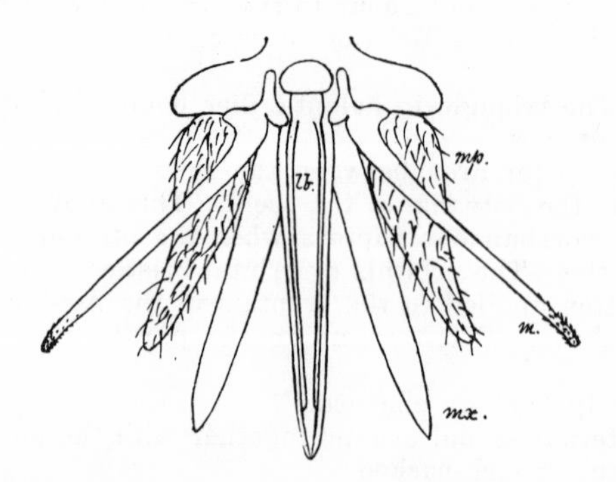

MOUTHPARTS OF FEMALE TABANUS.

lb, labium; m, mandible; mp, maxillary palpus; mx, maxilla.

Macrotrichia—The larger microscopic hairs on the surface of the wings.
Marginal cell—The cell lying between the first and second longitudinal veins (R_1).
Marginal scutellars—Bristles situated close to or on the margin of the scutellum.
Media—The fourth longitudinal vein.
Medial—Pertaining to the media or middle.
Median—Along the middle.
Mesad—Toward the middle.

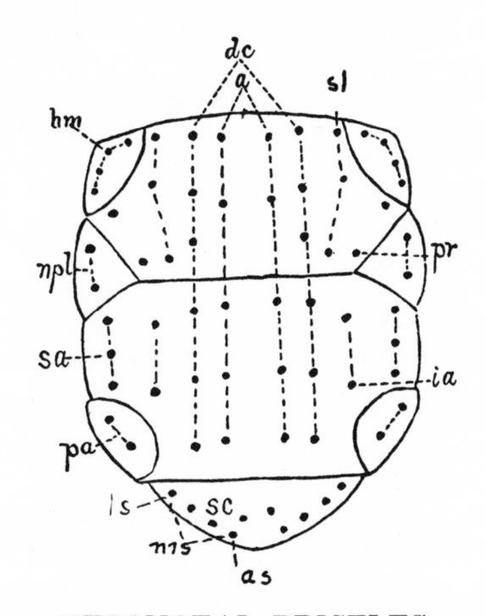

MESONOTAL BRISTLES

a, acrosticals; as, apical scutellars; dc, dorsocentrals; hm, humeral; ia, intra-alar; ls, lateral or basal scutellars; ms, marginal scutellars; npl, notopleural; pa, postalars; pr, presutural; sa, supra-alars; sc, scutellars; sl, sublaterals.

Mesonotum—The dorsum of the mesothorax or the main part of the back. Sometimes termed the mesoscutum. According to morphological usage the divisions of the mesonotum are, from front to rear, prescutum, scutum, scutellum and postscutellum.*
Mesopleura—A so-called pleurite or sclerite of the pleura bounded above by the mesonotum, in front by the propleura, below by a more or less distinct suture and behind by a suture extending down from in front of the wings. The so-called suture separating the mesopleura and sternopleura is merely a fold leaving an exterior furrow.
Mesoscutum—See mesonotum.
Mesosternum—The under side of the mesothorax.
Mesothorax—The second and largest segment of the thorax. The wings and second pair of legs arise from this segment.
Metacephalon—The area behind the mouth extending up toward the neck.
Metanotal slopes—Swellings on the sides of the metanotum or its sloping sides (pleurotergite).

---

* While not professing any great knowledge of morphology I am far from being convinced that the **Metanotum**, as used by taxonomists is actually **part of the Mesonotum**: there is a distinct, membranous suture between this part and the scutellum, such as one expects to find between true sclerites.

Metanotum—The dorsum of the metathorax, lying behind the scutellum. (*According to recent morphological usage this is the postnotum or postscutellum and is part of the mesonotum: the true metanotum is found only in the lower Diptera, as Psychodidæ.) See footnote, p. 487.

Metapleura—The part of the metathorax above the hypopleura and outside of the metanotum. It is a poorly defined area and not really separable from the metanotum.

Metasternum—The under side of the metathorax, situated behind the middle coxæ and extending to behind the posterior coxæ.

Metatarsus (si)—A term applied to the basal segment of the tarsi.

Metathorax—The third segment of the thorax. The posterior legs and halteres arise from this segment.

Micropterous—With small or vestigial wings.

Microtrichia—The smaller abundant hairs of the wing. When these are present the wing is said to be villous.

Moniliform—Resembling a string of beads.

Neuration—The arrangement of the veins of the wing.

Node—A swelling or knot-like knob.

Notopleura—A depression, more or less triangular, situated immediately before the transverse suture and behind the humeri.

Notopleural suture—The suture extending from the humeri to the base of the wings.

Notum—The dorsal surface; particularly of the thorax.

Ocellar bristles—Bristles arising within the ocellar triangle or on either side of the anterior ocellus.

Ocellar triangle—The triangle formed by the ocelli or the triangular, well marked area surrounding them. This triangle has sometimes been termed the frontal triangle in cases where it extends almost to the antennal base.

Ocellar tubercle—A term applied to the swelling on which the ocelli are sometimes situated, especially in the Asilidæ.

Ocelli—The simple eyes, located on the front, usually near the vertex.

Occipital cilia—The row of bristly hairs behind the eyes.

Occipital fringe—The fringe of fine hairs behind the eyes.

Occiput—The back of the head. Morphologically the subtriangular area limited by the vertex between the eyes and the neck.

Onychium (ia)—A pad between the tarsal claws.

Orbit—The part of the head immediately surrounding the eyes.

Orbital bristles—Bristles, usually proclinate or divergent, situated on the parafrontals between the frontals and orbits.

Ordinary crossvein—Anterior or small crossvein, r-m (Schiner).

Ovipositor—The female genitalia with the adjacent parts, composed of several segments and usually telescopic, but often variously modified.

Palpi—The maxillary palpi.

Parafacials, parafacialia—The part of the face between the facial ridges and the eyes.

Parafrontals—The part of the front outside the frontal bristles.

Pectinate—With branches like a comb.

Pectus—The under side of the thorax.

Pendulous—Hanging from one end.

Peristoma—Correctly, the region surrounding the mouth, but used in various senses. The part of the cheeks nearest the oral opening. The anterior oral opening. The anterior part of the cheeks. The term should be avoided as being too confusing.

Petiolate—Attached by a stalk or stem.

Phytophagous—Feeding on plants.

Pilose—Having long, fine hair, usually dense. The term is loosely applied to include any hair that is not coarse.
Pleurites—A term applied to the sclerites or sections of the pleura.
Pleurotergite—The hypopleura; morphologically the lateral division of the metanotum (postscutellum), at least in Nematocera.

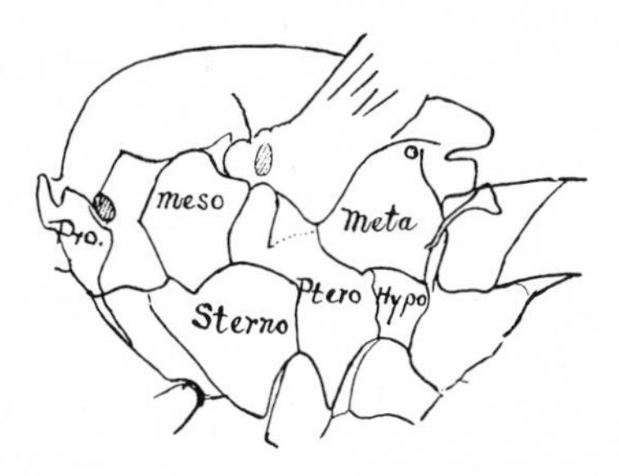

PLEURAL DIVISIONS OF SYRPHUS

Hypo, hypopleura; Meso, mesopleura; Meta, metapleura; Pro, propleura; Ptero, pteropleura; Sterno, sternopleura.

Plumose—Having rays on both sides like a feather.
Pollen—A fine, dust-like substance on the integument.
Pollinose—Covered with "dust" or "bloom".
Posterior calli—The swellings at the posterior corners of the mesonotum, present in the Calypteratæ, and other families, but absent in the Acalypteratæ as a rule. (Posterior callosities).
Posterior cells—The cells on the apical part of the wing lying between the third and fifth veins, exclusive of the discal cells (R_5 to Cu_1). Some of these cells may be closed by the union of veins apically.
Posterior crossvein—The vein or veins closing the discal cell apically (m and M_3). According to Schiner the basal section of Cu_1 of the Comstock-Needham System.
Posterior orbits—The part of the head immediately behind the eyes.
Posthumeral bristle—A bristle situated behind the humerus.
Post ocellar(s) (bristles)—A pair (or more) of bristles arising just below the vertex on the occiput and behind the ocellar tubercle, sometimes termed post-verticals.
Postscutellum—A convex, transverse swelling below the scutellum; actually the upper, posteriorly produced section of the metanotum.
Postvertical(s) bristles—See post ocellars.
Præfurca—See prefurca.
Pra—Prealar bristle.
Præscutum—The part of the mesonotum in front of the transverse suture.
Prealar (bristle)—The anterior supra alar bristle. This is frequently absent or reduced. It is used particularly in Muscidæ.
Prefurca—The petiole of the second and third longitudinal veins. Base of R_{4+5} (The Radial sector Rs).
Preapical bristle (of tibia)—A dorsal, short bristle situated before the end of the tibia.
Prescutum—See præscutum.
Presutural bristle—A bristle situated in front of the inner end of the notopleura in front of the suture. The lateral bristle situated in front of but close to the suture.

Proboscis—The mouthparts exclusive of the palpi; always more or less tube-like. They may be slender and adapted for piercing, or thick and adapted for lapping.
Proclinate—Curving or directed forward.
Pronotum—The dorsum of the prothorax.
Propleura—The sides of the prothorax. This is usually a depressed area, but also includes the area above the front coxæ.
Propleural bristle—A bristle situated on the propleura immediately above the front coxæ.
Prosternum—The under side of the prothorax, between and in front of the anterior coxæ.
Prothoracic bristle—A bristle situated immediately above the anterior coxæ (See propleural bristle).
Prothorax—The first segment of the thorax. The first pair of legs arise from the prothorax.
Pruinose—Covered with a hoary dust. (See pollinose).
Pseudosutural foveæ—Impressed polished areas on the humeral portion of the mesonotum (humeral pits); in Tipulidæ and elsewhere.
Pteropleura—A sclerite lying below the base of the wings.
Pteropleural bristle(s)—Bristle or bristles on the pteropleura.
Pteropleurites—The upper and lower sections of the pteropleura.
Ptilinum—An inflatable sac, occurring in Cyclorrhaphous flies and pushed out above the antennæ by the insect in emerging from the pupa (or puparium). This sac is coarsely grained or pubescent and when forced out thrusts the face into a horizontal position and when retracted after emergence leaves the frontal lunule exposed and is concealed in part beneath the facial ridges.
Pubescent—Having very short, fine hair.

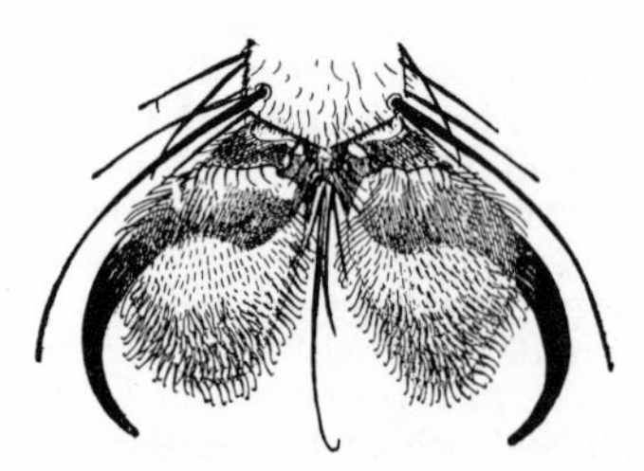

Foot of house-fly, showing claws, pulvilli and the hair-like empodium.

Pulvilli—Pads borne on the apical segment of the tarsus between the claws.
Pulvilliform—Shaped like the pulvilli.
Punctate—Pitted; covered with small pits.
Puparium—The pupa when formed within the hardened larval skin.
Pupiparous—Giving birth to larvæ ready to pupate.
Radial—Pertaining to the radius.
Radial cell—Any cell bordered in front by a branch of the radius.
Radius—The first to third longitudinal veins. R_1 to R_5 of Comstock-Needham system.
Raptorial—Fitted for grasping prey.
Reclinate—Curving or directed backward.
Recurrent—The anterior end nearer the base of the wing than some other part.
Reniform—Kidney-shaped.
Reticulate—Having a network.

Rostrum—The beak or snout.
Rugose—Wrinkled.
Rugulose—Finely wrinkled.
Scape (of antennæ)—The basal two segments in those flies having six or more antennal segments. These segments are differentiated from the remaining segments, although the first may be small and ring-like; the second segment is sometimes called the pedicel.
Sclerite—Any piece of the body well surrounded by sutures.
Scutellum—A (usually) convex sclerite attached to the back of the mesonotum. Sometimes termed the shield.
Scutum—The part of the mesonotum behind the transverse suture.
Second basal cell—A cell lying immediately behind the first basal, rarely united with it, more often open apically and united with the discal cell, but closed in most cases (Cell M).
Second vein—The vein (frequently absent), lying immediately behind the first vein, its base always united with the base of the third vein (Rs and its anterior branch R_{2+3}).
Serrate—Toothed along the edge like a saw.
Sessile—Broadly attached; incapable of movement.
Seta—A bristle.
Setaceous—Bristle-like.
Setigerous tubercles—Tubercles, occurring on the scutellum or legs, each bearing a spine or bristle on its top.
Setulæ—Very short hairs, sometimes coarse.
Setules—Setulæ.
Setulose—Bearing setulæ.
Sinuous—S-shaped, winding back and forth.
Sixth longitudinal vein—The first anal vein. The second anal is usually absent or represented by a fold extending around the anterior apex of the alula. (Anal vein).
Small crossvein—The anterior crossvein (r-m).
Spatulate—Broadened apically, narrow basally.
Spiracles—The external openings of the tracheal system.
Spurs—Either movable spines at the end of the tibiæ or strong production of apex of tibiæ or a tapering production of some part of the body, usually on the legs.
Spurious vein—An extra, usually very weak vein crossing the anterior crossvein.
Squamæ—The scales or connecting lobes connecting the wings basally with the thorax. There are two lobes, the upper and lower. The lower lobe is often greatly enlarged and is generally referred to as the squama.
Squamose—Scale-like. Refers particularly to scale-like hairs.
Sternites—Ventral sclerites or the under side of the segments.
Sternopleural bristles—Bristles situated on the upper part of the sternopleura on the posterior half.
Sternum—The under side of the thorax, comprising the pro-, meso- and metasternum.
Stigma—A darkened and often thickened area lying immediately behind the costa, either beyond the tip of the first or second veins.
Stylate—Bearing a style.
Style—A thick, terminal portion of the antennæ arising from the third segment, sometimes simulating segments, but usually tapering.
Stylose—Bearing a style.
Subantennal groove—See facial grooves.
Subcosta—The vein, usually present, between the costa and the first longitudinal vein.

Subcostal cell—The cell between the subcosta or auxiliary vein and the first vein or radius.

Subcostal crossvein—A crossvein, sometimes present, connecting the subcosta or auxiliary vein and the first vein. This is used taxonomically in the Mycetophilidæ and the Tipuloidea (Morphologically sc_2).

Subcostal vein—The vein lying between the costa and the first longitudinal vein. It is sometimes absent or greatly reduced.

Sublateral bristles—Bristles situated in a line with the intra-alars but in front of the suture. The anterior two are sometimes included as posthumerals but the term is deceptive.

Submarginal cell(s)—The cell or cells lying between the second and third longitudinal veins (R_3 and R_4).

Sulcate—Grooved or furrowed.

Supernumerary cells—Additional cells occurring in the wings due to the presence of extra crossveins (See Nemestrinidæ, Bombyliidæ, etc.).

Supernumerary crossveins—Crossveins, other than those normally present.

Supra-alar bristles—Bristles close to the edge of the thorax behind the suture.

Suture—A line separating the parts of the body wall.

Tarsus (si)—The feet, composed normally of five segments. The apical segment bears the claws, pulvilli and empodium when these are not obsolete. In rare cases the number of tarsal segments is reduced to two. The tarsal segments are numbered from the base, segments one to five, although the first segment is sometimes termed the basitarsus or metatarsus.

Tegulæ—See Squamæ.

Tergites—Dorsal sclerites or the upper side of the segment.

Third longitudinal vein—The vein arising jointly with the second vein and branching from it, sometimes branched. Behind it is the first posterior cell and behind or before its base, the first basal cell (R_{4+5}; Posterior branch of Rs.; Cubital).

Thorax—The middle part of the body bearing the wings and legs.

Tibia(e)—The part of the leg beyond the femur.

Transverse suture (of thorax)—The depressions extending inward from the sides of the mesonotum near the middle, but not true sutures. In the Muscoids this is said to be complete or extend entirely across, but this is not always the case. Usually the suture is obsolete in the middle. In the Tipulidæ it is V-shaped. The suture divides the anterior series of bristles from the posterior dorsocentrals and acrosticals, whether it is complete or not.

Trichostical bristles—Hypopleural bristles, used especially in the Asilidæ.

Trochanter—The small, ring-like portion connecting the coxæ and femora. This often appears more or less triangular as only part of it is generally visible.

Truncate—Ending transversely or with cut-off apex.

Tubercle—A conspicuous, more or less rounded swelling, sometimes elongate as on the face of Syrphidæ, etc.

Tuberculate pits—Paired shiny dots at or near the anterior margin of the mesonotum, one on either side of the median line; in Tipulidæ.

Ungues—Claws.

Venation—The arrangement of the veins of the wings.

Venter—The under surface of the abdomen.

Ventrad—Toward the venter.

Ventral—Pertaining to the under side of the body.

Vertex—The uppermost edge of the front; usually that part between the ocelli and the back of the head, or behind and between the upper angles of the eyes.

Vertical triangle—The space, in holoptic flies, surrounding the ocelli.

Vibrissæ—The large bristles arising from the vibrissal angles at the sides of the mouth in many Cyclorrhaphous Diptera. This term has been misapplied to include the bristles sometimes found on the facial ridges.

Vibrissal angles—The more or less rounded angles formed by the facial ridges just above the oral margin.

Viviparous—Bringing forth living young.

LITERATURE

For the convenience of those who may not be familiar with American literature on Entomology lists of general works on Diptera and periodicals, etc., published in North America is given. This list is not complete but includes the more important publications. Occasionally descriptions are published in other journals but the number is small. Certain journals contain more papers dealing with flies than others, but there is a great deal of variation over a period of years. Monographic work on American insects is greatly handicapped because there is no medium of publication, most journals accepting only short papers.

General Works for Students of Diptera

Aldrich, J. M.—Catalogue of North American Diptera.

Lœw, H.—Diptera Americæ Septentrionalis Indigena, I to X. (Latin). 1000 new species. The types are almost all in the Museum of Comparative Zoology, Harvard University.

Lœw, H.—Monographs of the Diptera of North America. Dolichopidæ, Ephydridæ, Otitidæ, Tetanoceridæ and Trypaneidæ. Most of the species have been elucidated in later work.

Lœw, H.—Neue Beitrage zur Kenntniss der Dipteren. (German). Partly North American.

Macquart, J.—Diptêres Exotiques, nouveaux ou peu connus. Vols. I, II and Supplements I to V. (French).

Say, Thomas—The Complete Writings of Thomas Say on the Entomology of North America (Two volumes).

Wiedemann, C. R.—Aussereuropaische Zweiflugelige Insecten. Vols. I, II (German).

Current North American Periodicals Dealing Entirely With Entomology

Annals of the Entomological Society of America.
Bulletin of the Brooklyn Entomological Society.
Canadian Entomologist.
‡ Entomologica Americana (Published by Brooklyn Entomological Society).
Entomological News.
† Insecutor Inscitiæ Menstruus.
Journal of Economic Entomology.
Journal of the Kansas Entomological Society.
Journal of the New York Entomological Society.
‡ Memoirs of the American Entomological Society.
Pan Pacific Entomologist.
Proceedings of the Hawaiian Entomological Society.
Proceedings of the Entomological Society of Washington (D. C.).
Psyche.
‡Thomas Say Foundation of the Entomological Society of America.
Transactions of the American Entomological Society.

---

* No parts on Diptera published.
† Publication discontinued. Mostly Diptera and Lepidoptera.
‡ Irregular publications.

Scientific Publications Containing Entomological Papers

American Journal of Hygiene.
American Museum Novitates (American Museum of Natural History).
Anales del Instituto de Biologia (Mexico City).
Bulletin of the American Museum of Natural History.
Bulletin of the Buffalo Society of Natural Sciences.
Bulletin of the Illinois State Laboratory of Natural History.
Journal of the Washington Academy of Sciences (D. C.)
Kansas University Science Bulletin.
Occasional Papers of the Boston Society of Natural History.
Ohio Journal of Science.
Proceedings of the Biological Society of Washington.
Proceedings of the California Academy of Sciences.
Proceedings of the United States National Museum.
Transactions of the Royal Canadian Institute.
Transactions of the Royal Society of Canada.
Transactions of the Wisconsin Academy of Sciences, Arts and Letters.
Zoological Record (London, England). Separate parts may be obtained. Lists all new species described each year.
See also Government publications of the United States, Canada and the States and Provinces.

CORRECTIONS

Page 327. **Leucophanga** Mik. Most species of this genus will trace to couplet 10, where they may be distinguished by having the costa ending at the third vein.

Page 359. For **Microdiopsis,** n. g. read **Pseudodiopsis** Hendel. The genotype is the same.

INDEX.

[PUBLISHED, AUGUST 25, 1934]

APPENDIX

Revisions and Corrections

P 21	Cpl	10	Discal cell present (except in Axymyia, Anisopidae) 21
P 22	Cpl	30	Line 3 Wings not pointed, usually with crossveins 31
P 25	Cpl	64	For 65 read **66**
P 25	Cpl	65	Delete couplet
P 25	Cpl	69	For 70 read — (P310) **PIOPHILIDAE**
P 25	Cpl	70	Read: Mesonotum, scutellum and abdomen flattened: legs and abdomen with hairs and bristles. face deeply concave (P. 376) **COELOPIDAE** Not with all these characters; both mesonotum and scutellum rarely flattened 71
P 76			**Isoecacta** Garrett = Alluadomyia, and not **Dasyhelea**
P 82			Third line for **Amopheles** read **Anopheles** and for algypti read aegypti.
P 165	Cpl	2	After; palpi absent, add: mesopleura haired behind.
P 165			Note: Heteromydas bicolor Hardy (n.g. n.sp.) descr in Canadian Entomologist p. 227, 1944.
P 179	Cpl	74	**(Panamasilus Curran)** = **Smeringolaphria** Hermann
P 195			3rd line from bottom: for 409 read 404.
P 257	Cpl	44	For 50 read 51
	Cpl	46	For 47 read 46a.
P 257	Cpl	46a	Face conspicuously tuberculate (25, 99) **Ferdinandea Scopoli** — Face not conspicuously tuberculate 47
P 257	Cpl	50	Delete couplet
P 259			Footnote: The signs for Malloch and Shannon should be transposed.
P 274			For fig 29 in middle of page read 24.
P 279	Cpl	54	Add: Costal cell normal: anal cell drawn out into a long point — Pareuxesta Coquillet.
P 286			Captions: For **Oedacarina** read Gymnocarena.
P 289	Cpl	23	For **Oedicarena** Snow read — **Gymnocarena** Hendel
P 291			**Straussia** possibly should be **Strauzia**
P 317	Cpl	15	**Steganopsis** is not American.
P 336	Cpl	14	After Melander add: Leptometopa (Becker)
P 399			3. paragraph, 4th line; for fourth read fifth.
P 341	Cpl	7	For Ephi — read: Epi —.
P 343	Cpl	14	For **Pseudohippelates** Malloch read **Lasiopleura** Becker
P 343	Cpl	18	For Duda read de Meijere
P 351	Cpl	31	For 32 read 31a
	Cpl	31a	Scutellar bristles arising from very strong tubercles; two pairs of frontal bristles (12, 74) Gastrops Williston
P 351	Cpl	38	Scutellars arising from at most weak tubercles 32
P 352			Delete cpl 39
P 353	Cpl	40	For elongate read: angular
P 353	Cpl	52	For 23 read 32
P 359	Cpl	5	For **Microdiopsis ng:** read **Pseudodiopsis** Hendel

P 369	Cpl	8	1st line for **Renocera** Hendel; read **Antichaeta** Haliday. 2nd line for **Antichaeta** read (2, 3) — **Renocera** Hendel.
P 381	Cpl	21	Transpose **Morpholeria** and (5) **Acantholeria**
P 395	Cpl	94	For 104 read 140
P 397	Cpl	123	First line after eyes, add: or male
P 399	Cpl	143	For Coquillett: read Malloch
P 401			Last paragraph; for Clark read Leach
P 407	Cpl	17	For **Pachyophthalmus** B & B read Amobia Desvoidy
	Cpl	21	For **Amobia** Desv. read **Amobiopsis** Townsend
P 409	Cpl	46	For **Camptops** Ald. read **Pachygraphia**
P 413			Last paragraph, first line for formed: read found.
P 420	Cpl	5	After bare delete 6 and replace with 1st two lines of Cpl 6. 2nd line cpl 5 — for 7 read 6.
P 420	Cpl	6	Read: Palpi absent or extremely small. **Tachinomima** Brauer & Bergenstamm. Palpi well developed 7
	Cpl	7	Robust hairy species .... **Pseudohystricia** Brauer & Bergenstamm. More slender, abdominal hair appressed and coarse dorsally .... **Arthrochaeta** Brauer & Bergenstamm.
P 423	Cpl	38	Line 2 for long: read short
P 425	Cpl	48	Line 1, after margin add: second abdominal segment with marginals. Line 2, after margin add: or second abdominal segment without marginals.
P 431	Cpl	93	After bare add: on basal half
P 441	Cpl	152	For **Ginglimyia** read: **Ginglymia**
P 441	Cpl	158	For **Blondelia** read **Anetia** Desvoidy
P 442	Cpl	168	(**Websteriana** Walton) = Lachnomma Townsend
P 443	Cpl	184	Transpose 186 & 185
P 444	Cpl	202	**(Coloradalia n.g.)** = **Parahypochaeta** Townsend
P 444	Cpl	209	**(Polidaria n.g.)** = **Lydina** Desvoidy
P 445	Cpl	220	After bare add: pleura black haired
P 445	Cpl	221	After bare add: pleura white haired
P 447	Cpl	247	For Townsend read Macquart
P 448	Cpl	255	After Bristles add: or a strong upwardly directed bristle.
P 448	Cpl	259	**(Vorialia n.g.)** = **Paedarium** Aldrich
P 452	Cpl	312	3rd line, after eyes insert: Usually
P 455	Cpl	361	Line 1, after geniculate add — or the labellae projecting forward
P 457			Last line: for lxix read lxxix.
P 459	Cpl	408	Second line; replace 3rd c with s.
P 462	Cpl	458	For second 458 read 459
P 491			Line 8 for well: read wall.
P 499			**Cuphocera** for 47 read 447

REFERENCES
and
Some Important Publications 1934 - 1964

Nowell, W. R. 1951 The dipterous family Dixidae in western North America. Microentomology 16: 187-270

Cook, E. F. 1956 The nearctic Chaoborinae. Minn. Agr. Exp. Sta. Techn. Bull. 218: 1-102

Stone, Alan, Knight, K. L. and Starcke, Helle. 1959 A Synoptic catalog of the mosquitoes of the world. Ento. Soc. Amer. Thomas Say Foundation vol. 6 358 pp.

Hardy, D. E. 1945 Revision of nearctic Bibionidae including neotropical Plecia and Penthetria. Kansas Univ. Sci. Bull. 30: 367-547

Laffoon, J. L. 1957 A revision of the nearctic species of Fungivora. Iowa State College Jour. Sci. 31: 141-340

Hardy, D. E. 1943 A revision of nearctic Dorilaidae (Pipunculidae) Kansas Univ. Sci. Bull. 29: 3-231

Cresson, E. T. Jr. 1938 The Neriidae and Micropezidae of America, North of Mexico. Am. Ento. Soc. Trans. 64: 293-366

Steyskal, G. C. 1961 The genera of Platystomatidae and Otitidae known to occur in America, north of Mexico. Ento. Soc. Amer. Annals. 54: 401-410

Steyskal, G. C. 1951 The genus Sepedon Latreille in America. Wasmann Jour. Biol. 8: 271-297

Steyskal, G. C. 1954 The American species of the genus **Dictya** Meigen. Ento. Soc. Amer. Annals. 47: 511-539

Bequaert, J. 1953-57 The Hippoboscidae or Louse flies (Diptera) of mammals and birds. Parts I and II. Ento Americana 32: 1-209; 33: 211-442; 34: 1-232; 35: 233-416; 36: 417-611.

Hall, D. G. 1948 The blowflies of North America. Ent. Soc. Amer. Thomas Say Foundation vol. 4: 477 pp

Sturtevant, A. H. and M. R. Wheeler. 1954 Synopsis of Nearctic Ephydridae (Diptera) Trans. Amer. Ento. Soc. 79: 151-257

Wheeler, M. R. 1952 The Drosophilidae of the Nearctic Region, exclusive of the genus **Drosophila.** Univ. Texas Publ. 5204: 161-218

Wirth, W. W. 1952 The Heleidae of California. Univ. Calif. Publ. Ent. 9: 95-266

Hennig, W. 1948-1952 Die Larvenformen der Dipteren. Akademie-Verlag. Berlin. 3 Vols.

Guide to the Insects of Connecticut. Part VI. Fifth Fascicle. Midges and Gnats Tendipedidae (Chironomidae) (O. A. Johannsen and Henry K. Townes) Heleidae Ceratopogonidae) (O. A. Johannsen) and Fungivoridae (Mycetophilidae) (Frank R. Shaw and Elizabeth G. Fisher) Connecticut Geol. & Nat. Hist. Survey Bull. 80: 1-255, 1952.

Hull, F. M. 1962 Robber Flies of the World. The Genera of the Family Asilidae U. S. Natl. Mus. Bull. 224: 1-907

Hull, F. M. 1949 The Morphology and Inter-relationship of the Genera of Syrphid Flies, recent and fossil. Trans. Zool. Soc. London 26: 257-408